The Agony in the Garden, by El Greco.

EXPRESSIONISM
IN ART

BY SHELDON CHENEY

REVISED EDITION
WITH 210 ILLUSTRATIONS

LIVERIGHT PUBLISHING CORPORATION
NEW YORK · 1958

PREFACE

MANY artists and students will face a new essay on Modernist art with the sort of impatience manifested by John Marin. I had asked for photographs of his paintings.

"What!" he exclaimed. "Another damn book?"

Contemplating the burden of recent works in this field, I too am impelled to ask why I—who once reformed and wrote no books for seven years—should now offer a volume about Expressionism.

My reason, I think, was this. There are books enough serving as introductions to Modernism, recounting its early history and paving the way to the first glimmers of understanding. But there is, in English, no book pretending to *analysis* of the characteristic elements in Expressionist art.

Eleven years ago I wrote a frankly introductory work. Therein I was concerned to break down prejudice against "the new art." I was trying to remove the blinders placed by academic teaching over the eyes of the average citizen, was hoping to pry open, a little, the too tightly closed mind of the student and observer.

In those days, in the early 'Twenties, Modernist art was on the defensive. One broached the subject with apologies and explanations. One took up arms self-consciously, even heroically, under the barrage of writings laid down by academic critics in defense of what is now obviously "the old art." The whole subject of Modernism was surrounded by an atmosphere of battle, with the radicals on the challenging side. The introductory and apologetic books, my *Primer* and the variously admirable works of Wilenski, Bell and Eddy, belong to that earlier time, when the public was unconvinced and the Moderns a beleaguered minority.

Today conditions are reversed. If the battle is to continue, it is

< vii >

the conservatives who find themselves on the defensive, who must sue for an audience. Expressionism—if you will allow me the word probationally—is widely accepted, studied, even respectable.

In this book, therefore, if I am wise, only minor effort will be expended to convince the reader that radical Modern art is logical and inevitable. I shall take for granted open-mindedness, if not a practiced appreciation of old and contemporary Expressionist works. After some clearing of the ground, and the establishing of definitions, I shall explain, so far as my present understanding serves, the special means by which artists are accomplishing a return to essentially expressive and creative art. I plan to describe technical methods, report theories, and sketch so much of the social background as may seem to have characteristic influence upon advanced practice.

My first aim is to aid the student in opening the way to understanding and enjoyment. I hope, in addition, that practicing artists will find the book clarifying; though I want no one to seek herein a *formula* for creative accomplishment. True Expressionism goes deeper than that.

The book is at once my most independent and personal expression upon art, and a confession that I have no original theory of Modernism. Even while relying upon my own reactions to and study of living art works, I can claim no originality for the explanations and analyses set forth; and certainly I make no pretense to omniscience in any part of the vast field surveyed. I have merely collated more recorded opinions and expositions than any earlier writer, and I am attempting a digest in readable form, along the line of my own "seeing."

The skeleton of the book is that of a course of "lectures"—a rather pretentious word in the circumstances—prepared in 1932 for discussion-groups at my briefly existent *School for Open-Mindedness,* in Berkeley, and repeated informally that year at art schools in the neighborhood. Teaching, in my case, is a give-and-take affair, and I think my students brought me as much knowledge and

< viii >

new understanding as I imparted to them. The whole book, indeed, reflects a view of creative art that has developed in a series of contacts with students and practicing artists. Parts of the material have been "talked out" with Joseph Sheridan and Glenn Wessels, painters, and with my nephew, Warren Cheney, sculptor. All of these, moreover, have put at my disposal unpublished articles or notes, for which I hereby express gratitude and admit indebtedness.

By far my largest debt, however, is to Professor Hans Hofmann. It was study of his two articles in *The Fortnightly,* doubtless, and the reading of a part of his unpublished work on *Creation in Form and Color,* that crystallized in its present form my "theory of plastic orchestration," elaborated here in the chapters on Picture-Building. I had already incorporated ideas of Albert Gleizes, Dr. Barnes and others into a framework of theory which I was placing before my fellow-students; but Hofmann's exposition of the formal part of the Expressionist synthesis seemed to me clarifying beyond any previous statements. References to these and other sources will be found in the footnotes on the following pages.

I wish to make acknowledgment also for courtesies extended by many artists and galleries in connection with the illustrations. I owe thanks particularly, for groups of photographs, to Alfred Stieglitz (prophet and early leader in the field we are entering), A. E. Gallatin, Pierre Matisse, Adolph Lewisohn, The Weyhe Gallery, The Downtown Gallery of New York City, and the California Palace of the Legion of Honor and the Adams-Danysh Gallery, San Francisco. In other cases I hope that the specific acknowledgment under the reproductions will seem sufficient token of appreciation, to those many who generously co-operated to make the set of illustrations representative and full. Three of the larger museums have been particularly helpful in offering the use of illustrations from their collections: the Art Institute of Chicago; and the Metropolitan Museum of Art, and the Museum of Modern Art, New York.

A more indefinable but heavier debt is owing to two individuals: J. B. Neumann has been generous with gathered material, both

< ix >

factual and photographic; and Martha Candler read the manuscript, and made invaluable suggestions leading to corrections and
rewriting.   To both I am sincerely grateful.

I started the writing of the book under a more particular title—
since discarded—*Expressionism in Art: The First Fifty Years.*
This was phrased to suggest a truth too often overlooked: although
Expressionism is commonly considered so young that its only possible merits lie in the fields of novelty and undirectioned experiment,
the "movement" can be traced, in several arts, through the course
of a full half-century.   In the early 'Eighties Cezanne already had
retired from Paris and Impressionism to Provence and to painting
for the sake of plastic rhythm and emotional realization; and in the
later 'Eighties Gauguin and van Gogh spent memorable productive
months together at Arles, and Rousseau was sending his first
strangely different works to the exhibition halls. Daumier earlier
had been packing his paintings with a sort of structural organization
just now being recognized as a variant achievement of the typical
Modernist expressive form.

Cezanne of course is recognized as prophet and first master by all
Expressionists (whether they admit the label or not) ; and the other
four helped to lift the new movement to the importance of a world-
shaping revolution.   While these events were occurring in France,
Sullivan in Chicago was laying the foundation of a new world architecture, actually creating the first expressively Modern buildings.
And in San Francisco a girl named Isadora Duncan was practicing
those dances which, by example, were to revolutionize another art.
In the theatre Craig and Appia were to follow soon with their dis-
ruptive insurgent theories.   Not only in its roots but in many aspects
of its practice, Expressionism goes back a half century.

I realize that I am using the term Expressionism to cover these
several phenomena at a time when it is still bitterly challenged by
those who would give it a pathological and a German significance.
My reasons are too varied for treatment in a preface: they will have
a chapter later, under the title "Why Expressionism?"   But I may

< x >

usefully summarize my thought here: I believe Expressionism to be the name history will assign to the development in art that began with Cezanne in painting, with Sullivan in architecture, with Duncan in dancing, with Craig and Appia in the theatre. It seems to me the only term exact enough to describe alike the works of Cezanne and Picasso and Orozco and Wigman and Wright and Lehmbruck; even while broad enough to embrace the varied contributions of the so-called Post-Impressionists, Fauves, Cubists, Functionalists, Purists, etc.

But it is for the book itself to explain what Expressionism is: how the artists now arrive at a more intense expressiveness (instead of simulating aspects of nature, or echoing Greek architectural idioms), and what it is that they express. In all reverence I may say, God help me!

S. C.

< xi >

Note on the Revised Edition, 1948

This is a revised edition of a book written almost fifteen years ago. I have received more letters from artists commending the work than in regard to any other writing of mine. Much as I should have liked to attempt a complete rewriting, in the interest of greater simplification, I have had to admit that a clear, effortless exposition of the subject is probably beyond me. The artists who have written to me, and the many favorable reviews, seem to warrant the present reprint, which carries, incidentally, twenty new illustrations, along with numerous text corrections and added footnotes.

The vogue at the moment seems to be for extremely simple art books, of the nature of "Morons Can Draw" or "How to Paint without Knowing How." Expressionism as a subject hardly admits elementary treatment of that sort. The chapters on Picture-Building, a relatively mysterious activity, are really the heart of my volume. It is chiefly on their account that I offer the book again, to artists and students, and to laymen who are willing to make a persistent and perhaps difficult effort toward comprehension.

I have resisted the temptation to add a paragraph on art in the Atomic Age. Nor have I trimmed my original chapter on socially conscious art, chiefly about Communism, though the word "Communism" has come to have sinister connotations not felt fifteen years ago. My broad, even idealistic use of the word was perhaps sufficiently guarded even then, through disavowal of political or party attachment.

"Expressionism" as a name identifying the main current of creative art in the 20th century has steadily gained adherents among artists, writers and museum people. This is still one of the very few books in the language that try to explain why the name applies.

Westport, Connecticut   S. C.

July, 1948

< xii >

CONTENTS

		PAGE
	PREFACE	vii
CHAPTER		
I.	EVOLUTION, TRADITION AND PROGRESS	3
II.	ART JUST BEFORE EXPRESSIONISM	29
III.	THE MAIN PATH OF MODERNISM: THEORY	45
IV.	WHY EXPRESSIONISM?	69
V.	ATTEMPTS TO EXPLAIN FORM	97
VI.	PICTURE-BUILDING: THE FRAME, THE FIELD, AND THE MOVEMENT-PATH	119
VII.	PICTURE-BUILDING: HOW MOVEMENT IS CREATED	163
VIII.	PICTURE-BUILDING: VOLUME, SPACE AND TENSION	201
IX.	PICTURE-BUILDING: COLOR AND TEXTURE	243
X.	PICTURE-BUILDING: DECORATION "FLAT"	273
XI.	ABSTRACTION AND MYSTICISM	313
XII.	FEELING AND MEANING	347
XIII.	THE ARTS OTHER THAN PAINTING	373
	CONCLUSION	409

< xiii >

LIST OF ILLUSTRATIONS

NUMBER   PAGE

1   The Agony in the Garden, by El Greco . . *Frontispiece*

2   Self-portrait, by Oskar Kokoschka 2

3   Four Houses, by Matthew Barnes 7

4   Portrait of Madame Cezanne, by Paul Cezanne . . 10

5   Lower New York, by John Marin 13

6   Gold Mining: Mural, by Diego Rivera 16

7   The Quarry Pool, by Joseph de Martini 19

8   Madonna and Child, by El Greco 24

9   Ecce Homo, by Honoré Daumier 28

10 Death of Socrates, by David 32

11 Death of Sardanapalus, by Delacroix 32

12 Old Kentucky Home, by Eastman Johnson . . . 33

13 Franconia Range: Water-color, by John Marin . . 35

14 Landscape, by Paul Cezanne 37

15 Spectators at the Print Show, by Honoré Daumier . . 38

16 Path of Discovery, by Paul Klee 41

17 Moby Dick, by Boardman Robinson 43

18 Circus Dancers, by Georges Rouault 44

19 Landscape, by Maurice de Vlaminck 47

20 The Garden, by Darrel Austin 51

21 Landscape, by Paul Cezanne 53

22 Hilda: Sculpture, by William Zorach 54

23 On Morse Mountain, Maine, by John Marin . . . 59

24 Sea Lyric, by Matthew Barnes 62

< xv >

NUMBER		PAGE
25	Winter Twilight, by Georges Rouault	65
26	Head of a Young Woman, by André Derain . . .	68
27	Still Life, by Karl Knaths	71
28	Anna de Zborowska, by Amadeo Modigliani . . .	74
29	Landscape in Maine: Water-color, by John Marin .	79
30	Tiger, by Franz Marc	83
31	The Artist on the Way, by Vincent van Gogh . . .	87
32	The Dream, by Henri Rousseau	88
33	The Big Trees, by Paul Cezanne	90
34	Landscape, by Pablo Picasso	91
35	Improvisation 33, by Vasily Kandinsky	93
36	Abstraction, by Georges Braque	94
37	Christ on the Cross, by El Greco	96
38	The White Horse, by George Bellows	101
39	Young Girl, by John Carroll	103
40	Skating, by Yasuo Kuniyoshi	105
41	12th Century Chinese Painting on Silk	108
42	L'Estaque, by Paul Cezanne	111
43	Macbeth and the Witches, by Albert Ryder . . .	114
44	Don Quixote, by Honoré Daumier	118
45	Dancing Trees, by Matthew Barnes	121
46	Ice Floes, by Max Beckmann	123
47	Chinese Landscape—12th-13th Centuries	125
48	Spring Is in the Air, by Frank Kleinholz	127
49	New Mexico: Water-color, by John Marin . . .	131
50	Clam Bay Farm, by Cameron Booth	133
51	Still Life, by Henri Matisse	137
52	The Elder Degas and His Secretary, by Edgar Degas	138
53	The Drinkers, by Honoré Daumier	140

< xvi >

NUMBER		PAGE
54	Mount Sainte Victoire, by Paul Cezanne	141
55	The Agony in the Garden, by El Greco	143
56	Christ and the Fishermen, by Georges Rouault . .	145
57	Mount Sainte Victoire, by Paul Cezanne	146
58	The Agony in the Garden, in the manner of Andrea di Giusto	147
59	The Lamentation for Jesus, by Giotto	148
60	Bridges, by Marcel Gromaire	150
61	Sunday on Grande Jatte, by Georges Seurat . . .	152
62	View of Toledo, by El Greco	153
63	Landscape with Red Spots, by Vasily Kandinsky .	155
64	Outward Bound, by Albert Ryder	157
65	The Unknown Singer, by Nicholas Roerich . . .	159
66	Christ on the Cross, by El Greco	162
67	The Uprising, by Honoré Daumier	165
68	The Reapers, by Maurice Sterne	167
69	Pink Vase and Green Leaves, by Georgia O'Keeffe .	169
70	Self-portrait, by Joseph de Martini	171
71	The Feast in the House of Simon, by El Greco . .	173
72	Chinese Landscape Painting on Silk	174
73	Music, by Georges Braque	177
74	Composition with Figures, by Fernand Leger . . .	179
75	Crucifixion, in the manner of Bernardo Daddi . .	180
76	Houses in Horta, by Pablo Picasso	181
77	Pierrot, by Pablo Picasso	182
78	The Bridge: Water-color, by Paul Cezanne . . .	183
79	Pines and Rocks, by Paul Cezanne	184
80	Boy with a Red Vest, by Paul Cezanne	185
81	Cow Barn, by Heinrich Campendonk	187

< xvii >

NUMBER		PAGE
82	Detail of Mural, by José Clemente Orozco . . .	188
83	Child with Cat, by Jules Pascin	190
84	Christ and the Fishermen, by Georges Rouault . .	191
85	Maine, 1928: Water-color, by John Marin . . .	192
86	The Parade, by Georges Seurat	194
87	Port en Bessin, by Georges Seurat	195
88	Moses Defending the Daughters of Jethro, by Nicholas Poussin	196
89	Bathers, by Paul Cezanne	197
90	Minnesota Farm, by Dewey Albinson	198
91	Self-portrait by the Sea, by Henry Mattson . . .	200
92	Court Scene, by Jean Louis Forain	202
93	Dancers, by Henri Matisse	205
94	Christ on the Lake of Galilee, by Tintoretto . . .	206
95	Blue Horse Composition, by Franz Marc	207
96	Christ on the Cross, by Giotto	208
97	Christ Mocked, by Georges Rouault	209
98	Jack-in-the-Pulpit, by Georgia O'Keeffe	210
99	Lamentation over Jesus, by Tintoretto	213
100	Three Horses and Two Riders, by Honoré Daumier .	215
101	Ruined House, by José Clemente Orozco	216
102	The Card Players, by Paul Cezanne	217
103	The Young Bather, by Gustave Courbet	218
104	Pegasus, by Albert Ryder	219
105	Crucifixion, by El Greco	220
106	Crucifixion, by George Bellows	221
107	Landscape with Red Spots, by Vasily Kandinsky . .	222
108	Painter in the Landscape, by de Hirsch Margules . .	225
109	Hills, by Bernard Karfiol	228

< xviii >

NUMBER		PAGE
110	Gesture, by Max Weber	229
111	The Crowd, by Georges Rouault	230
112	Artist at Beach, by Max Beckmann	231
113	Hilda, by Bernard Karfiol	232
114	Hound, by Marguerite Zorach	233
115	Old Woman Cutting Her Nails, by Rembrandt . .	234
116	Portrait of a Man, by El Greco	235
117	Woman Sleeping, by Max Kaus	237
118	Self-portrait, by Paula Modersohn-Becker . . .	238
119	Oriental Head, by Abraham Walkowitz	239
120	Acrobat in White, by Walt Kuhn	240
121	Flowers in a Vase, by Paul Gauguin	242
122	Reclining Nude, by Henri Matisse	247
123	Interior, by Arthur B. Davies	248
124	Ploughing, by Vincent van Gogh	249
125	Portrait of Madame Cezanne, by Paul Cezanne . .	251
126	The Taffeta Dress, by Henri Matisse	252
127	Nude with Flowers, by Henri Matisse	253
128	La Madelon, by Roger de la Fresnaye	255
129	Still Life, by Morris Kantor	259
130	The Jungle, by Henri Rousseau	261
131	Girl in Green Dress, by Henri Matisse	265
132	Arabesque, by Henri Matisse	266
133	*Vive La France*, by Pablo Picasso	267
134	Nude with Goldfish, by Henri Matisse	268
135	The Good Samaritan, by Rembrandt	270
136	Madonna and Child, by Duccio	272
137	The Baptism of Jesus, by Giotto	277
138	The Railroad, by Vincent van Gogh	279

< xix >

NUMBER   PAGE

139   Head of a Tahitian, by Paul Gauguin 280

140   St. James the Less, by El Greco 281

141   Winter Landscape, by Henri Rousseau 283

142   Coronation of the Virgin, by El Greco 284

143   Hina Tefatu, by Paul Gauguin 285

144   Mural in the Social Chaos Series, by Diego Rivera . 286

145   Maternity, by Paul Gauguin 287

146   Chinese Red Army: Distributing Grain, by Jacob Burck 288

147   Pouring Steel, by Diego Rivera 290

148   Russian-Oriental Panel: Mural, by José Clemente
        Orozco 292

149   A Vision of Antiquity, by Puvis de Chavannes . . 293

150   The Laboratory, by Albert Besnard 294

151   A Santo from the American Southwest 295

152   The Nativity, School of Giotto 297

153   Rustam Capturing the Horse Rakhsh: 15th Century
        Persian 299

154   A Santo from the American Southwest 300

155   Painted Marriage Salver, Florentine 301

156   Girl and Goldfish, by Henry Matisse 303

157   Ia Orana Maria, by Paul Gauguin 304

158   The Jungle, by Henri Rousseau 306

159   Landscape with Blue Birds, by Paul Klee . . . 307

160   The Huntress, by Marie Laurencin 308

161   The Boulevard, by Pierre Bonnard 309

162   Orbits: Pencil Drawing, by Raymond Jonson . . . 312

163   Earth Rhythms, Number 9, by Raymond Jonson . . 315

164   Composition Eleven: Rain, by Raymond Jonson . . 319

165   Majestic Tenement, by Arthur Osver 322

< xx >

NUMBER		PAGE
166	Vital Storm, by Kenneth Callahan	326
167	Wind, Clouds, and Water, by Arthur G. Dove . .	329
168	Figure Abstraction, by Joseph Sheridan	331
169	Green Still Life, by Pablo Picasso	333
170	Improvisation, by Vasily Kandinsky	335
171	The Artist and His Model, by Pablo Picasso . . .	336
172	Construction, by Jean Helion	338
173	Abstract Portrait of Savadsky, by Katherine S. Dreier	339
174	White Iris, by Georgia O'Keeffe	340
175	Abstraction—White Iris, by Georgia O'Keeffe . .	341
176	The Gale-swept Orchard, by Keith Vaughan . . .	342
177	Near Somewhere, by Karl Fortess	342
178	The Apparition, by Revington Arthur	344
179	The Death of a Communist, by Jacob Burck . . .	346
180	The Race Track, by Albert Ryder	351
181	Modern Inquisitor, by Philip Evergood	352
182	His First Crossing, by George Biddle	355
183	The Lynching, by Ben Kopman	357
184	The Civil War, by Diego Rivera	358
185	Thanksgiving 1884, by Mitchell Siporin	360
186	The Slaves, by José Clemente Orozco	363
187	Incumbent, by William Gropper	364
188	Bombardment of Workers, by Marion Greenwood .	365
189	Ilustration, by Phil Bard	366
190	Illustration, by Phil Bard	367
191	Haymarket 1934, by Mitchell Siporin	368
192	Division and Depression, by Diego Rivera . . .	370
193	Mural, by Diego Rivera	371
194	The News Building, New York	372

< xxi >

NUMBER		PAGE
195	A House in Illinois, by Frank Lloyd Wright . . .	377
196	Karl Marx Hof: Modern Apartments in Vienna . .	379
197	Model for a Functionalist House, by Norman Bel Geddes	380
198	Functional Houses, by Edward Stone and Donald Deskey, and by Walter Gropius	382
199	Falling Water House, by Frank Lloyd Wright . .	385
200	Head, by Wilhelm Lehmbruck	387
201	Young Pegasus, by William Zorach	389
202	Seated Nude, by Aristide Maillol	390
203	Camels: Early Chinese Sculptures	392
204	Bird, by Constantin Brancusi	394
205	Woman Looking Up, by George Kolbe	396
206	Setting for *Electra*, by Gordon Craig	399
207	Two drawings, by Adolphe Appia	400
208	Two Sketches for *King Lear*, by Norman Bel Geddes .	403
209	Stage Design for *Dr. Knock*, by Louis Jouvet . . .	405
210	City of Lights, by Umberto Romano	411

< xxii >

EXPRESSIONISM IN ART

Self-portrait, by Oskar Kokoschka.
(By courtesy of J. B. Neumann.)

CHAPTER I

EVOLUTION, TRADITION AND PROGRESS

THE scientists speak of a beginning in chaos; though there may have been, then as always, an eternal order which the time-counting human mind cannot comprehend. The picture of an initial chaos, at any rate, then at a first apprehensible moment a movement toward order, an integration—this picture may afford the most vivid backcloth for any appearance of the still mysterious figure, art.

This is how it would be: Chaos. Then somewhere in unorganized infinitude a clot of atoms, an integration of forces: next, emerging design, ordered movement, form. Finally a rough stabilization of the physical universe, as men of today, within limits, know it: stupendous nebulae and galaxies, millions of light years in extent, within a controlled complex of movements, orbits, weights and tensions. A physical machine-universe, kept "running" by prodigious burnings, radiation, condensation, motion: a continual cosmic transforming of energy. And at the other end of the scale, each physical atom existing by virtue of infinitesimal wave-spurts of that same energy.

Off in the remoter distances of one galaxy, one among millions, exists a not very important star, the Sun, and pendant to that a tiny ball of burned-out ash known as the Earth. Ultimately and unaccountably the life-spark is on Earth, the beginning of vital evolution—and of all man's mysteries of being, experiencing, creating. Rudimentary plants appear and lift crowns toward the sustaining

< 3 >

Sun. Living creatures evolve, adapt, become complex. Millions of years later, man has emerged, recognizably. For further aeons he is man-animal, while that master tool, intellect, grows, functions ever more clearly, points the way to ultimate conquest of all that is on Earth. Deeper, a link with the Universe-Self, unlike the intellect in being knowable only by experience and intuition, the Spirit has its separate, sometimes rapturous, existence.

Linked with Spirit, with creation, with beauty beyond explanation, is the thing men call art. As the spiritual vision of man develops, as the Spirit flames—at times almost to control over intellect and life—artistic effort is born, aesthetic understanding and enjoyment are extended.

No one "knows" what the spiritual is, whence wells up the divine apprehension, the creative impulse and expression. No more can anyone write assuredly of the aesthetic. But there it is: art, the impulse toward it, creative or appreciative, its "works" and the satisfaction or rapture they afford. And men are curious about it.

Now it is not usual to begin a book concerning the arts with a confession that there still is mystery about the subject: a baffling fog which the searchlights of reason fail to penetrate. One is expected rather to lay down a definition on the first page, and stick to it through thick and thin, as guide to interpretation and as final refuge from questioning. It is perhaps a sign of our modernity that we recognize the cloudiness, that we distrust such easy aphorisms as those guiding our immediate ancestors. "Art is imitation," they said, and lapsed into the practice of shallow imitative illustration. Or "Beauty is truth," and interpreted truth as photographic simulation or moral lesson.

We—you as reader impelled to seek understanding of a change that has obviously occurred in all common paths of art, and I as

< 4 >

explorer, having gone ahead in an effort to mark a main road—we shall be wary of too-tight definitions and too-limiting formulas. You will not ask too exact a report. I shall not pretend that I am setting down a precise sheet of directions or a permanent chart. We shall proceed as befits those who know that there are mysteries still not to be cleared by exercise of the human intellect, or by spiritual apprehension at its present pitch and intensity.

The art mystery has immeasurably deepened within the quarter-century. For the practice of the arts has epochally moved, in our time, away from the obvious, superficially real, and demonstrable, toward values not observable, imitable or reasonable. Artists and explainers alike look for the key to the secret in the realms of intuition, intimation, creation, expression. If we are even tentatively to consider Expressionism, we are compelled to renounce the shallowly bright truths and easy enjoyments of Victorian Realism, and to admit that we have climbed, in our search for more satisfying aesthetic enjoyment, into regions intellectually mysterious, perhaps explainable only as mystic. The most creative artists of our time have led the way, and we can object only if the sensitive ones among us fail to experience a sharper aesthetic response.

It is, moreover, meet that we should proceed for a time without too many fast-set guide posts, because our whole temper, as Moderns, impels us to resist the ideas of setness, limitation and finality. In short, we believe in evolution—and not alone in our conception of biology. We recognize, if we are wise, that all living philosophy has been profoundly influenced by the enunciation of the doctrine of evolution. Life is change, growth; institutions are passing means toward change; art and the spiritual life of which it is a part— expression and experience—are never more than an accompaniment of a stage attained by man along the way, geared to his compre-

< 5 >

hension, which is ever enlarging. Thus no matter how much we may learn about art in one era, there will be uncertainty about its next direction. Even as we attempt to measure one flower, there will be unaccountable life-stuff flowing, and changed environment, to shape another and different blossoming. There is no absolute in matters of art.

Nonetheless it is my business here to find what of immediate certainty there may be within this mystery. It is my duty to discover what rock islands may exist at the point in the current now reached by man. We do not pretend to begin at the heart of the mystery, pontifically, and work outward. We can, however, push from certain known points, inward, toward the hidden center. By bringing clear what has happened, in the name of art, at different times, and then noting by comparisons the changed direction, the tangent intent, the different enjoyment, we may find clues to understanding.

UNDERSTANDING BY CONTRAST

Art has arrived, at various periods in man's history, as formal expression. At other periods it has been, instead, imitational activity. It happens that there is between the present Expressionist practice and the immediately preceding imitational art, a contrast so striking that even a superficial study of the one in relation to the other affords light toward a main path of the present Modernism.

If one can see, for what it was, the shallow, literal, imitative painting and sculpture and architecture of the Victorian period, just before the current outpouring of Expressionist works; if one can place 19th Century art in relation to the rigidly institutionalized society, the materialistic and academic philosophies, and the intel-

< 6 >

Four Houses, by Matthew Barnes. (Photo by Ansel **Adams**, by courtesy
of Joseph A. Danysh Galleries.)

lectualized cultural structure of which it was a part: then one has
the perfect contrast to all that the Modernist artists are striving for.

The literalism and dogmatism of bitterly divided Christian sects,
the superficiality of "scientific" philosophy, the tendency to pigeon-
hole and label every object, action and impulse, these characteristics
of the times, as well as the actual photographic surface art, go
some way, as opposites, to explain the almost fanatic devotion of
the Expressionists to intuitional and mystic values, and formal
"unnatural" expression. The Landseers, Bouguereaus, Sargents

< 7 >

and Besnards among painters, the Baryes and Saint-Gaudens of sculpture, and the Eclectic historic-imitative architects, all belonged to the age of set-mindedness, of imitational molds-for-art. Cezanne and Lehmbruck and Sullivan belonged to some later era: partly to the period of revolutionary confusion and birth, between two ages, partly to an emerging new world.

Just before Expressionism, indeed, there was a crystallization of living and of art into approved and recognized molds. Morals were codified, a rigid model for living was set up, every activity of man was charted, and sanctioned or forbidden. Realistic minds settled, assertedly for all eternity, what art is, canonized Raphael and Donatello and Gainsborough, embalmed standard examples in tomb-like museums, and formed academies to perpetuate the true faith and protect the orthodox.

The Modern considers all such codifying and canonizing futile and limiting. He is as certain of evolution in art as in organic life. He points out that in spite of all the damming tactics of schools, academies and critics, the flood of Expressionism has swept over the Western world, so changing practice that the devotees of trans-fer-from-nature art cry out that beauty is destroyed, nature violated, chaos come again. Of the works of visual art flowing into the exhibition galleries today, three-fourths are of such nature that in 1890 they would have been turned away from all doors as having nothing to do with finished art. Similarly, to the cultured Eclectics of 1870-1930, Modernist architecture is barren of beauty, nakedly awkward, and utterly un-understandable as art. So great is the revolution immediately behind us.

The artists themselves, impelled by forces totally overlooked by Victorian criticism and practice—forces impossible to codify and difficult to detect—have changed not only the outward aspect of the

< 8 >

arts, but men's understanding of the reasons for art activity, and of the essential thing that the observer experiences as art.

Whether we are yet ready, or not, to employ the word Expressionism, we cannot escape the conclusion that the Western world's interest in and attitude toward the arts have shifted epochally since Cezanne saw a vision beyond Impressionism, since Duncan flung away the ballroom slippers which for generations had confined the art of the dance to variations of Louis XIV ballet-interludes, since Sullivan dared to design functionally.

EVOLUTION AND OUR TIME

If one grants vital evolution—and who does not among educated people?—how can one avoid realization that all that *is* changes? Everything material, from nebulae and stars to chairs and human bodies, exists by virtue of movement, change. Beyond the immediate physical-chemical transformation there is the longer progressive movement, which might be called chain-growth. The intellect too changes, grows, age after age (though obviously it is commonly utilized to only a fraction of its occasionally glimpsed powers). Within our time, indeed, new knowledge of the brain has been uncovered, and men foresee controlled growth, with unprecedented mental achievement. Expression of the spiritual life of man has been a shifting current; though in the failure to understand the march of evolution, every great religious establishment has tried to stop the flow, to set up final laws, only to be swept down in time.

Art too changes, assumes new outward appearances, presupposes man's finer sensitivity and enlarged capacity for aesthetic experience. The senses that thrilled to Monet's color harmonies, fixed from nature's tenderest fleeting aspects, and the mind that ah'd

< 9 >

Portrait of Madame Cezanne, by Paul Cezanne. (From *Cezanne*, by Julius Meier-Graefe.)

over Sargent's uncanny exposures of character and dashing portrayal of clothes and bric-a-brac, are stilled, in a later time, when some inner faculty of the observer responds to the plastic dynamics, the universal architectonics of a painting by Cezanne. Educated men should accept as natural this growth of human-aesthetic faculties, and the accompanying deeper current of creativeness in art practice: a creativeness triply expressive, in the current outpouring, as I shall try to show, and amply warranting the name Expressionism.

It is part of my thesis, then, that Expressionism represents a new stage reached in art's upward climb: that it is the art proper to the present-day expanding world, and rightly different from the art of the tight-bound 19th Century society. As represented in its early phases, by the Expressionist experiments that we see, so various, so confusing, on all sides of us, it is the art born of the struggle between two worlds, of the death-confusion of an expiring civilization, and of the birth-pains of a different human society. The works we may mark as finest, noblest, intensest, in the Modernist achievement, as the most revelatory, may be found fully worthy of man's increased artistic expressiveness in the world as it will next be stabilized—a world still vague in its outlines because man is entering into it in utmost confusion.

Let us not fool ourselves into believing that that world either will be a final one. The current of change will flow strong again, after a period of ebb, other unforeseen changes will follow, another society and another art will eventuate: perhaps an art never fixed in paint or stone or sound, but created and at once enjoyed within the one creator-enjoyer's faculties. But it is enough for us, today, that we understand the living art of this our time, and of the age opening before us. If we are alert and living, we shall desire to

< 11 >

know the achievement, and to enjoy the revelations, of the fully living, fully creative artists of these exciting Nineteen-Forties.

When the student sees art thus, fitted into the evolutionary scheme of things, subject to the influences of evolutionary change in surrounding life, and creatively evolutionary in its own right, he has established a perspective very useful in evaluating Expressionism.

TRADITION AND MODERNISM

Evolution implies change *within a continuity*. The main portion of this book will be concerned with change, growth, the differences; the remainder of this chapter, and the next, however, will have to do with continuity, with the tradition of art practice and theory, with the immediate historic background against which the phenomenon Expressionism discovers itself.

It is likely that nothing of artistic impulse and understanding that is once born into the world is completely lost in times after. Just as physical man carries about, along with his directly useful parts, a strange assortment of survivals from his periods of growth, ears related to fish-gills, a stub of a tail that he can't even wag effectively, a vermiform appendix, etc.—as well as a consciousness stored (though not "normally" to be tapped at will) with everything he has ever seen or heard, upon a lower foundation of racial inheritance—just so, the contemporary art stream carries along surviving elements from all the epochs of man's adventuring among the arts.

Certain characteristics—even the most creative and revealing— may be obscured for a time; as occurred during the long reign of Realism. A scientific and imitative spirit brought to the surface of the current, in Renaissance times, a mirror-like art, bright with

< 12 >

Lower New York, by John Marin. (By courtesy of
An American Place.)

easily understood transfers from nature's storehouse of beauty;
and men were satisfied, forgetting an inheritance of more profound
aesthetic discernment.

Even in that time, however, El Greco could refuse to be swept

< 13 >

with the surface current, could carry on a more intensely creative tradition, and add to it from his own rich and expressive genius. And at the very moment, three centuries later, when the Realistic achievement was touching the ultimate point in refinement and technical effectiveness, another genius, Cezanne, guessed the shallowness of contemporary art, perceived some of the glories that had been obscured, and set to work to recover the main tradition of creativeness, fusing it, within his own vision, with the color-brilliancy learned out of his own time.

The world is quick to label Cezanne a revolutionary, because his practice was so widely divergent from that of his contemporaries. In the longer view he is the historic evolutionary figure, picking up the forgotten main tradition: continuing, from a new start, the solid classic art-expression that lasts through the ages. Just so with Sullivan, the initiator of a new architecture, but first of the Moderns to link with the giant creator-builders of the past. In these figures tradition and Modernism meet. A temporarily forgotten heritage is recovered; at the same time a new release initiated.

Therein is the whole answer of the "radicals" to the academicians who cry out that Expressionism negates history, presupposes destruction of the entire treasured achievement of past artists. The Moderns instead, even while claiming a new intensity of creativeness, born partly out of the patterns of these times, point out that their practice links with the deeper tides of the art of the past; that it is only the weak photographic-ornamental art of the 17th-19th Century period that they violently oppose and scornfully ridicule.

The conservative critics, nurtured on Victorian sentimental Realism, clinging to a distorted Aristotelean dictum—"art is imitation" —and seeing no deeper than an intellectual-sensuous appeal, totally

< 14 >

overlook the characteristic abstract, emotional and pictorial-formal values in Modernist art, and gird at the surface distortion, the "unnatural" aspect of it. They believe that their battling is in defense of the main tradition. But it is, I believe, they, the conservative critics, and the surface-nature artists for whom they battle, who will be judged by history to have been out of line. It is the Expressionists, rather, who are the true traditional artists. For *the evolution of art, in the historic view, is along a path of creativeness.*

As art evolves, the "works" changing, and man's perceptive faculties growing, along the path men call tradition, it is the newly expressive bursts of activity that mark progress. Realistic-photographic and selective-Realistic painting, and historic-imitative architecture, wherein creative values were almost totally obscured, are now seen to have marked the pause between evolutionary spurts. Modernism brings art back to the vital tradition. I realize that I must, in order to make this clear to the reader, prove ultimately that the Expressionists have introduced substantially new elements into art—even while they were returning to the main ages-long stream of creativeness.* But here I wish only to note that Expressionism, far from being merely an attempt to "attract by novelty," is claimant to the right of main succession, in the purple line. Incidentally, if the reader still is employing the word "radical" as a term of reproach, he should look up its essential meaning: "from the foundation," "connected with the root."

---

* Chapters VI to XI, roughly, embody my attempt to explain the joining-on process, and to identify the formal values that are new—or perhaps it should be phrased, the understanding that is new. Expressionism is newer as theory than in practice; for in various historic eras, artists achieved, perhaps intuitively, values that critics of today term Expressionistic. Examples will be noted particularly in the chapters on Picture-Building. Note too the book's frontispiece.

< 15 >

Gold Mining: Mural painting by Diego Rivera.

The Moderns, indeed, go to man's past reverently. They recognize the life of the ages as soil from which contemporary art takes nourishment. But they ask that recorded history be fairly rewritten, with less emphasis on the near-barren era (as regards the visual arts) since the Renaissance, and more attention to originally expressive ages. Claiming creativeness as a principle, they damn 19th Century society for lacking or subordinating creative ability, for enthroning imitativeness, and for setting up models and molds for the eternal confinement of art. Even if the molds had been more elastic and better chosen, they could have been useful in only the most transitory and incidental way. The Expressionist recognizes a tradition, but not molds, of creativeness.

Let the student, then, turn to the historic ages freely, for enlightenment, for understanding of the ways in which the creative spirit came to flower at various times and places. Let him cultivate the ability to search the past, and to find works of art moving and intense in relation to the life of their own times. Enjoyment of ancient Chinese paintings, and the Sienese Primitives, and El Greco and the Mayans, will afford him a sense of identification with the great art stream of the past, the stream that comes unaccountably from the original source of life; and that mystic identification will aid him to express with deeper insight and in quintessence the life-currents of this his own time. But never should he copy, or fix himself within the limits of a past achievement in art, whether negro-primitive, Chinese, pre-Raphaelite, or shallow Victorian.

If someone come, in defense of the academicians, saying that their understanding and practice evolve too, are in the ascending scale, let the student not be misled. Their activity has only a reflective relationship to living art, is not a part of it. It will be pointed out that whereas forty years ago the academies were fight-

< 17 >

ing and excluding Impressionism, in favor of the more naturalistic and frankly literary-romantic painters of an earlier time, today their exhibitions are given up almost *in toto* to the belated Impressionists. To them this spells progress. It is, rather, a way of keeping the grave decently decked. It is the dead hand of Victorianism reaching forward in an attempt to forestall further change or creation. The academicians merely have altered the molds, forty years after invention has passed. They believe in final molds as before: but public opinion has forced a readjustment. They still suspect and exclude tangent art, art creative in its own time.

Revolutionary evolution is always accomplished by marginal groups, by minorities suspect among the ruling majority. Each new band of innovators finds the world encumbered with the litter of a dead past. But the Moderns today find the road to acceptance doubly obstructed: not only are the works of the dead all around, but the dying hand holds grimly to those instruments which should serve as guides to advancement, to progressive living, to new life. I refer at the moment to museums and the printed word.

OBSTRUCTIONS: PSEUDO-TRADITION AND THE MUSEUMS

Long ago I wrote at some length about mis-education of the eye and understanding, as a determining factor in closing the average mind against Modernist art. A false conception of art *as illustration* was developed in one's school years: by the pictures and statues in classroom and home, and by the actual illustrations (properly literary and Realistic) in popular magazines. By these agencies the young student or casual observer is led, as a matter of course, to evaluate a work of art by the degree of its likeness to nature. Casts from the late Greek or Roman statues, penny

< 18 >

The Quarry Pool, by Joseph de Martini. An illustration of the
Expressionist effort to render the picture plastically alive and unified.
A near-abstraction, but without denial of nature. (By courtesy of the
Addison Gallery of American Art, Phillips Academy, Andover.)

prints after all the carefully photographic painters, from Raphael
and Murillo to J. G. Brown and Sargent, magazine covers by Max-
field Parrish and Harrison Fisher, and colored "masterpieces of
modern painting" as chosen by the editors of the women's periodi-
cals, more particularly for the saccharine Christmas issues—these
form the bulk of the school and home repertoire of art: afford the
contacts by which youth shapes its conception of what art is.

   To me it seems clear that this pushing forward of illustrative
works in various forms, in place of creative art, is a chief reason

< 19 >

why any deeply expressive painting puzzles or repels the student at first meeting; and I urge the reader to be sure that he has brought clear in his own mind the all-important distinction between Realistic-illustrative activity and truly creative art. But now let us go farther: considering the case of the student who is not wholly satisfied with the home and school offering, who turns to the two instruments that should serve to break down the obsession with obvious photographic art—the museums and the art-history books.

Both fail him. The academicians choose the pictures that shall be shown to him in the great treasuries of art works, and they determine the names of artists and the modes of art that shall be exalted to him as reader of history. The Modernist finds his way to acceptance blocked, so far as may be in an inevitably changing world, by mis-education in the early school years, mis-education by the museums, and by distortion and suppression in the commonly circulated text books. Since we are considering the relationship of Modernism to tradition, let us pause a little over these obstructions, lest they continue to confound those who wish to approach Expressionism with an open and unconfused mind. Discrimination, and rejection of nine-tenths of what is offered as masterly art, must precede immediacy of vision and independence of judgment.

In recognizing the extraordinary material progress made by their museums, Americans have been, perhaps, too blind to the perversion of function commonly developed. The grander institutions, while acquiring princely materials for display, housed in palatial buildings, have slipped over from being art museums in the stricter sense, to being historical-cultural museums.

Among the several obvious faults in such institutions—which include overcrowding of exhibits, grandly elaborate or coldly tomb-like buildings (dwarfing the art within, rendering intimate enjoy-

< 20 >

ment of the exhibits impossible), and confusion of function—this
lack of directive conviction is most significant to us as students
of Modernism. The curator is scholar, antiquarian, teacher. Insofar as he considers it his business to deal with living art, he turns
for advice to the academies. He meets art always forty years
behind the times. The student is led to believe that original and
vital art is here treasured and shown for his benefit. But when
actually creative work is included, in the vast pageant of samples
of everything ever manufactured anywhere in the name of art, it
is lost in oceans of secondary stuff. The point of view of the
selectors, in regard to what is creative, is always a generation out
of date, and is timidly all-inclusive.

A vivid instance of the influence of the academies is to be found
in the newspapers as I write. In a mid-western city a two-million-
dollar museum building is being dedicated. Ample provision is
made for the purchase of paintings, out of the eleven-million-dollar
endowment. But the directors are prohibited from buying any work
of art *if produced by an artist dead fewer than thirty years.*

Thus the dead hand lingers on to discourage creativeness and
hinder growth. Creation in a certain time would seem to presuppose
a fitness of the work to the aesthetic-responsive faculty of the observer bred in that time. Yet here is a munificent gift limited
to works of past generations.*

Average folk have become so accustomed to considering the
museums purely historic and antiquarian in function, as tombs-

* It is possible to add, in 1948, that the museum situation has changed conspicuously
for the better in the fourteen years since the paragraphs above were written. Opportuni-
ties now exist for the student to see modern paintings in most large American cities.
Similarly the textbooks of art are no longer so biased and inadequate as in 1934. It
seems well, however, to retain the passages about the museums here, and the criticisms
of textbooks a few pages forward, because there is abundant room for improvement
still, in both matters.

< 21 >

for-art, with usually a mortuary solemnity of aspect in both architecture and exhibits, that the incident does not deeply shock them. But the Modernist, believing that a new intensity of creativeness is being achieved, and certain that an epochal revolution has occurred in men's understanding of the distinction between intensely living and secondary art, sees serious danger in these historic institutions masquerading as the chambers and exemplars of true art.

Already the Modernist has crystallized another ideal, of the art museum for these times, the museum living up to the implication of its name, "Place of the Muses": a place colorful, intimate, unified, giving back an aesthetic response, rather than instructing the mind. But only a Modern conception of what essentially constitutes creative art, expressive art, can lead to inspired and unified design of the collections and galleries. The Expressionist believes that the modern art museum, like the modern work of art, can afford sustained aesthetic pleasure, a consistent experience of art— as does a symphony program or a theatre production—related to creative practice and appreciation in this our own time.

It will be in order, when that is achieved, to take down the present motto over the proud museum portals: "We show everything." It will be necessary to sweep out, into frankly historical-cultural museums, the clutter of secondary, impotent, reproductive stuff. Living art will be the basis of art-museum design, as living expression is at the heart of the practice of the Modern artist.

In that day the curators and academicians will not use the public galleries in their business of canonizing artists and schools forty years after they have been at their intensest significance. The dead hand will no longer stay the living. Meantime let the student not be blinded by the sacro-sanct air and gilded framework of the museum displays. Let him realize that they are based on 19th Cen-

< 22 >

tury conceptions and molds. The dealers' galleries are still the likelier places for study of art that is vital; though one must discriminate there too. To come back to the starting point of this digression, the academicians control the museums, and they not only are laggards in the evolutionary advance—they even fight the Modernists from the rear.

MODERNIST ART AND HISTORY

When we turn to published annals of the past, we find that the historians too have betrayed us. The art-history books, like the museums, are designed with no conviction as to what creative art essentially is; and in general—since they were written in the Victorian era—they glorify the artists and schools that achieved a neat illusive art, the tasteful sentimental-natural and romantic painters, and the smooth naturalistic sculptors. They are concerned especially with the types of art from which the 19th Century molds were patterned: notably late Greek Realistic sculptures, Renaissance Italian painting (more especially that of the period after the discovery of scientific anatomy and natural perspective, which largely nullified the form-values achieved by the "Primitives"), the flashy British portrait painters, and the various forms of romantic and photographic 19th Century French art.

To the Modern this obsession with the shallow imitational products of uncreative ages is misleading and unfortunate. He prays for the coming of an historian who will begin with a passionate belief in the creative and expressive elements as fundamental, who will relegate illusion-art to its secondary place, and tell the main story in terms of the works of greatest creative intensity. Notable reversals would result from such an approach. Chinese painting,

< 23 >

Madonna and Child, by El Greco. Illustrating typical "distortion" of natural aspects, for expressive-formal intensification. (From *Domenico Theotocopuli El Greco,* by August L. Mayer.)

Persian miniature painting, Primitive drawing and painting, from the cave artists to the Italo-Byzantine development, and many periods of primitive sculpture, even to the contemporary African negro figures, early Chinese sculpture—all these would come into increased appreciation. Fading back into lesser prominence would be the recently popular physical-culture exhibits of the later Greeks, such "safe" masters as Raphael, Veronese, Murillo and the entire "British School," and 19th Century favorites from the polished Neo-Classicists and dreamy Romanticists to the gross-feeding Realists and spineless Impressionists. In short, the Expressionist asks for a revision of recorded history, on the basis of a fresh conception of what constitutes vital art, in order that the student may no longer be infected with the obsession that "Art is imitation."

In analyzing existent art-histories, we should find, no doubt, as much insidious propaganda and wilful distortion as in those now discredited "patriotic" history books out of which my generation—schooled in the opening years of the 20th Century—learned the record of men and nations on earth. There was wilful discrimination, and "interpretation" of fact, to make out my country, its ideals and its leaders, pre-eminent. Military victories were glorified, defeats minimized—or forgotten—and the *status quo* shamelessly bolstered. Presidents, kings, generals, patriots, churches, constitutions, were inordinately extolled. As all this fabrication and falsifying was done for the home-land and womanhood and Christianity, there was only negligible criticism of it, or challenge. One belonged within the tight-set system of which it was a part. One accepted, patriotically, without question.

Histories of art seem to have been written almost as servilely, with propagandist bias—and by people ignorant of the profound values of plastic order and dynamic rhythm which the Moderns

< 25 >

believe basic. Academicians, church painters, flatterers and photographers were glorified. Easily understood surface-art from the past was paraded as immortal. National pride was properly served. Even today there is not a published history of art which the Modern will recommend without apologies, reservations and warnings.

That the Expressionist movement already has had strong influence upon world opinion, outside circles ruled by the historians, is obvious. El Greco has been elevated to supreme desirability and widespread recognition, though he was not considered worthy of mention in Reinach's *Apollo: An Illustrated Manual of the History of Art throughout the Ages*, or in Goodyear's *A History of Art*—two Victorian works still standard at public libraries and schools. The popular thousand-page *Outlines of the History of Art* by Lübke did better, according him a single line. As late as 1923, H. B. Cotterill wrote, with special reference to "the origins and evolution of European art," *A History of Art*, in two fat volumes, and dismissed El Greco with a slighting paragraph. But today collectors search the markets for even the least intense works by this "master," and clear their walls for these obviously Expressionistic prizes. Less dramatic reversals in ranking, due to "discoveries" by the Modernists, may be illustrated in the resurrection of Daumier as a painter (after his near-obscuration, as a mere cartoonist), and in the canonization of William Blake and of Albert Ryder.

In a larger view, it is obvious that the museum curators and the historians alike will be forced hereafter to study negro sculpture, Chinese paintings and Mayan-Amerindian developments—not to forget individuals like El Greco, Daumier and Hans von Marées— as belonging integrally in the classic stream of art evolution. Where art lives, the radicals have overturned rankings, brought forward forgotten creative artists, changed the approach to world

< 26 >

art. But let the student beware still of published histories; or at least let him form his own conception of creative values, before he reads. Much current confusion exists because recorded history fixes in the student mind a theory of and approach to art utterly disrelated to living practice and advanced thought upon the subject.

The current Modernism must persist a little longer as radicalism, before it is accepted officially as in the tradition: before it yields up the name "Modernism" to some later development. Evolutionary progress brings Expressionism daily closer to that time when it will be standard in practice, and a touchstone for judging the creative past. Popular education, museums and historians still dissent: but it becomes more obvious every day that they are the dissentients, a diminishing group, on a side road.

< 27 >

Ecce Homo, by Honoré Daumier. (Photo by courtesy of the Museum of Modern Art, from original in the Folkwang Museum, Essen.)

CHAPTER II

J UST what was it that typical painters and architects and sculptors were doing when Cezanne and Sullivan and Lehmbruck emerged to initiate their contributive revolutions: breaking down the dams which had been erected across the historic streams of progress?

The art of painting offers the neatest illustration of the shift from Realistic practice to Expressionist practice. The change is most cleancut, most typical, most illuminating; and the works of the earlier period are surprisingly innocent of the values especially prized by the Moderns.

Painting in the 19th Century was, as a whole, overwhelmingly Realistic. In my definition—each new writer must frame his own, so muddied are the critical waters—Realism is that type of art concerned with transcribing, without noticeable distortion of surface aspects, the beauties, picturesqueness or other "interesting" values of observable nature. Realism thus includes a considerable group of schools: from Naturalism—with every hair of the beard separately depicted—to the widely variant Romantic and Neo-Classic developments, which were characterized, until recently, as at the very pole from Realism.

Thus the so-called "Classic" art of David and Ingres and Prud'-hon (and in sculpture Canova) seems in longer perspective essentially Realistic, because, in illustrating "ideal" and legendary scenes, with meticulous smoothed-down technique, the artists still

< 29 >

never departed from what could be seen on the surface of nature with the eye. In the search for flawless beauty they arrived at mechanical and effeminate refinement and dry rhetoric, that are at the far extreme from the truly Classic, in the root sense. They were concerned, to be sure, with nature as seen through the scholarly books of Greek and Roman history—but it *was* nature transcribed.

I include the Romanticists likewise among the essential Realists: they sought exotic far-off nature, or they poetically fuzzed up the edges of nature near at hand; but they never departed from a substantially photographic objective view, never distorted or re-arranged surface likeness, in a search for expression and order—never dreamed that art was other than interpretive imitation. From Delacroix with his melodramatics to the Barbizon painters in their misty or glamorous woods, there is a wide range of Romantic "interpretation"; but seldom a detail that could not have been picked up with the camera-eye, sharply or fuzzily focussed.

Along with the Naturalist-Realists, the Neo-Classic-Realists and the Romantic-Realists, there were the groups more commonly termed just plain Realists—painters devoted to nature but too selective to warrant the Naturalist label, and neither coldly idealistic nor yearnful for far-away places and exotic variants from nature's types. Stemming from Courbet, they flourished up to the time when Impressionism capped the progress toward refinement of surface transcription. Within this range one finds the sentimental anecdote-painters, the *genre* painters, the flattering portrait painters, and the purveyors of the charms of the nude, from the hothouse and twilight variations to the straight physical-culture display.

(The definition of Realism is not a point of cardinal importance here: we need not agree absolutely on a permanent terminology before getting on with our study. If you prefer to hold to earlier

< 30 >

conceptions of Realism, considering it opposed to Romanticism and Classicism, you need merely grant me, tentatively, that *beyond* such distinctions there exists a more fundamental division: between formal-expressive or Expressionist art on the one hand, and, on the other, grouped Realism, Romanticism and pseudo-Classicism, all bound within a servility to observed natural detail.)

Within Realism many are the varieties: many the efforts to lift the type out of the category of heightened photography. Attempts are made to render Realism significant, during the 19th Century, by idealizing nature, by serving patriotism or God, by offering escape into vicarious experience, into life as discovered by the artist in parts of the world inaccessible to the ordinary citizen. Attempts are made to build up its importance by pushing technique to a new brilliancy of surface appeal: as in the brushwork of Sargent, or the amazing meticulousness of Meissonier, or the soft-focus poetizing of Carrière. New tricks of composition are achieved, a new posteresque independence of casual detail, new ways of framing and balancing the main motive; and certainly there was gained at this time final intellectual knowledge of mechanical perspective and of physical anatomy. But—summarizing it from the later viewpoint—as long as art remains primarily illustration, as long as its business is considered to be transfer to the canvas of beauty or picturesqueness seen in outward nature, or the telling of a story in nature's objective materials, it is Realism, and to the modern mind more shallow than art that begins with a search for order, form, revelation, expression.

Impressionism as a variety of Realism demands more specific notice. In its scientific advance it put new potentialities into the hands of the later rebels; in its pushing of the Realist search to the last point of accurate surface transcription from nature, it hastened recognition of the shallow character of all Realistic art.

< 31 >

Three types of art here classed within the Realistic method, as distinguished from Expressionism. Opposite, above, The Death of Socrates, by David: illustrating the Neo-Classicism of a century ago, with legendary subject matter and "refined" technique, but pictorially hard, dry and shallow, and camera-exact in detail. Below, The Death of Sardanapalus, by Delacroix: an example of 19th Century Romanticism, full of natural movement but plastically disordered; exotic in subject but photographic in detail. Above, on this page, Old Kentucky Home, by Eastman Johnson: an example of Realistic exactness glorified for its own sake, as unashamed Naturalism, without understanding of pictorial-plastic aims. All of these, whether marking escape into idealistic-Classic or exotic-picturesque realms or abiding by a familiar sentimental milieu, are held strictly within fidelity to outward Realistic-illusional detail: and so distinguished from Expressionism. (From originals in the Metropolitan Museum of Art, the Louvre, and the Gallery of the New York Public Library.)

Impressionism was concerned with the depiction of fleeting aspects of nature. Story interest was wholly suppressed, and the object as·such was subordinated. The surface of nature under light, and the nuances of the component colors in light, became all-important. Structure, depth, organization, were largely forgotten. Art became luminous, hazy, scientifically accurate. That the painters then discovered a new way to make color fresh, alive, brilliant, by juxtaposition of minute strokes, patches and wedges of pigment, was enormously important in the technical advance of painting. But the method was used by the Impressionists themselves for shallow illusional ends.

Thus out of Impressionism the first Expressionist experimentalists were to inherit an incalculably precious asset: a scientific knowledge of color, and with it a pure external colorfulness that belongs essentially to the art of painting. They were to carry on, too, the convention of confessing their brush strokes, no longer smoothing down the pigment to hide the mark of the painter-tool. But the very first revolutionaries were to depart diametrically from the method and "look" of Monet and Pissarro. Whereas the Impressionist aimed at recreating an impression of nature received at one moment of time, in a flash of the eye, the first Expressionist painters returned to a search for order hidden beyond the momentary aspect of nature; and they aimed to fix in the canvas a plastic design, implying movement of the beholder's eye along a carefully designed track of vision. The painter is immediately off on a search for values almost totally absent from typical Impressionist works: values which we may term, tentatively, dynamic structure, plastic rhythm, spatial vitality, formal organization.

< 34 >

Franconia Range—Mist and Rain: Water-color by John Marin. (By courtesy of Alfred Stieglitz.)

Painting just before Expressionism, then, was the brilliant thin color wizardry of Monet, Signac, Hassam and Frieseke, mixed with the heightened photography of Sargent, Besnard, Carrière and Boecklin. These vied with belated practitioners of all the other sorts of Realism perfected during the Victorian era: pale Romantics carrying on the Barbizon tradition, followers of Delacroix discovering new theatrical effects in brighter colors and spotted rendering, the naked figures of Courbet become more brutal and scientific, or else warmly poetized by Henner or coldly literalized by Bouguereau.

< 35 >

Art was, through a wide range of variations, illusion, illustration, clever transcription.

In the midst of it came Cezanne, and van Gogh and Gauguin. It was during the flood of painting of those Realistic sorts that the first true revolutionaries appeared. The imitative tide continued, to be sure, for a long time after, and even today its latest flotsam may be seen in the academy exhibits on 57th Street. But in the last quarter of the 19th Century there were those divergent figures: artists who have taken on the stature of giants in the history of painting.

Out of the mid-19th-Century current, himself an Impressionist at first, came the leader Cezanne: out of a group of imitationists, a profoundly creative artist. As the world sees it now, Daumier had earlier achieved a strength of organization that is typically of the Moderns; and soon after Cezanne's defection from the regulars, there stood beside him van Gogh and Gauguin. These are the men who successfully challenged the values, methods and theory of painting as it was practiced by the final Realists, just before Expressionism. (The fact that it was so practiced by the *majority* of conforming "artists," during the first forty years of "the new movement," alongside the increasing stream of creative work, need detain us no longer.)

CONFIRMATION FROM THE STORY OF SCULPTURE

The story of sculpture is not quite so cleancut: the contrast between orthodox Realism and insurgent Expressionism not so suddenly achieved, not so immediately pronounced. To be sure, the art of the sculptor had degenerated through a period of three and a half centuries after Michael Angelo: had been weakly Realistic or frankly ornamental, from Cellini to Barye and Saint-Gaudens.

< 36 >

Landscape, by Paul Cezanne.   (By courtesy of the Metropolitan Museum
of Art.)

Barye may be marked as the type Realist of the Victorian era,
photographing in clay the interesting poses of animals, for transfer
into more enduring bronze.   Saint-Gaudens is the typical illustrator,
fixing in monumental compositions subject pieces that would be
noble as wash drawings.   Neither of these celebrated artists cut his
own work in stone—sufficient condemnation, in the mind of the
Modern, to exclude them from the roster of great creative sculptors.
The art had become something wholly untrue to name, not sculp-

< 37 >

Spectators at the Print Show, by Honoré Daumier. A cunningly organized
picture by a master of the plastic or movement element in painting. (By
courtesy of the Corcoran Gallery of Art: W. A. Clark Collection.)

tural, but an exercise in modelling, seeking painty effects, obsessed with natural postures and pretty surfaces.

There came, in the midst of the Realistic culmination, no single genius-sculptor of the stature of Cezanne among the painters. Rodin, greatest of the Realists, touched only slightly into a new art: never got clear the distinction between art as illusion of nature, as mirror of the picturesque, and art as primarily expression or revelation. Rodin was, through his middle period, the perfect Impressionist, catching his model at a single moment of time, in a significant attitude, fixing that pose cunningly in stone or clay. He also played up the surfaces of his statues to a brilliant luminosity, rippling his planes with minute variations, affording a sweet evanescent appeal parallel to that of Monet's paintings. But only rarely did he let his inner emotion rule, or permit his "feel for the medium" to dictate paths of improvisation beyond the minor truths of the objective image. He will be known in history as the climactic figure of the Realistic tradition—though he guessed, at the end, that a truer creative art of sculpture was coming. The revolution was to be accomplished by less known artists: Metzner, Maillol, Gaudier, Epstein, Lachaise, Archipenko, and that singular genius whose few works will some day raise him incomparably higher than Rodin: Wilhelm Lehmbruck. These men accomplished a revolution as complete as that in painting, but more gradually.

ARCHITECTURE IMITATIVE AND EXPRESSIVE

Architecture just before Expressionism offers a perfect parallel to the Realism of painting and sculpture. The building art, of course, is never concerned with photography, illustration and illusion. But if those were ends so pursued on their own account

< 39 >

that creative values were largely forgotten, in what were then called the "reproductive" arts, *imitationalism* is the exact counterpart in architectural history. In the one case it is imitation of nature, in the other, imitation of past styles and masters.

Almost from the time of Michael Angelo, architecture had been an exercise in tasteful re-arrangement of re-discovered decorative "motives." During the final quarter of the 19th Century it had become a basic principle of criticism and teaching that all the styles had been invented. The student was trained to take plan and decorative covering from the treasury of the past, and an extraordinary array of books, containing measured drawings of all "masterpieces," was made available to the contemporary designer of architectural veneers. Invention could not go beyond "creative adaptation." The professional architect had been tamed into being an accomplished Eclectic.

During the entire 19th Century, architecture had been Neo-this and Neo-that, with the Renaissance tradition, itself sprung from a Neo-Roman source, barely able to hold its own against revivals of Gothic or Greek or Romanesque. Shadows battled shadows.

Stepping aside from the arena where "the battle of the styles" was being fought, Louis Sullivan in the 'Eighties inquired simply why there could not be an architecture based upon the building materials, the building uses, and the altered ways of human living evident in the machine age. He damned out heartily all renaissances and revivals: all clothing of modern railway stations, meeting houses and office buildings in the garments stripped from Greek temples, Gothic cathedrals and Venetian palaces. And he essayed some buildings in which the materials and uses of the structure actually were reflected in the aspect. He returned the building art to the tradition of creation. He is the grandfather

< 40 >

Path of Discovery, by Paul Klee. (By courtesy of J. B. Neumann.)

of the Modern architecture of America and Europe today. His pupil and co-worker, Frank Lloyd Wright, is more strictly speaking the father, by reason of richer creative sensibility, and an ability to fight unscathed through any battle at any odds—to victory, because the future is on his side. These men, with Berlage in

< 41 >

Holland and Wagner in Austria, initiated the new expressive architecture, which is the exact antithesis of the imitationalism of the Victorian era.

It is not necessary here to seek into all the arts for evidence that practice and theory in the 19th Century were Realistic-imitational: exhibiting values at the very pole from the quality held most precious by the Moderns. I hope to have established sufficiently the point that, in general, art just before Expressionism was un-Expressionistic: uncreative, unoriginal, inexpressive. In literature the lines of revolution begin farther back, and interweave more confusingly with continuing traditional creative practice and with common Realistic activity. There is no suddenly apparent contrast, and there are subtler shadings of imitative and expressive elements. In the theatre, a multiple art, the prophet Craig changes the course of visual stage practice, but the advance is hampered because there are no co-revolutionary playwrights of comparable stature.

In the dance, however, a genius appears, against the typical background of a run-down, imitative and stultifying tradition. She galvanizes the world into attention, and, by example, revolutionizes practice on two continents. It is not so certain that Isadora Duncan carried through to intensest Expressionistic creativeness—Mary Wigman is more typical of the new world—but Duncan ended a centuries-long imitational era: closed a period during which evolution had all but ceased, and initiated a new cycle of creation.

The arts before Expressionism, then, had run a long and varied course within the blinders of Realism and imitationalism. It is necessary to remember the extent to which artists submitted to this limitation, through three centuries: that the graphic work had to

< 42 >

Moby Dick, by Boardman Robinson. (By courtesy of the Kraushaar
Galleries, New York.)

give back the illusion of the appearances of nature; that the architect and the dancer had to keep within the limits of what had been
done in their professions in the past. Institutionalized education,
the museums, written history, still glorify the Realistic painting,
the imitative building. But we have come together to study another
sort of art—which I hope will be more understandable after this
brief glance at what went immediately before.

< 43 >

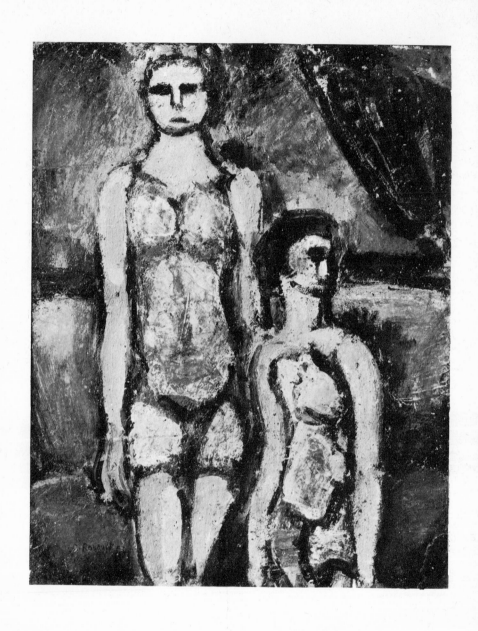

Circus Dancers, by Georges Rouault. Typical abandonment of natural
detail for strong plastic organization. (By courtesy of
Pierre Matisse Gallery.)

CHAPTER III

B ENEDETTO CROCE once opened a book with this definition: "Art is what everybody knows it is." Thus an aesthetician who had spent years wrestling with the subject intellectually, summed up his impatience and his doubts. The statement is far more than a quip. It acknowledges the uselessness of attempting to intellectualize conclusively about art, of trying to explain it literally and reasonably. At the same time it grants that all men feel what art is, intuitively—before they call on the brain to settle whether it is primarily perception or communication, intuition or imitation, content or form, or other of the alternatives which have been endlessly and confusingly debated by the philosophers.

The practicing artist is notoriously contemptuous of the experts who theorize about art; and certainly most of the aestheticians writing today overlook those very qualities or values which the Modernist believes to be the essence of creative work. The case is very much the same as in the realm of speculative philosophy: life itself escapes the philosophers while they are discussing whether it is seeming or being, the reality itself or the perception of it, the while men go on living. The aesthetician is far from being a direct help to either artist or art-lover. In the face of the mystery of creativeness, he has taken refuge in quibbling and abstruse evasion.

And yet we cannot easily and understandingly explore the field of produced art without recognizing some basic "principles." We

< 45 >

cannot advance in a discussion of Expressionism, or any other creative development, without agreeing upon, at the least, a tentative definition. What each student would like to feel, no doubt, is that after reviewing all the standard theories, he has dismissed as many as are outmoded; going on, then, with a few sifted truths that hold good in the light of latest exploration and practice.

It probably does no one any permanent harm to read the books of the learned aestheticians—both the philosophic and the empirical sorts. It is even possible to gain insight thus, if one resolves not to get lost in the disputatious jungles of thought, not to lose one's eyes for seeing, and one's intuitive faculties of enjoyment.

In Croce's works, for instance, the clearing of the ground * is of practical benefit: when he brings art free of the intents of instruction and moralizing, and when he distinguishes the "lyrical or pure intuition" of art from the logical thinking and critical classification of history and natural science. (Much that masquerades as original art, in our museums, is merely illustrative history or nature study.) He also puts back into perspective the earlier systems that aimed at an absolute definition or theory of what art is; he notes that aesthetic is ever growing and renewing, as understanding enlarges. His own first explanation of art as at once *intuition and expression* might afford as likely a starting-point as one could find for a simple book like this, which pretends to record little more than an outside view of one phase of art practice.

---

* Leo Stein remarks: "The principal service of Croce to aesthetics has been to almost wipe out the subject, while leaving the word. This service is considerable, because aesthetics had been on the whole so enticing and so unprofitable that its removal from the field of practical attention was a real boon." Stein, however, went on to complete his own book, *The A-B-C of Aesthetics;* though he notes in the Preface: "There are no authorities and it is somewhat doubtful whether the subject exists."

< 46 >

Landscape, by Maurice de Vlaminck. (By courtesy of Adolph Lewisohn.)

It should be emphasized, certainly, that all the elder systems of aesthetics (and some students would include that of Croce), all *a priori* systems, by which laws were laid down for the eternal confinement of art, seem to the Moderns futile. Reasoned canons, based on "the search for perfection"—a search carried on in the natural world—will always be inadequate, in the face of the mysteries and unaccountable reaches of creation. Intellectual concepts of art are necessarily based on observation in the realm of nature and inductive logic; and no amount of study with the sense-equip-

< 47 >

ment and the brain can explain the formal and rhythmic elements in art. The empirical aestheticians, trying to come at the mystery from another side, that of the observer and appreciator—tracing the modes of emotional reaction—are in somewhat better case; but the theory of empathy, of art as stimulation of sympathetic response, seems to many practitioners to leave out more than it takes in. It relates appreciation to a concept of an unchanging ego—as much a limitation as those to be discovered in the "absolute" systems.

The only aesthetician who has attempted, with any show of success, to formulate, in English, a theory specifically applicable to Modernist art, is Herbert Read. He goes largely to the German empirical school for evidence; but he finds in the writings of Bergson (who never treated aesthetics separately) the single statement that he considers broad enough to allow for the phenomena of Modernism.*

For our part, approaching the subject of Expressionism in an effort to clear away obstructions to enjoyment, we too may find

* The student should read a summary of the theories of Croce; he may be considered the end of the old line of aestheticians. His article in *The Encyclopædia Britannica*, 14th edition, is perhaps a better brief statement than any to be found in his books. The quotation at the beginning of the chapter is from the essay translated as *The Essence of Aesthetic*, London, 1921. One has to make allowances for Croce's hostility toward the empirical theorists and their "hopeless attempt." For the other side, see Herbert Read's *Art Now*, New York, 1934. One has to make allowance, in turn, for the author's impatience with Croce; but Read is the most persuasive and readable writer on aesthetics as applied to Modernism. *Art Now* is doubly useful·in having 128 collotype plates of contemporary painting and sculpture. (Too many books on aesthetics can get along without reference to produced art.) Read's terminology seems to me confused and confusing: he attempts exact divisions into groups that are "Subjective Realists," or "Subjective Idealists," etc., but his book is informative and stimulating; and today perhaps no terminology is good outside the volume in which it is used. The student should read also *The A-B-C of Aesthetics*, by Leo Stein, New York, 1927; *Art*, by Clive Bell, London, 1920; Book I of *The Art in Painting*, by Albert C. Barnes, New York, 1928 (second edition, revised and enlarged); and *The Modern Movement in Art*, by R. H. Wilenski, London, n.d.

< 48 >

most hope and sustenance in Bergson. The philosophy of change, of which he has been the most eloquent advocate, would seem to offer the only foothold for relating modern art to modern life; and his emphasis on intuition as basic and the mystic as normal, is in line with our study so far. At the moment, an acceptance of the theory of creative evolution—supplemented perhaps by a vague knowledge of the principles of Relativity—will prevent us from offering any definition of art with the expectation that it will prove permanent, absolute or final. We are seeking a means for understanding, in a changing world.

A WORKING DEFINITION

As a basis for discussion to follow, we may start with this:

Art is the formal expression of a conceived image. As an alternative, we might phrase it: *Art is the formal expression of an imagined conception.*

In adopting this definition tentatively, we are not evading the issue as does everyone who explains art as "beauty"; that is merely a transfer of the problem into another unlighted alley. No more do we take refuge in "that which gives pleasure in a special way," or "that which affords aesthetic enjoyment"—evasions both. We are facing the mystery of art with the most definitive words we can find.

But since they still are words, which are inexact, and many notoriously loose, let us try honestly to pin down our meaning as neatly and suggestively as may be—examining each word of the definition for overtones and implications.

Art is the formal expression of a conceived image.

"Formal" carries the implication of order, plan or rhythm in the

< 49 >

expression. It immediately lifts the meaning above imitative functions, beyond art as descriptive, inventorial or explanatory. The Oxford Dictionary defines "formal" first as meaning, "(Metaphys.) of the essence of a thing"—furthering our sense of flight from the casual, natural and ephemeral. There are those who would prefer the phrase "ordered expression" to "formal expression." To this student there seems little difference intrinsically, but "formal" outwardly ties in to the "search for form" which is a main path of Modernist experiment—and talk.

"Expression," as a word, affords another defense against the common conception of art as imitation or interpretation. Croce is careful to free expression from connotations of communication. We need not be so solicitous for a difference: for communication must be a link somewhere in the chain: whether we consider art as complete in the processes within the artist's faculties, with communication a sort of extension, or as the whole chain of processes from conception to appreciation. In either case, "expression" seems the fittest key word in any modern definition of art, because it implies the importance of the processes before the giving-out, of the feeling, the emotion, *personal to the artist*—and is therefore in line with practically all Modernist credos, and the bulk of practice.

"Conceived": this word, in its prime meaning, "become pregnant with, originate," establishes just the point I should like to establish, before going forward to talk about the greater *creativeness* of Expressionist art, as distinguished from Realist. "Conceived" also suggests directness of creation, and overtones of emotion, lyricism, ecstasy.

"Image": used not in the sense of representation or semblance, but as denoting *a production of the imagination given form.* But as some people, timid about abstractions, referring everything pos-

< 50 >

The Garden, by Darrel Austin. (By courtesy of the Perls Galleries, New York.)

sible to sense-images, might find a loophole here, permitting the escape of art back to nature-imitation, I have worded my alternate definition not "conceived image" but "imagined conception," which seems to me a slight weakening of the idea behind "conceived," but safer to some minds in that there is removed the possible likeness-to-nature connotation in "image." (There should be a word with the

< 51 >

implication of concreteness felt in "image," and the intuitional and non-representational sense of "imagination.")

The whole book is in a sense an elucidation—I hope that I am not implying too much!—of this definition. I have recorded earlier my opinion that the contemporary Expressionist movement constitutes partly a return to basic creative art (after a period when men turned to secondary, uncreative imitative activities); and any treatment of a serious phase of art practice, any analysis of a newly expressive or revelatory accomplishment, upon the upward scale, must be shown to come within a definition that embraces Chinese, Greek, Byzantine and other still valid manifestations. In studying Expressionism, in other words, one should begin with a theory basic enough to underlie all creative or primary art; but at the same time one may recognize that the very definition of art is broadened or sharpened by reference to latest achievement.

ART AND ITS MATERIALS

It is obvious, then, that I am trying to frame a definition broad enough to embrace intensely creative art of all past time, and of all sorts, yet a definition shaped somewhat by the conclusions to be drawn from Modernist practice and appreciation.*   It is under-

* The hostile reader—there always are such, when Modernism challenges Fundamentalism—will find here an apparent breach in our walls. "First he forms a definition of all art, to which presumably he will reconcile Expressionism, in an effort to bring about its acceptance.   Then he admits that he has framed that definition specifically to fit the Expressionist's case! Obviously illogical!"   And indeed there is no logic in discussions of creative art: there are no laws to deduce from, nor absolute practice as a starting-point for induction.   One throws a little light on the latest phenomena by reference to the main stream of past achievement; one opens appreciation to the latest product, and goes back better prepared to summarize in a definition the essence of past creative effort, in a statement temporarily useful. It is a see-saw effort to let in a little illumination; not an attempt to fix final standards. There seems to me no other method where spiritual and aesthetic values are under discussion.   From practice to theory, from theory to practice: and somehow one's understanding widens, one's experience of art deepens.

< 52 >

Landscape, by Paul Cezanne. Typical pictorial-plastic treatment, with the medium declared.

standing of the Expressionist achievement, for instance, that leads to the substitution of "expression" for "imitation," "interpretation," etc. The words "illusion" and "representation," common to many earlier definitions, are not included either.

There is, however, one primary lesson artists have learned out of Expressionist experiment and practice, as distinguished from Victorian-Realist, which I have not permitted to influence my wording. It has to do with the importance of the medium: the enormously expressive values to be derived from characteristic use of paint on a two-dimensional field, or stone in the mass, or archi-

< 53 >

Hilda: Marble sculpture by William Zorach. Typical Expressionist return
to capitalization of the virtues of the stone medium.

tectural steel-and-glass, or movement of actors on a stage. The Modernists have signally capitalized upon the materials and methods particular to each art, have purified the medium: so that the literary values tend to disappear from painting, the plastery-painty values from sculpture, the 19th Century literary-intellectual over-emphasis from the art of the theatre. Expressionism attempts a return to the typically theatrical elements in the stage art, to the stone of sculpture, to the strictly pictorial problems of painting. But the wisdom of his seems to me too elementary to demand recording in a definition of art. Capitalization upon the materials particular to the art in hand can be taken for granted in all intensely creative eras. (During the digression, in the 17th-19th Centuries, from the great tradition, in the seeable arts, men found special delight in sculpture tortured into wash-drawing technique, in anecdote pictures, and in cast iron ornament imitating wood carvings.)

Some of the most understanding of writers on Modernist art stress this matter in their definitions, refusing to consider the sense complete unless the idea of expression is conditioned from the standpoint of material-technique. There is no reason for quarrel with people who prefer to look from a slightly different angle— since we are putting forward no claims to universality or exclusiveness. I may therefore note that my wording might be elaborated thus: *A work of art is the formal expression of a conceived image, in terms of the particular medium employed.*

There is one other word commonly insisted upon, which I have omitted from the basic definition as too obvious: *feeling.* It seems to me patent that creative expression must arise out of feeling or emotion, in any case where conception has occurred, followed by image-forming. But this matter is treated in later chapters: one upon Abstraction, enquiring to what extent the formal image may

< 55 >

exclude the recognizable symbols or materials of objective reality, and one directly upon "Feeling and Meaning." Summaries of the ideas presented in those chapters are included in the numbered paragraphs a few pages forward.

My definition no doubt implies a point of view: it is obviously not worded with the intention of spreading over everything ever done in the name of art. Victorian definitions, like Victorian museums and histories, sometimes suffered from an amiable all-inclusiveness. Here we are definitely disinterested in "art" that is mere transfer from seen nature, that is photography. The emphasis is, instead, on the artist's conception, on essence, on form, on expression; and I take for granted the importance of feeling, and of the potentialities of the medium.

With that emphasis in mind, we shall now enquire whether there is one well-marked main stream of Modernist art. We shall ask whether there is warrant for considering such contributory "schools" as Post-Impressionism, Cubism, Abstractionism, etc., as integral to one current, within one movement. What are the features that characterize the most *typical* Modernist art? If there is such a thing as Expressionism, we should be able to find a certain continuity of experimental endeavor, a like achievement among many artists, a main path of progress—to which, perhaps, the name will prove more appropriate than any other.

THE MAIN PATH OF MODERNISM

I recognize that there are other currents of experiment and advance—and almost innumerable eddies and side-streams—beside the main course I shall now try to chart, roughly. But since I am conductor of the present party of exploration, I shall ask that, for

< 56 >

the moment, the reader follow my tracing of what seems to me the essential Expressionist thing. Some of the lesser currents will be examined later.

In the main, modern Expressionism (regarding, at this time, painting only) may be explained in these few statements.

1. There is an increased precision of thinking in regard to the artist's problem *in relation to his medium.* In painting, this results in an unprecedented respect for the canvas as a two-dimensional field, which, in completion, must have an integrity or unity of its own. The picture frame is no longer a window upon nature, within which a naturally beautiful scene or object is fixed, with or without a measure of selection and interpretation. To preserve the picture field, to endow it with a creative value, which makes it different from nature, is a first aim of Expressionist art.

2. Within the picture the artist arranges certain elements—volumes, planes, lines, colors, textures—in an order determined by a feeling he has experienced, perhaps stimulated by a natural scene, or a memory thereof, or perhaps first stirred at some deeper perceptive source, by an experienced emotion. The order thus achieved, the unified abstract design or plastic architecture of the picture, is of greater importance than the surface appearances of natural objects that may be incidental to the design. The achievement of this formal order, as a common attribute of modern painting, is of the essence of Expressionism on the material and compositional side.

3. While obviously it is too early to pronounce judgment on the artists and schools concerned, with any pretense of finality, it seems clear that the main current of Modernism proceeds in a line from Cezanne through the Fauves and the Cubists to the several contemporary groups that are usually explained as "form seeking."

< 57 >

That is, Expressionism has continually fed on the achievements of painters, in various schools, who were willing to sacrifice all else in order to reveal a bit of the precious rhythmic organization, the formal architectonics noted in the paragraph above. Intensest creation, moreover, seems to lie with those artists who differentiate this essential rhythmic-dynamic element from the static compositional values commonly found among the "Old Masters," and even, at times, in recent superficial Realistic painting; the distinction depending upon understanding of plastic orchestration: the correlation of dynamic elements, of tensions and forces set up by volume-space organization, recessive colors, etc. The nearest lucid explanations (for we are deep now in the clouds noted in the first chapter) are those dealing with *movement* in the canvas: meaning not depicted natural movement, but the backward-forward design, the poised or coiled tension-path, the thrust and return and contrapuntal variations of the plastic elements. There are ways of opening the picture, of carrying the attention, of stabilizing the sense of movement, which afford the observer a perception of underlying abstract order, a revelation of a plastic "structure." Some of the commoner means to fixing this movement in the canvas are by superimposed or overlapping planes, by bent planes, by tension of volumes (understood best by reference to the planetary system), by heavy or faint texture, and by manipulation of the forward-coming and receding properties of colors. These several elements are commonly utilized, in conjunction, to achieve not only a main direction of movement in the picture but also an enriching minor counterplay of backward-forward fluctuation.

4. The passionate search of the Expressionists for means to fix the play of movement in the canvas, to reveal the expressive form quality, the dynamic order, has led to increased *abstraction.* There

< 58 >

On Morse Mountain, Maine: Water-color by John Marin. Expressive-abstract values displacing illusive and Realistic. (By courtesy of An American Place.)

has been progressive neglect of nature's casual aspects, even what some would call nature's beauty; distortion of natural shapes and textures; and in frequent cases, utter abandonment of recognizable objectivity. Purely abstract relationships have become of greater significance than transfers from nature's storehouse of the beautiful and the "picturesque." It may be stated, indeed, that there are two main divisions of the Expressionist current: one in which the abstract values are sought for their own sake, independent of natu-

< 59 >

ral appearances, or with only incidental relation to the objective world; and one in which a picture ordered with nature's materials and rich in "feeling" contains a supporting skeleton or structure of the abstract, the latter being the more important reason for the picture's existence, aesthetically considered—though there may be a range of over-values, depending upon the nature of the subject, affording human and social interest and stimulation.

5. Implicit in the attempt to achieve a revealing bit of the creative formal order, the abstract architecture in the canvas, there is a universal-mystic significance. An intensely creative abstract work of art, affording an enjoyment that may border upon rapture, links with the mystic's search for personal identification with the rhythm at the heart of the universe, with the consciousness of dynamic order and harmonious progression of the cosmos, beyond time and space. It is not necessary for the reader to accept this statement in order to follow the discussion through following chapters—if he distrusts mystic analogies and speculation in the region of a fourth dimension. Nevertheless, many Expressionist artists are proceeding with a sense of direct connection of abstract values in art with the deeper spiritual aspects of living; and many of the rest of us have found our understanding of Modern art clarified by a study of those contemporary spiritual movements, of both Western and Eastern origin, that attempt to bring the individual soul into conscious identification with the source of all-being. Knowing something of the mystic's conception of the structure and meaning of all that is, we find our faculties better able to identify, and enjoy, the echo of universal-eternal architecture in creative art. The habit of apprehending the infinite in the finite is an aid in seeing through to the picture's abstract core. Art here becomes a sensuous means to revelation of cosmic order. Expressive form, achieved,

< 60 >

opens four-dimensional vistas. (The Modern is here aided and fortified by study of ancient Chinese art, in practice and theory.)

6. The increased precision of feeling in regard to materials and method, the capitalization upon freshly discovered or understood potentialities of color, movement, etc., in relation to the basic picture plane, lead to a new *intensity of expression*, a fullness and vividness typically Modern. This intensity is re-inforced by that other attainment, the plastic orchestration in the picture: the formal order which may be marked by one as mystic revelation, by another as merely mechanistic dynamic rhythm. Besides these factors contributing to the "fullness" of Expressionist painting, the one material, the other rhythmically structural, there is—except in wholly abstract examples—the element drawn from nature or human experience, which cannot yet be charted. It is too soon, it seems to this observer, to attempt to judge how far this "life" element, the reflection of a fullness and intensity of common living, in the machine age, may contribute, in the picture's "content," to the already increased intensity of Expressionist art. Decades from now, historians will be able to look back and estimate the influence: assess the enriching subject values, human and social, in early 20th Century Modernism.

Even today there are critics, holding to literary and moral values in painting but pretending to "sympathy" with the Moderns, who contend that all the achievement since Cezanne has been in the nature of perfecting a shell, into which more inspired artists may in the future pour something significant by way of subject matter. (Thomas Craven opines that the Cubists painted as they did because "they have nothing to say." He adds, writing in 1931, that "in France the more intelligent men . . . are gradually returning to representational art.") Others of us believe that a whole de-

< 61 >

Sea Lyric, by Matthew Barnes. (Photo by courtesy of Joseph A. Danysh Galleries, from original in collection of Mrs. Sigmund Stern.)

partment of painting—abstract and near-abstract—justifies itself by the enjoyment afforded without reference to objective nature or intellectual idea. The compositions of Kandinsky and the near-abstract "landscapes" of Cezanne, in no sense transcriptions from nature or comments on subject-matter, yield us pleasure as do the equally abstract works of Beethoven and Bach.

In a second range, where objectivity enters in, the core of abstract formal order seems to us the truer source of our enjoyment, rather than called-up memories of apples, trees, bathers and other

< 62 >

incidental content. In the third range, where compelling subject-matter is indissolubly fused with the formal elements, there simply is not enough evidence to warrant final conclusions. There will be, this observer believes, a development upon the foundation already built by the Modernists, a structure of art more humanly and socially significant, with the satisfying architectonic quality at its core; and as long as that core remains, and the subject elements lend emotional rather than intellectual intensification, it will still be Expressionist achievement. One can only say meantime that the Modern advance so far has been primarily in finding the means to achieve that core, which seems to some immeasurably worth while on its own account; and that there probably will be a further extension toward enrichment with intenser "life stuff." (The more extreme Communists, of course, stand with the old-fashioned critics in insisting upon the first importance of sentimental or intellectual content or message. For them the picture is not significant unless it promotes the workers' revolution. Some of us who believe in the inevitable and just coming of a workers' world, in the widest sense, still admit a value in art separate from propaganda or urge to action. Art with a social "drive" seems to me preferable to most of the product that we have now, with neither abstract values nor social significance: pretty, photographic, sentimental and trivially flattering art, subtly propagandist for the tired world that is passing. But the Communists will come to see that an abstract type of painting is worth preserving on its own account, as music and dance will be preserved.)

OTHER APPROACHES, AND EXCLUSIONS

Now obviously these six statements form a merely *personal* summary of what one observer considers the characteristic values and direction of Modernist art. After, roughly, ten years during which

< 63 >

I have sought for the most expressive, revealing and intense works of contemporary painting, first for enjoyment, then for study and analysis, I have come to the belief that the search for a deeper order in the canvas is the essential mark of today's Modernism; this leading to a conception of the picture as a thing apart from and beyond nature. Next in importance is the conception of that revealing order not merely as a compositional element but as a dynamic value, to be studied and attained in terms of movement, plastic rhythm and tension.

There are other ways of approach to an understanding of the typical thing. Once the point is made that transfers from nature are of only secondary importance, that imitation is giving place to expression—and any representative display of Moderns will suggest as much—one might turn immediately to the question, "What is it that the artist expresses?" The briefest study might lead to this answer: He expresses primarily his feeling for life and order, growing out of his own experience of universal abstract values, perhaps as apprehended from a sense-experience of an object or subject in outward nature; his expression being intensified also by a special mastery of the materials and methods of his art. And indeed, that approach, in turn from the three "sources," in the artist's feeling and imagination, in the subject, and in the materials, will determine the way of our analysis of Expressionist elements in the next chapter.

The reader who knows his "Who's Who in Modernism" will recognize that, in setting down the credo above, I am excluding from the main current several schools and isms which have bulked large in art news during the past thirty years. This is in addition to ruling out, as uncreative, all the streams of Realistic-photographic art: Naturalism, Romanticism, selective-Realism, etc.

< 64 >

Winter Twilight, by Georges Rouault. (By courtesy of
Pierre Matisse Gallery.)

Thus the following groups claiming the "Modern art" label are
left outside the definition: Futurism, because it ended by being
merely *illustration of movement,* however novel its photography;
Sur-Realism, because in its most characteristic phase it returned to
depiction of the objective, albeit the objects and symbols illustrated
are drawn from the subconscious rather than the surface mind
(though it is to be noted that certain creative members of the Sur-
Realist school have shied away from the Freudian dream-exposing
group, these others being recruits from German Abstractionism,

< 65 >

French Cubism, etc., and better explained with those experimenters); and the devotees of The New Objectivism, because they head straight back toward rearranged photographic Realism. I have thus simplified my task—and I hope that of the reader—because I have come to feel that Expressionism, as the name history will apply to the creative art of this time and the period immediately ahead, is the antithesis of Realism in all its varieties. Although allowing, as noted in statement 6, for the entry of incidental objective values, emotional stimulus and social significance, as contributory, the attainment of dynamic-formal elements, instead of Realistic illusion, is the type-fact of present-day Modernism.

There is something to be said for, or about, this conclusion from another side: the appreciator's. A recognition of abstract values, among those not professional artists, is growing. Perhaps, even, men are coming to a time when this factor in painting will be generally recognized as the prime essential, a touchstone. Our consciousness today is more attuned to it than has been that of any earlier generation, by reason of wider spiritual exploration, clearer understanding of the artist's problem, and increased opportunity to compare the arts of all times and all peoples. It is my belief that as men develop aesthetically and spiritually, in the era now opening, their faculties will be increasingly eager for revelation of the architectonic-universal rhythm, the plastic synthesis. Its guises are various, as discovered in the works of—for instance—Cezanne, van Gogh, Matisse, Picasso, Kandinsky, Klee, Rouault and Marin; but the true Modernist picture is characterized by a value common to the achievement of these artists, and not to be discovered in the works of typical 18th and 19th Century painters.

We are opposed, of course, in our willingness to place a primary importance upon the formal and plastic elements in art, by critics

< 66 >

of the older school, from the Fundamentalist Cortissoz to the "liberal" Craven. Their opposition is based upon the flat statement that they can see no such values, and doubt their existence. (Craven, in a sprightly attack on the Modernists, suggests that the appreciators, far from being humans with broader sensibilities, are those few who consider themselves divinely endowed, but really have shrivelled until their "receptive apparatus is no longer capable of responding to anything but abstractions." He speaks of the Modernists in the past tense—"The Modernists were men of the strongest anti-social propensities"—and he finds Cezanne the only near-master.)

But the swing of informed appreciation toward the form-seeking artists, even to the most abstract, has been evident enough to warrant us in claiming recognition, on the part of perhaps the widest "art public" in history, of formal values. People who can't experience that element simply can't experience a thing common to a large and growing number of their fellow men. These latter ones are ready to stake their faith and a great amount of their study and time upon the existence of a compelling expressive-rhythmic value: believing that it is far more than a self-delusion of a few esoteric wanderers from the normal paths of experience. There is, indeed, something like a landslide among young students of the arts, toward Modernism, and toward recognition of what I have called the formal values of Expressionism.

This all might be put in a nutshell—the beliefs of the Modernists tend to one conclusion: *Things not imitable can be revealed, expressed, presented in another form.*

< 67 >

Head of a Young Woman, by André Derain. (By courtesy of the
Museum of Modern Art: Bliss Collection.)

CHAPTER IV

WHY EXPRESSIONISM?

IF I have not lost my way, I have now placed before the reader these basic thoughts: Art inevitably changes, grows, expands into new forms; and tradition marks the main path of progress (Chapter I). Victorian art was the culmination of a progression, or digression, during 350 years, along the lines of Realism and imitationalism; today's Modernism constitutes an utter revolution from Victorian theory and practice, and a return to the creative tradition (Chapter II). Among the multiple currents, eddies and contributing streams of Modernist art, one main direction of advance is discoverable (Chapter III).

If you grant me, on this showing, that there is an epochal revolution, and within it an identifiable main current, it is right to ask: What warrant is there for terming the new creative art "Expressionist"?

In the fifty years since Cezanne and Sullivan effectively started two of the creative streams that have flowed in steadily toward collective Modernism, there has been a welter of confusion over the nomenclature of the subject. The thing must come before the name. Controversy has raged over theory and practice, over the importance of individuals and schools, and over the naming of the main stream. Even today the student who would specifically label the art that is crowding out Realism, if only for convenience in discus-

< 69 >

sion, finds himself attacked and decried. But at the undisputed age of fifty years revolutionary Modernism deserves a recognized name.

The word "Modernism" itself is sometimes insisted upon as sufficient. But if we believe in evolution in art, we know for a certainty that tomorrow's Modernism will be different from today's: that the word can have no lasting historical meaning. It has no character of its own, is only temporal and relative. A century ago, in painting, the current Modernism was Romantic, with the more Modern "Naturalism" already foreshadowed. A half century ago, in the theatre, Modernism was the crusading intellectual Realism of Ibsen (which some universities count Modern still). The label, indeed, has no claim to permanency. If there are any definite characteristics marking off revolutionary art today from Victorian practice, the word is inadequate: a makeshift to be passed on progressively to later generations of innovators.

Similarly "Post-Impressionism" is a relative and negative label, though once useful and expressive. For a time, in the first confusion, it adequately tagged those painters who were pushing beyond current mass-practice. Already it seems to have passed into history, as designation of the very small group of original rebels against Impressionism. The only authoritative place where it is still used in the broadest sense, I believe, is in the pages of *The Encyclopædia Britannica* (14th edition, 1929). It is there praised as a "safe" term, though "Expressionism" is noted as more apt— but unfortunately of German origin!

As to "Futurism," it is the term most often employed—misused —by people who know little about contemporary creative art, except that it puzzles and therefore annoys them. It is another temporal and makeshift label, with no innate character, and is, moreover,

< 70 >

Still Life, by Karl Knaths. (By courtesy of A. E. Gallatin and the Gallery of Living Art.)

the self-chosen tag of a minor but vociferous school of painters and writers. Nor is "Cubism" a possible general designation for Modern art, considering its technical and limited connotations; although the Cubists have made the largest contribution to the main stream, in their experiments and their clarification of theories.

< 71 >

R. H. Wilenski, a leading and widely respected writer on this subject, sums up the main Modern development as "Cubist-Classical," by which he implies that Cubism constitutes the latest creative phase in the great or classical tradition of world art. But the name is rather too clumsy, if not contradictory, to live on definitively. Cubism will bulk large in histories, but as a contributory stream.

It seems to this observer, indeed, that—meaning considered— there are only two current terms possible to criticism and history, as summarizing the Modern movement: "Purism" and "Expressionism." As between the two, "Expressionism" is incomparably the more suggestive.

The antipathy to "Expressionism" as a label comes largely from France. French artists and critics, along with American and British writers trained in Paris, are hostile to a word originally associated with a German school; even though that school was obviously in the main line that began with Cezanne and progressed through Fauves, Cubists and Abstractionists. In a decade, nevertheless, the circulation of the word has widened, outside Germany and France —its significance enlarging too—in a way that argues its appropriateness and expressiveness. It promises, despite Paris, to persist as the label for the typical creative art of the early and middle 20th Century.

Putting aside the external fact that our own "authorities" make increasing use of it,* let us inquire into its appropriateness.

* C. J. Bulliet, in *Apples and Madonnas, Emotional Expression in Modern Art,* rather grudgingly admits that "Expressionism . . . is the best term that has been suggested to give a general idea of the aims of the new men." Helen Gardner, in *Art through the Ages,* notes that "The chief movements that have grown out of the 19th Century, beginning with Cezanne, may be loosely called Post-Impressionism, or as the artists themselves prefer, Expressionism." Frank Jewett Mather, Jr., in *Modern Painting: A Study of Tendencies,* accepts the word in its broadest significance; as does Mary-Cecil Allen in *Painters of the Modern Mind.*

< 72 >

If "Expressionism" is the ultimately right term for the thing this book treats of, it will be true that the word *express* is in some sense a summary of the characteristic elements brought into or restored to art at this time. In a general way the earlier chapters have labored to stress the shift of emphasis from illusion to expression, from imitational aim to expressive aim. The thought was brought to focus at the end of the preceding chapter: "Things not imitable can be revealed, *expressed*." It is necessary now to explore the expressive elements, analytically.

Just what, it is fair to ask, does the Modern artist express? *What* is revealed in his art, that existed not at all in the average art of the Realistic-Romantic era, or only in very subordinate measure?

There is an element, or a quality or value, sometimes identified as "Form," which may be considered (in a sense and tentatively) the outward crystallization, elusive but vaguely recognizable, of the thing we are here approaching as "expression." Even in the visual arts, we are accustomed to say that form cannot be seen so much as felt. There is still so much of mystery about the ways in which it is achieved and the ways in which it appeals, and so much of wrangling over the question of its existence, that I shall later treat the subject in a chapter cautiously entitled "Attempts to Explain Form." Meantime we are beginning our inquiry farther back, before considering the realization of the quality, in the finished work of art: inquiring what is *behind* the form, beginning with "expression." This inquiry may be divided, arbitrarily, for convenience, into three parts, one concerning the process within the artist's creative faculties, the personal-expression element, one concerning the expression of deeper values or attributes in the subject or object

< 73 >

Anna de Zborowska, by Amadeo Modigliani. (By courtesy of the Museum of Modern Art: Bliss Collection.)

(beyond imitable surface aspects), and one concerning the expressible or expressive values of the medium and materials as such.

The first small coteries of artists to whom the name "Expressionists" was applied, in Germany, were attempting to fix in the picture non-representational, non-objective values: "subjective" and formal elements similar to those they had detected in the works of the French Fauves and Cubists, by whom they had been strongly influenced; and to these they added something learned out of the Abstractionism of Kandinsky, one of their own number—he called it soul-expression—and a heritage of intense emotionalism from Edvard Munch. There entered in also, from non-pictorial sources, an emotional intensity coupled with heedlessness of nature, from Strindberg most notably. The German critics settled upon the name "Expressionism" for this group movement "that put more stress on expression of the artist's own feelings than on the objective materials of Realist art."

Certainly if the word was coined to cover the Cubism of Marc, the naïve child-primitivism of Klee, and the dynamic impetuousness of Kirchner, Schmidt-Rottluff, Heckel, Pechstein and Nolde —and these are among the men mentioned in the earliest articles and books—it should be broad enough to denominate the entire creative stream from Cezanne and van Gogh to Rouault, Lurçat, Marin and Arp. The name was invented, indeed, not to suggest a special quality which the Germans had detected in their own radicalism—what the *Britannica* terms "the excessively brutal German contribution"—but to summarize the newly expressive international achievement up to that time. Writers as early as 1919 were treat-

< 75 >

ing the subject under headings that indicate this breadth: "Dynamic Expressionism," "Abstract Expressionism," "Arabesque Expressionism," etc.*

Of the influences out of the French development—as noted by the German critics, in the war years and immediately after—the main current of Cezannism through Matisse and Picasso was doubtless strongest.   But van Gogh proved an extraordinary stimulant, and found in Germany first recognition as one of the Masters.   Of the less known influences, that of Munch, who had lived long in Germany, giving impetus particularly to the Dresden secessionists, was most potent.   But the Swiss Hodler was becoming known, and the works of the 19th Century German "eccentric" von Marees were being re-discovered.   It is useless to try to disentangle the threads of these several influences; they all led away from Realism—toward a deepening of expression.

The broad significance of the term Expressionism, as used, could scarcely go farther than it did in 1919, when Herwarth Walden in one of *Der Sturm* publications stated that Impressionism—the final variety of Realism—was only a phase, a vogue, but Expressionism a world movement, of the universal spirit or feeling, linked with Creation.   To him the two things were patently Non-Art and Art: nature and expression.   He carried the thought over from painting to poetry, music and the other arts.   Various writers pushed

* See particularly *Die Deutsche Expressionistische Kultur und Malerei*, by Eckart von Sydow, Berlin, 1919-20. Most of the literature of the subject is still confined to the German language.   J. B. Neumann, who has done much to increase American understanding of Expressionism, by exhibitions and lectures, dates the movement, as a recognized international development, from 1911.   He held then the first Munch one-man show; and in 1912 there was the great Cologne exhibition which challenged and crystallized understanding in Germany as did the famous Armory Show in this country a year later.   The first artist groups to which the Expressionist name was applied were, I believe, *Die Brücke* in Dresden, and the more widely celebrated *Blaue Reiter* in Munich.

< 76 >

the inquiry into other fields, and prepared books on German mediaeval Expressionism, Expressionism in peasant art, etc. What they all were tracing was art as expression of the artist's feelings or imaging, instead of art as illusion or transcription.

It did not escape these early critics, as you see, that "Expressionism" offers the perfect antithesis to the immediately preceding movement, Impressionism. Rudolf Bluemner even went back, in his search for appropriate connotations and explanations, to Thomas Aquinas and Scholasticism. There he found the distinction between *species impressa* and *species expressa:* the one pertaining to material and sinful corporeality, and the other to the angels and the pure human soul. The old objective art—or pretense of art— was to give way to an art freed from materiality: become subjective, expressive. There was, of course, much talk about the mystic element, particularly in abstract Expressionism, and of the individual artist-creator as an individualization of the universal Creator. Of course you and I will have no quarrel with this ranging of the Modernists on the side of the angels.

Some of the earliest summaries prove illuminating still. This one is to be found in Dr. Oskar Pfister's extraordinary psychopathological study, *Expressionism in Art: Its Psychological and Biological Basis:* "The Expressionist objects to the low level of the photographer's camera, reproducing natural colors. The Expressionist wants to reproduce the intrinsic meaning of things, their soul-substance. But this grasping of the intrinsic, i.e., the only genuine reality, is not done through an intellectual study of the external world. . . . From this view-point Impressionism appears as mere surface-art, and therefore a superficial art, a mechanical craft and no art at all. The Expressionist on the other hand creates out of the depth of things, because he knows himself to be in those

< 77 >

depths. To paint out of himself and to paint himself means to reproduce the intrinsic nature of things, the Absolute. The artist creates as God creates, out of his own inner Self, and in his own likeness."

Again Pfister has said that "the Expressionist's world is the Expressionist himself as *the* world." Fritz Burger in 1917 wrote: "The modern picture [aims at] the embodiment of that incommensurable realm which constitutes our innermost Self. . . . It will bring about our enjoyment of the world's inner magnificence, the wonderful abundance and richness of the Creative Power itself." Kandinsky wrote: "That is beautiful which is produced by the inner need, which springs from the soul." And again: "The artist must search deeply into his own soul, develop and tend it, so that his art has something to clothe, and does not remain a glove without a hand."

While we are still exploring this question of the supreme importance of the artist's subjective process, or contribution, in early Expressionism, let me note that two of the writers quoted offer a direct contrast in their interpretations of the source and impulse within the artist. Kandinsky is a mystic and Theosophist, and is himself a creator, with keenest formal sensibility. Pfister is a scientist, psychologist, Realist; he is a skeptic, intolerant of mysticism, and wholly insensible to formal values and aesthetic response. Up to a certain point they see eye to eye, as regards an epochal change that has developed in the arts; their differences beyond are illuminating.

Pfister defines Expressionism as the art of inwardness: but since he recognizes no mystic-creative sources, he must trace back to a psychosis every objective element in the painting. "There are, behind the design planned by the artist-poet, secret personal remi-

< 78 >

Landscape in Maine: Water-color by John Marin. (By courtesy of the Art Institute of Chicago.)

niscences and aims which could be found only by Psycho-analysis. What the artist indicates as its contents is always rationalization. . . . The deepest meaning . . . is always the self-representation of the artist's psychical state." Pfister then goes on to the usual sequential ideas: every artist is a sufferer; "All his pictures contain the fulfillment of secret desires, which are wholly hidden even from himself"; "Whoever is conscious of a wave of emotion when looking at Expressionistic works proves thereby that he experiences the same distress"—a warning to the reader! Ultimately, of course,

< 79 >

Pfister reaches the typical material-scientist's conclusion that expression constitutes a psychic discharge. Art is made a funnel for belching up from the subconscious.

Kandinsky, on the other hand, vaults both the subconscious and the upper objective mind, and arrives at a source beyond, in what he frankly terms the soul: art is an expression of the spirituality in man. Kandinsky begins not with distress but with harmony. It would seem to some a fairer starting point for creation. But there are many observers, in this time when men have not outgrown 19th Century materialistic philosophies, who are equipped exclusively for the recognition of Realistic harmony, and cannot respond to Kandinsky's type of art: who therefore lump it with the psychic-discharge sort, and tag it all as "abnormal." Nevertheless the recent trend has been toward acceptance of Kandinsky's general premise.

We shall, in a later chapter, return to the mystic aspect, examining the suggestion that the artists escaping from pre-occupation with objective reality are working toward revealment of the sanest and most beautiful thing to be experienced by man. Meantime we may note that even the later scientists cut under Dr. Pfister's assumption that every expression must proceed from a physical or worldly cause. It is a commonplace of latest scientific philosophy that the physical is only one phase of what is. The most ordinary of terms in the vocabulary of art—design, unity, rhythm, order—imply creative powers not measurable or chartable; and the delving of science into the atom and the nebula have failed to suggest any plausible physical source of first motion or life. Dr. Pfister himself weakens his case when, toward the end of his book, he quotes a remark by Worringer, to the effect that Gothic architecture is a "living document of the lofty hysteria of the Middle Ages." He

< 80 >

would seem almost to indicate that every exceptionally intense work of art is a departure from "the normal." Perhaps the world is progressing toward attainment of another "normal" than his.

These quotations sufficiently suggest the early revolutionary shift from illusional and imitational art to subjectively expressive art; and the advocates of Expressionism, as the name summarizing constructive Modernism of today, point out that devotion to an inner expressiveness was as much a characteristic urge of Cezanne, Sullivan and Craig—fathers and prophets of the "new art"—as it is a stated objective of many a practitioner a generation later. This is all we need to know, in this chapter, about the subjective element: we are merely establishing that it richly exists—in contrast with the spiritually poor, objective Realism of the centuries immediately preceding. The nature of it, and the methods of presenting it, will afford materials, and controversies for later chapters: treating of its revelation as form, and its significance as feeling and meaning.

GETTING TO THE SOUL OF THE OBJECT

Possibly a purely subjective art would be wholly abstract, without observable relationship to concrete reality. But only a very small part of Modern art is of that sort; though obviously the typical Modernist tends *toward* abstraction, as compared with the Realist confining himself to the surface look of nature.

In other words, the object survives, even though its natural aspect is subordinated, at times distorted. Expressionism is first of all an expression of the artist's own feelings or illumination; but there is also an element of expressiveness of a deeper reality, a hidden essence, in the object (or event) by which his creative faculty has been stimulated. The "inspiration" comes from nature, or memory

< 81 >

thereof, or an observed event; not in a photographic or illusional way, as in the Realist's case, but in some new, doubly expressive equivalent.

The Cubist may claim that he affords an abstract of the apple or the vase or the mandolin player. He has looked not only at the "front" surfaces, which happen to present themselves to the common eye; he has viewed the object from all sides, from front and back, below and above, from without and within. He has sought its essence, not merely its physical aspect under casual light. He reveals this "soul" of the object—let the appearances fall where they may.

"Abstraction" is defined as "an idea stripped of its concrete accompaniments." An "abstract" is the "essence" or "summary." To express this idea or essence or summary, perhaps without resort to nature's casual arrangements, disembarrassed of inconsequential concrete detail, is a first aim of the Expressionist.

There is, I believe, no way of distinguishing exactly between expression of the artist's feelings, as analyzed in the preceding section, and this expression of the deeper values in the object; though there are whole volumes on aesthetics that argue for absolute creation or for perception of nature as the one and only process of creation. The artist expresses something found in the phenomenal world, let us say; but it is the essence, superior to surface reality, only because it breathes relationship to the source of all that is, because it is microcosmic, crystallizing in little the architecture of the universe. That value in the object is hidden from the eyes of ordinary mortals, is detected only by the deeper visioning of the artist. There is, then, no delimiting his experience of it from his feeling over it. He apprehends its universality because his own faculties are extraordinarily attuned to the human-cosmic rhythm.

< 82 >

Tiger, by Franz Marc. (From *Expressionismus* by Herman Bahr.)

Expression in his art has found its source at once out of the soul of the object and out of his own intuitive visioning, out of a reaction and out of subjective feeling. Duncan Phillips entitled one of his books on modern art, "The Artist Sees Differently," with reference to this part of the creative process. He had written earlier an essay under the title, "The Power to See Beautifully."

There is, if you wish to put it that way, a power of mystic penetration, even where nature is concerned; and I think that we are

< 83 >

not laboring the point unduly when we say that expression of what is thus mystically "seen" provides a second warrant for terming Modernist art Expressionistic. What the camera sees can be imitated, depicted: the illusion of it given. The essence can be *expressed*, in other terms.

We might sum up the two kinds of expressiveness by saying that the artist expresses himself, but only when he has been stirred by something apprehended under the surface of nature or life. The two sources are one, if the process is traced back far enough; but in the product, the results may be dissociated and studied separately —as two aspects of expression.

THE EXPRESSIVENESS OF MATERIALS

In the search for an intensity of expression that had been lost by the Realists, the Moderns re-examined the methods and materials of each particular art, and arrived at new understanding of the limitations and capabilities of the several mediums. In some cases they not only recovered values long lost to the world, but, by capitalization upon newly existent materials, such as concrete and steel in architecture, and electric lighting on the stage, added to the intensity and range of expression.

Thus beyond the self-expression of the artist, and the expression of deeper values in the object or model or happening, there is this third sort of revealment which is common to Expressionism. The element of materials and method both shapes the final product by its limitations, and contributes by its special properties to the particular sort of beauty characteristic of the art in hand.

What the Expressionist has recovered is an attitude common to many primitive artists: a sense of directness of expression by the one most capable medium—a loving feel for color on its own account,

< 84 >

or polished wood, or the sensuous overtones of words. During less creatives ages, when imitation gave more delight than creative art, men lost sight of these values out of honest manipulation of materials. It became the fashion to copy the material idioms of one art into the practice of another. The so-called sculptors made plastery compositions with the swishy technique of painting or wash drawing. The painters told stories, or flattered courtiers or millionaires. Clever workmen tortured steel panelling into the semblance of grained wood. Imitational cleverness and transfer of "effects" won the popular and academic hearts. Integrity of medium was forgotten.

Then rose up a van Gogh to revel in color pigment on its own account; a Gaudier-Brzeska to cry out for the mountainous stone-quality in sculpture, damning the "light voluptuous modelling" that had usurped the place of cut-stone art; and a Gordon Craig to demand that the literary men—closet poets and journalists—and the scene-painters be subordinated to the artist of the theatre, who would bring back the typically theatric elements of movement, color, light and revelatory acting.

Expressionist artists speak often of the *purification of the means* of the art: a stripping away of the accretions of insensitive eras, and a sifting of the remaining basic elements for characteristic expressiveness. Isadora Duncan stripped away courtly ornament and literary purpose—as well as masquerade costume—from the dance: purified the art for direct expression of the body in rhythmic movement. Cezanne turned the course of painting from story-telling, photography and sentimental commentary to expression of an artist's feelings in terms of paints and two-dimensional canvas: purified the means and direction of his art. Craig and Appia startled a complacent theatre world by demonstrating that painters

< 85 >

and poets and pulpit-orators were appropriating the stage, blanketing the creative actor under bad pictures, torrents of words and a convention of naturalistic mimicry. They asked that the stage be purified: freed from intruders and returned to the artists of the theatre for *theatrical* expression. The modern theatre movement is sometimes summed up as a return to "the theatre theatrical"—an illuminating suggestion of the importance of an understanding of materials.

We are concerned here with a sort of expression that is instinctive with the artist *after he knows his tools,* after he has come to have a special feel for his materials. Perhaps he seldom thinks about the effects he is achieving specifically out of the virtues of his paint and canvas or chisel and stone: they have become an extension of himself, intuitively used. But the capitalization of the particular capabilities of his medium have put into the product values possible to no other art.

One should be a creative artist to realize the vividness of the artist's consciousness of potential beauty in materials, the poignancy of a sculptor's emotion over a certain quality of stone, or a theatre artist's leap to creative imagining in presence of a new type of stage.

I have so stressed, earlier, the "supreme" importance of the subjective contribution, as a factor in the Expressionist revolution, that the reader might be inclined to underestimate the actual change that has occurred in the attitude toward the medium. Watch the artists themselves, however: they are assiduous in studying their several arts, almost microscopically, for new resources; and conversely, there is a sense of outrage when a fellow artist "violates the picture plane," or fuzzes up the surface of a metal statue with clay-pellet untidiness.

< 86 >

The Artist on the Way, by Vincent van Gogh. The paint as such intensely expressed—plus pictorial organization.

There is more than at first meets the eye in an early slogan of the German Expressionists: "Away from nature—back to the picture." There is an implication of laws of picture-making, distinguishing this art from nature-photography: laws based on the flatness of the canvas and the properties of paints. The picture frame no longer is merely a pleasing border through which a vista is opened upon a fragment of reality. Rather it establishes the

< 87 >

The Dream, by Henri Rousseau. (By courtesy of the Knoedler Galleries.)

boundaries of a picture field, existing under incontrovertible laws. This plane can be violated—for instance, by carrying the eye off the edge, or by "leaving a hole"—only at cost of destroying the pictorial unity, corrupting the plastic rhythm, nullifying expressive form. There is much talk in studios about declaring the canvas, dividing the field, entering the picture, etc., all referring to phases of medium expressiveness.

This is the third, then, of the avenues or sources of that expressiveness which gives purport and significance to the term "Expressionism": after the artist's feelings and his imaging, and after the apprehension of deeper values in "what he takes in for expression," there is this capitalization upon the materials particular to his

< 88 >

art. Though really there is no "after" in the creative process. With the instinctive artist expression is undivided. It is only the miseducated critic and student who must separate the functions, for better understanding.

EXPRESSIONISM—DEFINITION AND SUMMARY

Henri Rousseau loved jungles: not necessarily tropical jungles as they are, but a half imaginative sort, lush, studded with flowers and fruits, designed with plane beyond plane of palm fronds and lotus leaves and sword-like grasses, all bound together in a color mosaic. Rousseau also loved a mistress, and perhaps he dreamed her too into something more than other men would have seen. In 1910 Rousseau painted a picture which is a perfect example of Expressionism at one end of its wide range: naïve subjective expression. He combined his feeling about his mistress and his nostalgic feel for the tropics in a tapestry-like painting. His lady, in a childlike idealization, is placed, nude, on a divan, in the midst of a gorgeous jungle, pleasantly peopled with birds and animals and a dusky piper. The plants and flowers are not botanically correct, and the juxtaposition of parlor sofa and tiger-haunted wilds is one of those distortions of reality distressing to the literal mind. Many people, indeed, fitted in their formative years with blinders shutting out all of art except "normal" transcription from nature, fail to be stirred by this beautiful canvas—except possibly to laughter and ridicule. Rousseau joined two things beloved and real to him in his inner life, and externalized them in expression, in something new in the world, different from nature.*

* I am indebted to J. B. Neumann for this instance. I first heard the work analyzed, as a typical example of Expressionism, at one of his lectures.

< 89 >

Paul Cezanne saw behind each contemplated landscape in his beloved Provence some hint of a cosmic structure, an architectonic rhythm; and he felt in applied paints a structural value and a means to movement—each stroke of the brush could be carefully laid to build the organism, or to turn the movement this way or that.

The Big Trees, by Paul Cezanne. (By courtesy of the Knoedler Galleries.)

< 90 >

Landscape, by Pablo Picasso. (From *Picasso,* by Maurice Raynal.)

He painted landscape pictures that violate the photographic aspect, distort nature. But in the dynamic organization of forces, in the plastic relationships, in the underplay of controlled planes, Cezanne expressed values absent from painting since El Greco; and he went beyond the Greek in color counterpoint. His canvases are revealment to an intensity unknown in painting before, except in El Greco.

Cezanne is a type Expressionist, over at the other end of the range from Rousseau. It is not so much *personal* feeling that controls here, as cosmic feeling, a consciousness of great impersonal forces underlying the order of the universe—to be revealed, if he

< 91 >

is lucky, through an artist freed from the obsession of "natural-
ness." Here, in addition, is an inventive understanding of color
as such, of the picture field as an entity with its own laws, of plane
arrangement as plastic expression.

It was Cezanne who started the Cubists on their search, and two
developments out of Cubism might be shown in example, with
Rousseau and Cezanne, as typical phases of Expressionism: in the
root sense, of something revealed that was not known to art in the
preceding era. The landscape built in flattened and squared forms,
by Picasso, exhibits an extraordinary pictorial completeness: it
affords a valid satisfaction—gained, I believe, from particularly
skillful capitalization upon the capabilities of the painting medium,
and very little from elements that might have been photographed
in nature. The "straight Cubist" picture by Braque is still further
stripped of objective interest, is abstractly expressive, wholly removed from ingratiating nature.

Finally, not in the Cubist tradition, but no less a product of the
impetus from Cezanne, I am placing here a picture by Kandinsky,
which he describes as "soul-expression." It is abstraction absolute.

These all are examples of Expressionism: paintings expressive in
ways unrecognized by the Realists and literalists. It seems to this
writer that there is no other word that so obviously describes the
varied anti-Realistic achievement of contemporary and recent
artists: an achievement constituting the main stream of Modernism. Therein is the answer to the chapter's title question. It remains only to shape our working definition of Expressionism, in the
light of this broad expressiveness.

I believe Expressionism to be art in which expressiveness of
hidden subjective and formal elements is put before imitation of

< 92 >

Improvisation 33, by Vasily Kandinsky. (By courtesy of *Der Sturm* Gallery, Berlin.)

aspects of nature or representations of surface life. Where Realism depicts the realities of the concrete world, Expressionism reveals the abstract rhythms or universal structure, sets forth the feelings of the artist, or illuminates the deeper essence of the object or subject, and expresses at highest intensity the values inherent in the medium. Realism offers primarily an illusion of actuality, an inventorial record of things seen outside, or a commentary in "natural" terms. Expressionism stresses instead the artist's imaging powers, however close to or far from nature: his inward penetra-

< 93 >

Abstraction, by Georges Braque. (By courtesy of the Phillips Memorial
Gallery, Washington, D.C.)

tion and shaping. In the product, the work of art, Expressionism
gathers these inward impulses, forces and deeper apprehensions
into an expression in which formal organization counts immensely,
where plastic rhythms, structure and thrust and color counterpoint,
enter creatively.

Expressionism is presentative where Realism is representative;
creative where Realism is imitative. From the 19th Century viewpoint, Expressionist art often is "distorted," because camera truth
is violated. But the artist claims that he has neglected or distorted
lesser truths only to reveal a greater: for the sake of expressing the
formal values and intensified feeling of an individualized image.

For further evidence, or example, in support of this definition,
one may go to any of the figures commonly called great, among the
artists of the half-century. Here is explanation of the dynamic

< 94 >

geometrics of Cezanne, of van Gogh intensifying sunlight in his painting as no one had ever purveyed (or perhaps felt) sunlight before, or universalizing the Postman; of Seurat organizing his picture space architecturally; of the fresh naively subjective visions fixed in paint by Rousseau; of the decorative-curtain compositions of Gauguin, less dynamic and less "distorted," but no less an arbitrary sensuous arrangement of color planes and volume tensions; of Matisse, escaping all that was literary and photographic in the old painting, to return to naked rhythmic expression, then to decorative organization, to mildly dynamic rhythms fixed in brilliantly harmonious color-structures; of the Cubists, who destroyed nature to re-arrange her planes and colors in more revealing order; of the Abstractionists totally abandoning concrete reality, pushing toward expression of mathematical harmonies and soul states.

< 95 >

Christ on the Cross, by El Greco. (From *Domenico Theotocopuli El Greco,* by August L. Mayer.)

CHAPTER V

ATTEMPTS TO EXPLAIN FORM

C LIVE BELL calls it "Significant Form." Dr. Barnes calls it "Plastic Form." I have called it "Expressive Form." The aestheticians and intellectualists mostly call it non-existent, and Thomas Craven has implied that it is an imaginary plaything of a few self-deluded esoterics.

Bell started the contemporary discussion of Form in a book entitled *Art*. Citing a number of varied art works, he wrote: "In each, lines and colors combined in a particular way, certain forms and relations of forms, stir our aesthetic emotions. These relations and combinations of lines and colors, these aesthetically moving forms, I call 'Significant Form'; and 'Significant Form' is the one quality common to all works of visual art." He attuned himself to an attribute of art overlooked by the Realists, and he sensitively evaluated historic masterpieces and the works of Moderns by reference to his conception of "the one quality."

Barnes, catching a glimpse of *plastic organization* as a determining element of painting, on the instrumental side, impatiently brushed aside Bell's "system," and offered a more analytic method of appreciation, by understanding and realization of "plastic form." My own modest contribution to the controversy came when I offered the suggestion that "expressive form"—as a term—had the advantage of linking the determinate creative quality with the achieve-

< 97 >

ment of the Expressionists, whom I considered the typical **Moderns**.

I saw no definitive value in the word "significant," and at that time I was afraid of the word "plastic" as applied to painting—technically it seemed to belong to sculpture, and some of us were passionately sure that the road to salvation lay in a strict confinement of each art within the chest of its own capabilities, uncontaminated by borrowed attributes. The plastic element, moreover, constituted only one part of the formal synthesis.

In any case, today "significant form" survives only in dry intellectual discussion, but the two other terms increasingly serve the practicing artist and the student. "Plastic" has become the commonest designation for the dynamic or "movement" elements in the painting, when talk is along the lines of methods and means; whereas "expressive form" is more in use when there is discussion of a fusion of the formal and the emotional elements.

The attribute form in art is like the unidentifiable quality the lover sees in his beloved. Hollywood is for once more sensible and expressive than most of us, and calls it "It." The materialist lowers it to his own highest thought, and names it "sex appeal." But to the lover it is a distinguishing individual loveliness in the beloved—understandable to all other men who have experienced the quality, who have experienced reasonless love. "And with Love . . . words are of no use, all our philosophy fails—whether to account for the pain, or to fortify against the glamour, or to describe the glory of the experience." So once wrote Edward Carpenter.

Nevertheless quite a few words have been written about love: and not a few are being written about form in art—because it too is a quality being widely experienced, and unexplainable under any other name, if only to be hinted at under this.

< 98 >

Certain it is that critics who claim to see intensely vital and universal values in art since Cezanne, cannot analyze or expound without accepting "plastic form," "expressive form," or some equivalent: which they may prefer to phrase "formal organization," or "rhythmic weight," or a similar still-undefinable term. And certain it is that the student can best approach the work of the several contributing groups of Moderns by asking what it was that each sought *beyond* the values known to Monet and Sargent and Boecklin. For the Expressionist advance has been made largely by schools that might reasonably be called "form-seeking." This is to say that a great number of artists are today setting out to capture and to fix in the canvas a felt quality or value unrecognized in the Victorian and earlier eras, a quality or value still denied by academic painters, by intellectualist critics, and by most admitted aestheticians.

Thus I, having come somehow to a deep enjoyment of El Greco's *View of Toledo* and Cezanne's *Mount Sainte Victoire*, felt in those works a value which I could not explain to myself or others in terms of subject matter, emotion, technique, imagination, composition, or any other of the definitive categories authorized by current criticism. The quality was—as near as I could understand it—the sum of the unidentifiable formal and mystically expressive values in the picture. I studied on for years, going back again and again to the canvases, to see if the thing that had become more memorable, more essential, than any other element, was still there. Finding it, now, a living thing, with vitality increasing as my sensitivity grows, and that it outlasts and outweighs all else, I judge that a label for it will be useful. I accept the least vague offered name, "form."

< 99 >

I try to pin it down a little closer to my own understanding—"expressive form." And immediately I am set upon by a pack of unbelievers, who claim that form is non-existent because they haven't yet seen it.

Half the world of art is sensitive to some such almost hidden, unexplainable quality in the creative painting; the other half fails to apprehend it, and denies existence or sense to it. Let us remember, however, that there are color-blind people, and tone-deaf persons, and materialists who judge that nothing is real that cannot be appraised by the senses reporting to the brain. The intellectuals in art are form-blind; and they are not content to accept their blindness as an absence of sight: they deny and ridicule the "seeing" of those others who detect plastic or expressive form.

We need not spend a great deal of time on the form-blind, though they challenge us continually—some of them even writing books on Modern Art. After all, the best that most men know of life comes by experience, beyond the sensory range. Even our knowledge of material things is scrappy and incomplete, if measured only by the reports of the senses. It is late to be arguing for the existence of mystic elements, when leading scientists of our generation have joined philosophers and spiritual prophets in affirming that the truer life and the animating cause lie beyond anything that is measurable by the physical senses and mind.

Increasing numbers of people, then, *experience* in works of art an aesthetic pleasure beyond anything to be attained by sense and reason; and because those are people who experience and treasure mystic values, in other groves of life, they are willing to speak of the form-experience in art as mystic. The revelation, communion and illumination that come with mystic apprehension—most commonly through art, love, and the religious experience—are for them

< 100 >

The White Horse, by George Bellows. (By courtesy of the
Worcester Art Museum.)

the realest part of living. That the nature of the experience and
the reality cannot be explained intellectually, that words cannot
compass the full truth, does not nullify the existence or the importance of what we are talking about.

The fight against admission of a hidden or mystic form-value in
art is carried on less by the older aestheticians—so few people read
them any more—than by the would-be "liberal" Realists, or intel-
lectual-materialists. And they tend, as certain phases of Modernism are progressively clarified—in the essays of Barnes,

< 101 >

Hofmann, Fry, and others—to become tangled in their own terminology. One has the impression that, having made up their minds that their own blindness is the only normal state, they are staggering around in an effort to shut out a light inevitably dawning.*

THE KINDS OF FORM

Let us pause to remind ourselves of the ways in which art was explained, in its service to mankind, before there was this doubtless confusing talk about plastic orchestration and expressive form. Art, of course, was photography, the mirror to nature, for long periods: far longer than the trivial nature of mechanical illustration alone would account for. There were ways in which Realistic or even Naturalistic art might be made to "serve society": when it took on purpose, moralistic, patriotic, etc. The vague thing called sentiment entered in: strongly in the moral-purpose and religious

---

* It is fair to note, I think, that Thomas Craven, who has made himself the exponent of all that is healthily masculine, physical and intellectual in recent art, while savagely ridiculing those who admit a mystic value, is obliged occasionally to fall back on citing those very excellencies he has denied, almost in the language of the attacked. Thus in *Men of Art* he writes: "How often have we heard artists and critics praising or condemning this picture or that! 'What marvellous form!' 'A master of form!' 'Utterly lacking in form!' And so on." Some pages later, having discovered "the rhythmical interplay of lines and volumes" of Rubens, Craven himself exclaims: "What infinite variety he gave to his volumes! What plasticity! What suppleness of articulation! . . . He had what artists call the profound feeling for form. . . ." Reading Craven's later book, *Modern Art*, one feels again and again that he is on the verge of recognition of abstract or mystic values: that he may have taken the trouble to read Barnes' chapter on "Plastic Form," or other of the explaining writers. But suddenly he throws in a contemptuous bit like this (about Soutine): "About all that can be said of his work is that it indicates some sort of tragic experience—what, I do not know. His art is supposed to be rich in plastic values." Craven is a brilliant writer; but his tragedy seems to be that after he began "debunking" the old art, with gusto and wit, his Victorian training in Realism prevented experience of the creative values in the new. The result is that he tries to destroy creators such as Picasso, Matisse and Rousseau, while glorifying men who are still essentially illustrators such as Benton and Curry. He has nothing less than a phobia regarding abstraction in art; and he narrows form to a technical attainment.

< 102 >

Young Girl, by John Carroll. (By courtesy of Frank K. M. Rehn Gallery.)

art; weakly, as sentimentalism over children, flowers, the sunset, etc. In all these cases, the "treatment" might vary from the idealized (neo-Classic, or pseudo-Classic) to the natural. Romanti-

< 103 >

cism led out into exotic subject-matter: to the picturesque and far-away. Another division of graphic art descended to being little more than ornamentation: the Court painters, and the portraitists to the millionaires. This sort of painting for grandification, in flashy technique, survives fitfully today, along with all the sorts of sentimental and journalistic Realism.

Victorian critics treated these matters as the end and all of the art of painting: writing endlessly of the Classic spirit, the Romantic spirit, technique, composition, subject matter, emotion. When they wrote of form in art, however, they discussed the *forms of things,* as observed in nature, and how those objective forms could be made effective in pictures; or of form as merely mechanical composition.

The Moderns claim that in comparison with form-revelation, in the Expressionist's sense, all those others are secondary values. Without abstract formal-rhythmic support, expression becomes sentimental reproduction, or mere manufacture of technically brilliant surface ornamentation. The formal-plastic orchestration—shaped by feeling—is recognized as the heart of the pictorial synthesis.

There is a distinction between forms merely as seen in nature—objects transferred in characteristic mass and lighting to the canvas—and forms as synthesized from nature, at a glance of the focussing eye; though both sorts are but incidentals to the organizational or abstract form of the Moderns. Mather in *Modern Painting: A Study of Tendencies* distinguishes between the inventoried forms and the fused equivalent thus (in a passage about Manet): "He set himself resolutely to the problem of form. This he conceived in another sense than had the professed realist, Courbet. Form is, for the painter, not what he knows to be, but simply what he sees at a given moment. The eye creates its world not by minute observations, but by swift interpretations of the more significant indi-

< 104 >

Skating, by Yasuo Kuniyoshi. (By courtesy of the Downtown Gallery,
New York.)

cations of mass. Resolve form into its constructive planes, find a
reasonable equivalent for these planes in paint, and your picture
is done. The eye will infer the mass creatively from such indications with far more zest and conviction than any minute inventory
can arouse."

This is, of course, merely a transfer from details of objective
natural forms to the summarized characteristic mass: is still within
the understanding and aims of the Realist. It is a parallel to the
Impressionists surprising nature in one of her tenderest and fleet-
ingest moods, or catching the model in a "revealing" pose. It is
form found outside, not expressed from within.

The form we are talking about here is rather the sum of all the
objectively unidentifiable qualities in the picture: it is inner struc-

< 105 >

ture, rhythm, plastic vitality, organic order, architectonics, coiled power—all this plus or shaped by the artist's individual way of revealing his feeling: the distinctive differences that make his painting other than Jones' or Brown's. It is the part of the painting you can't get at, though you know, from your aesthetic reaction, that it is there.

The following chapters embrace my attempt to elucidate what the Expressionists have accomplished in achieving expressive form; and since no exact word-definition is possible, I must leave to those chapters the throwing of whatever specific light is possible. By breaking the subject into two parts, exploring first the gain in plastic form, the revelation out of instrumental means newly mastered, and then going on to feeling and meaning, I may be able to afford the reader glimpses of the elusive quality in its two aspects.* It remains for this chapter only to trace the growth of thought—and controversy—on the subject; and to note some things that expressive form is *not*.

GROWTH OF THE FORM THEORY

Order is a first principle of the universe—"Heaven's first law," modern science's final explanation, and a foundation of all art. There is no finality, no absolute. But man progresses—progresses by setting up some far conception, perhaps some new intuitional understanding of order, and working toward that. The inferences of science precede the experiment and the proof; "ideals" of conduct and social organization outrun attainment; and the artist perspires over a possible revelation he has visioned.

* Herbert Read, in *Art Now*, speaks of form as of two sorts: "abstract form"—illustrated especially in the work of Matisse—and "subjective form," which, in addition to the abstract value, "can be the emergent sensibility of the artist himself."

< 106 >

The farthest thing glimpsed by vision-gifted artists at present is a sort of order that we call form. It may be termed an echo of the finally satisfying cosmic rhythm, a crystallization in little of the universal architecture (the mystic's view); or it may be subjective revelation of an image born to an artist out of the contact of his individual sensitivity with "life."

The Realists admit the importance of order; but limit their tests of it, in the abstract, to arrangement on the surface of the canvas (overlooking the plastic nature of the art, the depth-and-movement dimension); and denying other objective order than can be illustrated from outwardly-seen nature. Through the ages, however, there have been artists unseduced by the Realistic ambition: who have sensed the deeper order, who have intuitively created plastically and beyond-nature. The *theory* of form as the creative summary or essence, of this deeper order, was unknown to the Realists, and is new to the Western World. There has been historic practice—wherefore Giotto, Tintoretto, El Greco and others have entered into our text, and generously among our illustrations—but of theorizing about the quality, in the past, the only rich body of sayings is to be found embedded in the books of far Eastern wisdom.

Since most of the English translations were made in the time when the Western mind understood art only as illustration or interpretation of nature, one cannot be sure that even yet the full significance of Chinese foreshadowing of the "expressive form theory" is clear to us. Centuries ago, in a country now recognized as productive of extraordinarily beautiful paintings, the following statement was set down as "the first law" of the art: *"Rhythmic Vitality, or Spiritual Rhythm expressed in the movement of life."* That this law should have been recorded as basic is a remarkable co-

< 107 >

The Emperor Wen Meets the Sage Chiang Tzu-ya: 12th Century Chinese painting on silk.   (By courtesy of the Freer Gallery of Art.)

incidence of ancient Eastern and contemporary Western thought. The words used oftenest by the Expressionists in attempting to explain "form" are here brought together: "movement"—which is the key to the understanding of the "plastic" element (and the subject of several chapters to come); "rhythmic vitality"—there are those who prefer "rhythmic form" to "expressive form"; "spiritual," which is a synonym of "mystic"; and "expression."

Among the other Chinese laws, there is one which is variously translated as "composition and subordination, or grouping according to hierarchic order," and "Correct division of space." A variant reading of the first law is this: "Consonance of the spirit engenders the movement."

The translators have found the same difficulties of statement that beset every modern writer on form, because words are at best bungling in the realm of experience. But, considering the likeness of Chinese paintings and certain Western Expressionistic ones— even to those bugaboos of the Realistic mind, abstraction and distortion—there can be little doubt that the Orientals were getting at the quality we are approaching as expressive form.

So the Modern looks back to intuitive attainment of form, in all lands and in many periods, and to at least one formulation of a theory of art in which the hidden quality is counted fundamental. He goes on his way certain that he is following no "will-o'-the-wisp." He is equally sure that any present-day theory or explanation will take into account certain advances in knowledge accomplished in the machine-age: for instance, the abstract element as realized by Giotto, El Greco and the Orientals will be modified by scientific understanding of the dynamic properties of colors, and the plastic or movement relationships will be clarified by the analogies of modern physics: polarity, tensions, orbital pulls, and other mani-

< 109 >

festations of astro- and atomic dynamics will afford light on the nature of abstract pictorial organization. In short, there is reason to believe that the form-theory of the Modernists is firmly rooted in the traditional creative art of the past, even while reflecting characteristic reaches forward in the thought and experience of our own times.

The progression of theoretical thought has continued from the time when Clive Bell published his treatise on "significant form," through a decade and a half of controversy and downright wrangling. Those who accepted Bell's "discovery" as more or less epochal, found in Cezanne particularly a witness offering constructive testimony. For those who came to enjoy the paintings of the Master of Aix saw that a canvas of his, placed on the walls alongside any representative show of 19th Century works, made the others appear singularly empty, inert, and pictorially lifeless. Here was an object-lesson in paintings with and without vital form —significant, expressive, or what you will. On the one hand, Cezanne with expressiveness of a living truth beyond surface nature, with plastic unity, with rhythmic vitality. On the other hand, pictures copied from surface nature, illusional and reproductive, with plastic elements casually assembled—without pictorial movement, or unity, or dynamic correlation.

Cezanne had done little verbally to clear up the tangle of theory. His famous saying about seeking a "realization" fitted in exactly with the ideas of the mystics, who knew that he meant the crystallizing of a reality that lies within but not on the surface of nature. But the Realists might as easily convert the saying to their uses— and have. Cezanne's works, nevertheless, *exhibited* rich expressive form—and did more than any other easily available exhibit to prove existence of a characteristic creative quality.

< 110 >

L'Estaque, by Paul Cezanne. (By courtesy of Adolph Lewisohn.)

Barnes was more fortunate than Bell. He failed, to be sure, to
isolate the form so that it could be readily detected—and his own
analyses leave something to be desired in lucidity. But in his book,
The Art in Painting, he did a better job than anyone else writing on
the subject up to this time. He narrowed the conception to abstract
limits, and wrote of *"plastic form."* He posited that this quality
fundamentally gave creative painting its reason for being, affording
to the observer the satisfying aesthetic experience. "Plastic form,"
he wrote, "is the synthesis of the plastic elements or means—color,

< 111 >

light, line, space—in a rhythmic, unified whole." Again he wrote: "The conception of plastic form, as integration of all the plastic means, will be used in this book as the standard and criterion of values in painting." He implied that until observers came to the habit of evaluating a painting (sub-consciously) by the test of plastic unity attained, they would continue to judge superficially, by such secondary attributes as illusional subject-matter, flashy technique, etc.

All this is clarifying; and I am wholly in sympathy with the thought that, in future, appreciation will commonly begin with intuitive evaluation of the plastic synthesis, before other factors "register." If I prefer still to speak of "expressive form," it is perhaps only a difference of approach. It seems to me that my term implies a larger value: expressive form is at once plastic form (the values expressive of the typical painting-means), *and* form expressive of the artist's feelings (the revelation of an image individually conceived, out of the painter's special emotional sensitivity). Dr. Barnes allows for this element, when he notes that the artist's business is to find a plastic *equivalent* for his vision, for his emotional reaction to some human situation or objective scene (these are not his words, but I think a fair summary of his meaning).

R. H. Wilenski, in a book entitled *The Modern Movement in Art*, served to clarify informed opinion regarding the essentials of creative art. Particularly he emphasized the importance of formal order, and deftly deflated the pretensions to importance among descriptive, romantic and other popular painters. But his treatment of form seems to me less valuable than Barnes' because his differentiation of it as "architectural form" leaves out more than it takes in. He points out that the modern movement in painting and sculpture is essentially based on *the idea of architecture as typical*

< 112 >

art. He writes that "the architect as artist makes definite **organized** complete structures symbolizing and epitomizing special instances of his formal experience." He believes that the Modern painter strives to achieve, first of all, an equivalent "structure." In view of the nature of the painter's materials—and the new importance assumed by the "movement" element—it seems to me that his label "architectural form" is less suggestive than "plastic form." I believe, moreover, that Wilenski, who talks a good deal in terms of the old compositional discussions—"balance," "proportion," etc.— fails to penetrate to the secret of integrated plastic orchestration. His illustrations indicate confusion of three-dimensional plastic order and surface-structural order.* Nevertheless, his testimony is to be added on the side of those who count form—plastic, architectural, expressive—basic in the painting art.

I might go on to quote other writers and artists who have come to the use of equivalent terms for "expressive form": Read and his talk about art as genetic, about the expressive synthesis, and structural unity, and abstract form; Davidson, who tries obviously

---

* It is, of course, a ticklish business for a writer on art to criticize his fellows; and particularly to compare them, as regards the value of their service to students. But I am trying to show how each one cited—Bell, Barnes, Wilenski—has helped to formulate the typical Expressionist theory of what I prefer to term "expressive form." If I believed that any one had brought the whole subject clear, I should feel that there is no need for other books. Bell, Wilenski and others have had their contributive importance; but Barnes summed up better, and had a clearer vision of the plastic synthesis as of basic significance. But his understanding of *certain* of the plastic elements—dynamic color particularly—seems to me incomplete. And so I try to pick up the subject, which is ever growing, at the point to which he advanced it in his book, and I attempt to bring further light from artists who have clarified our knowledge of the individual plastic agencies.

This book, insofar as it treats formal order, is my effort to carry the discussion farther, reshaping the theory which you may consider Bell's or Barnes' by the test of Hofmann's discoveries regarding volume-space organization, and by the post-Synchromist understanding of color,—with perhaps some small personal contribution out of my own study of the expressive synthesis. It seems to me inconsequential who gets the credit, so long as we get on with our understanding, progressively.

< 113 >

Macbeth and the Witches, by Albert Ryder.   (By courtesy of
Ferargil Galleries.)

—though not very successfully, in his text—to differentiate the
"mystic picture" from the illustrational, and finds in Cezanne a
painter whose landscapes "leap and swell with form," in contrast
with the flat lifeless art of the academists; and Hudnut, who
speaks of the creative sculptor adding "to whatever formal harmonies he finds in that which he represents . . . other harmonies,
compelling nature to assume whatever new aspects of unity or completeness he has envisaged"—and again noting that the artist
"strives to realize in patterns of abstract form a symbol of that

< 114 >

cosmic order and unity which must exist beneath the disordered appearances of the world."

I believe that, space permitting, one could bring to the discussion so many quotations and so great a bulk of testimony that it would be obvious that the form advocates are in the majority among vitally interested analysts of modern painting. Living opinion has swung over to belief in a distinguishing formal-expressive quality or property in creative art. Those who oppose admission of a term equivalent to "expressive form" seem to me now on the defensive—a dwindling minority. Abstract form, whether narrowed to a summary of the plastic elements, or expressive of the synthesis of instrumental and emotional values, is understood as the basic excellence and test of the art of painting.

WHAT FORM IS NOT

It remains, for this chapter, to lay one misconception: that expressive form is only what earlier artists and critics termed "composition." There are many books on Composition, but I doubt whether one contains the word "plastic." Certainly I have found none that takes into consideration the depth element, the backward-forward movement.

Poore caught a glimpse of the movement element, and evolved a suggestive theory of the circular observation of pictures, but he traced his path of vision on the flat, with exits for the eye through the canvas—totally overlooking the organic and closed nature of the plastic "structure." Ross, Hambidge and the others seem to have been equally blind regarding recessive movement and plastic design, though very wise regarding the effects to be attained by plane proportioning and linear harmony.

< 115 >

In short, "composition" in painting has been understood, up to the time of the Expressionists, as a system of area organization, with reference to balance, proportion, measure, shapes, etc. "The divine proportion," "the golden proportion," and "dynamic symmetry" are measure-formulas applicable to spacing and object-placing on the surface of the canvas, irrespective of the penetration of linear perspective, or the newly understood tensions of volumes in space, or the dynamic properties of colors.

On the one plane, the composed areas and lines could be made to assume a geometrically stable and superficially pleasing appearance; though the inevitable penetrations and advances of volume, plane, color and texture were left unorganized, or only given a semblance of order, intuitively. Raphael, for instance, was an artist supreme in arrangement of balanced surface compositions, superficially pleasing, although in general his paintings are lacking in compelling plastic rhythms and dynamic unity. (It is for this reason that Raphael was, for the Victorians, "the world's greatest painter," whereas in the 20th Century he has lost stature, until he seems tame and over-sweet beside the plastically rich El Greco and Tintoretto.)

The sense of surface unity and structure gained from observance of the "laws" of composition, as set forth by Hambidge, Poore, Ross, Dow and others, is but a first dimension of the organizational unity or order implied in what I term "the theory of plastic orchestration"; and form, in the Expressionist's sense, is incomparably more than "composition." The test of dynamic symmetry or the divine proportion may even be used to prove the excellence of a painting that is, to the practiced eye, plastically unorganized, and thus expressively defective. The impressive and stirring rhythms of El Greco and Cezanne are possible only through the orchestration of the several plastic instruments in deep space.

< 116 >

Another approach to understanding is in the contrast between *static, balanced* composition, and *dynamic, organic* movement-organization. The discovery of the movement element, of order conditioned by an additional dimension, is typically a modern development, in line with "the new physics" and relativity. Plastic organization is spatial and voluminous, where the old composition was plane and linear. Implicit in the new idea of form are tensions, flow, volume, dynamics—whereas the materials of the old composition were the surface figures of rectangle, triangle, the "S-line of beauty," etc.

Nor can one escape the analogy of "composition" as sufficient for a material world, while expressive-plastic form belongs to art in a world scientifically based but spiritually conscious. Formal pictorial organization, on the instrumental side, accords with the planetary model of the universe, and with the conception of a sort of movement as the basic physical "element"; and, on the spiritual side, with the mystic apprehension of powers and qualities beyond the physical. Let the artist know the latest discoveries of astronomer and physicist, and let him see life with the most transcendent of the spiritual sages; otherwise form in all its fullness and expressiveness may escape him—though he may continue to compass the pleasing effects of the contributive "composition."

< 117 >

Don Quixote, by Honoré Daumier. (By courtesy of Dr. F. H. Hirschland.)

CHAPTER VI

PICTURE-BUILDING: THE FRAME, THE FIELD,
AND THE MOVEMENT-PATH

ONCE at a solemn meeting of war-service workers and theatre folk, a pompous official arose and said: "I am going to speak on Vice, about which you all know so much." We of the audience greeted this beginning with joyous applause. That we should be treated as experts in that particular field had not occurred to us.

Now I realize that framing formulas for explanation of picture-building became a minor vice of art criticism at the end of the Century; and I am not a little diffident in launching an attempt to explain Expressionist theories of pictorial organization. I should like to place a part of the burden on my readers. Many of them, doubtless, have a more detailed knowledge than I, in regard to the actual systems formulated to explain the "composition" of older works of art. They consort more familiarly with "the divine proportion," "dynamic symmetry," and similar measurable determinants. I have dabbled a little in those dangerous waters, as indicated at the end of the preceding chapter, and I know why artists in general detest all published formulas. But I think that I have explored deeper, to discover not (I hope) a system, but related clues, which go some way to suggest why the older formulas, overlooking the plastic dimension, lead to a mechanical or static sort of art. These same clues are useful, moreover, in explaining why modern Expressionist art is more profoundly affective, on the formal side, than any other group-development since Giotto laid down his brushes.

< 119 >

There can be no doubt that the Expressionists in painting have made more progress in this branch of their profession—in attaining to an understanding of *picture-building*—than in any other of the several correlative means to intense expressiveness. They have rediscovered principles that underlie the melodious-plastic rhythms of Giotto, El Greco and the Russian makers of ikons. Where those earlier artists arrived at intuitive creativeness with their paints on two-dimensional fields, the Expressionists have developed theories to account for the effects gained—and have proceeded with experiments toward intenser pictorial vitality. In short, the most obvious contribution of the Moderns, up to this time, has been in furthering the expressiveness of the pictorial medium as such, and in clarifying knowledge of the potentialities and limitations of that medium.

If, in the end, I slip into the habit of terming my bundle of clues a theory—the theory of plastic orchestration, perhaps—the reader will remember my warning that systems are makeshifts and are dangerous until forgotten, except as background for spontaneous understanding.

MOVEMENT IN THE CANVAS

In any explanation of the new understanding of two-dimensional canvas, paints, and the formal organization to be built with those materials, one comes immediately to the necessity to talk in terms of *movement*.

Movement is at once the most certain "element" in the universe, and the greatest mystery. Modern science traces the order of the spheres and the composition of matter down to movement, but offers not the slightest clue to its origin. Life is movement; all that our senses report as solid, static or material is, we now know, movement poised. Finally we are told that the primary element

< 120 >

Dancing Trees, by Matthew Barnes. (By courtesy of
Joseph A. Danysh Galleries.)

which pleases the observer in painting can best be described as
"movement in the canvas."

There are many names for the thing, and necessarily none is
exact. "Plastic organization," "spatial vitality" and "dynamic
rhythm" are some of the labels suggesting the movement-factor:
all more or less commonly used in discussion of the modern search
for formal values.

We may approach the subject here by saying that most theories
of Expressionist painting tacitly recognize an element of movement
in the canvas, of a sort unknown to 19th Century painters or theorists; and that study of one or another phase of "movement-

< 121 >

structure" affords the easiest road to comprehension of what are called (with perhaps too strong an implication of finality) "the laws of painting."

The nature of the movement of which Expressionist painters speak is wholly different from the *depicted* sort commonly found in Futurist paintings, and in Realistic battle scenes, dance pictures, sea-pieces, etc. The illusion of pronounced natural movement more often than not destroys the pictorial unity. In the 19th Century, artists recognized only objective movement illustrated, or that sort of pictorial-reportorial shorthand known as perspective. The Moderns think of movement as an element self-contained in the canvas, to which photographed action and perspective may contribute in a minor way. In other words, their sort of *created* movement has nothing to do with the mobility of certain objects and organisms in nature.

In the Modern canvas the "main movement" may often be traced along volumes, colors and textures, offering a guide to the observer's eye: according to a sense of rhythm or formal order experienced by the artist, out of his emotions and his attunement to cosmic order. It is movement within the enclosure of the picture, not illusion of movement in outward life.

Western artists and philosophers after Giotto and El Greco failed to identify or understand this quality or element in painting; and there is practically nothing recorded in our art histories or aesthetics that hints of it. But Chinese books of wisdom speak in terms strangely paralleling the pronouncements of Cubists and other Expressionists.

Regarding the art of China and Japan, Laurence Binyon, in *The Flight of the Dragon*, speaks of "expressive form" and of "rhythmic vitality." He writes: "It is not essential that the subject-matter

< 122 >

Ice Floes, by Max Beckmann. (By courtesy of J. B. Neumann.)

should represent or be like anything in nature; only it must be
alive with a rhythmic vitality of its own. You may say that the
waves on Korin's famous screen are not like real waves; but they
move, they have force and volume. We might in dreams see waves
such as these, divested of all accident of appearance, in their naked
impetus of movement and recoil."

Again he makes this "movement" even more integral to the picture, and less of outward nature, and identifies it with "the rhythm
of the spirit." He continues: "Every statue, every picture, is a

< 123 >

series of ordered relations, controlled, as the body is controlled in the dance, by the will to express a single idea. A study of the most rudimentary abstract design will show that the units of line or mass are in reality energies capable of acting on each other; and, if we discover a way to put these energies into rhythmical relation, the design at once becomes animated." He records, of the Chinese: "It was felt that the true artist, working when the mood was on him, was brought into direct relation with the creative power indwelling in the world, and this power, using him as a medium or instrument, breathed actual life into the strokes of his brush." The rhythmic vitality in the picture is thus interpreted as *creative* movement, a bit of the cosmic rhythm.*

There is, the Moderns point out, physiological reason for placing movement first among elements making for sense-satisfaction in paintings. The human eye cannot see either a comprehensive scene in nature or a complex picture as a whole, with equal attention to all the parts. The eye naturally roves, explores, focuses and re-focuses, before coming to rest (temporarily) at a center of interest. There is, in short, movement along a path of vision. In nature this results, usually, in selection of bits that hold the attention of the mind, pleasing the intellect. At other times, there is a fortuitous conjunction of elements in "a naturally beautiful" scene: masses of trees bordering a winding road, or a "composition" of lawns, shrubs and buildings—satisfying, in terms true to nature, some sense of compositional order. When pictures are made, the painter can transcribe such "effects" discovered in nature, or he can, creatively,

* See *The Flight of the Dragon*, by Laurence Binyon, New York, 1911, in the series "Wisdom of the East." It is an admirable brief introduction to the art of the Orient. In Vernon Blake's *The Art and Craft of Drawing*, Oxford, 1927, the first of the Six Laws of Chinese painting is translated thus: "Consonance of the spirit engenders the movement (of life)."

< 124 >

Chinese Landscape Painting of the 12th-13th Centuries. (By courtesy
of the Freer Gallery of Art.)

set out to fix, in the materials particular to his art, an organic complex of forms, perhaps along a traceable "path of vision," that will afford more intense satisfaction, speaking not only in terms of casual arrangements but rather in a deeper counterpoint understandable to the soul.* The eye no longer translates to the mind alone: it is consciously stimulated to convey a manifestation of order of a super-natural character.

Even in Realistic painting there is some recognition of the habits of the eye. Objective materials are selected, and arranged to bring one object to the center of attention. It is easy to see that if all objects or units in the picture are equally stressed, there is division of interest, resulting in confusion and restlessness. The corners of the painting are darkened or summarily treated. But the Realists are generally innocent of any intention to provide a carefully designed, carefully enclosed, path of vision or complex of forms. Particularly, they are oblivious of action inward and outward, having studied only superficial proportion, on the surface: plane movement, not plastic.†

* Laurence Buermeyer has a wise word to say about the way in which the artist goes beyond nature: "This design or form or vision is a grasp or understanding of what *is*, but it is creative in that the illumination is one which nature, unassisted by the artist, is powerless to provide." See the chapter "Art as Creative" in Buermeyer's *The Aesthetic Experience*, Merion, 1924. Gauguin once wrote: "It is said that God put a piece of clay into His hand and created all that you know. The artist, in his turn, if he wishes to create a really divine work, must not imitate nature, but use the elements of nature to create a new element."

† H. R. Poore, in *Pictorial Composition*, New York, 1903, written for and largely about Realists, includes a chapter on "the circular observation of pictures," and another dealing with the "ways of getting into and out of the picture." There is stimulatng material in the book; but the author sees composition as static, and "movement" as a relationship of surface objects, not as a plastic organism, with depth relations. His insistence upon an "exit" for the eye, and the leaving of openings therefor, negates the first principle of plastic order: that there shall be movement in a *closed field*, a final equipoise of dynamic elements.

< 126 >

Spring Is in the Air, by Frank Kleinholz. (By courtesy of the Associated
American Artists Galleries, New York.)

The Expressionist considers that a "skeleton of movement"—a
necessary perversion of terms, where a quality beyond measurements is concerned—is his first consideration. An order in arrangement of his materials is presupposed. Order may best be come
at as a structure of thrusts and counterthrusts. Where composition,
for the Victorians, was static, a thing of balance on the surface

< 127 >

of the canvas, varied only by depth as understood through the laws of perspective, it is to the later painters dynamic and recessive. To the surface movement is added back-and-forth thrust and return. Equilibrium is construed less as balanced objects, more as related paths of tensions between volumes. Just as cosmic speculation and exploration outgrew the model of fixed stars and pendant earth, in favor of planetary order and orbital progression, so the artist gives up static compositional models, and reads into organizational painting a reflection of the dynamics of the perpetually moving but poised cosmic system (an analogy to be considered later).

SEEING——UNDERSTANDING——CREATING

Since he is dealing with a visual art, comprehensible through the same eye that sees nature, the Expressionist grants that oftener than not the quantitative materials of his picture will be drawn from objective nature; though he insists that there may be intenser expression where the outward appearance is abandoned, in favor of a summary or abstraction. The eye recognizes not by the actual shapes of objects, but by appearances under cast light. After the eye-report, the mind's understanding is re-inforced by memory of reports brought, at other times, in regard to like-appearing objects, by the more fundamental sense of touch (by which we know thickness, roundness, etc.). Movement, as developed in the canvas, will have at least vague reference to these sense-experiences.

It will be related also to stored experience of weight, gravity, balance, etc. But most important—the Expressionist claims—it will link with the deepest rhythms, arising from universal order: with the cosmic machine, the flow of the worlds, the tensions of galaxy, star and planet. It is, he believes, an echo of that deepest,

< 128 >

most fundamental ordered movement that gives satisfaction to the observer—in Chinese paintings, in El Greco, in the typical Modernist.

Understanding is an adjustment of what we see at the moment, what we know from past experience, and what we deeply "feel." A work of art is a crystallization of understanding—and its vitality lies in the livingness of the movement-summary. The artist, then, parallels nature, in creating movement; and he is instinctively careful not to negate certain of nature's laws as illustrated in the phenomenal world. He must keep within racial comprehensions of equilibrium, gravity, etc., acquired through immemorial sense experience. It is not his business to transcribe to the canvas observed illustrations of the working of those laws, but rather to liberate in the picture other movements not directly revealed by nature. Ordinarily materials from objective nature are used, as Glenn Wessels puts it, "to build the bridge from ordinary experience into the pictorial world." But some abstractionists, while keeping within felt natural laws, have been able to reveal the deeper form-value with only the slightest reference to objective appearances.

We are dealing here with three orders of materials: what the eye sees physically, an "appearance"; what the mind images, three-dimensional reality, "appearance" plus knowledge gained from past experience through the other senses, and through having seen the same object from all sides, by walking around it, touching it, etc.; and the deeper intuitional image, after penetration to "the soul" of the object, an image conditioned by the artist's sensitivity to it as microcosm, as the universal rhythm in little. In expressing, by plastic means, the last image, the appearance may be distorted. In fusing the elements out of his feeling for nature and the elements out of his feeling for picture-building, the artist intuitively respects

< 129 >

certain laws underlying both categories; but since the picture is his primary concern, he violates the casuals of nature with impunity if thereby he attains a greater intensity of plastic movement and formal order.

The "plastic" is, by dictionary definition, that which is capable of being molded: that which can be worked in a third dimension. In painting, the essence of the plastic is penetration, relief, depth. "Plastic orchestration" implies the projection of the canvas plane backward, creating an understood box-like "spatial field," and the organization, within that field, of all relief or movement elements, in organic relationship.

BACKWARD-FORWARD MOVEMENT

Up to the time of the Expressionist development, artists had attained no clear understanding of backward-forward movement in the picture, as distinguished from linear or side-to-side and up-down movement. The movement across the canvas or up-and-down embraces only a beginning of the dynamic or plastic complex, which gains profoundest effect through mastery of thrust and return, within space beyond the picture "front." The one is two-dimensional, the other three-dimensional. Even superficial Realistic painters, such as Sargent, Bouguereau and Gainsborough, gained catchy effects with two-dimensional rhythms (and these formed the basis of many of the older treatises on composition). But the Expressionist theories, while beginning always with emphasis upon the inviolability of the picture plane, deal with movement in and out, backward and forward, as the fundamental means to pictorial effectiveness. The expressive form is fixed according to an imagined order of movement, linear, recessive, and contrapuntal.

< 130 >

New Mexico: Water-color by John Marin. (By courtesy of
Alfred Stieglitz.)

The Moderns point out that the Realists inescapably created
such movement, without understanding it, without order. The
moment a volume is placed in space, movement of the eye is
induced, forward or back; the moment a color is applied, there is
a physical sensation of recession or thrust forward; and texture
may be insistent or neutral or backward-pulling. The Realist's
painting is, so far as these plastic values are concerned, a chance
agglomeration, a hodge-podge—however engaging the linear surface rhythms and static balance of objects may be.

< 131 >

The Expressionist builds his picture by the movement values of those several elements. From a point of stability in the established picture plane, he creates his plastic rhythm, backward and forward, with the materials of volume, plane, color, and texture. Usually there is a dominant path of movement, varied with oscillations in smaller measure: main "way" and counterpoint. The rhythm has become consciously symphonic: not merely a harmonic arrangement amid the random, and ignorantly combined, thrusts of nature.

THE MATERIALS OF PAINTING: THE SURFACE PLANE

Once the insurgent painters at the beginning of the Century had gained glimpses of movement in this sense—finding the actuality without explanation in Cezanne, and then going back to El Greco, Tintoretto and Giotto for comparison, and perhaps to the flood of Oriental art just then released in European museums—they found themselves driven to a reconsideration of the materials of the painting art. If one starts expression with honest regard for one's medium, one may discover forgotten laws based on the nature of the materials used. Perhaps Cezanne had served to break into a new era by returning his art to a more direct and expressive use of the picture field, the plastics of volume and space, plane, and color movement. A considered search began for "laws" which would afford a clue to form-revelation and essentially pictorial "movement."

The first law of painting—insofar as one can find agreement in any group of Moderns—is that *the picture plane shall not be violated.*

Albert Gleizes was perhaps the first and certainly the most illuminating of writers advocating this law. His summary is still the

< 132 >

Clam Bay Farm, by Cameron Booth.

most suggestive: "Painting is the art of giving life to a surface plane. The picture plane is an organism of two dimensions. Its truth lies in its two dimensions."

By violating the two-dimensionality of the pictorial plane, by letting the movement escape from the prescribed and framed field, the Realist destroys the picture as a unity, as an art-organism.

The painter's problem is to vivify the picture-field: to build a picture which affords a living experience, within the laws of the two-dimensional unity—and not to make a picture merely reflecting an experience of nature's exterior world. Architecturally speaking, wall-sense is preserved: holes not pushed through.

< 133 >

Maxwell Armfield has said that "movement in art has no meaning apart from stillness." As I see it, in plastic organization, the sense of the picture plane preserved affords meaning to the thrust and return, the recessive rhythm. The plane provides the stillness that gives significance to the movement.

When one accepts the flat plane as conditioning the painter's problem, one uncovers a new set of principles, unknown to the 19th Century artist. Everything entering into the design must be organic to the picture, not to nature: must be pictorially authentic, not "natural." The artist no longer considers the canvas-frame merely a window upon nature, with picture beyond; he begins with a sense of a fixed surface, bounded by a frame integrally related to every unit within the enclosed field. This sense of the two-dimensional picture as removed by its nature from all else in life, subject to its own laws, is the beginning point of all understanding of Expressionist painting. (And, one might add, of early Egyptian and Chinese painting.)

That movement in the canvas shall be controlled, in relation to the flat, is fundamental. Expressive form is destroyed by uncontrolled movement, escaping the picture enclosure, or tracing purposeless representations upon it. The canvas field, complete in itself before the artist touches it, must remain complete when the painter has finished, when he has vitalized it: as a pictorial organism, its two-dimensionality must still be felt, its movement-elements enclosed and firmly anchored to the original plane. This law is implicit in the picture format.

Preserving the picture plane does not mean that the painting cannot have depth: it does mean that every thrust backward, by means of plane, color, texture or other agency, must have compensation, must be ultimately counteracted to restore the sense of

< 134 >

poise in relation to the two-dimensional field. The elements by which movement may be started, inward from and outward toward an established two-dimensional field, are planes, tilted, bent, etc.; volumes in space; colors, forward or recessive; line (which is usually shorthand for boundaries of plane or volume); and texture, fading or insistent. The design is an ordered complex of the movement values of these several elements, sometimes in the nature of main movement and support or accompaniment, sometimes one utilized as corrective of another (as a forward-pushing volume may be neutralized by a recessive blue, or negative empty space brought forward by heavy texture or live red).

In short there is room for complex backward-forward movement, in addition to the up-down and right-left movement on the surface; but, so to speak, that deeper movement must be anchored in the picture field. The constant play of penetration and return must be stabilized in relation to the original chosen plane: the plastic weight balanced within the closed, recessed field.

The infinitely difficult task of the creative painter is to marshal these elements, each in itself and at every move threatening the two-dimensional unity, into a vitalized formal expressiveness, without destroying the integrity of the flat.

There is, then, the *sense* of a third dimension in the expressive painting; the danger is that this will be instead an *illusion* of movement, an imitation of the third dimension of objective nature. Sensed pictorial movement, offering a way for the observer's eye, is at the heart of picture design.

Glenn Wessels writes that "to contrive a destruction of the essential flatness of the picture would produce a deception. One of the reasons that easel painting has fallen into disrepute and disrespect is because its purpose has been mistaken as the production

< 135 >

of such deceptions. Such lying expression is untrue to the nature of the medium and is in the same category as any other hoax." This is perfectly true from the standpoint of the *creator*; though some of us might argue that there is a minor place for "illusion-art," for reproductive illustration. But here we are dealing exclusively with expressive, creative art; and we should keep clear the distinction between the authentic pictorial creation, conditioned by the two-dimensional plane, and the casual, imitational, surface-of-nature thing.

The truth, in summary, seems to be that the artist accepts a convention of two-dimensionality, when he undertakes to create within the painter's medium; in introducing a certain type of movement into his canvas, he utilizes a three-dimensional element, this being only incidentally related to the third dimension in objective nature; and his profoundest aim is to liberate a sense of four-dimensional rhythm or order. If this statement seem muddling and vertiginous at first glance, there is behind the confusion a solution of some of the most difficult problems posed by modern art for the observer trained in the imitative tradition.

THE PATH OF MAIN MOVEMENT

In creating a movement-path and the various counterplay of plastic elements, then, the painter keeps before him the sense of a complete organism, of which the picture plane is the first conditioning, inviolable factor. In initiating movement in the canvas, he will be careful not to partition space, or drive deep beyond the surface, or push toward (or beyond) a border, in such way or to such degree that the plastic equilibrium or tension-poise cannot be restored. He will have before him at every stage of design the

< 136 >

Still Life, by Henri Matisse.

image of the movement equipoised, the path enclosed and centered, the pictorial unity preserved.

The secret of the variations lies in the fact that while the entire movement structure (so to speak) is designed to be in equipoise, one sort of movement will be irregular, far from symmetrical, with a vigorous main "drive"; with another movement element entering to counter-poise thrust or pause, or to "fill the holes." Thus a track of movement may be created by overlapping planes, leading off into one side of the field, and a cunning gradation of colors

< 137 >

The Elder Degas and His Secretary, by Edgar Degas. (By courtesy of Durand-Ruel.)

compensate for its steep inward thrust, or a heavy textured area or a volume-buffer stop its drive and turn its direction. Line is a less fundamental element, but is commonly used for variation.

In some paintings the movement of volume-space elements is so strong—the color-texture elements affording mere accompaniment —that it is possible at first glance to mark a vision-path. In others, the elements are so fused, or combined with such subtlety of counterpoise, that the complex counterpoint, the rich play of oscillating color and texture and minor melody, seems to be the characteristic element in the design. The practiced eye, however, will soon detect the larger movement beyond the variations: will mark the dominating volume or "sun," will note where the eye enters the picture, its main direction, where it comes to rest—without losing the sense of the enriching counterpoint.

Perhaps the greatest painters are those who learn to accentuate the main movement even while intensifying the emotional effectiveness by a constant play of fluctuating color-planes, small-volume complexes, etc. El Greco and Cezanne, masters of contrapuntal effects, seldom leave the eye in doubt as to a main rhythm. Matisse, perhaps the greatest living master of decorative color and texture, is, on the other hand, weak in understanding of the profounder rhythm; whence arises the criticism from many Expressionist painters that he is "only a light-weight," or "a mere decorator." *
Even so the main movement path can be satisfyingly felt in many of his canvases, although the recessions are less deep, the plastic intervals less pronounced. Rouault, Schmidt-Rottluff, Campendonk, Carra, Picasso, Marin, Kandinsky, offer better material for a study of the more vigorous rhythm. Although I shall leave

* My own partiality toward the paintings of Matisse will be sufficiently explained, I hope, in following chapters.

< 139 >

The Drinkers, by Honoré Daumier. (By courtesy of Adolph Lewisohn.)

Mount Sainte Victoire, by Paul Cezanne. (By courtesy of the
Phillips Memorial Gallery.)

analysis of the movement-path as such to later paragraphs, I am
introducing here two pictures, to illustrate the plastic rhythm
strongly accentuated, with little subtlety of counterpoint, and, on
the other hand, the main rhythm easily traceable but richly varied,
re-enforced, and answered by a multitude of minor rhythms.

OPENING THE PICTURE

When certain painters speak of "opening the picture" they
usually are referring to initiation of the main movement. The

< 141 >

moment a line is drawn across the virgin picture field, or a color plane laid upon it, movement is initiated and requires compensatory action. Once started in this way, the work is not complete until the structure has been poised, every tension anchored, every recession brought to return.

It is doubtful whether a creative painter ever begins a picture where the path of vision seems to the observer to take its rise: the artist jots down his main tension lines first, in all likelihood—sketches the forms with strongest pull—and works the path both ways, back to an opening point, and forward to a point of final stabilization. But for us who can study these matters not in the doing but only from the finished product, it is more convenient to consider the painter as opening his picture at that point from which the observer's eye seems to rise along a main path.

As if to afford validity to this approach, it is a fact that in an extraordinary number of modern paintings (and in many examples of the work of El Greco, Tintoretto, Giotto and others among master picture-builders of the past) the point of entry is along the lower border to the right or left of center. The internal structure of the picture is such that the movement, from there, pushes inward and up, and so into a more or less complex path.

We do not want to make a formula of this thing, either for guide to appreciation or—far less—for a system of creative picture-building. The path of vision varies as the emphasis on the several formal elements differs, and as the subjective or emotional elements affect the structural composition. But we may be sure that no creative painting is haphazardly built; and that all artists following the Cubist-Expressionist period will be profoundly indebted to Cezanne, Seurat, Braque, Gleizes, Hofmann, and others who served to make clear the nature of movement in relation to formal ex-

< 142 >

The Agony in the **Gard**en, by El Greco. (By courtesy of Arthur Sachs, Paris.)

pressiveness. We can, moreover, learn a great deal, I think, by studying the movement path in a typical manifestation—just as if it could be disengaged from the other elements within which it is fused.

This, for instance, is the commonest noticeable type of plastic structure, as I have found it in ancient and contemporary paintings: the eye is drawn into the composition somewhere in the right

< 143 >

half (observer's right) of the lower edge of the canvas; it moves, perhaps by artificially overlapping planes or by a sweep of terrain, upward and inward toward the left; above center it is turned across the canvas, perhaps by a buffer specially placed in the corner of the picture; comes down and forward on the right; is turned inward to the pictorial center—and comes to pause there.

Almost needless to say, no example exhibits so bald a structure, so *direct* a line of movement. The eye passes from volume to volume, takes in a minor complex of elements at one point, is attracted by a color or an angle or a face to another; and even the so-called point of stabilization may be the nucleus of a complex, or the tension-point *between* two weights. In short the vitality of the plastic structure lies largely in the variations and incidental enrichments, in the contrapuntal rhythms and the fluctuating fullness; and yet the expressive form suffers if the main line of movement is too long obscured or inadequately felt.

It may be that the path of vision is a secondary consideration, in that the observer's eye may be drawn first to a dominating form or volume, and only after "taking that in" drops to a point on the designed track, to continue from there the "round" of movement. There is, moreover, the probability that even observers somewhat trained to plastic appreciation have developed differing ways of approach, so that to suggest any absolute rule of observation is dangerous. Nevertheless, study of the most creative Moderns, beside El Greco and other early masters, indicates that the plastic order is oftener than not marked out visibly along a rhythmic path.

If the "line" were stripped of all incidentals, the typical path described above would be a spiral: but a spiral which cannot be diagrammed on the flat, because the plastic element in its essence supposes penetration. In trying to "read" the vision track in any

< 144 >

Christ and the Fishermen, by Georges Rouault. (By courtesy of
Pierre Matisse Gallery.)

given painting, the spiral should be felt as pushing *inward* from
the lower border, and returning outward, then inward, in the opposite half of the picture. Inexact and variable as it must be, the test

< 145 >

Mount Sainte Victoire, by Paul Cezanne. There is close likeness to the
third preceding plate, but significant variations in plastic manipulation,
for movement effect. (From *Cezanne*, by Tristan L. Klingsor.)

may serve the reader as one clue to the actuality of the vision path
in innumerable creative canvases.

For instances I am introducing here a landscape by Cezanne, a
"Primitive" interpretation of *The Agony in the Garden*, El Greco's
version of the same theme, and a composition by Rouault.
The in-and-out movement can be traced in all of these with very
little departure from the type form; though in the El Greco and
Cezanne paintings there is extraordinary variation and enrichment
all the way; whereas the compelling linear accentuation in the

< 146 >

The Agony in the Garden, in the manner of Andrea di Giusto. (By courtesy of the Gallery of Fine Arts, Yale University.)

Primitive and the Rouault make the coiled path stand out in almost naked relief.

Even in the most obvious of the examples, the Italo-Primitive, however, the line is varied, the nodes become complexes, and interest is enriched by minor elaborations. The eye, drawn in by the linear lift of the upflowing river, pauses momentarily at the group of Disciples; continues left and up, is turned from the corner by a complex of vaguely recognizable natural forms—mountains, town, wall; is carried along the heavily accented valley of foliage; is

< 147 >

The Lamentation for Jesus, by Giotto. (From *Giotto,* by Louis Gielly.)

drawn around the central peak by the bit of bush beyond; is pulled forward and right by the Angel; falls to the trees, turns inward again, and centerward, to come to rest at the head of Jesus. So varied is the most obvious example of what I have variously termed the way of vision, the tension-path, and the skeleton of the plastic structure.

I confess that I dislike this sort of analysis of creative works of art. But in the circumstances it seems justified: for the recog-

< 148 >

nition of some such underlying plan of structure, or designed movement progression, may afford to the student a key to the basic differences between casual Realistic and designedly Expressionistic painting. Remember, please, that any formula or diagram is a makeshift, a means to first recognition; get on, as soon as possible, to direct feeling of the thing we have been discussing. But if you still have doubts about the nature of the main plastic outlining of the picture, take time to trace out the paths of vision in these four works. The spiral form as given may be tested also, in only slight variations, in Georges Seurat's *The Parade* (page 194), in Kandinsky's *Landscape with Red Spots* (page 155), a perfect example, and, with greater concessions to nature, in Roerich's *The Unknown Singer* (page 159). Practically every illustration in this chapter "declares" its plastic order.

That the movement is not always to be diagrammed so simply, even in a painting with extraordinarily marked recessions, is made apparent by study of Giotto's *The Lamentation*, reproduced here. The first sweep of movement, by means of stepped-back figures, and inward-right instead of left, is strongly re-enforced by the oblique push of the wall. The path is then carried across by tree and angels, and ultimately downward and outward, almost to the corner of the canvas.

MOVEMENT AND THE SPECTATOR

There are principles concerning the origin and direction of pictorial paths of vision, which can be put down with some assurance of scientific sanction. Due to the way of seeing—this being a visual art—the point of opening the picture is somewhere at the base. The painting is conceived with reference to an imagined

< 149 >

Bridges, by Marcel Gromaire. (By courtesy of J. B. Neumann.)

observer. The spectator is thought of (at a varying focal distance) as facing the central portion of the picture. But the line of his vision is picked up practically never at the center of the frame. The picture opens from the bottom, at his right, leftward; or, less often, at a point to his left, rightward—and always *with' relation to the ground where he is* (*in imagination*) *standing.* Because subconsciously the observer carries over to his attitude toward pictures his sense of gravitation and equilibrium, the artificial created world of the picture must seem founded on stable ground, and must move away as the eye rises. Through establishment of the observer's position, by the apparent point of origin of the path of vision, these matters are related to his own foundation

< 150 >

and uprightness. The structure of tensions, between volume-axes, relates through him to order and stability in the universe. The new creation is integrated to the existing world.

Applying the principle to the movement path described above, the spiral has mathematical relationship to the ground upon which the spectator stands. The first movement is a sweep away from the frame before him at right, deep into pictorial space before him at left. The lower curve is the broader, aiding the sense of stability. It rises from a frame-edge paralleling the ground.

A group of Cubists were the first to promulgate a theory of the picture as related gravitationally to the spectator's standing-ground. And it is easy to see why we sometimes speak of the way in which the planes of a Cubist picture are "laid up." They seem to rise from a heavy base, close to the observer, and the skeletal lines or axes move up and away (though ultimately brought to poise, into integral relation to the other plastic elements and to the pictorial field).

In an illuminating essay on Cubism, Andrew Dasburg explains that there are "two considerations fundamental to the understanding of rhythm. One is the force of gravity, the other, the upward impulse in living things." * Certain it is that the path of vision *rises*. There is, in plastically satisfying paintings, the feeling of a heavy base. The picture is a *building*, on a foundation, not a random scattering of objects and accents.

Wessels adds to our understanding of the observer's standpoint when he writes: "We live visually in that part of space which is between the horizon and our toes. Unless special evidence to the contrary is brought into the graphic symbol. we assume all things

* "Cubism—Its Rise and Influence," by Andrew Dasburg. In *The Arts*, November, 1923.

< 151 >

Sunday on Grande Jatte, by Georges Seurat. (By courtesy of the Art Institute of Chicago.)

seen to be below us." We begin by looking from the ground upward and back.

Pictures are asymmetrical.* The picture field is partitioned, the movement initiated, and immediately there is disturbance of the balance. From then on, in creation, there is a series of processes, one element checking another, weight roughly balanced by counterweight, movement turned, enclosed, tied in—but never does the original static balance return. The life of the picture is in the adjustments, the varied thrust and return, that hold the movement stable, without symmetry.

* Symmetry is a condition of ornament or pattern, as distinguished from picture.

< 152 >

View of Toledo, by El Greco. (By courtesy of the
Metropolitan Museum of Art.)

In fact, there is quite commonly a general division of the picture
into a space side and a volume side. That is, in one half of the
design the path of vision seems to run off into deeper space; in

< 153 >

the other, it pushes out toward the spectator, before turning in again to a point of rest (not *too* far back) at the pictorial center. Only thus could a sweep of movement be accomplished, in the vision-path: only thus strong plastic rhythms be created.

The voluminous side of the picture, in the examples considered above, with one exception, is at the observer's right. It is at the foot of the volume, so to speak, that the spiral line takes its rise, swinging away into deep space leftward. In the Rouault and the Primitive, the matching of volume side against space side is very obvious. Even in the flatter Cezanne landscape, the practiced eye will detect the bulge forward of the hills at right. The Kandinsky landscape shown here perfectly illustrates the "displacement" of the two sides.

As one moves toward decorative painting—Gauguin, Matisse, the Russian ikon-makers—the recessions are less deep, the plastic rhythms less strong, and therefore one detects less easily the space side and the volume side; but illustrations might be cited from all these sources. Further examples of marked contrast between the deep space in one half, and forward push of volume in the other, are shown in nearby pages: Seurat's *On Grande Jatte,* and El Greco's *View of Toledo.*

Again let me say that the "principle" is variable, subject to almost infinite manipulation. If in many cases an entire half of the picture seems to be pushed away from the spectator, the poise being restored by the pull of important "volume interest" in the other half, more examples could be brought to illustrate a subtler counterpoise: the path almost obscured by minor counter-play of volume, plane, color and texture. Sometimes the sweep is almost wholly a matter of movement by complexes of planes leading up and away on one side, "returning" by other combinations to the

< 154 >

Landscape with Red Spots, by Vasily Kandinsky. (By courtesy of *Der Sturm* Gallery, Berlin.)

other—with volumes difficult to detect in any strict sense. Or else the interplay of oscillating color-areas all but obscures the linear vision-path and volume-space contrast. Yet here is a clue to the secrets of designed and completed plastic rhythm.

I have said that no artist would think of building a picture by consciously following the spiral (or any other) formula, from the beginning point of a path of vision, through logical progression to the pictorial center. The formulated theory is useful only as

< 155 >

a test, for appreciative and recognitional purposes. The artist's sense of planned movement, during creation, is more than half intuitional. It is none the less certain that the painter *feels* some such plastic structure, in its main outlines, as the picture grows under his hands. He senses the living movement, the lift and thrust and return, and final settling to poise; and is conscious of the effect upon the unity of the organism as he introduces each recession or advance, by line, plane, volume or color.

MOVEMENT START AND MOVEMENT CONTROL

Hans Hofmann notes that there is no way in which one can draw a line across a virgin canvas, partitioning space, without starting movement. The first line makes for the sense of two planes: there is departure from the absolute flat, from perfect balance, from symmetry. Let us say that the field is divided thus (A):

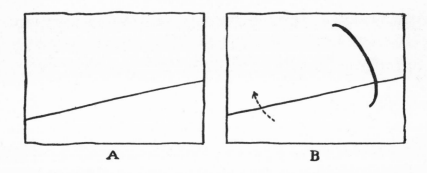

A   B

Due to automatic action of the eye, and relationship to observer's standpoint, there is the impression of movement from the area below the line upward and back; and in this case, due to the tilt of the line, leftward (as indicated by the arrow in B). Immediately the artist is faced with the necessity for further movement, for

< 156 >

Outward Bound, by Albert Ryder. (By courtesy of the Corcoran Gallery of Art: Loaned by the Estate of James Parmelee.)

compensation. It may seem to come (if he is thinking at the moment without reference to any but the line-and-plane element) by means of an arc as in B—which indicates a sort of skeletal equilibrium, but immediately opens the way to other compensatory steps.

Hofmann speaks of the partitioning of space as the "first animation of the picture plane," of reciprocal action, and of "spatial unity" restored. He is insistent that in the end the picture shall be "closed." The sense of completion and enclosure is what some

< 157 >

others have in mind when they insist above all else that the **picture** shall be considered as an organism: all parts related in movement, in harmony, in variety within unity, in completeness. Joseph Sheridan, who speaks more in terms of forces and tensions—(we shall consider plastic movement as the summary of tension paths, later)—states the thought thus: "The sum of all the forces must form a closed figure."

Cezanne, who has not been surpassed by any later artist in surety and richness of plastic orchestration in painting, worked deliberately to adjust the weights, tensions and directions of his planes of color, from first laying-out to final stroke. His paintings, which seem at first, to the observer trained in detailed Realism, so like an artistic shorthand, so summary and even careless, represent extraordinary labor: not so much in *thinking* through to the perfect relationship, and certainly not in order to catch a photographic effect, but in bringing each brush-stroke into consonance with everything gone before and everything planned to come after. We are told that not uncommonly he would, after filling the brush with color, hold it poised for a quarter-hour before laying it to the canvas: meantime he was feeling through to the movement relationship of that color plane to main plastic rhythm and contrapuntal effect. No later painter stripped himself more naked of casual detail; no one fixed formal rhythms more directly and more cunningly in paints. Those who made theories of his incidental idioms and abstractions, failed usually to approach his mastery of *all* the movement elements in controlled relationship.

I have said enough of movement by plastic means to indicate the importance of the plastic orchestration, the completed dynamic rhythm, as a factor in Expressionist painting; and I will remind the reader again that this factor was wholly overlooked by Realistic

< 158 >

The Unknown Singer, by Nicholas Roerich. (By courtesy of the
Roerich Museum.)

painters and by 19th Century academic critics. The formulas
developed by the intellectuals of the Century-end, to explain harmony of design—Dynamic Symmetry, etc.—fail in regard to painting because they accept static composition as the type excellence.
They make no allowance for backward-forward movement: overlook the plastic element that gives intensest life to Modern painting.
They content themselves with static balance, linear rhythms, and
"proportion": failing to guess movement in depth as the determining element in endowing a painting with pictorial vitality. Let
the student know the geometry of the thing miscalled Dynamic
Symmetry, but let him understand it as contributory to a mastery
of surface effects, in no wise explaining the dimension that counts
most.

< 159 >

Since mine is not a technical treatise, I will end my discussion of the movement path as a whole, except to summarize thus:

In creative painting, control of movement, of interrelated plastic means, is the first secret of formal design. From the opening of a picture with a partitioning of the field, through a main thrust into deep space, back to a stabilization or equipoise, with innumerable minor thrusts, tensions, recessions and returns along the way, the artist must foresee how the movement skeleton will be coiled within the picture enclosure.

The theory of plastic-spiral movement in recessed pictorial space happens to be a bit of the puzzle that I worked out myself; perhaps with memories of Hambidge's surface figures, modified by the knowledge of plastics brought in by Hildebrand, Hofmann, Gleizes, and Wessels. But I should add, here at the chapter end, that once upon a time there was in my town a teacher-painter named Vaclav Vytlacil, who developed a theory of picture-building under a name suggestive and illuminating. He called it "the Fifth Line theory." He postulated that a painting is conditioned by its two-dimensional field *within four rectangular border lines*. In relation to these four, the movement developed by the main slope into the picture constitutes a determining *fifth line*. This is, perhaps (as illustrated in the examples considered above) the beginning sweep of the way of movement—which I have oftenest termed "the path of vision," because treating it from the observer's standpoint. It may aid the student to comprehend the organic nature of the enclosed movement if he tests some examples as "resting on" a skeletal "fifth line," and through it related to the four.

The crystallization of my own thoughts upon plastic vitality and movement correlation came through reading the particularized essays of Albert Gleizes and Hans Hofmann; and I found con-

< 160 >

firmation in the more generalized writings of Dr. Barnes. But occasionally students have checked my statements, by their understanding of Vytlacil's teachings, and I cannot know how much of his theory I may have woven into my own—or Professor Hofmann's. The credit is perhaps unimportant. To be able to *feel* the structural line, in a Cezanne *Mount Sainte Victoire,* or a Giotto *Lamentation,* or a Kandinsky improvisation, is comparable to development of the ability to "hear" the architectural relationships underlying the counterpoint of a Bach fugue. And ordered movement is of the essence in both cases.*

* In the years since this chapter on the movement-path was written, scientists have conducted fruitful experiments in the observation of children's eyes while "touring" pictures. Their findings prove that the eye moves through the picture, and that Modern painters and such earlier painters as Giotto, Tintoretto and El Greco seem to provide a guiding path through pictorial space. The commonest path, moreover, is said to be the spiral one here suggested. But at least one scientist has reported that the majority of the observed observers of pictures makes the tour in the reverse direction from the inward and upward one here described. That is, the average person looks first at what I have termed the point of rest or pictorial center, and proceeds along the spiral path and *out* of the picture at the bottom—before repeating the round. This is probably correct. I have no reason to maintain that my theoretical way of "reading" the painter's composition is superior, for all observers. For analysis and technical discussion, however, with due regard to the observer's position in looking into the picture, the treatment here may stand; it seems to make clearer the method of organizing (intuitively) the spatial elements, with regard to the surface plane, the initiation of movement, and an orderly plastic rhythm. The Vytlacil mentioned is a well-known painter and teacher in New York.

< 161 >

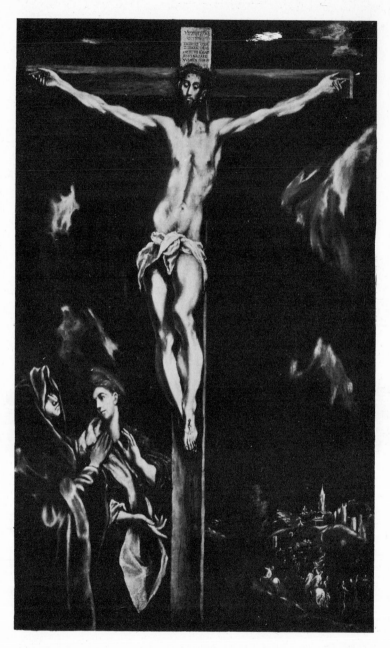

Christ on the Cross, by El Greco. (Photo by courtesy of the Art Institute of Chicago, from the original in the Johnson Collection, Philadelphia.)

CHAPTER VII

PICTURE-BUILDING: HOW MOVEMENT IS CREATED

IF creative painting is now considered a matter of plastic-dynamic rather than static design, if talk about the mysteries of composition centers no longer on balance and proportion but on spatial vitality and plastic form, what key can one find to the all-important movement-control?

There is no *master* key. The profound beauty of the paintings of El Greco, Cezanne and Kandinsky is so fixed in a fusion of the several formal elements that to pick one for analysis brings danger of undervaluing the interplay. Movement in the canvas exists by virtue of the perfect adjustment of such differing "materials" as colors, planes, textures, etc. Each aids the other by checking, neutralizing, re-enforcing, etc. In the end, plastic orchestration, the sum or result of all movements, is of supreme import.

Nevertheless there is light for us in discovering the actual means by which each element contributes to the movement. The listener gains from a symphony more rather than less if his ear is trained subconsciously to hear when the wood-winds come in, when the strings dominate, and so on. The knowledge sharpens rather than dulls the appreciative faculties (unless one fall into the degenerative habit of staying awake intellectually). The observer will lose nothing by recognizing the recessive values of colors, the thrust and

< 163 >

return of arranged planes, and the tension values of volumes in space; and he may thereby find unlocked the major mystery of plastic orchestration in painting.

And so—though there is no master key—we shall take one item out of the array of "movement materials," and see exactly how it contributes to the visual progression and the counterplay. We shall review briefly a number of incidental factors; but from the major ones we shall select *planes,* and investigate their movement-potentialities, dynamic slopes, etc. In the end the reader should understand why Expressionists grant that the artist-group known as the Cubists made one of the cardinal historic advances in knowledge of the technique of painting.

MOVEMENT BY "NATURAL" MEANS

The painter's problem goes so much deeper than a mere depiction, or interpretation, of something casually seen in the phenomenal world, that there is almost inevitably distortion of the surface appearance; and not infrequently there is total departure from objective nature, into a region of abstractions. When I first introduced the subject of movement in the canvas I stated—perhaps too emphatically—that the student must be careful not to confuse the plastic element with depicted natural movement. As a matter of fact, since totally abstract paintings form only a small fraction of creative work, objective materials enter into design in great quantity; and occasionally the manipulator of plastic movement utilizes the *direction of natural movement* as an item contributing to his plastic "structure." Thus one can discover examples in which the direction of motion of a horse, or the slope of land, or the pushing of a crowd, gives direction to the path of vision in certain segments.

< 164 >

The Uprising, by Daumier. (By courtesy of the Phillips Memorial Gallery.)

It is notable that the majority of paintings do not depict, even incidentally, objects in motion. In a large number of the minority, the movement is in the nature of casual photographic illusion, without relationship to a designed plastic rhythm. But in a few cases, painters who have attained mastery of plastic organization utilize objective elements.

Daumier exhibits many examples of combined natural and compositional "direction." *The Uprising,* reproduced here, shows the main figure accentuating the first long sweep of the path of vision, from lower right base to upper left corner. But note how the painter

< 165 >

artificially uses the darkened left edge of the canvas as a buffer; this, with the slight backward turn of the hand, serves to bend the track of sight rightward along the building wall (simplified into hardly more than a sloping plane); until the darkened block, in the opposite top corner, acting as buffer, pulls it forward and bends it down—to be picked up by the complex of heads, and brought to pause at the pictorial center. Others of Daumier's compositions incorporate moving animals in the same way. The point we should remember is that in utilizing these effects incidentally, the artist never forgot that his complete movement design, not the depicted figure, was the prime consideration: he artificially adjusted, counterpoised and ultimately stabilized within the pictorial enclosure the thrust "naturally" created.

El Greco made extraordinary capital of hands and limbs and draperies in furthering the essential rhythm, and in building up his flame-like theme-variations. Realistic-minded critics see in his "contortions" only a result of astigmatism, or an arbitrary departure from the natural. But El Greco literally twisted nature to his own uses. It is noteworthy that he dealt to an exceptional degree with elements that were "natural" to his public, yet could be endlessly rearranged for abstract purposes; draperies and clouds and rocks. He thus filled in with materials that could be "distorted" without offense to Realistic-minded observers. At other times he took refuge in combinations which could be "excused" because the miraculous subject matter had divine sanction. A man might arrange Biblical apparitions and the Kingdom of Heaven according to his fancy.

Thus El Greco could moderately satisfy an audience trained to Realism, and yet accomplish the miracles of plastic organization that place him among the very greatest painters of all time. The

< 166 >

The Reapers, by Maurice Sterne. (By courtesy of the
Phillips Memorial Gallery.)

figures in his canvases are not so much moving, in the usual sense,
as artificially energized—by attenuation and exaggerated gesture—
to carry out a preconceived plastic orchestration.

Much commoner is the utilization of the *implied* movement of
a slope of ground, or the directional effect of a figure facing left
or right, in or out. A bit of terrain leading inward is a common
device of the Realists as well as the Expressionists, for getting the
eye into the picture. But it is in the canvases of the Moderns that
one finds every natural slope incorporated into a closed rhythmic
design. Cezanne's landscapes illustrate at times an amazing com-
plexity of ground slopes entering into the intricate counterpoint of
color, plane and volume. In the early and less abstract work of the
Cubists—Braque and Picasso particularly—there is over-conscious
utilization of such "directions": it may be fields and roads, or table

< 167 >

top or bar. As classic examples one might study Chinese landscape paintings; and the famous *View of Toledo* by El Greco offers masterly material for test of the relationship between apparently natural topography and dramatically moving pictorial rhythm.

We are here on the verge of a consideration of "natural perspective." The reader trained to recognition of right or wrong perspective in pictures probably found himself thinking, when I first began speaking of recessive values and spatial depth, "Why, he is talking of the effect of perspective." On the contrary, nothing could be more confusing than to mistake plastic rhythm for merely a cunning manipulation of appearances in perspective. This factor, like depicted motion of animals, may be one item contributing (at points) to the main rhythm or to the plastic variations. But its rôle is incidental; and in great numbers of creative paintings there is conscious distortion of what are inaccurately known as "the laws of perspective."

These laws are merely a convention. Slavish observance of them, and playing with the resultant "natural effects," all but ruined Western landscape and genre painting from the time of Masaccio, "who was the first artist to attain to the imitation of things as they are" [Vasari], to Manet and Monet and Menzel and Sargent. (Perspective vistas even crept into sculpture—so help us God!) Chinese painting of the same period is incomparably richer in plastic values, in the profounder values of pictorial art.

PERSPECTIVE: MECHANICAL LAW OR CREATIVE INCIDENTAL

There is a supposition, among those who put a special value upon "natural" art, that a knowledge of scientific perspective enables a painter to fix on canvas views of nature exactly as the human eye

< 168 >

Pink Vase and Green Leaves, by Georgia O'Keeffe.   (By courtesy of
An American Place.)

sees them.   On the contrary, the eye sees in patches, each clear patch
shading off into blurred surroundings.   The Realist sometimes ap-
proximates this effect in a small painting, as when he places a portrait head in a field darkened at the corners.   In most larger pictures
he spreads over his canvas a series of views of adjoining bits of
nature.   By observing "the laws of perspective," he brings them
into a composition which is true to nature as the human eye would
see it *if* it could be focussed over many times the territory it actually
does cover.   It is a mistake to believe that we see "in perspective."
The "laws" are really an intellectual working-out of mechanical

< 169 >

truths—and were superstitiously adopted and observed, in an era when materialistic and intellectual forces came together.

The Western system of perspective is *one* convention. Today a great many people are coming to believe that the Chinese convention is truer pictorially, permitting a greater intensity of that sort of beauty pertaining essentially to the painting art. That the method of "laying up" the objective elements of a picture, in Chinese art or in Italo-Byzantine, violates the rules of natural perspective, no longer seems to argue inferiority in the product.

It is seen to be an unwarranted assumption, on the part of material-scientific minds, that perspective-art is true to appearances, and that transcription of surface appearances results in the highest art. In the Far East, painters seldom aspired to the triumphs of literal representation, and scientific perspective was not discovered. In the West, the student should learn the rules and quite consciously forget them.* The wise revolutionist knows thoroughly what he is rebelling against.

The rhythmic structure or plastic organization is, indeed, of so much greater significance than the observance of the mechanical rules, that the majority of paintings produced by the Moderns ignore or distort linear perspective as known to the conscientious 19th Century artist. This is not to say that there is never use of the formula, for incidental gain in primarily plastic design. What used to be called atmospheric or aerial perspective—almost independent of the rules of linear representation—is the greater source

---

* Vernon Blake, in *The Art and Craft of Drawing*, writes: "The visible universe, the terms of plastic art, are (or were) to the Chinese artist no more than the means of bodying forth abstractions. If the rhythm of pattern in a composition require it, that is, if one of the most important aesthetic factors require it, a Chinese artist does not hesitate to change the direction of a receding perspective line; rhythm is more essentially important, on account of its aesthetic suggestive value, than is exactitude of appearance."

< 170 >

Self-portrait, by Joseph de Martini. (By courtesy of the artist.)

of contributory "effects." The way in which a landscape seems
sometimes to be laid up in stepped-back atmospheric planes, could
not but be suggestive to the artist interested in all the resources of
recession and return. The contrast between forward-dark and
lighter-back, and the projection-value of succeeding edged planes

< 171 >

are items not to be overlooked as means to plastic movement. All this, however, is quite apart from the code of laws of linear perspective, which are framed with the stated purpose of making transcriptive art "look natural."

Linear perspective, indeed, presents exceptional dangers when incorporated into plastic design. The convergence of architectural lines toward vanishing points often starts movement that is never "headed"—the pictorial structure thus being destroyed. The museums are full of vaunted paintings which illustrate how the eye can be carried impossibly far back into space, or clear off the edge of the picture. Personally I find the extravagantly praised *Madonna with St. Francis and St. George* by Giorgione badly marred by the duality of focus. The front plane with its distributed points of interest accords to the best canons of static composition: but there must be a violent jump of the eye to embrace the two perspective inserts beyond. There is cunning surface design, almost architectural in its rigidity: though mechanical and dull as compared with the plastic architectonics of much of Tintoretto and El Greco. But the point of the illustration here is that only by an effort can vision be held in the picture proper. Titian is guilty of "breaking" several of his compositions similarly.

Linear perspective appears seldom in El Greco's work. Note, however, in the *Feast in the House of Simon,* how the architectural lines weave into the larger design; and how the artist has pulled in the pillar, spire and dome to close the arched space at back: stopping up what in another's painting would have been a "hole."

It may be of interest to the reader to note how seldom perspective backgrounds appear in the illustrations by contemporary painters, in this book—as compared with any representative series of 17th-19th Century pictures. No work was excluded *for* its perspective: it

< 172 >

The Feast in the House of Simon, by El Greco. (Photo by courtesy of the
Art Institute of Chicago, from original in the collection of Mr. and Mrs.
Joseph Winterbotham.)

is simply a fact that a strict regard for plastic unity demands the
elimination of many of the deep vistas and sharp linear descents
that graced shallow Realistic paintings, as added tidbits of reproductive fidelity.

< 173 >

Chinese landscape painting on silk, illustrating utilization of overlapping planes for movement effect. (By courtesy of the Freer Gallery of Art.)

Leaving the natural or objective means, let us see how the *formal* means for creating movement are commonly manipulated. In general it may be said that there are two large groups of formal elements, the one more directly plastic in that they can lead the eye in and out of the canvas by indicating shapes and slopes, the other with the properties of backwardness or forwardness but not "fluidity." The first category includes plane and volume. The other includes color and texture.

When plastic values are under discussion, it is too commonly assumed that color and texture are only secondary and corrective: as if design in painting could be complete without those elements: they being in the nature of added decorative values. Cezanne was the first Western painter to fuse the processes of drawing and coloring. Before his time almost all painting existed as colored drawing: the composition was built up by delineation, chiaroscuro, etc., and then color was superimposed objectively—grass green, sky blue, apple red, etc. The Expressionists in general have now learned the creative properties of colors, and commonly use them for recessive values; but very few have attained to the mastery of Cezanne in fusing this element with the other means to movement.

There are difficulties for the reader here: we can study these matters only by pulling one element free from the others—without which, perhaps, it cannot truly exist—and yet the end of our quest lies in the synthesis, the indissoluble unity of all elements. Thus color cannot exist independently: can be evident only in color-areas —which are essentially color-planes. In the same way line cannot be said to exist as a separate element: it occurs where planes meet.

< 175 >

Of the first group of elements, Hofmann writes thus: "The formal elements of painting are the line, plane, volume, and the resulting formal complexes. These are the elements of construction, and result, when properly utilized, in form." *

Hofmann has written elsewhere that the artist conceives his image in terms of volumes, but that he creates formally in planes. As a matter of fact, volumes are visually existent only as composites of planes shown out by light. The Cubists discovered this truth, and the related one that every solid in nature can be summarized by— "reduced" to—a cube; and they played with planes, wholly abstract, or disassembled from objective nature, or near-natural, until the world wearied of their endless packs of shingles, and patch-work mandolin-players and block landscapes.

But out of their researches came the first easily intelligible clue to the mastery of plastic movement—as exhibited long before by

* The quotations from Hofmann are from two exceptionally meaty articles entitled "Painting and Culture" and "On the Aims of Art," published in *The Fortnightly* (San Francisco) in the issues for September 11, 1931, and February 26, 1932. The one is set forth "as communicated to Glenn Wessels"; the other in a translation by Ernst Stolz and Glenn Wessels. I have quoted, scrupulously, only from these articles, though some of Hofmann's ideas are summarized from his unpublished work *Creation in Form and Color*, of which I read one volume in manuscript. It is to be hoped that this will soon be made generally available to students. The diagrams in following pages, "after Hofmann," are based on his originals in the manuscript, with his permission. The quotations from Gleizes are my own translations from his *Du Cubisme et des Moyens de Le Comprendre*, Paris, 1920. Quotations from Wessels are from a multigraphed syllabus entitled *Principles of Pictorial Composition*, generously put at my disposal. Quotations from Adolf Hildebrand are from *The Problem of Form in Painting and Sculpture*, translation and revision by Max Meyer and Robert Morris Ogden, New York, 1932. This essay, first published in Germany in 1893, was a remarkable reaching forward toward the present theories of plastic organization. Hildebrand wrote particularly of "the relief conception of painting," of the picture "spatially alive," and of "planes and depth." It was left to later artist-teachers to clarify the theory, and to co-ordinate knowledge of the several plastic elements; but Hildebrand's book is still one of the most suggestive and useful works on the subject of Picture-Building. The quotations from Kandinsky are from his essay *On the Spiritual Element in Art*, published in an English translation as *The Art of Spiritual Harmony*, London, 1914.

< 176 >

Music, by Georges Braque. (By courtesy of Katherine S. Dreier.)

their prophet, Cezanne. And the Cubists themselves rose at times to intense plastic expressiveness, with their best plane arrangements.

In learning to "read" planes in a canvas, the student should make sure that he is not merely following tracks from edge to edge, but rather feeling the tensions from axis to axis. Every plane has axes, meeting at a center of weight; and "planetary movement" may be said to be engendered by the tensions between axial points.

< 177 >

The following diagrams, after Hofmann, illustrate the commonest (and type) method of building in a path of vision by plane manipulation. Simple planes (considered, for the moment, as parallel to the picture surface) are set one behind another, with overlapping edges. The eye, due to the way in which the observer automatically looks *into* the picture, inevitably steps back from plane to underlying plane, sensing the weight-tensions from axial point to axial point.

A　　　　　　　　　　　**B**

Figure A illustrates the basic principle of movement engendered by planes. There can be no doubt that visual movement is induced by this formal means; nor doubt that the direction is changed by any rearrangement of the overlapping, as in Figure B. A different and less elementary set of figures, below, illustrates how movement

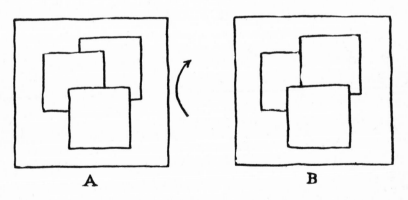

A　　　　　　　　　　　**B**

< 178 >

Composition with Figures, by Fernand Leger. (By courtesy of A. E. Gallatin and the Gallery of Living Art.)

can be reversed by lifting one edge from back to front. The arrow beside figure A indicates the path natural to the eye. In figure B the direction, though still inward, is reversed as regards right-left.

Such are the phenomena of planes manipulated to create movement. Seldom will they appear as bald as here; but the basic principle illustrated underlies the practice of one whole wing of the Cubist school. There are few Expressionists who do not utilize

< 179 >

Crucifixion, in the manner of Bernardo Daddi. (By courtesy of the
Gallery of Fine Arts, Yale University.)

Houses in Horta, by Pablo Picasso. (From *Picasso,* by Maurice Raynal.)

the device, more or less abstractly, in correlation with the other dynamic elements.

The effectiveness of overlapping planes in engendering movement was felt, if not intellectually understood, by Giotto and by many of the "Primitives" of his time and earlier. Duccio, Masolino, Daddi and Taddeo-Bartoli spread on their gold grounds rhythmic compositions, with definite backward-forward movement (though within shallow depth limits); and no element contributed more to accentuation of the vision-path than the stepped-back halos and the parallelism of figures of horses and men. As examples I am reproducing here a *Crucifixion* in the manner of Daddi, and (page 208) Giotto's *Crucifixion.*

< 181 >

Pierrot, by Pablo Picasso.

The Picasso *Houses in Horta* shows how, even when the device of overlapping planes is used very obviously, to carry the eye in and out, there is continual variation: edges accented, complexes formed to indicate volume, planes turned from the parallel, etc. This is an example, of course, from that period when the Cubists had first reduced to a formula the new knowledge of plastic values and of the mechanics of planes; and the device is self-consciously used.

The effects of parallelism are better studied in the works of those doctrinaire Cubists who, for a time, insisted that the integrity of the picture "flat" could be preserved only by ranging every element in

< 182 >

The Bridge: Water-color by Paul Cezanne. (By courtesy of the Museum
of Modern Art: Bliss Collection.)

the painting parallel to the canvas surface. They banished movement that carried the eye deep into the picture, even though that
plastic movement could—as Cezanne, Picasso and others had proved
—be anchored by tensions to an established pictorial plane. Gleizes,
Marcoussis, Ozenfant, Braque, Gris and Metzinger all passed
through periods of flat patch-work composition, of the sort illustrated here in a painting by Picasso.

One of the sub-groups of Cubists proclaimed that the recessive
values of *colors* also offered disturbance of the flat effect, and proceeded to compose exclusively in natural browns and grays. When
they had discounted plasticity and denied color, it seemed to some
outsiders that they had effectively denatured the painting art. And

< 183 >

Pines and Rocks, by Paul Cezanne. (By courtesy of the Museum of
Modern Art: Bliss Collection.)

mind you, these Cubists had started from hints found in the works
of Cezanne, the pioneer master of plastic counterpoint and creative
color.

Cezanne had utilized plane-arrangements more cunningly, I believe, than any painter in the earlier history of the art. Some of

< 184 >

Boy with a Red Vest, by Paul Cezanne. (From *Cezanne,* by
Julius Meier-Graefe.)

his more abstract water colors seem to the unpracticed eye little more
than pleasingly matched squares of color. In the more objective
Boy with a Red Vest, shown here, the artificial "playing with planes"
is evident; and in *Pines and Rocks,* opposite, the method is obviously the same, but with the typical mature Cezannish variations and
enrichments.

< 185 >

We must leave to Hofmann, Wessels, and other artist-teachers the task of elucidating ways of changing direction and indicating tension; explaining how the principle of overlapping planes is varied for outward rather than inward movement, at a distance from the painting's base, where the eye more naturally "moves in"; and the special effects to be induced with rotating planes, bent planes, interpenetrating planes, etc. My own brief treatment is introduced, first as one more proof of the reality of this newly explained element of plastic movement in painting (about which the reader may still be harboring skepticism); and then to suggest how much more significant this formal means may be than is the easy depiction of actual objects in motion in nature. In that part of the study of Expressionism dealing with the medium, with the technique of picture-building, a comprehension of the movement-values of planes is fundamental. I omit also treatment of that technical device known as "the light plane": the carrying of a consciously manipulated plane, at a certain depth, and with a uniform "value," through separated portions of the canvas, as a binding element.

As a last word on the difference between designed plastic movement and depicted natural movement, I suggest a comparison between works of a true Expressionist, Orozco, and one of the later objective Realists, Benton. The latter is praised for the fullness of his canvases and the extraordinary sense of motion conveyed to the spectator. But to those who expect pictorial as well as representational values, and a sense of aesthetic stability and completeness, Benton's murals often are restless, formless and confusing. We may appreciate his work intellectually, for many unusual qualities: intense liveliness, courageous satire, and—God save the mark!—a sense of bustling mid-Western Americanism. But the virtues are illustrational; the picture as an organization often falls to pieces—

< 186 >

Cow Barn, by Heinrich Campendonk. Illustrating interpenetrating planes. (By courtesy of *Der Sturm* Gallery, Berlin.)

figures seem in imminent danger of tumbling out of the wall to the floor at one's feet, parades march through the border-frame, the eye jumps from prize-fight to locomotive to cabaret.

Orozco, on the other hand, handles material of equal human and social significance with competent and sometimes inspired mastery of plastic design. He confines natural movement within a rhythmically closed field, makes it contributory to spatial design; and he

< 187 >

Detail of Mural by José Clemente Orozco. Illustrating utilization of
planes for plastic effect. (From original at the New School for Social
Research, New York.)

utilizes adroitly that particular formal element just analysed—over-lapping planes.

OVERRIDING THE PLANES

It cannot be recorded too often that mastery lies in the synthesis of elements, in effects gained by manipulating the *several* formal "means" in harmony, in contrast, in fusion. A too obvious and exclusive reliance upon plane-arrangement makes for thin results—and a good deal of Cubism seems, today, pinched and meagre. Having given so much of space to the matter of planes, let me say, then, that the most expressive painters hide their parallel arrangements beyond a continual play of harmonizing and corrective elements. Plane movement is balanced not only by color and texture, but by arbitrary introduction of other abstract elements. There is wilful overriding of planes.

An artist will seem to lay down a complex of planes, starting a thrust, only to cut across it arbitrarily, with a strongly linear element, an arc, a mast, or whatnot. The design, outside the main movement track, as fixed perhaps by planes, may be strewn with corrective accents, pointing angles, and minor "points of interest." These may be in the nature of objective features, or they may be merely smears of color, or an area emphasized with lines equivalent to heavy texture.

Pascin's paintings, for instance, seem often to present a clearly defined face or figure or volume, against a background of improvisation in fluid colors. The artist seems to strew mere "smears" through the space portions of his pictures. But where these have not a definite place in an arrangement of planes for recessive and return effects, they act as individual correctives. The careless

< 189 >

Child with Cat, by Jules Pascin. (By courtesy of the
Downtown Gallery, New York.)

"look" is deceptive. Note in the *Child with Cat* how the arc that
swings down along the left edge completes the main composition
(even in the black-and-white reproduction). In the original this is
accomplished by a long wedge of red-madder, running into a complex of greens darkened with reds and purples. The entire "back-

< 190 >

Christ and the Fishermen, by Georges Rouault. (By courtesy of
Pierre Matisse Gallery.)

ground" vibrates with rich color contrasts—but all within a scheme.
(What I see as a "smear," in a picture by Rouault or Pascin, may
be a carefully graded agglomeration of color pellets in Seurat's
work—placed arbitrarily, without objective reason.)

When I write of these smears and accents as correctives, I do not
mean to suggest that the artist sits down and considers intellectually
what effect is needed to balance or close the design. The process
is nearer intuitive. Nevertheless, the "feel" for the right plastic
relationship is there, is orderly.

In the matter of impromptu accents, Marin is a master. You may
read in so good a book as Pearson's *Experiencing Pictures* that
Marin understands only one of the plastic means, color—the inti-

< 191 >

Maine, 1928: Water-color by John Marin. (By courtesy of An American Place.)

mation being that he is weak in design. I should say, on the contrary, that he has few peers as a creator of organic plastic designs. These are seldom tied up neatly in static linear compositions. But where he seems careless with one element, another is intuitively brought into play. All things recognized, the design is closed, the rhythm poised in relation to the pictorial field. Other artists whose apparent carelessness has puzzled the Realists—but producing work richly repaying study for the variety of counterplay—are Rouault, Schmidt-Rottluff and Kokoschka. Many observers who are confused today by the apparent carelessness of "handling" in Rouault's paintings will progress, as their understanding grows, to enjoyment of the gorgeous orchestration of elements in a work such as *Christ and the Fishermen*.

Note how the plastic design is carried sometimes by the objective factors, sometimes by arbitrary "unreal" bits: the position of the figures and the direction of the boat initiating the movement, a faintly discerned arc of color carrying the vision across the horizon at the left, the sun placed to pick up the attention, then mere color planes "carrying on"; and so to the objective elements again. Rouault packs more of pictorial movement into a canvas like this than was ever created by the Futurist painters, "inspired to reproduce in their art the dynamic movement of modern life."

Seurat was a painter who went to the opposite extreme of meticulous neatness of handling. He used every brush-stroke in its exactly appointed place. Sometimes his design is almost static—rigidly architectural—rather than richly plastic. There is little of the fluid counterpoint that distinguishes Rouault or Kandinsky or Cezanne. But, without being profound, his achievement of thrust and return is sure, his carefully controlled recessive values integral to the pictorial structure.

< 193 >

The Parade, by Georges Seurat. (By courtesy of the Knoedler Galleries, from the original in the collection of Stephen C. Clark.)

Seurat, indeed, was one of the pioneer masters of picture-building, in the Expressionist sense—if a little removed from the group that carried along the main current after Cezanne. That he understood the plastic values inherent in stepped-back planes could hardly be doubted, after examination of the two reproductions here, and the *Sunday on Grande Jatte* on page 152. But like the flat-wing Cubists, he stuck by parallelism of planes, limited the depth of recessive elements, and achieved a gently melodic counterpoint.

A sort of flawless architectonics can be found in these canvases; and no summary of the advance in knowledge of picture-building could be written without attention to Seurat's work. But it misses

< 194 >

Port en Bessin, by Georges Seurat. (By courtesy of the Museum of
Modern Art: Bliss Collection.)

something alike of the full-blooded emotion characterizing the best
Expressionist art, and of the plastic richness of typical Expressionist
handling of formal materials.

It is easy to speak of the "architecture" of Seurat's paintings
where one speaks of the plastic organization of Cezanne's or Marin's
or Rouault's. Pictorial architectonics may be based, so to speak,
on a more or a less fluid conception or scheme; and the fact that
Seurat sacrifices something of plastic depth for a shallower structure does not remove him from the ranks of freshly expressive

< 195 >

Moses Defending the Daughters of Jethro, by Nicholas Poussin. (By courtesy of the Minneapolis Institute of Arts.)

painters. In all three of the pictures mentioned one can trace easily a designed track of vision; indeed, most of the means and tests of movement already described are illustrated—coiled path, a picture field spatially deeper in one half and voluminous in the other, recession induced by overlapping planes, etc. And yet here is a variation in which the movement is held almost rigidly within a structure with static architectural lines. One can actually see the scantlings holding the architecture together, in *The Parade,* and *Sunday on Grande Jatte.*

< 196 >

Bathers, by Paul Cezanne. (Photo by courtesy of the Art Institute of Chicago, from original in collection of Mrs. Rutherford McCormick.)

There is a forerunner of this particular sort of conscious picture-building in the 17th Century painter Poussin. He was perhaps a link between the Italian Renaissance artists who achieved an exceptional architectural organization, though more static than plastic— Raphael, Piero della Francesca, Giorgione, etc.—and those Moderns, beginning with Cezanne, who revived monumental structure and added the movement-dimension. It will be illuminating, perhaps, to compare the picture by Poussin, illustrated here, with

< 197 >

Minnesota Farm, by Dewey Albinson. Illustrating the heritage of plane
Cubism to later non-abstract but plastically ordered painting.

Cezanne's *Bathers* (over-leaf) and the three Seurats. It may be
added that Corot seems at one time to have experimented with this
sort of "architectural" structure.

What I started to illustrate in this chapter was the way in which
a single formal element may be used to carry the main direction
of movement in a picture, or to weave into other elements by
forwarding the thrust or return at certain points. I chose to show

< 198 >

graphically the effects achieved by overlapping planes. Then, recognizing the common vice of overstressing the first understood factor, I showed certain ways in which the experienced artist overrides the plane-arrangements: how he learns the formula for engendering movement by one element, only to be able to cast it aside when some other means will afford variety and deeper enrichment. Leaving to another chapter such other major factors as volume-tension, color and texture, I described some of the minor arbitrary means—accents, improvised linear movement, introduced perspective, etc.

Speaking of "improvised" forms, of what some would call "distortions," in relation to the abstract element in art, Kandinsky points to the numberless assets open to the creative painter: "These apparently irresponsible, but really well-reasoned alterations in form provide one of the storehouses of artistic possibilities. The adaptability of forms, their organic but inward variations, their motion in the picture, their inclination to material or abstract, their mutual relations, either individually or as parts of a whole; further, the concord or discord of the various elements of a picture, the handling of groups, the combinations of veiled and openly expressed appeals, the use of rhythmical or unrhythmical, of geometrical or non-geometrical forms, their contiguity or separation—all these are the material for counterpoint in painting."

< 199 >

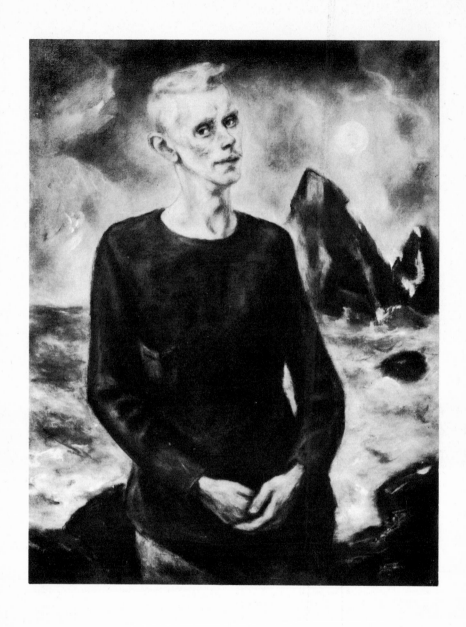

Self-portrait by the Sea, by Henry Mattson. (By courtesy of the Frank
K. M. Rehn Gallery, New York.)

CHAPTER VIII

PICTURE-BUILDING: VOLUME, SPACE AND TENSION

MAN moves forward by progression in two great fields of knowledge. He sheds fresh light on material phenomena, on all that registers in his brain through the senses; and at the same time his comprehension of the intangible grows and matures: his perception of the values that lie beyond sense-reporting and mental reasoning. Today he pushes forward epochally, in discovering laws of the mechanics of matter, and at the same moment millions of men feel a new impulse toward spiritual inquiry, and they sense an underlying principle or cause that will explain the accord or order underlying universe and creative life.

Art bridges the two divisions. A work of art appeals through the senses; but unless it achieve values beyond the material and the reasonable, it fails of the purpose ascribed to it by every prophet and seer through the ages.

Some people avoid both extremes: dislike the purely physical and mechanical at one end of one range, and the mystic at the far pole of the other. They ask explanation in a middle range. And so, having first written, in my exposition of a newly formulated theory of movement in pictorial art, about the most mechanical element or means—the plane—I will now approach the same subject from a viewpoint less isolated from objective life. The plane is an abstraction. The human eye and brain are more accustomed to deal with volumes.

< 201 >

Court Scene, by Jean Louis Forain. (By courtesy of Adolph Lewisohn.)

The eye itself, to be sure, has but slight stereoscopic powers: man is enabled to see only a little the roundness of objects, close by, by reason of bi-focality—through being in possession of two eyes. But the brain reënforces the sense of roundness, out of past sensory experience of like-appearing objects in nature. Even a one-eyed man, whose vision is not at all stereoscopic, who technically sees nature laid up in bounded planes, experiences an instantaneous impression of a head or a house as a volume: the limited two-dimensional sight impression, on the flat, is projected automatically into a three-dimensional image, because the observer has previously

< 202 >

touched those objects, and viewed them from other sides, often enough to *know* them as volumes. The trained artist will purposely view them as planes, breaking up the impression, against the time when he will re-arrange those planes for summary expression, stripped of the insignificant. But while the rest of us see "almost flat," we mostly comprehend nature as volumes in space.

Volumes related in space may also be reduced to abstractions, to geometrical equivalents: cubes, etc. But volumes may as easily be angels and cows and apples, and the other representational materials of picture-making. And so we come to an approach that offers fewer obstacles to the abstraction-shy mind.

By this other approach we shall, I believe, arrive at the same conclusions regarding the all-importance of plastic design, the existence of detectable movement in the canvas, the necessity of anchoring the complex of movements in relation to the rectangular picture field, etc. The painter's formal problem remains the same whether he thinks in terms of plane-manipulation or volume-space organization: the aim is preservation of the sense of two-dimensionality of the picture field, while affording an experience of pictorial-plastic movement, attained, formally, through orchestration of the several dynamic elements available to the painter.

VOLUMES IN SPACE

It might be said that all design begins with forms moving in space. There is here some relationship to the shift in scientific thought which makes the planetary-solar system a basic model of all that physically exists. The planets spinning in their orbits around the sun, held in space by a complex of reciprocal tensions, afford an analogue to the objects held within the picture limits by

< 203 >

felt tensions. The old conception of the picture as static, with its individual objects compositionally balanced, gives place to a dynamic conception: poised taut movement, fixed by the relationship of volumes in pictorial space—with a complex movement-path traceable along the invisible lines of tension.

A writer upon spiritual philosophy once noted that "Everything we see, or imagine, or dream, we have to perceive in space." Objects, or volumes, are anchored in a world of space. But where those objects used to be regarded with a sense of individual finality, as if set out separately and terminally, there is now a tendency to put first, as basic truth, the relationship between all objects. Relativity is a fundamental not alone of modern physics, of all that materially or organically exists in the universe, but also of that little stabilized world which each picture is.

The scientist or artist attempting to identify or explain the binding element, talks in terms of forces, energy, tensions, stresses and polarity. Glenn Wessels opens his syllabus on *Principles of Pictorial Composition* with this statement: "The world outside ourselves is a complex of forces interacting and continually shifting their relationships. We are equipped with senses which bring to our minds different aspects of this cosmos in flux. . . . Consciously or unconsciously, we arbitrarily divide the cosmos of qualities outside us into units, focal points, pieces of experience of convenient dimensions for comparison and differentiation. The world for us has primarily: mass, shape, measure, texture, color, movement, smell, taste, sound. No form can be clearly defined without recording by means of symbols of its perceptible characteristics." He goes on to differentiate between the "primary" characteristics, which are quantitative, have measure, shape, extension in space; and the secondary—texture, color, etc. Later he notes that the voluminous

< 204 >

Dancers, by Henri Matisse.   Illustrating linear rhythms and volume
tensions.   (Photo by E. Druet.)

primary materials are held "in certain relations due to their relative
tensions on each other."

In short, man's sense-equipment being what it is, there is no
more basic approach to the formal problem in art than by consideration of surrounding space, quantitative object or volume, and the
relating, interacting forces.   Sight and memory, acting together,
bring first recognition by contrasting volume and space, with an
understood web of forces between volumes.

In shifting from consideration of planes to study of volume-
space organization, we might seem to be abandoning certain artists
whose works entered importantly, as illustrations, in the preceding

< 205 >

Christ on the Lake of Galilee, by Tintoretto. An early example of manipulation of planes for plastic enrichment, and an interesting analogue to Cezanne's painting. (By courtesy of Arthur Sachs, Paris.)

chapters, and turning to others—perhaps more "solid" and "voluminous." This is true, I think, only in regard to those Cubists whose paintings rather self-consciously proclaimed reliance upon parallel planes. Most of the deeply creative artists earlier considered—Rouault, Kandinsky, Seurat, etc.—can be tested as easily for volume-organization. And as for the historic forerunners of the contemporary plastic-conscious painters, Giotto, El Greco and Daumier, all exhibit the solidest sense of related volumes. In characteristic works of each one, the employment of planes as an instrument to step the vision backward or forward can be marked,

< 206 >

Blue Horse Composition, by Franz Marc. (In the
National Gallery, Berlin.)

with the usual accenting of edges to speed the movement; but no
less there is the detectable and effective "structure" of volumes in
tension, the felt web of polarity and attraction.

Nothing could offer a better tangible beginning point for understanding of the finer adjustments of volumes in space than this

< 207 >

Christ on the Cross, by Giotto. (In the Pinakothek, Munich.)

Christ on the Cross by Giotto. Nor is the Rouault *Christ Mocked* less an exemplar of the two means in combination: activated planes, and volumes interacting. For similar orchestration of the two elements see also the El Greco *Crucifixion* at page 220, and Franz Marc's *Blue Horses*. Note, too, the way in which Cezanne, using

< 208 >

Christ Mocked, by Georges Rouault. (By courtesy of
Pierre Matisse Gallery.)

separated planes more effectively than any other painter, still
affords the feeling of voluminous roundness, in a landscape as
shown on page 141, and in a figure composition, page 251. Just
here I add also one of Georgia O'Keeffe's near-abstractions based
on flower forms, in which there is rich intermixture of plane and

< 209 >

Jack-in-the-Pulpit, by Georgia O'Keeffe. (By courtesy of
An American Place.)

voluminous rhythms. The painting is in the truest sense an orchestration of the plastic elements.

All volume study, like all plane study, must be undertaken with full realization that the beginning point of picture-building is the bounded two-dimensional field. What violates the flat, destroys the unity of the picture. In relating volumes in space, the artist builds a *system*; and this collapses if any solid escapes out of the tension holding it to other solids, out of the adjusted poise. But it escapes also if the system is not fully enclosed in the picture field, if the focal point is not fixed in relation to the established picture plane. Volumes may be presented as deep in space or as close to the observer, but the successful final adjustment is such that the weight as a whole rests firmly within the field. Just as a movement engendered by overlapping planes may carry the eye too deep beyond the focal plane, so the pull of a volume along a tension path may draw the vision so deep into space that the return to equipoise is impossible. All depends on the complex of tensions holding so that the path of vision is fixed, the plastic weights distributed, and the observer's eye never drawn into so deep penetration that the serene sense of equilibrium is upset.

In short, the aim of volume-space organization is to afford the pictorial experience *upon the two-dimensional field*. The tension organization is at rest only in relation to an enclosing frame.

It is necessary again to qualify my generalizations about *one* movement element or instrument, by reminding the reader that what I describe as typical of volume or plane alone is really true only when that element is adjusted or related to all others, primary

< 211 >

or secondary, that contribute to the movement. Thus the painter can and often does place a volume too deep in space, or too close to the observer plane, for the poise to be right while the structure is still stripped of color and texture. He can bring the too-deep volume forward by the advancing properties of certain colors or by insistent pattern, or he can set back the volume (to a certain extent) by the use of withdrawing colors and lack of texture interest. I have preferred to postpone consideration of these "corrective" agencies, in the array of movement materials; in order to attempt first an explanation of the main *structural* means.

No one else has written quite so clearly as Hofmann, I think, regarding the matter of basic volume-composition. He points out that volume and space as materials may be conveniently considered as filled space and empty space: as positive space and negative space. In *The Aims of Art* he writes:

"Form must be balanced by means of space. We differentiate the animated form and the space pervaded by energy. Form exists because of space, and space exists because of form.* A work of art which expresses only the objective form always has an over-emphasized naturalistic effect. The spatial counterbalance being omitted, the painting misses the inner rhythm."

Relating the element of volume-space organization to color rhythm, and the whole movement in the picture field, Hofmann writes, in the same article, thus: "From the depth-sensation, movement develops. There are movements into space and movements forward, out of space, both in form and in color. The product

* Hofmann here uses—or perhaps his translators make him use—the word "form" interchangeably with "volume"; though in the only other published essay, the text explicitly relates space and *volume*. For data about sources of these quotations, see footnote on page 176.

< 212 >

Lamentation over Jesus, by Tintoretto. (In the Brera Gallery, Milan.)

of movement and counter-movement is tension. When tension—
working strength—is expressed, it endows the work of art with the
living effect of co-ordinated, though opposing forces. Tension and
movement, or movement and counter-movement, lawfully ordered
within unity, paralleling the artist's life-experience and his artistic
and human discipline, endow the work with the power to stir the
observer rhythmically to a response to living, spiritual totality.
The picture swings, oscillates, vibrates with form-rhythms integrated
to the purpose of spatial (and volumnar) unity and it resonates with
color rhythms balanced, focussed and so ordered as to produce the
richest intensity of light contrast. It is not the contrast of two or
three, but the contrasted balance of many contributing factors,
which produces the paradox of life within unity."

< 213 >

Wessels notes that "objects must be given their due of space surrounding them. It is a common failure to pass over the space between objects as unimportant. When we are cognizant only of objects and draw them unrelated to their surrounding space, the composition is crowded." It might well be added that, obversely, volumes can be lost in space. Objects are less often crowded, in too little space, perhaps, than separated in too much. There is such a thing as an economy of space: a perfect adjustment of the negative element to the positive. The early Expressionists had a slogan that summed up the idea: "Banish the dead spots in the canvas." Realistic paintings are brimming over with dead space. (A notable parallel exists in one of the principles of the Imagists, who determined, in their poetry, "to use absolutely no word that does not contribute to the presentation." Ezra Pound comments that free verse "has become as prolix and as verbose as any of the flaccid varieties that preceded it. . . . The actual language and phrasing is often as bad as that of our elders, without even the excuse that the words are shoveled in to fill a metric pattern or to complete the noise of a rhyme-sound." Meaningless space is less shoveled into the casual-Realistic picture than left negligently there. It no less makes the picture tedious and thin.)

AXES AND STRESSES

The living axial relationships of volumes across space cannot be reduced to law. For one reason, there are those other elements to enter in and modify or correct: color, texture, etc. The task of creation is bound up in almost intuitive counterpoise of the several movement-means. But this much can be recorded confidently: the Moderns as a group recognize main movement and counterplay of

< 214 >

Three Horses and Two Riders, by Honoré Daumier. Illustrating masterly
volume-space organization.

movement as resulting chiefly from tensions between related volumes; and what is sometimes termed the focal point of the picture
is where the coiled power of the tension system centers.

The new philosophies start with two essentially Modern conceptions: that life is not static, perfectable and statable, but an evolutionary growth, change, a progress; and that relatedness rather than
isolated individuality is basic. The new physics begins not with
solids, the tangible, but with movement, spurts of energy; and it
recognizes a basic relatedness of all phenomena, material or organic: the fields of investigation, electrical, gravitational, etc., tend
to merge into one. Modern painting, on the formal or instrumental

< 215 >

Ruined House, by José Clemente Orozco. (By courtesy of the Delphic
Studios, from original in the Albertina, Vienna.)

side, likewise arrives nearer to understanding of basic principle by
study of dynamic relativity. The unity of the creative picture
grows out of a poised inter-relation of potentially energetic volumes,
each with weight and direction exerting stresses on all the others—
they in turn exerting a combined pull on it. The paths of tension
are from axis to axis (the axial center being determined by the
crossing of the two rotational axes of the volume).

To restate our fundamental thesis in still another form: the
vitality of the picture depends upon the completeness of the move-
ment-function within the limits allowed by the axial pulls. The

< 216 >

The **Card Players**, by Paul Cezanne. (Photo by courtesy of the Knoedler Galleries from the original in the Stephen C. Clark Collection.)

sense of completeness is achieved when the movement has been strongly initiated, curbed, brought to poise: the stresses equilibrated.

The galleries of recent favorites are full of paintings illustrating how little the Realists guessed the existence of volume-tension and axial relationship. The fashionable portrait painters—Sargent, Lavery, de Laszlo—concocted pictures as superficially organized as those of Besnard, Bonnat, Henner and Bouguereau. Even Manet, who helped to rescue painting from "mere" Realism, exhibits practically no understanding of volume-attraction. I have chosen a Metropolitan Museum masterpiece by Courbet to illustrate 19th

< 217 >

The Young Bather, by Gustave Courbet. Illustrating the Realist's entire neglect of plastic correlation and volume poise. (By courtesy of the Metropolitan Museum of Art.)

Century neglect of fundamental plastic-formal principles: to exemplify mishandling of weight and space. There is nothing in the canvas to hold the so-forward woman to the picture field. She is suspended, a naturalistic physical-culture exhibit, and beyond her is painted a pretty, naturalistic landscape, pictorially unrelated to

< 218 >

Pegasus, by Albert Ryder.　(By courtesy of the Worcester Art Museum.)

the figure.　The Moderns might analyze this typical painting with regard to many other principles, and find it equally unsatisfying: its only "movement" is illustrational, its color is pictorially destructive, etc.

On the opposite page I have reproduced Ryder's *Pegasus,* as an example of volume-placing by an artist with a strong sense of func-

< 219 >

Crucifixion, by El Greco.

Crucifixion, by George Bellows. (Photo by courtesy of the Art Institute
of Chicago, from the original owned by Emma S. Bellows.)

tional design. More powerful tensionally, is the *Crucifixion* of El
Greco, with its intricate but consciously related arrangement of
many figures. Against the "structure" of axially related volumes
in space, there is a gorgeous counterplay of fluctuating planes and
flame-like undulations: a sort of enrichment too often overlooked,
perhaps, by the Moderns who doctrinairely practise the new theories.
No other artist, I believe, ever energized the space in his canvas as
does El Greco: he vitalizes the spatial intervals through which pass

< 221 >

Landscape with Red Spots, by Vasily Kandinsky. (By courtesy of *Der Sturm* Gallery, Berlin.)

the tension lines from volume to volume. The rhythm is dynamic and vibrant throughout.

In the dwarfing company of El Greco, indeed, the paintings of most of the present-day Purists and belated Cubists seem meagre and over-precious. Only a few of the avowed Abstractionists have been able to present a full pictorial portion: adding to their carefully adjusted balances of weights sufficient counterpoint to enrich the field satisfyingly. Kandinsky (who seldom is *absolutely* abstract) escapes the fault. The main movement is commonly answered by multitudinous minor patterns of recession and return:

< 222 >

heavy weights poised against complexes of minor weights, the tension paths between main volumes crossed and varied by minor stresses. The "Landscape" shown here is a variation of the pictorial arrangement illustrated on page 155: with greater weight, deeper recession, added solidity.

In these two pictures by Kandinsky there is a perfect illustration of two different pictorial means used to the same end; and a reminder that we are considering planes and volumes, in two consecutive chapters, not as mutually exclusive formal materials, but as related devices, really inseparable—but, studied separately, affording convenient *approaches* to the plastic-form problem. The movement is strong in both canvases, and the vision path is identical. The too obvious regularity of the movement is daringly checked by the same thrust-in shaft. But in the example shown here the movement is engendered mainly by volume-space manipulation, by a rich complex of axial relationships. In the flatter version at page 155 the vision track is traced primarily by means of overlapping planes and color areas. But neither is the plane wholly absent as an instrument in the one, nor the volume in the other.

VOLUME-SPACE AND "MERE" PROPORTION

There can be no doubt that critics and teachers who have talked about *proportion* in painting have had in mind some of the weight effects inherent in adjusted volume-organization. But the understanding has generally been intuitional, and published statements have invariably evaded the issue of recessive values. In short, all formulas for proportional "space division" have dealt with relationships on the flat, as if the movement never pushed beyond the surface plane. "Dynamic symmetry" seems to the Moderns mis-

< 223 >

named, so far as application to painting goes: because it provides a test for design up-and-down and right-left, but totally ignores the plastic forward-backward thrust and return—the dimension in movement that affords the sense of power and dynamic vitality. There is a less deep sort of harmonic vitality, appertaining to pattern and pleasing decorative design, which can be charted by the space-division systems.

Painters with an exceptional sense of static balance and flat geometric relationship—Raphael particularly—seem to have proceeded with a strong intuitional or theoretical knowledge of the laws of harmonic proportioning (as since codified by Hambidge); but those laws are incidental to whatever mathematical truths may underlie the powerful dynamic effectiveness of the paintings of El Greco and Cezanne. That such truths will ultimately be mechanically explained, I have no doubt: that is, they will be codified to "explain" the satisfying mathematical relationships of weight, tension and volume which underlie plastic unity or formal dynamics; but they will go only so far as the so-called "dynamic symmetry" theory has gone to explain surface design—that is, they will offer a test of framework only, leaving out of the case the variations and complexities by which the artist enriches and individualizes the picture.

Hambidge developed his system in such ways that one or another of his formulas will fit almost any average pleasing pictorial composition: conversely, any painter trained to the usual surface-compositional principles will arrive at a result conforming to the coded laws. Raphael or Sargent, Hokusai or Harrison Fisher—their diagonals and root-rectangles will prove to be mathematically right. And yet it is possible that El Greco and Cezanne will often fail, on the surface, to pass the test: because what is a violation of the rela-

< 224 >

Painter in the Landscape, by de Hirsch Margules. (By courtesy of the
Feigl Gallery, New York.)

tionships of surface harmony will be corrected by effects resultant
from manipulation in a deeper dimension, by the plastic element.

It may come to be recorded, ultimately, about Cezanne, that he
totally revolutionized painting in the Western world by turning the
current of theory and practice away from Realistic recording of
nature, and also away from static surface composition. He under-
mined the centuries-old faith in the importance of reproductive art,
with its superstitious regard for anatomical truth, light effect, and

< 225 >

mechanical perspective; he abandoned that faith to express the deeper realities of universe and self. Equally he exposed the shallowness of surface design: initiated the modern search for dynamic movement and symphonic fullness: for the powerful pictorial rhythms that had been all but lost out of painting for centuries— though still enduring in the works of unnamed Orientals, in Giotto, in El Greco, in Tintoretto, and even, rather uncertainly and flamboyantly, in Rubens. It was in the passionate effort to understand and capture the profound plastic values, that Cezanne "distorted" the anatomy of man and landscapes, telescoped natural perspective —and so far departed from orthodox practice that he was execrated by every guardian of respectable painting. Today, nevertheless, he emerges as one of the historic revolutionary and creative figures.*

* There would be little point in calling attention to the total lack of understanding of Cezanne's contribution, on the part of the dwindling group of reactionary Realists, except that certain critics with Victorian standards still hold command of the commoner channels of education: schools, libraries, "art news" columns, museum lecture-series, etc. So recently as 1925 Royal Cortissoz wrote, in *Personalities in Art*, that Cezanne was "commonplace, mediocre, a third-rate painter." Thomas Craven is even more dangerous, because he makes a pretense of understanding Modernism, and grudgingly accords a certain significance to Cezanne's "meagre and unfulfilled art." Craven actually exhibits no comprehension of the values restored or discovered by Cezanne, and he remarks in 1934 (*Modern Art*), that "his influence on the leading American painters of today is imperceptible"! His summary and dismissal of later critics is illuminating: "I am aware of the hundred and one theories put forth to explain the finality and indefectibility of Cezanne's art: the crooning praise of his plastic form, his functional color and his logical consistency—as if these abstract properties were the end of art; the strange descriptions of his little world as a microcosm in which every patch and particle, every distortion, plane, and indefinite contour, was preordained by the omniscient creative wisdom of God Almighty; the comparisons of his worst things —those 'figure compositions' of deformed, slanting females differentiated from the other sex by the ungainly prominence of buttocks—with Raphael's *The School of Athens*. I can only account for such aberrations by mentioning once more the muddled condition of modern art: originality in painting is so rare an article that the presence of a little of it in a slow-witted French provincial is enough to cast a spell over artists and critics and to deprive them of all sense of values." It might have served toward clarification if Craven had paused, just once, to attain to comprehension of plastic design.

< 226 >

Again we must leave to artists and schoolmasters exposition of the more recondite principles and facts involved, as they relate to the placing of volumes in pictorial space. Contrast of volumes, while still preserving equipoise; how a scale of volumes is established, the relativeness put within limits; the mathematical methods of figuring or feeling axes: these are problems proper to technical books—outside the field of a book aimed to establish only the point that there *is* a revolutionary theory of picture-building, sketching enough of the formal means to emphasize the reality and aesthetic vitality of the effects attained.

THE CUBED VOLUME

The Cubists doubtless made more *theoretical* progress than any other group of Modernists; and while we are dealing with volume, it is as well to note that they were given the Cubist name because one step in their advance was marked by the discovery, or re-discovery, that all solids in nature can be reduced to a few geometrical equivalents, of which the cube is basic. They over-did the cubing at first—as is natural when artists have become dissatisfied with mere fact-reproduction, and have glimpsed a means of moving nearer to revelation of universal truth.

Critics and artists who fail to understand the importance of the reach after plastic unity, who wish therefore to destroy the whole edifice of Expressionist attainment, have been quick to herald the shallowness of an art that *merely* cubes objects out of nature; and they have elatedly unearthed diagrams by Leonardo da Vinci, Dürer and other early painters, to prove that "the masters" knew all about this geometrical business, but rejected it as worthy of no more than passing interest.

< 227 >

Hills, by Bernard Karfiol. (By courtesy of the Downtown Gallery, New York.)

Such critics miss the entire significance of the Cubist contribution to the advance of painting: a new theory of formal creation, of plastic structure; and an advance in understanding of the instrumental means, embracing not only geometrical equivalents of solids, but methods of breaking solids into planes (or building by complexes of planes to afford a sense of related volume-weights)—the whole resulting in a conception of plastic movement or organic rhythmic organization as the fundamental compositional factor. The student must know why the Cubists played with cubes—and cones and spheres—at one stage of their explorations; but to pretend that Modernism stands or falls by proof of the newness of the statement of cubic equivalents is childish.

< 228 >

Gesture, by Max Weber. (Photo by courtesy of J. B. Neumann, from collection of Dr. F. H. Hirschland.)

The rest that need be said here about volume-space organization can best be presented in relation to illustrations. In these two pages and overleaf I have juxtaposed some examples suggesting how compactly the volume structure may be compressed into the picture field, and how widely "distributed" it may be in other examples. The Max Weber *Gesture* contrasts strangely with the *Hills,* by Bernard Karfiol; but each painter has proceeded with a sense of volume-placing which will be apparent to the trained eye. The simple balance of weights in Beckmann's *Artist at Beach* is a sort of elementary statement of a principle that finds complex expression and rich variation in Rouault's *The Crowd.* In the latter

< 229 >

The Crowd, by Georges Rouault. (By courtesy of Pierre Matisse Gallery.)

the separation and distribution of certain volumes, their weight emphasized by comparative isolation, and the combining of others into inseparable weight-complexes—these are details of volume-space adjustment worthy of serious study.

In the Karfiol *Hilda* and Marguerite Zorach's *Hound* there is evidence of a different approach to the problem of volume,in relation to picture field. A single volume dominates the canvas; but is, in a sense, cradled back into pictorial space by means less voluminous than plane and linear. In the one, the figure would fall from the field if the draperies below or the sofa-back above were removed. In the other, the dog is plastically "set" in relation to the frame by the "filling" before and behind. In both cases it might be claimed

< 230 >

Artist at Beach, by Max Beckmann.   (By courtesy of J. B. Neumann.)

that the plastic effects are not very deep—though the painters are obviously working creatively, pictorially—not merely realistically. The counterpoint is, perhaps, too generally linear.

Immediately one has "discovered" volume tension as a separately distinguishable means to plastic understanding, the temptation is to

< 231 >

Hilda, by Bernard Karfiol. (By courtesy of the Downtown Gallery, New York.)

look for actual solids with traceable stresses between. But few artists deal with volumes so baldly as, occasionally, do Weber and Rouault and Karfiol—as did El Greco and Blake and Daumier. Balance may be achieved by other than tangibly weighty objects. Sometimes the old device of balanced chiaroscuro becomes more important than any detectable equipoise of volumes. Some Moderns have been ready to dismiss Rembrandt as summarily as they do superficial painters like Murillo and Gainsborough. But the best of Rembrandt's paintings seem to this student extraordinary examples of calculated plastic organization; seldom with the depth and richness of an El Greco, but with cunning placing of volume in space, made more effective by light-dark contrast. What is the

< 232 >

Hound, by Marguerite Zorach.

exact relationship between light-heavy and light-dark as plastic instruments, no one, I believe, has yet pretended to demonstrate.*

It would be easy to read axial relationships into Rembrandt's *Old Woman Cutting Her Nails:* with tension lines traced between the

* Investigators of this particular relationship will do well to go back to a book published nearly a half-century ago: *Practical Essays on Art,* by John Burnet, New York, 1888. From the Moderns' point of view, Burnet would seem to approach the problem backward: how to place volumes for a pleasing composition of light and dark. But the text and illustrations both are richly suggestive. There is a thought, too, in Kenyon Cox's contention, in *The Classic Point of View,* that "Modelling does, indeed, insist upon the body—true chiaroscuro conceals it." Again he writes: "Just because light and shade is so mysterious and absorbing, because it tends to take the place of design and drawing and even color, it is a dangerous tool." If Cox had guessed that all the formal elements might be approached as factors in a deeper synthesis—a fullness of plastic design—he might have seen the "dangerous tool" as an enriching asset. But he was right in believing that misuse often resulted in "a rather paltry picturesqueness."

< 233 >

Old Woman Cutting Her Nails, by Rembrandt. (By courtesy of the Metropolitan Museum of Art.)

figure, the chair arm, and the background mass of drapery. But the more natural approach is by a study of the lights characterizing these "objects." The painting is voluminous, with plenty of plastic fluctuation; but as in most of Rembrandt's major works, whether painted or etched, there is exceptional capitalization upon the move-

< 234 >

Portrait of a Man—sometimes called Self-portrait, by El Greco. (By
courtesy of the Metropolitan Museum of Art.)

ment values of light-dark contrast. Considered as volume-space
organization, the positive volume structure seems perfectly fitted
into the enveloping negative space. The spatial portions are of the
organism, living. If you doubt this, cover a quarter-inch strip of
what you may consider dead space at the top of the reproduction;

< 235 >

and note how the composition loses as a formal pictorial organization. Plastically speaking, half a Sargent or half a Gainsborough may be as good as the whole. Not so the organisms built by Rembrandt, El Greco, Cezanne. It would be instructive to test *The Anatomy Lesson* or *The Descent from the Cross* for volume dynamics and the livingness of space.

TENSION BETWEEN VOLUME AND FRAME

The most puzzling question, when one has begun to sense the volume-space structure in plastically rich paintings, arises in connection with canvases wherein a single object appears. One of the earliest principles sensed is that a volume well forward can be anchored, so to speak, by a network of tension lines to other volumes deeper in space. But what of a single volume? The answer is that the entire structure within the picture field is built in relation to the frame: the volumes have tension-relationship not only to each other but to the enclosing borders. It is obvious that there cannot be the rich voluminous counterplay in a portrait bust which one detects, for instance, in the El Greco *Crucifixion* or the Cezanne *Mount Sainte Victoire*. But certainly El Greco's *Portrait of a Man* has, within its limitations, essential plastic weight and spatial depth. The satisfying sense of fullness with perfect poise is accomplished by a cunning adjustment of volume to field. Perhaps the axial center of the single solid is made to coincide with the understood focal plane (of which more in a later chapter).

It would almost go without saying that when the volume structure is limited to one main motive in relation to adjusted frame, the plastic elements other than volume-space are likely to assume increased importance. Additional functions of balance and correc-

< 236 >

Woman Sleeping: Water-color by Max Kaus.

tion are exercised by color and texture. The *Woman Sleeping* by
Max Kaus is an example in which the single volume would be in
danger of falling forward if not held in tension by the extraordinarily heavy texture interest or "streaks" introduced into the upper
right corner of the picture field. This texturing has the effect of a
weight with tensional pull upon the woman's head and figure.

This same painting illustrates the way in which strength is attained by filling the frame almost completely with the single volume.
Obversely, a single volume placed deep in space may appear weak,

< 237 >

Self-portrait, by Paula Modersohn-Becker. (By courtesy of
J. B. Neumann.)

lost, though perhaps with a gain in restfulness. There is, of course,
a place for strength, and a place for restfully remote isolation.

The strengthening of pictorial impression by cutting down the
space in the field, to "gain volume," is a device not uncommon to
Oriental art; and the Expressionists have been quick to sense certain possibilities in relation to the pace and timbre of modern life.
Picasso went through a period of sculpturesque largeness of volume

< 238 >

Oriental Head, by Abraham Walkowitz. (By courtesy of the
Downtown Gallery, New York.)

design. The earlier German "radicals"—Pechstein, Paula Moder-
sohn, Schmidt-Rottluff—by this means filled their galleries with
such a show of unaccustomed power and drive that the public educated on Boecklin, Menzel, Liebermann and Thoma all but fled in
terror. And a great many artists have occasionally utilized the
device with excellent judgment: as Walkowitz has in this pastel
Oriental Head. It is instinct with structural understanding. Modig-

< 239 >

Acrobat in White, by Walt Kuhn.

liani was an Expressionist with an uncanny sense of volume-equi-
librium in restricted space. Walt Kuhn often places a dominating
single object solidly in framed space, as in his *Acrobat in White*.

In these examples the artists in bringing the volume forward, in
relation to frame (and therefore to observer), have not permitted it
to fall out of the picture. Hofmann devised what he calls the plumb-
line test for volumes "sticking out." A projection too far forward
is as destructive of the always understood two-dimensionality as is

< 240 >

a "hole" too deep. If, Hofmann says, a plumb-line dropped from any point on the frame to the corresponding opposite point apparently cuts through a projecting volume, then the plastic structure is defective. In other words, the tensions have not been adjusted to hold each unit in its appointed place in the equipoised structure. One sticks out.

I chose to criticize the murals of Thomas Benton, in the preceding chapter, partly because there is too often the effect of volumes spilling out. The essential fiat of pictorial integrity—that the field enclose the initiated movement—is violated. One no more wants figures to be pushing from pictures into the room, than one wants pictures to simulate windows upon nature, like holes in the wall. Pictorial volume and pictorial space must live, but in their own pictorial character, not as illusion: must preserve an identity of their own, separate from nature, within pictorial limits.

< 241 >

Flowers in a Vase, by Paul Gauguin. (Photo by courtesy of the California Palace of the Legion of Honor, from the original in the collection of Mr. and Mrs. W. W. Crocker.)

CHAPTER IX

PICTURE-BUILDING: COLOR AND TEXTURE

A PICTURE field is established. The theory of plastic orchestration posits that the observer's eye will travel a constructed
but hidden track winding from the framed front plane back to,
and beyond, a focal plane fixed within that field. The "structure"
is mainly determined by the weights and axial relationships of
volumes in space; though the eye may be led on partly by complexes of planes artificially overlapped, bent, etc. All this is stated
as though the design were an organism without that characteristic
asset of painting, color. (And there is, indeed, a picture-art of
black-and-white.) But, in painting, it is discovered that each color
has in itself a movement value. The hue, at its established pitch
or intensity, tends to push forward from the surface upon which
it is applied, or to draw away. If the plastic structure is adjusted
without allowing for the recessive or advancing colors, the rhythm
is bound to be distorted or destroyed when color is added.

Until Cezanne fused the processes of drawing and coloring into
one operation, practically all picture-making in the Western world
had been a matter of arranging the other factors satisfactorily, and
then adding color. The Modern affirms that the other formal elements cannot be fitted into the organism unless the living color
finds its appointed place at each step of creation. Few have come
to Cezanne's deliberate and unerring delivery of stroke and color

< 243 >

effect together; but the best have learned constantly to *see* the color with the structure.

Today one knows, for instance, that a red is insistent, comes forward, and that a certain shade of blue-green is retiring, recedes into distance. Suppose, then, that the painter has been cunning enough to build a certain amount of plastic rhythm into the skeleton of his picture—(and many an artist has outgrown loyalty to other surface aspects of nature, but remains a Realist in his loyalty to objective coloring—fails to guess that colors too have individual dynamic properties). He has somehow balanced his black-and-white picture so that the voluminous cow in the foreground is anchored within the field; nor does the bit of landscape vista at the back recede too far and carry the eye out of the canvas. Then he adds "natural" colors: the cow red, the field vista green. Immediately the combined effect of volume and red color pulls the cow forward, while the green pushes the vista hole deeper: the balance is upset, the plastic rhythm stretched awry—because the colors have not been taken into account as movement elements. The point is that, whether designedly or not, the color *will* have inward-outward motion effect. Added ignorantly to a composition which is already "right" without it, it destroys the rightness. Used constructively, in co-ordination with other motion means, it furthers and completes the plastic unity.

THE NEWNESS OF THE THEORY OF PLASTIC COLOR

If you will look into any of the older treatises upon the art of painting—up to 1900, say—you will find learned and true observations upon certain of the properties of color; but nowhere will you find mention of these recessive values. The subject usually

< 244 >

has been treated according to certain coded principles: harmony of colors; tonality, or the unification of the picture by relating all colors to the chosen "tone" of one; and values, or the harmonizing of the degree of black-and-white in the colors. Many books begin with still another problem: reasonable conformity to nature. How can we, the painters and critics asked themselves and each other, endow the picture with harmony, tonality and a proper scale of values, and still not noticeably violate nature?

In a day when study of the art begins with a flat declaration that the painter's business is creation of an organism distinct from nature, subject first to its own pictorial laws, there is less talk about the problems of truth to natural coloring. But books on design and composition continue to appear, and to discuss tonality, values, etc., without even suggesting that there is a dynamic property of colors, entering constructively and vitally into the modern plastic synthesis.

Repeatedly, in the chapters on picture-building, I have been at pains to remind the reader that no one of the instrumental means treated—whether plane or volume or color or texture—appears independently, in any richly creative or plastically complete painting. What are sometimes termed the *structural*-formal elements can be separated, perhaps—they can at least be isolated, for discussion, theoretically—these being the truest plastic-formal materials, for building in positive-negative space. A picture can be wholly conceived for expression without color. But it is questionable whether any important black-and-white picture escapes exhibiting some suggestion of color and texture. Even the most nakedly posteresque woodcut is likely to take on variety and fullness by the enrichening of grained cutting; the simplest etching gains by the cross-hatching of the shadows or the tonal wiping of the plate. And the painting in wash, from which true color has

< 245 >

been scrupulously excluded, will gain "colorfulness" from devices of shading, stroking, etc.

But exceptional cases and non-color arts aside, the revolutionary truth is that color and texture have been discovered recently as harboring properties of "movement" totally unrecognized in the preceding era. Important as may be the principles codified by the adherents of tonality and scaled values, this other matter of the dynamic properties of color is incomparably more important to the student of Expressionism. The discovery and conscious utilization of the dynamic effects of advancing and receding colors is one of the major phenomena of the Modernist advance.

MATISSE AND COLOR ORCHESTRATION

Probably the surest manipulator of color today, for plastic effect, is Matisse. Whatever else may be lacking in his art—and there are some who scoff at him as a "mere decorator"—he is a master of rich but perfectly balanced color-orchestration. The charge of "lightness" arises from his repeated use of the same emotionally inconsequential materials: flowers, a couch, an Oriental woman, a rug, a bowl of goldfish, etc. Aside from values of feeling and meaning, moreover, the plastic rhythm is ordinarily shallower than in El Greco, Cezanne and Rouault. Matisse is distinctly on the decorative side: historically allied with the Orientals; in the contemporary advance, with Gauguin and Rousseau. Whatever his "place" in Modernism, he offers the perfect example of color expertly used for plastic effect.

Matisse ordinarily relies upon texture values to complement his color-design—no other Western artist uses richly textured areas so abundantly—and it is difficult to analyse his employment of color

< 246 >

Reclining Nude, by Henri Matisse. (By courtesy of
Pierre Matisse Gallery.)

without reference to this other factor. (Black and white reproductions are make-shifts at best; but I have tried to present illustrations of paintings that suffer least distortion of values in the
transfer.) In the example on this page, it might be claimed that
the initiated movement from front-right to left-back is stopped and
turned by the extraordinarily heavy texture of the wall (in conjunction with the slight natural perspective effect); and that it is
the large-spot texture of the sofa-head that draws the track of vision
around, down and in to the figure. But examination of the original
would show that the wall-texture is lightened by just the recessive
colors proper to modify the "insistence" of the stripes. Similarly

< 247 >

Interior, by Arthur B. Davies. (By courtesy of the Minneapolis Institute of Arts, from the collection of the St. Paul Institute.)

the "weight" of the sofa is a resultant of the combined volume, texture and color values.

More strictly an effect of color correction alone, the space around the couch, which would be in danger of fading out to a deadness, leaving holes in the plastic composition, if painted a receding color, is filled with reds, that "bring up" the "space around." Obversely,

< 248 >

Ploughing, by Vincent van Gogh. (Photo by courtesy of the California Palace of the Legion of Honor, from original in the collection of Mr. and Mrs. W. W. Crocker.)

the body, the weightiest element in the canvas when regarded as volume alone, is "brought down" by recessive colors.

Again and again in Matisse's pictures the student will find this device of space filled with reds, and figure or other dominating solids set back with colors chosen from the receding half of the scale. At times the bodies almost assume a grayness—if a rosy one. Since Matisse conceives the plastic play as held strictly within limits, kept at all times within a range close to the focal plane, his pushing back of volumes and his pulling forward of space are more pronounced: his use of color and texture for cor-

< 249 >

rectives of too deep or too advanced volume-space elements more obvious than in any other leader among the Moderns. He seldom avoids the single dominating solid as do several of the most distinguished practitioners in the decorative group: Rousseau, Klee, Bonnard, etc. Therefore, having chosen strong volume-space contrasts, he must use color and texture strongly for correction. To put it another way, having chosen to be a decorative practitioner, avoiding the deeper plastic rhythms, and yet utilizing voluminous figures and objects that otherwise would imply deep recessions and strong axial pulls, he builds up heavy weights of the less usual plastic means, texture and color—counterpoising weighty volume with heavy color, or "pulling down" volume-emphasis by modifying color.

In Cezanne and El Greco the volume-space organization ordinarily reaches deeper into space, the fluctuations before and beyond the focal plane occupying a less limited range: and color-texture values carry less obviously the burden of plastic oscillation and balance. It is easy to find in Cezanne, nevertheless, examples of the more decorative, shallower-range organization. His work, indeed, afforded a main instigation to the researches of the Fauves, the group with which Matisse first came into prominence. There is, for instance, this *Portrait of Mme. Cezanne* to indicate Cezanne's understanding of the compensating values of texture. His color orchestration is as sure as Matisse's, but more delicate.

There are few things more pleasing to the eye, as sheer decoration, than the best of the Matisse canvases—in the entire range of art. Don't let me give you the impression that I consider them merely superficial arrangements of color and texture. Matisse knows the principles of plastic design as thoroughly as any living artist. If he practically denies the importance of subject-matter—

< 250 >

Portrait of Madame Cezanne, by Paul Cezanne.   (By courtesy of
Adolph Lewisohn.)

carrying to extremes his reaction from the over-literary picturing
of the 19th Century—he has made himself the unchallenged master
in a medium that will continue to delight generations of men not
too sophisticated to enjoy melodic music and sensuously rich verse.
Nor is his reliance upon color and texture values quite so bald as
this brief analysis may have suggested.

< 251 >

The Taffeta Dress, by Henri Matisse. (By courtesy of
Pierre Matisse Gallery.)

In the picture here, for instance, every one of the formal means
so far described is utilized: the stepping back by planes, the volume-
space adjustment, the axial pulls (figure, bouquet, vase and stand),
color, and texture. But the interplay of elements is all-important.
The bouquet near the upper left corner is at once volume, color

< 252 >

Nude with Flowers, by Henri Matisse. (By courtesy of
Pierre Matisse Gallery.)

and texture—cunningly fused, as you will realize if you ever
happen to see the original. Note how line is utilized, too, just
beyond: to prevent the eye from travelling out the window—
instead, directing it across to the next strong item in the plastic
chain.

< 253 >

The amusing and vigorous water-color by Roger de la Fresnaye, shown opposite, from the original in the Gallery of Living Art, New York, illustrates the play of color, against plastic movement engendered by a structure of overlapping planes and poised volumes. If one studies the three faces, in the original, one will find the nearest head grayed down—otherwise it might tend to push forward of the understood plumb-line—while the face farthest back is, in color, the most "advancing" of the three.

One of the puzzling facts, when the dynamic potentiality in color is understood, may be stated thus: color movement may be capitalized independently or dominantly, in certain parts of a picture; or it may serve, throughout, a merely *corrective* rôle. Perhaps the highest point in creative painting is touched when, as in certain works of Cezanne, the drawing or modelling is fused with the color application. The several movement instruments are then manipulated together in the grip of one plastic intention.*

THE THEORY STATED

The theory of recessive colors, in brief statement, is this: All color effect is the result of broken-up light. (Scientists no longer study the subject by means of colored materials, but primarily through phenomena of light-rays and light-waves.) All that exists visually is made known to man as illuminated forms in space. Whether material object or living organism, light makes it comprehensible to man's brain through sight, by means of radiant energy. The surfaces have no color in themselves: they have

---

* Some of the later Purists exactly equilibrate their planes or volumes, and leave to contrasting colors the whole task of dynamically vitalizing the organism. This is possible, I believe, only in a starkly abstract painting—of a sort to be mentioned in a later chapter. The commoner method is to let the space-volume structure carry the main burden of movement, color merely re-inforcing, answering, or correcting.

< 254 >

La Madelon, by Roger de la Fresnaye. (By courtesy of A. E. Gallatin
and the Gallery of Living Art.)

properties of reflecting or absorbing rays in such manner that the
resultant radiation induces a sensation in the beholder. According
to the degree of reflection—measured on a wave-length scale
called the spectrum—man judges the object as colored red, green,
violet, etc., though more properly the color resides in the reflected

< 255 >

light. Amount of reflection vs. absorption determines hue, or place in the spectrum. Other modifying factors enter when colors are "used": values, from the degree of lightness or darkness, and intensity, because in pigments the purity of light cannot be attained. But the modern revolutionary fact about color, in relation to the art of painting, arises from the discovery that it is not primarily a static property of objects, but a living activity, with dynamic potentialities.*

The conception of color as a portion of light returned to the eye in vibrations, opened a new world of possibilities to artists already exploring the field of plastic design, of "relief" effects. If color determination was to be a matter of certain vibrations being absorbed, and others reflected outward, there must be in color composition a factor potential in developing the plastic unity or synthesis. In short, as color varied, the eye would push deep into the picture or be brought out. Scientific investigation determined the values of recession and return. Roughly, the red-yellow range advances most insistently, corresponding to positive volume in the volume-space organization; while blue-violet recedes farthest, having retiring effect comparable to negative space.

Knowing this much about the movement values of colors, the Modernist was able to go back and discover one more reason for lack of plastic unity in the works of great numbers of historic painters. If the average Realist between 1600 and 1900 had not effectively destroyed the integrity of his picture field in manipulation of the other elements, he was pretty sure to have used color—copied objectively from nature—with damaging rather than unify-

---

* My terminology accords, I believe, with that developed by Rudolph Schaeffer in formulating his "Theory of Rhythmo-Chromatic Design." The material of the entire paragraph is more or less paraphrased from notes taken at Schaeffer's lectures.

< 256 >

ing effect. The theorists of that period had not even guessed at dynamic values. But through the ages there had been a very few painters who felt, intuitively, the relationships of plastic structure and dynamic color. During most of the history of Western art, the destructive possibilities of dynamic colors had been limited because painting consisted largely of dark-light compositions slightly colored over. But since the Impressionists had driven the blacks, grays and browns even out of shadows, this factor of recession or advance by color seemed destined to prove a primary asset when constructively utilized, or a violently destructive agent when ignorantly used. One had only to look in at any academy show to note the disorganizing effects.

Willard Huntington Wright long ago pointed out that study of color in the painting of the past, since the Renaissance, would show that it had been used *naturally*, to increase the illusion of appearance-reality; *ornamentally*, to add to the pleasing aspect of pictures as decoration—this trailing off into the voluptuousness of court painting, etc.; and *dramatically*, to heighten the feeling of the spectator by color-contrast. The Impressionists might be said to have deified color for its own sake, wresting it free from the other elements of design; and certainly they paved the way to discovery of its independent plastic-dynamic properties. It was left for the Expressionists, led by Cezanne, to pick up color thus purified and fuse it constructively with the other plastic elements: to recover the volume-organization that had been thrown away by the Impressionists, and to co-ordinate it with color orchestration.

The Synchromists, Morgan Russell and S. Macdonald-Wright, were the first, I believe, to codify the recessive values, a service summarized by Willard Huntington Wright thus: "With him a yellow, instead of meaning an intense light, represented an advanc-

< 257 >

ing plane, and a blue, while having all the sensation of shadow about it, receded to an infinity of subjective depth. The relative spatial extension of all the other colors was then determined, and a series of color scales was drawn up which gave not only the sensation of light and dark but also the sensation of perspective. Thus it was possible to obtain any degree of depth by the use of color alone, for all the intermediate steps from extreme projection to extreme recession were expressible by means of certain tones and pure hues." *

Wright further says: "At an early date artists had recognized that blue and violet were cool and mournful colors, and that yellow and orange were warm and joyful ones. They applied this primitive discovery with the feeble results to be found in Neo-Impressionism. That these colors had any further character they never suspected. Their insight extended only to the emotional and associative characteristics of the colors; the physical side was overlooked. Had the painters been more scientifically minded they would have known that these characteristics, which were the feminine traits. could not have existed in isolation; they would have searched for the colors' dominating and directing properties which represented the masculine traits. Such a search would have led them to the meaning of colors in relation to volumes, that is, to colors' formal vibrations which alone are capable of expressing plastic fullness. . . .

"The ambitions of the Synchromists went deeper. They desired to express, by means of color, form which would be as complete

* *Modern Painting: Its Tendency and Meaning*, by Willard Huntington Wright, New York and London, 1915. See pages 286-304, embracing the best available exposition of Synchromism. As with so many self-consciously revolutionary groups, the Synchromists ran on to the shoals of an art too scanty and empty, because they overcapitalized their one epochal discovery to the neglect of other elements.

< 258 >

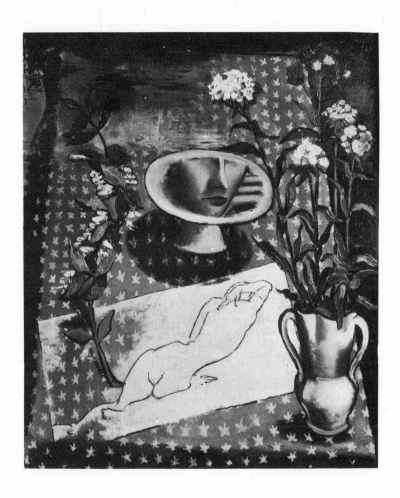

Still Life, by **Morris Kantor**. (By courtesy of A. E. Gallatin and the
Gallery of Living Art.)

and as simple as a Michelangelo drawing, and which would give
subjectively the same emotion of form that the Renaissance master
gives objectively. . . . The Synchromists' chief technical method
of obtaining this abstract equivalent for materiality was to make
use of the inherent and absolute movement of colors toward and

< 259 >

away from the spectator, by placing colors on forms in exact accord with the propensities of those colors to approach or recede from the eye."

INTUITIVE CAPITALIZATION OF DYNAMIC COLOR

There is in the Yale Gallery of Fine Arts a long panel-painting by the 15th Century artist Sano di Pietro, which establishes a rhythm with a series of foreground hills, mostly in receding dull greens. In the background appears a series of answering forms, comprising the hills seen between, painted in advancing colors— with castles in madder, and figures in reds and yellows. One would swear that the painter consciously "brought up" the far hills with forward colors; that he had insight into the dynamic values of colors, and intentionally stopped the holes in his picture field— in the best manner of the Modernists trained to plastic design. This painting, in short, has a definite affinity with Matisse and the Cubists and Synchromists.

But the history of Western painting forces the conclusion that such understanding was intuitive, and usually uncertain. In general the painters before Botticelli and Leonardo da Vinci had more instinctive feeling for preservation of a plastic balance in the picture field, with color considered, than had the later generations who became entangled in the search for exact equivalents of surface nature. In the rich and glowing paintings of the school and time of Giotto—fertilized by the influences of the Orient—the shallow volume-space rhythms often are accentuated and vitalized by structural color. It may be said, in general, that artists working in the less profound reaches of space, like Giotto—with what is sometimes termed a decorative flatness—have been more fortunate in

< 260 >

The Jungle, by Henri Rousseau. (Photo by courtesy of the Art Institute of Chicago, from the original in the collection of Mrs. Patrick J. Hill.)

their "feel" for the dynamic effects of color. Some of the others attained to the negative virtue of seldom destroying the picture by wrong use of color, because they approximated monotint painting.

El Greco, the great master of spatial rhythms, used color less creatively than the other elements. Many a later artist who came to be known as a brilliant colorist totally overlooked recessive values, gaining his title for a factitious natural glow or for dra-

< 261 >

matic heightening of emotion. But after all, it was not until the Impressionists had purified color, in the late 19th Century, that ignorant misuse of the palette invalidated whole galleries of pictures.

One does not like to criticize painters who may be serving very laudable purposes, who have evident faith in their own methods. But it will help to clarify our study of constructive color if I record that many of the so-called "progressives" among practicing artists today—even men exhibiting at the Museum of Modern Art, and termed "Moderns" by the newspaper critics—have only an imperfect comprehension, if any, of plastic-dynamic coloring. These painters obviously please large educated audiences, and therefore perhaps will the more easily forgive my personal opinion that they fail in one direction. I have noted, for instance, at recent exhibitions, that the coloring seems to push certain objects out of the canvas, or to dig holes, in paintings of Bruce, Burchfield, Benton, Brook, Beaux, Speicher, Hopper—and many, many more.

Whatever the other accomplishments of these eminent artists, they fail at mastery of the plastic synthesis which is increasingly recognized as the basic excellence of painting on its formal side. They fail worse than many a "Primitive," who could not have known the theory of dynamic coloring: because the Primitives often *felt* the color weights, and endowed their paintings with a plastic unity later lost, when art slid into Realism.

SUMMARY OF THE THEORY OF PLASTIC COLOR

The Expressionists, then, are certain that they have shaped a new and epoch-marking theory of the art of painting—which I have termed the theory of plastic orchestration, or the theory of

< 262 >

dynamic correlation—based on the conception of counterplay of the movement elements as basic; and they consider color as most important in respect to the dynamic values it contributes to the formal synthesis.   Colored pigments have been found to possess properties of advancing toward the eye or receding therefrom: positive and negative properties corresponding roughly to those of volume and space.   Movement may be engendered by colors in series.   Colors in balance or in contrast may be made to create effects of weight and tension—by manipulation of the dynamic-recessive values—comparable to those achieved by adjustments of volumes in space.   The movement, weight and tension effects of color may be used directly or dominantly, in parts of the plastic organization; or to clothe and reënforce the plastic-volume structure. In the former case, it may "lead" in the orchestration of the move-ment elements, or it may "answer" the play of volume-space melo-dies.   While the dynamic element is supremely important among the properties of color, it is an asset only as it correlates with the other plastic instruments in the formal synthesis.

Of the technical refinements that have been worked out in accord-ance with the theory of plastic color, this book cannot treat; though the chief framers and practitioners have pointed out new subtleties of relationship between coloring plastically considered and the other formal agencies.   To mention only one instance, a plane when colored not only "takes on color," in the old sense, but actually appears to the eye as enlarged or contracted, according to the thrust or return value of the pigment.   In the future any artist working without a definite comprehension of such dynamic influ-ence, of a recession scale, opens the way to disunity and confusion.

Joseph Sheridan puts down this summary: "Each color has its own rate of vibration.   Hues in juxtaposition, vibrating at different

< 263 >

rates, create tensions. They repel or attract one another. . . . Atmospheric color is distributed with regard to a certain advancing and receding character." Again Sheridan has written: "Universality in art exists in the picture. As in poetry the meaning lies not in the words, but in the flow along over the words." He speaks of the flow-elements as forces, adding that "the sum of all the forces must form a closed figure." Color has at last been analysed as dynamic force, a part of the "flow along over": entering integrally into the plastic rhythm, the coiled movement-figure within the picture enclosure.

In closing the section it is not inapropos to add an often-quoted saying of Cezanne: "When the color has the greatest fullness, the form attains the greatest richness."

TEXTURE AS PLASTIC WEIGHT

There is no need to repeat regarding texture the theory of plastic correlation and contributive animation. Texture "vibrates" as color does: except that the painter directly creates the degree of vibration desired. An area can be made to push forward or "disappear." The observer's eye can be unerringly—even violently—drawn to a corner or to center. An otherwise weak spot can be strengthened by building-in vigorous texture. Volume poise, tensions, weights, can be corrected with this factor.

And yet it is the least profound of the major plastic instruments. It remains, when obviously utilized, something added. If one cares to insist that everything existing has texture—smooth or rough, retiring or insistent—then all painters traffic in it. But of the positive thing we more commonly term texture, adding "interest" or frankly drawing the eye's attention, the average Expressionist

< 264 >

Girl in Green Dress, by Henri Matisse. (By courtesy of the Museum
of Modern Art: Bliss Collection.)

is chary. He wants the quality built in, so integral that it won't
be noticed until after the main plastic rhythms have registered:
like the fluctuating color-spots on a Cezanne hillside. But a lesser
group of Moderns has capitalized texture frankly, compellingly—
and, within a strictly limited range, beautifully. Gauguin, Matisse,

< 265 >

Arabesque, by Henri Matisse.

Leger, Klee, Chagall, Severini, Kandinsky—these all have experimented with the element, since Cezanne brought it significantly into the plastic synthesis.

In the arabesque-like pictures of the mature Matisse, texture enters strongly, gorgeously. In Klee there are likely to be shy little patterned patches, cunningly devised to pick up a rhythm dropped by some other instrument. Among the Cubists who eliminated or ruthlessly subordinated colors, texture is often set to do the work of the missing hues in building up another sort of "color-

< 266 >

Vive La France, by Pablo Picasso.   (By courtesy of Sidney Janis.)

fulness"—as in the Picasso panel illustrated here.   The problem
was primarily a plastic one, and certain parts are obviously pushed
forward by the applied pattern.

But Matisse again offers the richest material in illustration of
the principle.   In the run of five reproductions in nearby pages,
the reader can note the large number of areas frankly enriched by
repeat and all-over patterns.   Seldom are the volume-space element
and plane relationship so subordinated to the Arabesque effect as
in the reproduction opposite.   It does indeed approach the estate

< 267 >

Nude with Goldfish, by Henri Matisse. (By courtesy of
Pierre Matisse Gallery.)

of "mere decoration" which the more intellectual critics and the
emotional-mystic painters alike frown upon. But in its field it is
richly successful.

The *Girl in Green Dress* seems a transitional example between
that sort of "Oriental" composition and a later Matisse type of
volume-color-texture synthesis (still with little subject interest).
The *Nude with Gold Fish* illustrates the texture values more cunningly fused with the other elements, less insistent on their own
account. And yet in the carpets and in the wall behind the figure,

< 268 >

the color is strengthened, and the otherwise negative space brought toward the positive by half-concealed pattern.

Texture in pictures, however, need not be interpreted as merely depicted pattern, where in nature pattern would be: as in introduced carpets, wallpapers and Arabesque hangings or grills. In the nicer sense, every surface suggesting nature has distinctive texture, whether skin or wood or jewel or flower. Matisse is master of the one sort as of the other. There are bits in his canvases, if one cares to fix attention momentarily upon a segment—like listening intently for a certain passage in music—which give back intense pleasure for the sheer sensuous beauty of surface handling. And beyond all individual bits of texture, there is a further achievement, a harmonious conjunction of sensuous values, an achievement that might be termed inter-texture. I feel that if it could be isolated it might have a contributive excellence similar to the marvelous enriching counterpoint of Cezanne's fluctuating color-planes. It endows with recognizable *character* the paintings of Gauguin, Matisse, Rousseau, Klee. It need not be merely glamorous, though it often degenerates to that, in painters less masterly in command of the other plastic means.

There is, also, the device of arbitrarily organizing light-dark for texture effect. The departures from natural chiaroscuro in Rembrandt's paintings might be considered less as distortions to emphasize volume, than as thrusts toward a compelling pattern. El Greco is, of course, the outstanding master of dark-light manipulation for contrapuntal enrichment. The textural or patterned effect is often opulent, but seldom by reason of patches of applied ornament; rather the rich grain or light-dark variation is integral to the flow of voluminous elements.

< 269 >

The Good Samaritan, by Rembrandt.

For further study in the field where chiaroscuro and texture meet, Rubens and Tintoretto are historically important—as witness the illustration on page 206—and among the typical Moderns, Cezanne, the Picasso of the so-called Blue Period and of early Cubism, Kokoschka, Heckel, Vlaminck. In these painters there has been, at times, an apparently conscious effort to arrange the effects of light-dark in a surface play approximating the weight-values of texture, within the plastic synthesis.

The painter, then, beginning with respect for the inviolability of the picture plane, and knowing that the first disturbance of equi-

< 270 >

librium, the first initiation of movement, must be compensated through a complex interplay of the dynamic elements—the painter so grounded will add the weight values or plastic properties of texture to his repertoire of force-creating instruments: to volume-space adjustment, plane arrangement, and color dynamics. If he is wise, he will study texture for attainment of all that its rather limited capabilities can contribute; then return to the truth that ideally all the elements will work together, in a harmonious fusion from which no one element stands out: in a plastic orchestration.

< 271 >

Madonna and Child, by Duccio.

CHAPTER X

THERE are the cathedrals and temples of painting, and also the pleasant pavilions and intimate meeting-rooms. The vast reaches, impressive spaces and profound contrasts of the larger monuments need argue no deficiency of essential art-of-painting virtues in the lesser and "lighter" structures.

Some of the most enlightening critics have utilized the architectural analogy in explaining the formal composition of modern painting: Hildebrand finding "the architectural structure of a work of art the paramount factor," and Wilenski pitting the new "architectural" against the old "descriptive" art. I too have utilized the figure: have grouped the five chapters dealing with the instrumental side of Expressionism under the sub-title "Picture-Building": believing that only a knowledge of the organic *structure* of the picture can bring understanding of the typical expressive form. In distinguishing "decorative" painting from a more profound sort, here at the opening of the last formal-technical chapter, I believe that the thought of spacious cathedral and intimate colorful living-house will be suggestive and illuminating.

El Greco was the great cathedral builder among picture-makers. Cezanne aspired to similar monumental building, and was the first master to use modern materials for profound and spacious creation. But the other range has its prophets and masters too: less deep in intention, less stirring and less likely to dwell in memory; but

< 273 >

certainly no less ingratiating and inventive and companionable. The builders of the pleasant pavilions and colorful houses of modern painting are Gauguin, Rousseau, Matisse—and a smaller group of followers than one would expect, considering the easily comprehended loveliness bequeathed to the world by these masters.

The "decorators" accept a lesser problem, conceive their sort of creation as filling out a lesser framework; and the excellence of their contribution should be judged in relation to the limits consciously acknowledged.

There is more than mere metaphor in the thought of the structure of decorative painting as less spacious and less deep. In the theory of plastic orchestration, it is the actual extent of the thrust into space that determines the profundity of the plastic rhythm. Decorative painting is an arbitrary division of examples within which penetration is deliberately curbed, and a different sort of fullness achieved, usually with larger reliance upon melodious linear rhythms, sensuous color-harmonies, and texture interest.

THE UNIVERSAL CREATIVE ELEMENT

There is no painting without depth. Decorative painting merely *approaches* the flat: does not exclude recession values, but only holds them within shallower limits.

Realistic and expressive-formal artists alike initiate movement into space. The Realist copies the casual movement and space effects of nature, and recognizes no need to control the plastic thrusts and returns. He affords the illusion of natural movement. The Expressionist starts movement in the canvas with the conscious intention of controlling every plastic element. He knows that the first partition of the picture area creates the "feel" of plane beyond

< 274 >

plane, every volume implies recession, every color pushes toward the observer's eye, or withdraws, into space. Depth is an inescapable actuality in all painting. The decorative sort is that in which the depth is purposely limited, the play of plastic elements controlled within a shallow depth-range. In short, decorative painting is not flat, but merely flatter than the other sort.

I am frank to say that I did not see the matter in that light until recently. Not many years ago I wrote, ignorantly, of "the flat composition approaching pure decoration" of Gauguin, as follows:

"If its essential quality is to be called form at all, it is form dependent on surface organization of lines, masses and colors; it is not voluminous form, dynamic poised form."

Insofar as I had comprehended the idea of plastic form, I was attempting to apply it solely to the complexly structural painting of El Greco, Cezanne, and similar but lesser "symphonic" practitioners. I had not arrived at the truth that in the nature of men's way of seeing, *every* painting has depth; that every completely designed picture gains something of its satisfying formal unity by plastic orchestration. Today I believe that the so-called decorative canvas of Gauguin or Matisse or Klee, no less than the profounder things of Cezanne or Rouault or Kandinsky, must be equilibrated according to the principles of correlated dynamic elements. The sole difference is in the depth or shallowness of the plastic range.

When I say "sole" difference, I am thinking at the moment in terms of the formal elements: not emotional or subjective. I am postponing—since we still are concerned with structure—the question of a lessened importance of the life-content, in a decorative work. For the moment, we will leave aside also the question of a possible accord between the decorative and the abstract. Some commentators mark decorative painting as close to ornament:

< 275 >

imply that it merely adds to the elegance of a place—and that abstraction may serve such a secondary ornamental purpose, although a drawback to more "serious" painting. But we are concerned here with the formal means, not with the elements of feeling and meaning.

When one gets clear the truth that plastic correlation is a fundamental of all creative painting, one no longer tries to classify painters in mutually exclusive pigeon-holes. One may say that there is more of the cathedral or symphonic element in El Greco, whereas Giotto is over toward the decorative group. There is no dividing line. The plastic synthesis is no less attained in the best of Gauguin than in the average work of Cezanne; but the one conceived his compositions *nearer* the flat, while the other delighted in seeking realization through the play of forms and colors reaching deep into space. The one sort of painting is, we say, "decorative," for lack of a more definitive word: as against the other sort—for which we have no distinguishing name at all. Some critics and artists would call that other sort "serious painting": implying a lack of significance in the decorative. We can best meet that by asking a question: "What then of Giotto?"

Giotto's murals, indeed, exhibit most of the "decorative" earmarks: recession values held within a strictly limited range, background "interest" suppressed, large-area coloring, melodious surface rhythms, parallelism of planes, even flattened volumes. And yet Giotto retains "significance"—apparently for conservatives and radicals alike.

There is extant a "curtain theory" which is suggestive of the special qualities considered proper to decorative painting. It found its origin, perhaps, in the speculations of certain Cubists who, in the search for flatness, denied validity in the picture to anything

< 276 >

The Baptism of Jesus, by Giotto. (From *Giotto,* by Louis Gielly.)

inappropriate to a rug or wall-hanging. Some of the old tapestry-makers had arrived at a compromise of pictorial aim and architectural purpose which ranged them with the most accomplished pictorial-plastic creators in history. Their respect for the curtain as such was comparable to the Moderns' respect for the two-dimensional integrity of the canvas. Their tapestries can be compared to the works of the decorative group of Expressionists, because they sensed that a deep plastic play into space would destroy architectural wall-sense.

Some readers doubtless will find their comprehension of the aims of Gauguin, Matisse and Rousseau sharpened by thought over the disposition of volume and space in relation to "the curtain." The problem may be stated thus: how to animate the surface, without recessions disturbingly deep.

PLASTIC DEPTH AND THE FOCAL PLANE

In decorative painting, then, a knowledge of plastic orchestration *in relation to an established picture field* is fundamentally important. There is one principle, in connection with the stabilization of the movement-complex in the field, which has not been elucidated— so far as I know—by Hildebrand, Gleizes, Hofmann, Wessels, or other artist-teachers. I have termed it tentatively the principle of the focal plane.

What most commentators speak of as "the picture plane" is meant to be understood as the actual field bounded by the frame: the plane from which the movement "into the picture" starts. Too often this *front* plane is by implication identified as the plane in which the plastic movement "centers," the plane in which the eye is brought to rest after travelling its pictorial journey. Confusion of front-plane or picture-field with focal plane can only serve to puzzle and disconcert the student.

From the nature of the painter's means, and of the human eye by which the observer "takes in" the picture, space seems to open away from the base of the frame. The eye is drawn in; and the plastic orchestration starts—"the picture begins"—at a point in the plane established by the bordered canvas. From there it travels back, from plane to plane (volumes being considered here as complexes of planes), until at some point it touches deepest, and is turned across and outward.

< 278 >

The Railroad, by Vincent van Gogh. The main planes clearly stressed.

But a return movement never pushes forward to the full extent of the recession. *The eye never returns to the front plane.* If we visualize the eye-track, for instance, as the organic spiral (pushing into space, and winding back, not merely traced on the front plane), we see the movement initiated at the picture border, stepped back by the several dynamic means, reaching deepest point on the large far sweep, then rounding forward toward the picture-front, and finally settling back to a focal point where the eye is (temporarily) brought to rest.

When artists insist that the flat must be respected, the picture field never be violated, they do not mean that the observer's eye is

< 279 >

Head of a Tahitian, by Paul Gauguin. Illustrating a very shallow plastic range, as compared with the El Greco portrait opposite. (By courtesy of the Museum of Modern Art: Bliss Collection.)

to be held in the front plane. No power on earth can keep the picture from being three-dimensional in effect, once the first line is drawn or color-plane applied. The observer's eye inevitably pushes in, and stays in (if the design is truly organic). The crux of the

< 280 >

St. James the Less, by El Greco. (Photo by courtesy of the Art Institute of Chicago, from the original in the Charles Deering Collection, lent by Mr. and Mrs. Chauncey McCormick.)

matter, it seems to me, is that a focal plane be established *part way back*. It is in that plane that the pictorial equilibrium will seem to be stabilized. There the final focus will be established. That plane will be mathematically related to the front plane or original picture

< 281 >

surface, from which the movement started, and thus equally related to the frame.

Too often, I think, when the main picture plane is mentioned, meaning the front plane, and the idea of recession and advance is added, the student tries to visualize the movement as to and from the actual canvas. But obviously any movement forward from there would bring the object out of the picture. It is rather what I term the focal plane which affords the *mean* of movement backward and forward. This is the plane in which pictorial center, or the focal point of the plastic rhythm, is to be located. It is an inner plane fixed in relation to front plane and to point of deepest penetration. Once the eye is in the picture, it is from this plane that the backward-forward elements seem to act, into depth or toward the frame: whether recession and advance of color, or draw and push of volume in space, or slopes of planes, or forceful textures.

We are accustomed to say that colors advance and recede. From what? Except at the bottom edge of the canvas, they do *not* act from the picture surface. Visual phenomena are such that they act, pictorially, from planes at certain depths within space, determined by volume organization. In the average, all movement elements considered, the action is from the inner focal plane.

The *spatial* field is space between framed front-plane and focal plane, plus space between focal plane and the plane touched by plastic penetration at its deepest. Pictorial center, in the focal plane, is the point of stabilization of the axial pulls through space. The plastic "structure" seems to "rest" there.

After the plastic element has entered, when the picture is first animated, the front plane, the fixed canvas surface, actually disappears. The nature of three-dimensional design is such that the eye and the attention are carried beyond. The problem has become

< 282 >

Winter Landscape: Snow Effect, by Henri Rousseau. (From *Rousseau,* by Christian Zervos.)

spatial, and whatever "anchoring" is necessary, of forces inward and outward, will be accomplished in direct relation to a plane in mid-space, not to the front plane. In short, the plastic organism, moving in space, acts entirely beyond the frame. In the paintings and prints of the Far East, the front plane is often emphasized by a panel containing title or signature, obviously on the "picture surface." This marks the beginning point of observation, and, as the Japanese artist says, "gives depth." Whistler experimented with the device when he was working in arranged receding planes.

How far back from the frame the focal plane is "normally" fixed cannot, I believe, be arbitrarily established. The limits might be

< 283 >

Coronation of the Virgin, by El Greco. (Photo by courtesy of the Art Institute of Chicago, from the original in the collection of Max Epstein.)

determined, perhaps, by the analogy of the observer looking into a mirror. Automatically he will find the proper "range" for shaving or tying a tie, or what-not. There is a considerable latitude of satisfactory focus, as one approaches or recedes from the mirror; or, if the observer remains fixed, a considerable range of image planes beyond the glass that can be comfortably realized. There are rough limits of the area of visual clearness, from any given observer-standpoint.

Certainly there can be no *one* normal depth for the focal plane, for all picture-making. Otherwise, there would be no difference of

< 284 >

Hina Tefatu, by Paul Gauguin. Illustrating plastic depth strictly limited,
as compared with the El Greco opposite. (By courtesy of the Museum
of Modern Art: Bliss Collection.)

Mural in the Social Chaos Series, by Diego Rivera. (From *Das Werk des Malers Diego Rivera*.)

recessive penetration between an El Greco and a Gauguin. If the focal plane of any given picture is, to put the thought another way, at the average depth of focuses demanded of the observer's eye, as it travels the vision-path, the distance of that focal plane beyond the frame will be established by the pulls of all dynamic elements; an El Greco thrusting figure beyond figure into space, will establish his mean of focuses farther back than Gauguin, who seldom ranges solids in recessive series, who flattens bodies and tree-trunks, and spreads color not in fluctuating waves and turned planes but in simple areas.

It is a temptation to suggest that a picture might be simplified down to the point where its focal plane could be demonstrated as half-way between front plane and plane touched by deepest thrust; but there are so many movement agencies contributing to the plastic

< 286 >

Maternity, by Paul Gauguin. (By courtesy of Adolph Lewisohn.)

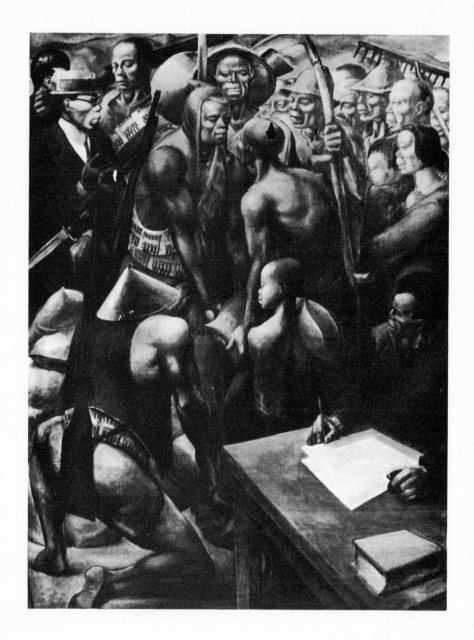

The Chinese Red Army—Distributing Grain: Mural by Jacob Burck.

synthesis, that any such summary statement would be extremely hazardous. One sort of thrust is modified by another instrument, and it is the total "effect" that creates a center of stabilization, of focus. Nor would "half-way back" be an accurate designation, since we are dealing with the organic spiral (in the one suggested example of eye-path), and the longer recessive swing is in the front space, the lesser in space beyond the focal plane. All we can conclusively say is that the artist initiates movement into space, and utilizes several interacting dynamic means; and that the web of plastic animation is poised between front plane and back plane, with a felt median of vitalization in what I am naming the focal plane.

DECORATIVE PAINTING AND MURAL SENSE

What is termed decorative painting, then, is simply a sort in which the focal plane is established especially close to picture-front, and the total recessive depth thus deliberately shallowed. This is accomplished in two ways: by keeping *all* elements near the flat, as in Rousseau's tapestry-like jungle pictures—where there is no violent movement of any sort, no "bright" colors, no insistent texture, no strong axial pull of volumes or precipitately descending planes; or by immediate *correction* of any strong movement in one element by the forward or backward properties of another, as in Matisse's rich interiors-with-nudes, where the dominant solid is "toned down" in color, or potentially deep space is brought forward by advancing color and texture. In both cases the artist has worked toward an equilibrium centered near the frame.

All the decorative painters are likely to close the background against perspective effects (the commonest cause of the "hole-in-the-picture" fault of even eminent Realists), and many are accustomed

< 289 >

Pouring Steel, by Diego Rivera. Illustrating flattening of volumes in a mural painting. (From *Das Werk des Malers Diego Rivera*.)

to make more than usual capital out of frankly linear rhythms. Thus what is lost in deeper rhythms is partially gained on the surface. There are other compensations: a general enrichment by

< 290 >

sensuous means—texture and color both leaning to the sensuous; there is less of volume-space manipulation, which works by axial attraction through space, and more reliance on the dynamics of color and texture, acting from surfaces.

It is easy to see why "decorative painting" and "mural painting" are accepted as synonymous terms. If the artist has a wall to paint, and begins with the obligation to preserve the sense of a flat plane bounding the room, he will automatically exclude the deep recessions: will work with a sense of the focal plane only slightly recessed. The "extra flatness" becomes a concession to architectural fitness. The great modern muralists from Puvis de Chavannes to Orozco and Rivera exhibit many of the idioms already ascribed to the decorative easel-painters: Gauguin, Rousseau, Matisse. (The distinction is, of course, an artificial one. Gauguins and Matisses and the Cubists are bought by those who feel that such pictures will not "disturb the architecture," as would compositions with profounder plastic rhythms, extended into deep space.) Broader areas, flattened volumes, parallel planes (preventing the extra movement of slopes), restrained color, linear harmonies: these are typically "mural."

There are Moderns who deny any validity to Puvis de Chavannes. But I think they argue, in general, from a restricted viewpoint, that of the Cubists or the Abstractionists or those insistent upon art as a social stimulus. Certainly there is, in the murals at the Sorbonne and in the Boston Public Library, a sustained loyalty to the wall, and at times a complete animation of the picture-surface within a controlled plastic unity. The coloring and the disposition of forms both indicate a possible fear of upsetting an equilibrium attained instinctively rather than through conscious knowledge of dynamic values. There is here none of the vigor or intensity of Orozco

< 291 >

Part of the Russian-Oriental Panel of a Mural Series by José Clemente Orozco, in the New School for Social Research, New York. Typical shallowing of plastic elements.

and Rivera. Perhaps it is Expressionism at its lowest intensity, in its most delicate manifestation—at a time when expression would seem, on its emotional side, to demand drive and strong contrast. But since we have accepted the attainment of plastic unity as the type earmark of Expressionism on the *formal* side—and have not yet ruled out abstract and "unmeaningful" subject art as insignificant—there is reason to mark Puvis de Chavannes as a pioneer experimenter in plastic-decorative organization.

He lived in a time when the Realists ruled, and it is noteworthy that he resisted the melodramatic devices and superficially clever light-effects by which his contemporaries were enlivening their canvases—even while destroying any plastic order. He did not

< 292 >

A Vision of Antiquity, by Puvis de Chavannes. (By courtesy of the
Department of Fine Arts, Carnegie Institute, Pittsburgh.)

escape a rather pale literary yearning; but he was the first muralist
in many generations to preserve wall-sense and create ordered
plastic movement.   There were many artists among his contemporaries—and even a few critics—who called lustily for a return to
architectural painting, to the wall unviolated and flat pictorial effects.   But most of them went on strewing their murals with casual
movement patterns—because they neither understood the principles
of dynamic volume and color, nor possessed Puvis' intuitive plastic

< 293 >

The Laboratory, Mural by Albert Besnard in the *Ecole de Pharmacie*.
Illustrating how wall-sense is destroyed by Realistic perspective pictures.
(From *Albert Besnard,* by Gabriel Mourey.)

sense. I reproduce here one of the murals of Besnard, for example of all the effects that destroy the wall and negate plastic order and expressive form.

Confusion has arisen in many quarters out of the fact that an artist *can* establish the feeling of wall-flatness and yet compose

< 294 >

A Santo from the American Southwest.   (By courtesy of J. B. Neumann.)

spatially, with plastic depth.   It cost the Parallelist group of Cubists many years of near-futile experiment, after they had enunciated the principle of flatness, of integrity of the two-dimensional field, before they returned to volume-space organization and dynamic colors.   In a chapter on "Decorative Painting," a leading aesthetician writes: "Yet most of the great decorators have been satisfied with very moderate concessions to flatness. . . . Giotto, who has been more highly praised for flatness than anyone else before Puvis, has been praised with equal enthusiasm for the solidity and rotundity of his figures!"   He adds the exclamation mark to register his own amazement that anyone could claim a "flat" value for any picture in which solid and rotund figures appear.   Such criticism is based on ignorance of the nature of the plastic element in painting, common to teachers of the old school.   The fact is that solid items are not at all denied to muralists: the flatness is a matter of the adjustment of *all* the movement factors—the holding of the several recessive elements within a shallow depth-range behind the canvas.

A study of Orozco's compelling murals will indicate some of the ways in which a fine solidity of figures can be achieved without destroying the sense of flatness.   Sometimes Orozco flattens the figures—as indeed did Giotto on occasion—in the manner common to Gauguin's later work.   But a voluminous effect can be prevented from going too deep, by color correctives, volume buffers, etc.   It is because he seems to me to lack a knowledge of these dynamic adjustments that I have freely criticized, in earlier pages, the murals of Thomas Benton.   His insistent figures, which might be "relieved" by the other plastic elements, are given high objective coloring, and

< 296 >

The Nativity: attributed to the School of Giotto. (By courtesy of the
Metropolitan Museum of Art.)

spatial effects are deepened by naturally recessive hues: till the figures spill out of the picture, and the wall is punched with holes. Nothing but a knowledge of plastic correlation can bring richness plus flatness to decorative painting, whether on walls or canvas.

ORIENTAL AND WESTERN DECORATIVE PAINTING

The Orient has been more successful than the Occident in attaining to the lighter loveliness of sensuous decorative painting. Persian art is a delight for the way in which the shallow plastic range is animated with eye-filling color, delicate texture, and restrained movement from plane to plane. It is only with the coming of Expressionism in the West that recognition grows of the superior decorative achievement in the East, whether in the "deeper" paintings of the Chinese, or the "lighter" achievements of the Persians, Hindus and Japanese.

It would be well if, in the histories of European art, more emphasis were laid on the influences that came into Italy from the Orient before the Renaissance. The Italo-Byzantine painters afford the most pleasurable exhibition of sensuous-melodious painting in the whole pageant of Western art. This group were called "Primitives," by the critics and historians of the long Realistic era, because the formal conventionalizations and distortions—necessary for the achievement of the plastic rhythm—were mistaken for crudities of artists who would have been Realists if only they had known enough. It is more likely that, like the Orientals (and many true Primitives too), the Italo-Byzantines were content if they created pictures with complete formal expressiveness: it did not occur to them that accurate copying of nature would come to be considered art. In any case, they are taking a belated revenge today, when the early Florentine

< 298 >

Rustam Capturing His Horse Rakhsh: Persian painting of the early 15th Century. (By courtesy of the Metropolitan Museum of Art.)

A Santo from the American Southwest. (By courtesy of J. B. Neumann.)

Painted Marriage Salver, Florentine, Early 15th Century. (By courtesy
of the Metropolitan Museum of Art.)

and Sienese panels are being brought up from museum basements, to
displace the illustrative painters of the three Realistic centuries. Our
galleries will be infinitely richer, aesthetically, for the change.

The Byzantine tradition as such persisted in Russia till our own
time. The ikons, even those of the 19th Century, surpass in rich
decorative effect any other products of Europe since "natural"
painting came in. Curiously enough, there is a parallel achieve-

< 301 >

ment in the "Santos" of the American Southwest and Mexico. Native artists, by some intuitive return to the Byzantine directness of expression, swung Catholic church painting back to formalized decorativeness.

Even the historians of Post-Impressionism and Fauvism are likely to forget the significance of the inflow of Oriental influence during the formative years 1870-1900. Some of the root-nourishment of Expressionism can be traced to the treasures imported from the East. If Whistler made rather superficial application of the decorative principles of Japanese art, in most of his later work, he again attained to an exquisite adjustment of shallow plastic and delicately sensuous elements. His small contribution to Expressionism is rather more secure than some of the intolerant historians of Modernism admit.

But this is not the place to attempt ranking of the various artists concerned in the transition from Realistic to Expressionist art. We are interested in learning what it is that constitutes the progress, the revolution, during the fifty years past, and we need summon the artists and their work only as light may thus be thrown on the special qualities of Expressionist painting—just here the formal-decorative qualities. Whistler is useful to the student for evidence of a cautious return—revolutionary in his time—to an ideal of what he termed "arrangement," as against the current obsession with observed natural effect; and for his preservation (in the best of his work) of the two-dimensional integrity of the canvas. If often he let that regard mislead him into an art too flat and linear and slight, he again attained an ordered synthesis into which the plastic elements entered.

Another lesser but still significant figure was Hans von Marées, within whose mural compositions the geometric-plastic structure is

< 302 >

Girl and Goldfish, by Henri Matisse.

implicit.   One might go on to other border-line figures, to Manet—
who seems to me, despite his praised "good painting" and "styliza-
tion," to exhibit less of expressive form than Whistler, to have less
pictorial sensitivity, in the Expressionist sense—and Degas, and
Hodler.   But it is more to the point that we return to the artists who
summarize the decorative phase of the Modernist advance.

"Exotic" is the adjective applied to Gauguin more frequently
than "Oriental."   And there is no profit in laboring the matter of
this source or that.   Gauguin is allied to the Orient, to Africa, to
the South Seas: to all places where art has remained a formal-
decorative exercise rather than illusional transcription.   In this one

< 303 >

Ia Orana Maria, by Paul Gauguin. (By courtesy of Adolph Lewisohn.)

man's work there is illustrated the sum of the Modern decorator's likeness to the other Expressionists, and of the differences between decorative and other "wings."

Gauguin is of the Expressionists because, within limits, he attains to a formal-plastic orchestration; because he is essentially colorful, revelling in sensuously-compelling color-harmonies—"expressing the paint" with a new intensity; and because he expresses his emotional self in relation to life, freely distorting the actuality of nature —anti-Realistically.

He is of the decorative group, rather than the Cezanne-Fauve-Rouault succession, because the plastic range is deliberately limited: the flatness consistently affirmed, by broad color areas, by flattened volumes, by linear rhythms, by parallelism of planes. Patterned texture is frequent, and color harmonies are utilized for exceptional sensuous loveliness.

All of these characteristics are illustrated in the plates in nearby pages.

Where Gauguin arrives at a simplification out of long study and many influences—less out of the savage isles than out of the civilization he sought to escape—Rousseau the Douanier was lifelong the incorruptible child. It is said that he longed ardently to achieve the academic fatuities of the popular painters. Fortunately he seldom got beyond being himself.

It seems a miracle that an artist supposedly untutored could so often achieve the plastic effects so consciously labored after by other Moderns, could so unerringly avoid the deep unstopped recessions of the Realists, and their piling of advancing objective colors on prominent volumes. Again, it is that a very few artists through the ages have been born with an instinctive sense of plastic co-ordination. Rousseau is the true modern intuitive-Primitive.

< 305 >

The Jungle, by Henri Rousseau. The "curtain" idea **illustrated**. (By courtesy of the Museum of **Modern Art: Bliss Collection**.)

Note how backgrounds are **brought** forward, men and tigers naïvely conventionalized, the botany stylized, the houses flattened: and all brought into relation within the slightly recessed spatial range.

Of other artists who have chosen (usually) to renounce the deep plastic rhythms, but have attained to organic expression by correlation of the movement elements, I am illustrating Paul Klee, Marie Laurencin and Pierre Bonnard.

Klee has an uncanny way of making every canvas "live," no matter how slight the subject-matter, and the formal means. Almost

< 306 >

Landscape with Blue Birds, by Paul Klee. (By courtesy of A. E. Gallatin and the Gallery of Living Art.)

invariably there is a satisfying "adjustment"—which I take to be a plastic unity achieved. People complain that his paintings are like the scratchings and daubs of children: and yet there is "something they like." It is, perhaps, the hidden plastic structure. This patchwork picture is engagingly decorative. It is hardly more than a fluctuating pattern of turned planes of color, with accents to indicate trees, birds and house.

Marie Laurencin seems to me less sure pictorially; though you personally may find her pale paper-flat ladies and cool colors more

< 307 >

The Huntress, by Marie Laurencin.   (By courtesy of Adolph Lewisohn.)

to your liking than Klee's near-abstractions.   She falls back on linear rhythms to an extent that removes her a little from the builders of plastic organisms.   The art of line is only incidentally the art of the painter.

In emphasizing that (in general) the decorative Expressionists move away from the plastic-symphonic technique of El Greco and Cezanne, toward a territory where sensuous values help to compensate, we have moved still another notch away from seriously "meaningful" art.   It is not difficult to hear certain readers—the

< 308 >

The Boulevard, by Pierre Bonnard. (From *L'Art d'Aujourd'hui*, Autumn, 1927.)

mere Realistic illustrators, the intellectualist followers of Craven, the crusading Communists—muttering "Does the man mean to claim that decorative art is self-sufficient, just because it is decorative?" It happens that I do. But I postpone the arguments to the chapter on Feeling and Meaning. Here we are arbitrarily limiting discussion to the instrumental phase, the plastic skeleton, if you will. For

< 309 >

that reason, too, we will put over all treatment of the mural painting of Rivera, Orozco, Siqueiros.

SUMMARY

Decorative painting, no less than the other sort, finds its formal vitality in an achieved plastic order. Within a pictorial, not an illusional, unity, there is movement: engendered of volume-space tensions and planetary thrusts, modified by strong or weak texture, and color (with hue and intensity both considered in relation to depth of recession). When movement is poised, and fills the closed spatial field behind the frame, the plastic orchestration is complete. The aesthetic experience of the observer is more poignant and more intense, as the pictorial-plastic organism is achieved with this vitality and fullness.

In the Orient, up to the recent invasion by Occidental "ideals," abstract-formal values have been at the core of creative art. Once upon a time Western art, open to Byzantine currents, was rich in the same values, as one may realize by going back to the Sienese and Giotto and the ikon-makers. But with the dawn of the Renaissance, Europe proclaimed its independence from the East, and Western artists began that glorification of superficial appearances which culminated centuries later with the Impressionists. During the reign of Realism the abstract values, the skeleton of expressive form, almost wholly disappeared.

Expressionism—speaking still without regard to feeling and subject—is the beginning of the rebirth of creative formal painting in the West. It derives impetus, on the traditional side, from a return to study of Giotto and those in Giotto's line. At the same moment there is a spontaneous reaction against accumulated shallow Realistic

< 310 >

art; and again, it happens, currents are flowing in from the Orient and have their influence—due to a new familiarity with the East, possible only to the age of instantaneous communication and easy machine-transportation. History will, I believe, mark the first fifty years of Expressionism as the beginning of an art revolutionarily different from that of the 17th-19th Centuries: due to its abstract-formal core, which is partly a recovery and partly new evolutionary development, in consonance with the times.

The theory of plastic orchestration tries to explain the gain of this art on the formal or instrumental side.

< 311 >

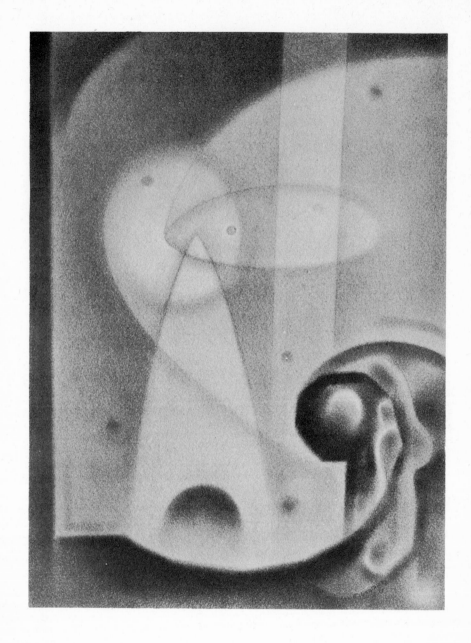

Orbits: Pencil Drawing by Raymond Jonson.

CHAPTER XI

ABSTRACTION AND MYSTICISM

THE chapters on picture-building have been concerned with a certain way of use of the *materials* of the art: with orchestration of the several plastic elements, for achievement of an ordered movement within the closed spatial field, a dynamic unity, an organic pictorial vitality. In those chapters I have attempted an elucidation of the methods employed to attain one part of expressive form: an intensification of the potentialities and properties of the specialized medium of painting. This might be termed the formal achievement out of masterly use of the instrument. But form-organization in this sense, as a plastic organism, is but one part of the larger creative synthesis, the full pictorial expression. The instrumental orchestration—harmonizing, correlating, organizing the tensions of volumes in space, axial pulls, movements of planes, dynamic colors, etc.—is but one important unity achieved within a larger unity. It is the mastered means of expression, not the end of expression.

Continually in those and earlier chapters the implication has been that subject-matter drawn from surface nature had, in Expressionism, receded in importance, as mastery of ordered plastic design increased and the "hidden" elements of expression became intensified. It was even suggested that, where creative art is concerned, distortion of objective nature might be "natural"; even to a point where the recognizable visual aspect disappears, in total abstraction.

< 313 >

If the values of photographic or selective imitation of nature—of Naturalism and Realism—are thus discounted, one may ask, what is it that enters as the primary value of painting? If depiction is dropped for expression, what is it that is expressed?

The answer "Form" is not enough, if we continue to consider form merely as a capitalization of the instrumental means: as a plastic achievement, a mechanical-dynamic order fixed in the canvas. Where does the instinct come from that impels the artist to formal creation? What is the *feeling* inseparable from form-conception and image-fixing? Form is revelation—of what?

It is revelation not merely of a plastic organism, but *through* the plastic of something that might be termed universal or cosmic truth, and, commonly, of human emotion.

Leaving out of consideration here the human or "subject" aspect, we are seeking clues to the reality of the cosmic or universal value that lies between the mastered means of expression and the human-feeling content.

In truth there is no separating the values, in either creation or appreciation. When the Expressionist claims that the attainment of a structural order, a plastic unity, is basically important, he doubtless is thinking of the order or synthesis both in the mechanical, measurable aspect (which can to a certain extent be diagrammed mathematically) and in an abstract-mystical aspect. That is, he creates a little world with a living order and vitality of its own; and at the same time an image of the macrocosm, echoing the relatedness and order of all that is. We have explored the nature of the immediate pictorial order. Now we are asking to what extent the universal enters in.

There are those who see all abstraction as merely a mathematical and mechanical thing, explainable by its surface aspect of geomet-

< 314 >

Earth Rhythms, Number 9, by **Raymond Jonson**.

rical relationships.   There are others—the majority now, I think—
who link the abstract with the mystic: who consider it an expression
at once of the mathematical and of the spiritual or cosmic.   Whether
the painter feels that he is, in "turning abstract," instinctively expressing what is only a mechanical-physical order, or is proceeding
in accord with a mystical aesthetic philosophy—apperceiving a
deeper meaning in objects and relations than those explainable
mechanically through senses and intellect—in either case, he is
furthering a main advance of modern art: the march *toward ab-*

< 315 >

straction. Whether one grants or not that *pure* abstraction in painting is possible or desirable, there can be no doubt that the world of art has recently moved in the direction of intenser capitalization of non-objective values.

It is my belief that the greatest art compasses form in the three aspects: as plastic-mechanical, as abstract-universal, and as expression of human feeling. I believe, moreover, that the increasing abstract significance in art is one phase of mankind's contemporary advance in spiritual apprehension. In other words, I take the mystic's view of the artist as creator, and count the mystic artist the true Modern.

If I am right, we shall see, in the 20th Century, a phenomenal increase in abstract art. I might put it better by saying that there will be both an increase in the amount of totally abstract art, and enlarged emphasis upon the abstract element in art which, in "content," still deals frankly with the objective world, with symbols, with events. In the Expressionist advance so far, there have been two easily-marked divisions: a small but challenging group of artists abandoning objective reality, to seek expression in the absolute abstract, and a larger group who inform their "more natural" work with an abstract "structure" or design. When I speak of abstraction in painting, I include both those pictures in which abstract "meaning" is the central content, and those in which the human-subject values lie over a support or core of the abstract. In the latter case, it is the support or core that gives most significance, aesthetically, to the picture.

It seems to me, moreover, that the art of the ancients will survive for future generations, as vital expression, largely because of the intensity of the abstract realization. I have noted that many artists, Western and Eastern, have achieved, perhaps intuitively, those very

< 316 >

formal values that the Expressionists are consciously striving to attain. And while the subject-matter—of, say, Christian legendry —may register with observers still, it is less the personal or human expressiveness than the abstract expressiveness that makes the pictures "live" for us of today. Therein is the explanation of the return to popularity, within your lifetime and mine, of El Greco, the Chinese landscapists, and the Italo-Byzantines—in all of whom the abstract skeleton is obvious, the cosmic implication evident. If there is a universally valid "quality" in graphic art, it is on the abstract, rather than on the "subject" side. It is this value more than any other that links Cezanne, Rouault and Marin with Giotto, El Greco and the Persians—or Lehmbruck with Michael Angelo and the Romanesque carvers.

IS PAINTING NORMALLY ABSTRACT?

For those who still cannot see significance in pictures from which objectively recognizable nature is wholly or practically excluded— Kandinsky, O'Keeffe, the "flat pattern" Cubists, etc.—there is solace, perhaps, in the fact that most of the "great" painting preserved from the past compasses objective content as well as abstract-pictorial form; though, as just noted, that art in which the abstract element is strongly emphasized tends, in the 20th Century, to displace "merely objective" painting. This point may well lead us to the question whether there is, possibly, a *reasonable norm of abstraction* in each art. I am not ready to admit that a picture entirely innocent of the camera-symbols of the phenomenal world, divorced from sense-known nature, is necessarily without meaning, reality and aesthetic validity. But for those who cannot experience abstraction except mechanically, it may be illuminating to inquire

< 317 >

about the balance of objectivity and abstraction in the other arts.

Music is widely considered to be cheapened when the actuality of nature is introduced: as in program pieces wherein one can hear the babbling stream, the lion's roar, the storm, etc. Hardly less contemned is the subject piece, built not around actual sounds but limited to emotional-interpretive equivalents of living: as too often in the works of Tschaikovsky or the Impressionists. But take a composition of Bach, that we all might admit as great, and immediately it is clear that creation has been arbitrarily divorced from anything heard in nature: is primarily an exercise in the abstract. (It is not, as so many Victorian commentators averred, *intellectual* music, but richly abstract-expressive—or as I would say, abstract-spiritual and cosmic-expressive.) In other words, it is almost universally accepted that music is essentially an abstract art; that it departs from abstraction only at cost to its highest aims and potentialities.

The Expressionist inquires, then, why the materials that are detected by sight cannot be utilized to afford stirring aesthetic experience as readily and purely as the materials addressed to the sense of hearing. Sight and sound afford many parallels: why should the one be bound, as art, to portrayal of objective nature, the other freed for absolute creation? It may be answered that a picture *can* reproduce a view in detail, or tell a story circumstantially. But that is no conclusive argument against there being a department of painting aiming at a degree of abstraction as advanced as that normal to music.

Literature seems to be in different case, because the prime material of the art, words, came into existence as a set of intellectual symbols for sense experience. Words primarily stand for things. Inventorial, descriptive and story-telling aims are natural to the

< 318 >

Composition Eleven: Rain, by Raymond Jonson. Considered by the painter "fairly Realistic," this is, like the preceding plate, a far step from illusionistic painting, but less abstract than the chapter frontispiece.

word-art, and abstraction may here be a will-o'-the-wisp (though one cannot dismiss offhand the experiments of Gertrude Stein and James Joyce). Certainly abstract elements exist richly in the highest literary form, poetry, in which the sensuous values of words, and formal structure, enter expressively. But there may be a bar to absolute abstraction in the very nature of words. There are, however, no such medium-limitations upon the art of painting—of line, plane, volume, color, texture.

Architecture and dancing are other arts on the abstract side. The one became imitative in the Realistic era—imitative not of nature but of the outgrown but sanctified forms of the past—but under Expressionism, architecture returns to abstract creativeness, upon a foundation of expressiveness of use, function and materials. Dancing purges itself of descriptive and story-telling accretions, and returns to abstract creation. The lesson of these arts, as of music, would seem to be that the painter is being modernly Expressionistic in pushing the search for abstract-pictorial effectiveness just as far as he can without losing his "public." Certainly no one would deny that Kandinsky and Braque and O'Keeffe and Klee have an audience today; though there are critics who stand off and jeer at that audience as deluded and self-hypnotized.

In all this I am trying to ease the way for those who are still afraid of abstraction. To me, as appreciator, the question is beside the point. I derive a real and direct enjoyment out of certain purely abstract painting; though that is but one small division of the range of pictures from which I gain aesthetic pleasure. It seems to me that the measure of a certain sort of expressive form is perhaps greater in the abstract picture, say an O'Keeffe or a Jonson; but when I turn to a Cezanne or an Orozco, the lessened

< 320 >

expressiveness on that side is matched by the gain on the subjective-expression side.

I honestly believe that man's aesthetic-appreciative faculty grows with individual use, and, in the mass, with the evolution of the race. It is no assumption of a special sense of superiority when one who has lived intimately with manifestations of the arts claims to experience the values of abstract-pictorial form. It is merely an earlier arrival at a sort of sensitivity that will be universal—as the present generations outgrow their false education to Realism, and as the opportunity increases for living with varied sorts of art. At the present stage of comprehension—retarded by education —a few people but an increasing group are sensitive to absolute abstraction, which they may or may not consider a sort of mystic revelation of harmonious cosmic order; and a larger group turn to partially objective painting in which the abstract skeleton or core is richly dominant. They will detect the quality in greater purity as understanding and sensitivity grow; perhaps the individual will march on till he commonly demands abstraction washed of the last remnants of objectivity. In any case I ask the reader to grant me the possibility that this is not mere self-delusion: to go on with me, probationally, to an examination of the mystic significance attributed to abstract pictorial form by many Expressionists.

ABSTRACTION AS MYSTIC REVELATION

The commonest explanation put forward by the Expressionists, regarding the mystic element, is that the abstract form fixed in the picture is a direct revelation of cosmic architecture, of the rhythmic order of the continuing universe. That is, the plastic organism, or coiled and poised movement in the spatial field, is

< 321 >

Majestic Tenement, by Arthur Osver.   (By courtesy of the Pennsylvania
Academy of the Fine Arts, Philadelphia.)

not merely of the sort that geometrically pleases the eye—as an old armchair fits the body—but carries with it cosmic and spiritual implications. The order created by the artists is an echo—rather, an implicit part—of first creation, a manifestation proceeding from the Center of all that is, a pulsation in little of the rhythm self-perpetuated at life's Source.

Formal expression, at its intensest and most significant, embraces, in this view, cosmic and spiritual revelation: the artist touches upon final unknowable truth about life, crystallizes a fragment of the beauty and order that lie beyond the field of sense knowing and intellectual explanation.

The Expressionist's business, then, in creating the plastic synthesis, is to reveal through it the ultimate hidden principle, the all-relating harmony, the sense of cosmic unity. In Realistic art the surface of nature is reproduced or portrayed, and neither the hidden universal value in the object nor the cosmic emotion of the artist enters into the product. But in Expressionist art the two sorts of hidden value primarily determine the excellence of the work. The painting partakes more of the reality of the spirit than of the commonly accepted reality of outward nature.

The picture, with a vitality of its own sort, determined physically by the nature of its materials and means—flat field, spatial sense, voluminous organization, dynamic colors—is in itself a universe in little, yet exhibiting the laws of original creation, and the rhythm and poise of celestial movement. In its finite way, it echoes, in one more manifestation, in one further push of evolutionary achievement, the harmonious order of the infinite. A bit of the equilibrium, of the utter clearness, of intuitively divined Perfect Order, is fixed, beyond any incidental copying of disordered outward nature.

< 323 >

We have been talking here in terms common to mysticism—a word demanding definition wherever it is used, so great are the differences between one man's and another's interpretations of it.

The mysticism which enters into the conception of Expressionist art is not the playing with veils that too often cheapens the word, and confuses the uninformed public. It is a philosophy of life and a release into richer living.

The mystic believes that the world as known to senses and intellect is only one phase or manifestation of the universe and experience: that there is a world of the spirit, more directly connected with, or expressive of, first principle or Divinity. Each man is potentially divine, and through his consciousness maintains a link with original Spirit. The individual can purposely develop his consciousness of relatedness to creative Spirit, and can illumine every object and event on the immediate material plane of living, by bringing light and understanding to bear from the deeper plane. He may even withdraw occasionally from the surrounding disorder of human-physical life, into blissful self-identification with the divine Spirit, experiencing the rapture of perfect realization of harmony and order. Whether one prefers to term this identification with God—in the Christian mystic's words—or merely elevation into a region of harmonious accord of spiritual and physical living, there is presupposed a realm beyond the comprehension of the senses, but open nonetheless to human experience: where there is total release from the bondage of material and worldly things, where the individual partakes of the life of the Spirit.

The Expressionist in art believes that he brings material or "meaning" from that realm beyond, when he endows the picture with form affording experience of an unexplainable harmonious

< 324 >

order; and that he does this by means of the abstract elements, not the objective, with which he works.

The "scientific" materialists of the late 19th Century—when the Spirit, and love, and art, were all in line for explanation by test tube and chart—denied reality to everything unexplainable by sense experience and reasoning. They rejected the idea of divinity, denied the Spirit, and ridiculed the mystic. They set up sense-Reality as the only truth, and reason as the only guide to living. A later generation of scientists have helped to discredit materialistic philosophy; but mankind had already descended into that excess of animalism, cupidity and will to power that brought the earth to its present disordered state. The pendulum swings back; the interrupted continuity of spiritual-material expansion is re-affirmed —and the world of man will inevitably resume the march toward order and perfect understanding. But there are artists and critics still who would interpret Modernism from the crassest materialistic viewpoint. There have even been books on 20th Century painting that belittle the mystic implication, that make out Expressionism as largely a by-product of scientific-mechanical discovery, and material—even fleshly—living.*

* The rise of Modern painting is ascribed to Parisian Bohemianism, and more particularly to freed sexual impulses, in at least one widely advertised book on Modern Art published this year. In the opening chapter the words prostitute, whore, harlot, tart, strumpet, pimp, bawd, procurer and the like appear at least twenty times, and the politer cocottes, grisettes and mistresses as many more—with mention also of fornication, cohabitation, brothels, Lesbians, etc. It implies no sense of aloofness or assumed superiority, I believe, when one criticises a writer who thus sensationalizes or animalizes the subject of art. Certainly we all have learned to live, in these realistic times, without wincing at the mention of prostitution on its own grounds. But why, in the larger view, should that way of facing life and approaching art be considered superior to—or more realistic than—the one which involves talk of the spiritual, the mystic, the formal, etc.? The men who write such books, denying the mystic overtones and the abstract significance of Modern art, are obviously of the surviving group of scientific materialists. Having failed to establish any spiritual orientation with life, they deny the possibility of spiritual experience, and they carry the negation over into their statements in the field of art.

< 325 >

Vital Storm, by Kenneth Callahan. (By courtesy of the artist.)

The Realists having so recently been in the ascendancy, popularly, and my own position being so far distant, at the very pole, I think it wise to state, briefly but with some exactness, what sort of philosophy of life lies behind my linking of the Expressionist artist with the revelation of spiritual truth and the opening of four-dimensional vistas. If there is validity in the suggestion, made in another chapter, that there is in process today a regathering of spiritual forces, a push toward a possible universal belief, my own statement of its outlines may be serviceable precisely because I speak for no sect or church or system. What I think has become the belief of millions is this:

There is a unity of all that is, life undivided flowing from a single principle or source, of which man can feel but not explain the nature. This is the great well of Spirituality, the creative Center, and all phases of life known to man are manifestations in the finite of that infinite and universal power or flow. The wise individual recognizes the relatedness of all that is; and he attempts to shape every detail of his living in the light of the intuitive guidance of Spirit. The only particularization of creative Spirit functioning on man's plane is in his own consciousness: the only divinity is in man—but he is, exceedingly slowly, escaping animal bondage, as evolution proceeds. As he recognizes his own creative power, his oneness with the universal whole, himself as channel for expression of the divine, he puts himself in position to advance evolution by creation of new manifestations of order and grace. There is no other way out of the disorder and the accidents of casual nature, than by returning first to the sense of in-forming divinity—of God in man, if you will.

This is how the modern philosophy so stated applies to the creative work of the artist:

< 327 >

Life is a progression, originating from a *Creative* principle or power, and proceeding, by manifestations of that Spirit or power, in new designs of order and beauty. Each individual may make himself the instrument of creation, in the measure of his awareness of the oneness of all life and his realization of Spirit. Knowing himself a particularization of originating Spirit—with, therefore, control of material and thought in immediate surroundings—the artist is enabled to push forward creatively, originating manifestations of order beyond any accomplished theretofore, taking the step that advances evolution toward ever-purer crystallization of Spirit. The creative march, in art as in every department of man's activity, is toward intenser expression of order, relation, union, and unity.

Far from limiting expression, identification with Spirit affords the artist at once the inspiration of universality, of inexhaustible harmonious forms, and absolute freedom of creation on his immediate plane, up to the limits of his mastery of his chosen artistic medium. The artist's creative faculty both lives in the originating Spirit or power at the center of all-related life, and continually becomes a fresh center of creative manifestation.

The intellect is but a tool along the way, as the technique of one's art is a tool. Sense knowledge and mastery of one's instruments are necessary; but the greater understanding and power must be from the spiritual center, if one is to illumine life movingly.

In short, the artist is God and man, Creator and creator, drawing from the center of all life and creating new life. For the work of art is itself a living thing, manifesting vitality, order, growth, rest. The greatest art is that which expresses the apprehension of Source, Spirit, Cosmos, and at the same time expresses the creating, feeling self of the artist. Form in art is at once the expression of this dual power or origination, and expression of the poten-

< 328 >

Wind, Clouds and Water, by Arthur G. Dove. (By courtesy of
An American Place.)

tialities of the particular medium employed: as manifested in the
living plastic organism in painting or the typically theatric flow of
the stage art.

I might quote from endless books and articles to support my
own view in these matters: but it hardly seems necessary to bring
varied testimony, when so many artists and critics have turned or
are turning to the mystic view. There is an excellent chapter on
"Art and Mysticism" in Barnes' *The Art in Painting*. Hofmann,
despite his usual preoccupation with the methods of plastic organization, goes back continually to the affirmation that creative art is
spiritual and transcendentally revelatory. Claude Bragdon is the
most prolific writer on the relationship of art, mysticism and four-

< 329 >

dimensional mathematics; and the reader is urged to search out his several books. Farther afield, but richly suggestive, are the works by Troward: from which my own summaries are derived, more than from any other source. But the few quotations I am adding here—not for corroboration, but because they seem to open further vistas—are from practicing artists.

Kandinsky speaks of the artist as having "a secret power of vision," and of art as "belonging to the spiritual life." He avers that "that which has no material existence cannot be subjected to a material classification. That which belongs to the spirit of the future can only be realized in feeling, and to this feeling the talent of the artist is the only road. . . . In dancing as in painting we are on the threshold of the art of the future. The same rules must be applied in both cases. Conventional beauty must go by the board and the literary element of 'story-telling' or 'anecdote' must be abandoned as useless. Both arts must learn from music that every harmony and every discord which springs from the inner spirit is beautiful, but that it is essential that they should spring from the inner spirit and from that alone."

Joseph Sheridan has expressed the whole relationship of artist, cosmos and rationalization in a few sentences: "Man the microcosm is endowed with the attributes of that, all that, which lives; the pulsing of the macrocosm, the oneness with the universe, that which makes man the part of the whole, and so sensing that there is a whole—and so endowed he has no choice, would he move upward, but to seek to create, for creation is the activity of the macrocosm. . . . The futility of creation out of rationalistic endowments, the incurring flow, during their exercise, of confounding intuitions or whispers out of the ether, awaken a new sense in a degree free from matter: a sense which catches vibrations of the Eternal, and

< 330 >

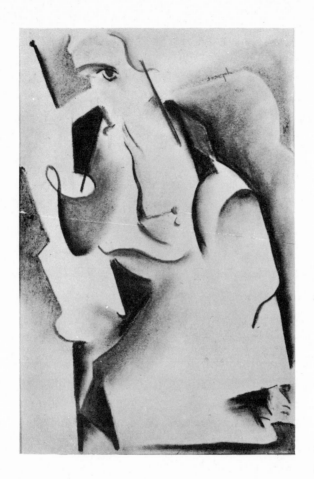

Figure Abstraction: Crayon Drawing by Joseph Sheridan.

re-expresses them in the matter-organization in which the recipient
works, a re-expression attaining to that degree of clarity to which
this vehicle styled 'artist' has himself achieved, through the elimination of worldly enchainments or weightments. Let this be named,
if one will, mysticism. Or let it be called sensitivity."

Herbert Read quotes Picasso as having said (to his biographer,
Zervos): "Whilst I work, I take no stock of what I am painting

< 331 >

on the canvas. Every time I begin a picture, I feel as though I were throwing myself into the void." Read counts this subjective method—or as I would say, "intuitive" method—revolutionary in its significance. Read adds: "We have to realize that we are now concerned, not with a logical development of the art of painting in Europe, not even with a development for which there is any historical parallel, but with an abrupt break with all tradition, with all preconceptions of what the art of painting should be. . . . Let us realize, however, that all links with the objective world are broken; that that love of the concrete which has characterized the art of Europe for centuries, and which has become inseparable from the very concept, is deliberately renounced. The painter instead turns all his perceptive faculties inwards, to the realm of his subjective fancies, his day dreams, his preconscious images. He replaces observation by intuition, analysis by synthesis, reality by symbolism."

As a footnote to this description of Picasso's subjective-intuitive method, let me add Bragdon's observation that *the intuition works mathematically*.*

We may go back, for the sake of those who possibly are wearied by so much unaccustomed talk of the Infinite, the Source, and intuitive creation, to the fact that there are artists who admit the

---

* A bit culled, I believe, from Bragdon's *The Frozen Fountain*, New York, 1933. The quotations from Read and from Kandinsky are from books already cited: bibliographical details will be found in earlier footnotes. The quotation from Joseph Sheridan is from a letter. The volume by Troward which touches closest the artist's problem and method is *The Creative Process in the Individual*, by T. Troward, New York, 1917. I may add that, having quoted freely from the Chinese "Six Laws" in earlier chapters, I have forborne to cite again those ancient maxims that so strangely parallel "Modern" mystical theories of the painting art; but the student should not omit Binyon's *The Flight of the Dragon* from any list of books illuminating the subject-matter of this chapter.

< 332 >

Green Still Life, by Pablo Picasso. (By courtesy of the Museum of Modern Art: Bliss Collection.)

value of the abstract but discount the mystic meaning and the cosmic significance. It is just natural, they say, that man craves the *feeling* of mathematical order: he gets the same satisfaction out of certain pictorial arrangements, designs, that he does out of seeing a tree depicted upright, with a sense of firm rooting; or out of the artificially ordered elements of a sweetly functioning machine. "And that's all there is to this talk about echoes of a universal architecture, and identification with the harmonic pulsation at the heart of life." Just crystallized geometry or mechanics: a matter of mathematical ratios, proportioned magnitudes, and pleasingly measured adjustment. One critic has posited that the

< 333 >

key to all creative Modern art is to be found in the *ratios* between the different parts of the picture.

And by way of further relief, we may return the rest of the way, and remind ourselves of those who oppose abstraction and mysticism as meaningless, in a society of intellectually emancipated men. We find a curiously mixed company in this grouping of "antis": the academicians holding to the sanctity of "normally" depicted nature; the Realist-Intellectuals; and the one-object Communists, barring abstract art because it bears no message, puts forward no promise of a workingman's world. Thomas Craven, in *Men of Art*, has summed up wittily and perfectly the intellectual-academic view: "Art at last was pure, perfect, abstract, absolute— and intolerable."

THE VARIOUS APPROACHES TO ABSTRACTION

If there is a sufficiently general and unified advance toward abstraction to warrant the claims that this is a main path of Expressionism, there is still a very great variety of approach. I have scattered through nearby pages illustrations of many sorts of example: absolute, near-abstract, and objective with strong abstract emphasis. Notes on the methods, and sometimes the intention, of the individual artist may help to illumine the points already theoretically made.

Kandinsky, of course, is the type exhibit of the mystics who state flatly that creative painting comes from the soul. In most of his mature work the objective element has been so slight that there can be no doubt that his aim is to crystallize some other-worldly order. And yet there is the point that seldom does his work lack, somewhere, a minor link with recognizable objectivity. Kandinsky

< 334 >

Improvisation, by Vasily Kandinsky.

is an avowed mystic, seeking to bring the light of the spiritual
realm to the illumination of earthly life. There was a time when
he studied painting by the analogy of music. But he seems to many
to have arrived at a point as near pure creation in the terms of
his medium, without dragging along suggestions of the other art,
as any living painter.

In the paintings of Nicholas Roerich, another frankly mystic
artist, there is a suggestive contrast: in that he commonly uses
subject-matter to stimulate thought upon an imagined world; though
he considers the creative design-elements of his pictures a revelation direct from the soul. I must confess that I find Kandinsky's
works richer in spiritual or four-dimensional implication or feeling.
It may be that the difference is due to Kandinsky's superior formal

< 335 >

The Artist and His Model, by Pablo Picasso. (By courtesy of Sidney Janis.)

mastery; or perhaps awakening the intellect does definitely inter-fere with intuitive-spiritual response. It seems to me that Roerich seldom touches upon the creative intensity of that Far Eastern art from which his best qualities seem derived. The serenity is there, and often a richness of coloring, but the rhythms are not compelling, the plastic depth and adjustment lacking. Farther down the scale—and illustrating a sort of vagueness that is too often miscalled mystic, because reality is poetically veiled, are the shallow har-monies of Arthur B. Davies. As a matter of fact, the abstract element is only weakly expressed in most of his canvases.

< 336 >

Of those who seem to approach abstraction without mystic intention—with a mechanistic understanding of order, perhaps—there is a considerable group centering in Paris; another that worked fruitfully, before Germany was purged of "radicalism," at the Bauhaus, Dessau; and a considerable number of scattered painters here in America. I have chosen to illustrate, as representative, works of Jean Hélion and Raymond Jonson. These are as stripped of objective materials and symbols as the extremest purist could ask. As it is not within the province of this book to push out into the manifold theories—but only to record the generalities of the advance toward abstraction—I will put into a footnote some references to published statements of the Purists and Mechanists.*

The Cubists were the most significant "school" in the long progression between Cezanne and the abstract-Expressionists—or Purist-Abstractionists. They returned painting definitely to a search for the nature of the abstract plastic organism; and the compositions of Braque, Picasso, Gris and Marcoussis are likely to rank high among the early accomplishments of non-objective Expressionism. Their works lean to the mechanistic side, rather than the mystic-formal. They seldom attain to anything comparable to the profound rhythms of El Greco and Cezanne. Their range is as lim-

* The A. E. Gallatin Collection in the "Gallery of Living Art," at New York University, leans strongly to the most advanced abstractionists. The instructive catalogue contains an essay by Jean Hélion, on "The Evolution of Abstract Art," which is an excellent summary of the progress from the time when Cezanne broke the tradition of "submitting the picture to the model," to the "free treatment of elements" in Arp, Mondrian, etc. Hélion believes that "the artists do nothing but indicate the paths for the eyes through the surface of the pictures. Whether this path follows the known line of a nose or the anonymous trajectory of a parabole, is of no decisive importance in itself." His own work is concise, balanced, clear—he wants it to be "as clear as a sign." The same catalogue includes an excellent essay by James Johnson Sweeney, on the development of the plastic organization under and after Cubism. One of the best books on the "Functionalist" theory is *The New Vision*, by Moholy-Nagy, New York [1932].

< 337 >

Construction, by Jean Helion. (By courtesy of the Becker Galleries.)

ited as that of the "decorators," Gauguin and Matisse—and for the
same reason: they consciously hold the spatial field to a constricted
depth, with planes closely paralleling the front "surface." The
illustrations of Cubist work indicate their virtues within those limits.

The approach to abstraction in painting by definite parallelism
to the qualities or "effects" of music, is illustrated in the portrait
of Dr. Savadsky—himself a musician—by Katherine Dreier. The
subject of the portrait has written thus: "This form of art is the
result of the acuteness and vigilance of the spiritual insight rather
than of the sharpness and keenness of the eye. Katherine Dreier's
enigmatically interwoven lines, forming here and there geometrical

< 338 >

Abstract Portrait of Savadsky, by Katherine S. Dreier.

proportions, resemble combinations of harmonic chords of music. These crossing rays of light, throwing different colors on fantastic unknown forms . . . are reminiscent, in music, of a masterly design of the contrapuntal order. . . . Thus, like music, these paintings compel us to join in the process of their unfoldment, stimulating our senses and directing our emotions. This property of abstract painting brings about the co-ordination of emotional vibration and gives it the music-like quality of fluidity."

Georgia O'Keeffe in one series of abstractions was obviously influenced by meditation upon the comparable elements in musical creation. I have chosen to illustrate here, however, other phases

< 339 >

White Iris, by Georgia O'Keeffe. (By courtesy of An American Place.)

of her work—which is, to me, strangely potent and beautiful. The two plates of a white iris, the one retaining strongly the objective "natural" forms, the other a pictorial-formal organization "abstracted from" the natural object, afford an illuminating lesson in the way in which nature may *serve*, without enslaving, the artist.

< 340 >

Abstraction—White Iris, by Georgia O'Keeffe.

There are few painters whose work would so well repay study for detection of the intensified abstract element: whether "absolute" or as pictorial skeleton or core. (Though I doubt not that O'Keeffe would deplore "study" of paintings for any such outside purpose: she creates her pictures, out of her own special understanding and

< 341 >

The Gale-swept Orchard, by Keith Vaughan (above); Near Somewhere,
by Karl Fortess (below). (By courtesy of the American British Art
Center, New York, and the Associated American Artists Galleries,
New York.)

urge, and if they speak to people with like aesthetic sensitivity, that is enough. But I add a wide range of her expressions, abstract and otherwise, for the benefit of those still in the period of intellectual groping: who are trying to find mental comprehension, that they may the more freely dismiss the mind.)

We might have come at this whole question of abstraction by two approaches, differentiated as the attempt at inner subjective expression, with practically no reference to, or stimulation from, the phenomenal world of objects—Helion, Mondrian, Arp, etc.—and the attempt at expression of the deeper structural or four-dimensional secret divined in the object. The latter approach—suggested by the *White Iris* compositions of O'Keeffe—reminds one of the dictum of Troward, not specifically directed to artists but nonetheless apropos, that: "The great duty incumbent on all who have attained to this knowledge is to impress on their fellow men that there is an *inner side* to things, and that until this *inner* side is known, the things themselves are not known."

Abstract expression in art may be revelation of something detected as a deeper value or hidden truth in the object, or it may be a manifestation direct from the well of truth beyond all objects. In either case the artist, in being creative at all, inevitably creates a world nearer final truth and cosmic harmonious order than is the casual one of outward visible nature.

ABOUT SUR-REALISM

I have left out of consideration one exhibit that many another commentator would bring prominently into view, in any exposition of the position of the Abstractionists—if only because the "school" is currently very much in evidence. I refer to the Sur-Realists, and

< 343 >

The Apparition, by Revington Arthur. (By courtesy of the Joseph
Luyber Galleries, New York.)

I dismiss them thus casually because only confusion can result
from mistaking the retreat into fancy, and into dream-symbolism,
for a true escape into free creation. The Sur-Realists, as a typical
group, substitute the images of the sub-conscious for the object
portrayed (by the Realists) direct from nature; and they juggle
these familiar images in new and "unreal" combinations. But
oftener than not the images carry so great a burden of intellectual

< 344 >

(and perhaps Freudian) significance, that the mental response precedes and nullifies the aesthetic.

This is not to say that the group affiliated under the Sur-Realist banner includes no artists endowed with rich plastic sensibility, and no creators who place attainment of abstract expression first. But these latter are in general accessions from other schools—Klee from the German Abstractionists, some graduated Cubists, etc.—claimed by the Sur-Realists, but better explained with their earlier affiliates. Giorgio di Chirico cannot be overlooked as a creative force, and even the dream-fantasy group, Miro, Ernst, Masson, etc., rise above their Sur-Realistic fetters at times: forsaking dream symbolism and intellectual baiting for absolute plastic aims. But the typical Sur-Realist credo is as essentially opposed to the main current of Expressionism as is the so-called "New Objectivism." I may add that my chary use of the word symbol or symbolism—which is occasionally employed to explain the values beyond the objective aspect—is due to the fact that most so-called symbolism in art has been a matter of placing one *intellectual* concept to suggest another. Symbolism remains on the objective and mental plane. If in Sur-Realism the artist rises above casual reality as visible in nature, it is only to re-arrange the objective symbols of nature according to a fanciful or dreamed arrangement. This is not an approach to abstraction in the chapter-meaning of the word.

< 345 >

The Death of a Communist: Mural by Jacob Burck.

CHAPTER XII

S INCE Realism was discredited, and the tyranny of the object destroyed, art has re-spread its wings. It now covers a territory wide and varied, from absolute abstract to purposefully meaningful. There is no authoritative warrant for claiming that one sort is exclusively valuable, or superior. The view that all serious painting is message-bearing seems to me to grow out of a narrowness, an intellectual bigotry. The counter-claim that the "highest" art is purged of objective elements, innocent of the language of phenomenal nature, is brought without the confirmation of history —and the contemporary evidence, though compelling in its narrowed field, is hardly of a volume or of an intensity to warrant dismissal of the several sorts of non-abstract art as inferior.

In the preceding chapter I affirmed my faith in abstract values: both in the occasional absolutely non-objective picture, and in the basic importance of the abstract element—skeleton or core—in the "content" picture. I have marked the swing toward apprehension and capitalization of abstract factors as a typical and healthy part of Expressionism. But this is not to say that painting is through with human or social content. I think only a few fanatics among us would insist that today the major portion of our enjoyment out of paintings is derived from purely abstract examples. Most of us will be quick to report that it derives from pictures where there is obvious understanding of the *underlying* abstract elements. But

< 347 >

we admit human-feeling and social-meaning values as still commonly entering, and valid. Without returning to Victorian preoccupation with the camera-subject, we oftener than not expect a fusion of the formal-abstract and feeling-meaning factors.

When I state that subject-matter importantly exists in the bulk of Expressionist works, it is necessary to add that *more* progress has been made in establishing a norm of abstract-formal expressiveness —in an understood plastic correlation—than in attaining a main road of human or social expressiveness. The reason lies perhaps in the confusion of contemporary life: the disorder in the spiritual and economic fields, the lack of conviction regarding purpose in present-day living, the inability of the mind to cope with the surface disorganization of a material world transitionally deranged and involved. Where subject matter exists, there is no social focus, no common agreement as to what is significant.

In approaching this matter of subject and meaning, we should by this time be free of the misconceptions and limitations that turned an earlier generation aside from an evaluation—or enjoyment—of typically pictorial expressiveness on its own account. We are happily released from the belief that there is an uplift in being "classical," insofar as that term implies devotion to the conventions and lifeless symbols of an intellectually idealized Greek-world. Nor are we seduced by the Realistic-Romantic offering of a detailed exotic world. to carry our thoughts out of our own too pressing surroundings: as a "relief" from life, rather than—what art should be—intensification of one of life's most precious experiences. When we Expressionists turn to the human and social content—the part of the picture beyond formal expressiveness and spiritual or cosmic connotation—we insist that the materials be of life as lived today, a reality of the present world. Only we dis-

< 348 >

count, in picture-making, the photographic view of that world: the depictions and inventories easy to the camera, and the longer descriptions and narratives natural to the literary art. The "realization" sought alike by Cezanne and Kokoschka and Orozco, escapes the definitions of Classicism and Romanticism; it escapes, also, both naturalistic and selective Realism, but is of the essence of the familiar world and common living.

THE CASE FOR CONTINUING OBJECTIVE CONTENT

I imagine that I hear our Abstractionist friends still asking why there is this confession of attachment to concrete subject-matter, after so complete an affirmation of the *basic* importance of the plastic-abstract and spiritual-architectonic elements. The answer of the "subjective" Expressionists is this: in the nature of Evolution, men cannot swing so quickly from an art with centuries-old traditions of human-life content, to an art purged of every element of objective reality.

Progressively man attains to spiritual awareness, achieves new manifestations of order on the immediate material plane. The artist renders himself a channel of creativeness, bringing the life of the Spirit to the pictorial organism. The picture, or the expressive form in the picture, is from the central well of all-creativeness; but the manifestation is here on earth, to be "lived in" by men whose awareness is still largely conditioned by what they have experienced in the phenomenal world. The projection of the universal or cosmic is therefore still—at this stage of progress—clothed more often than not in the symbols of life as objectified for the earth-bound human faculties.

In other words, men's grasp of the spiritual is weak—though strengthening; and the trammels of the immediate concrete world

< 349 >

are still numerous and strong. Creative geniuses arise, to speak more directly than ever before, out of the Source of life, to the spiritual consciousness in upward-struggling man. In another field —of absolute wisdom, shall we say?—Jesus, Buddha, Lao-tze, and a very few others, were such seers and prophets. But even they, so eloquent of the divine, so clear-seeing in regard to human life— even they must bring their revelations to humankind in terms of accustomed objective understanding, manifesting within an order natural to the plane upon which man has his day-by-day existence. The impulse of art is to the higher plane, toward realization of the vitality of the Spirit; yet most of us climb but laboriously to grasp of the cosmic and the abstract, out of the consciousness of a conditioning natural world. For a time yet the comprehending faculties will demand that the images of objective experience serve as carriers of the purports and suggestions of formal and spiritual order.

In time, the concrete, the lowest form of manifestation, may be burned away, as man's faculties become alight with spiritual truth. But we are not in an era when the individual man can more than illumine material living—not escape it—by devotion to the inner being. And it is likely that our artists yet awhile will subordinate, not deny, objective nature.

WHAT IS MEANING?

I will attempt to set up no boundary lines between feeling and meaning: between the emotion of the artist and the stimulus to the observer. Most of the writing on the relationship of perception, emotion, expression, and communication seems to me more confusing than clarifying. The fusion of processes is fundamentally important; the synthesis of expressive elements the prime requisite

< 350 >

The Race Track, by Albert Ryder.

for the creator, and the conditioning achievement for appreciation.

We may, however, profitably remind ourselves of the many senses in which the two words "meaning" and "feeling" are commonly employed by artists and critics; trying, then, to delimit their application under Expressionism. I have doubtless, in pages past, used the terms "aesthetic meaning" and "mystic meaning"; but these are extensions of the word beyond the implications intended in this chapter. When the Abstractionists and those opposed to abstraction use the word, they are talking about human and social

< 351 >

Modern **Inquisitor,** by Philip Evergood. (By courtesy of the A.C.A. Gallery, New York.)

significance as distinguished from formal and possibly fourth-dimensional substance or suggestion. Particularly meaning is that which stimulates, by stirring recollection, sympathy, moral sentiment, etc. Meaning may be a stimulus to the observer's feeling: cheaply and shallowly, as in popular sentimental art, or profoundly, as in deeply religious art. It may further be a stimulus to action,

< 352 >

through arousing feeling—and that is what the extremer Communists demand of "typically Modern" art today.

Meaning is the thing that stirs the artist to creation, and it carries through to the product and the effect on the observer. In the end it is compelling in measure of the intensity of the artist's feeling.

The artist "sees for others." Because his sensitivity was exceptionally keen, Cezanne penetrated through to meanings of nature hidden from most eyes, beyond the camera aspect. Because his grasp of the plastic medium was extraordinary, he was enabled to present in vitally living pictures his double "realization": of something divined beyond ordinary seeing, and of a new plastic order. He got down to some inner significance and structure of the object, stripped of trivialities and casual detail, and, in intensely pictorial terms, carried a sense of the fundamental character of the thing, its universal import, over to the observer (who, however, first had to be cured of his "educated" taste for the photographically correct or sweetened depiction of surface aspects).

In a true sense, Cezanne created a world in each picture: created, because it was a world not seen by other men, a world of new meaning for them. He offered them the two inseparable experiences of great objective art: enjoyment of a complete pictorial-plastic adventure, and a revelation of essential truth in something they had known before but in lesser significance.

SOCIALLY SIGNIFICANT ART

There are those who claim that we still have not come to meaning of the sort that characterizes the greatest painting. How, they ask, can any deep significance be attached to the endless landscapes and apples and bathing figures in Cezanne's pictures? In short, they

< 353 >

want *socially* significant subject-matter. They want the art that starts the mind to unwonted thinking, that stirs the observer to action. We are on dangerous ground here: for most of the Moderns believe that aesthetic expression can be brought to its intensest when the mental faculties are not unduly aroused. They draw a line between richly formal art and intellectualized art. The literary art, because it deals with the mind's symbols for objective things, words, necessarily is closer to a combined formal-intellectual expression; to carry the plastic art into the realm of intellectual stimulus is to render it unduly literary, mental and objective.

Perhaps the deciding factor here is that contemporary artists find so little in modern life worth re-expressing: that there is no objective-intellectual material that appeals crucially or universally. Let us grant for the moment the claim that achievement of the formal-expressive synthesis is only half the battle: that the plastically complete picture is only a shell, unless an equally moving "content" is provided. What is there in modern art to compare with the religious symbolism and story-telling of the Middle Ages and early Renaissance? Or, for that matter, with the fleshy neo-Paganism and courtly pageantry of the late Renaissance (which endowed the world of the artist and his appreciators with a certain unity and significance—though later generations detect the inherent elements of falsity)? The answer is, mighty little. Today it is a world disorganized, without unity, and a society dangerously divided and without convictions, that present themselves to the artist's social consciousness.

That is not to say that there are no new elements in life, typical of the age, that cry out for re-expression. The magnificent vistas opened by the scientists, upon cosmic glories and marvelously delicate manifestations of order, no less than the epic struggles into

< 354 >

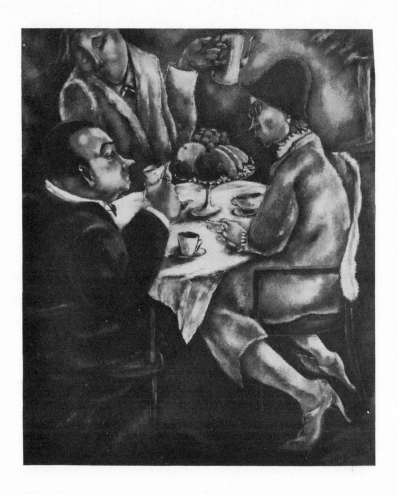

His First Crossing, by George Biddle. (By courtesy of
Frank K. M. Rehn Gallery.)

which mankind is plunged in the search for just government and a
new spiritual vision, afford the artist stirring materials and unique
inspiration. The splendor and stupendousness of the newly dis-
closed universe of nebulae and galaxies, the dwarfing grandeur of
the new physical cosmos, linked with the sweet precision of its

< 355 >

mathematical order; the compelling design of microscopical atomic matter, and its microcosmic echo of a universal dynamic rhythm; the mass struggles of class-divided men, still fighting one another although at last there is abundance for all—with the gigantic irony of persisting ignorance and selfishness and enslavement amid Utopian assurance of physical sustenance, and unlimited tools for intellectual and spiritual study and enjoyment; the collapse of royal dynasties and the march toward world unity; the decay of centuries-old churches—at a time when men crave spiritual experience and release as of old: all these are phenomena of our times, of the essence of life and progress—and so grist to the mill of the contemporary artist. No age has offered more stirring external stimulus to the creative faculties, and the painter or dancer or sculptor is deliberately blind if he fail to place himself in timely and sympathetic relationship with these conceptions and events. The sharp crisis and the cosmic perspective, the penetrating, poignant insight and the epic sweep of human issues: these all are background for the contemporary arts—but largely unexpressed.

Certainly there is little to compare with the way in which, during the Mediaeval era, the symbols and beliefs of the Christ-obsessed painter and builder entered into the mural pictures, the ikons and the idols, even into the church edifice. What is lacking today, to afford the artist grasp of the titanic elements and profound significance of the machine-age world is, of course, a binding faith, a unified attitude, an all-embracing conviction. Instead, a materialistic individualism, a surviving will-to-fight, a wide smattering of superficial education, have prevented the formulation of a world philosophy and the discovery of a comprehensive viewpoint. And perhaps that is natural, just after science has destroyed centuries-old beliefs about the universe and the physics of life; in the near-

< 356 >

The Lynching, by Ben Kopman. (By courtesy of J. B. Neumann.)

chaos when invention has rendered obsolete an economic system built up through all the known ages, and men seek frantically to establish the foundations of another; when the venerable churches are deserted; when nationalism and self-destroying imperialism approach the final phase of break-up and disappearance. In the midst of these changes, man is still too confused to attain to the philosophic belief, to gain a comprehending perspective.

And yet the artist should be prophet as well as reflector or spokesman of a society in the forming. With his special sensitivity and his profounder awareness, he should perceive before others, and give expression in his formal fashion. If there is to be meaning in painting, it should be eloquent of these things of which I have

< 357 >

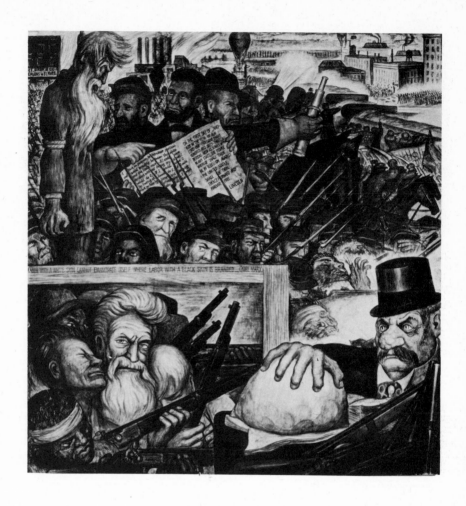

The Civil War, by Diego Rivera, in the mural series at the New Workers'
School. (By courtesy of Covici-Friede.)

spoken. Perhaps it is not too much to ask of the artist that he be
the first focusing agent, the perceiver and the herald of a new world
order, nearer to the spiritual type, underlying all still-chaotic surface manifestations.

< 358 >

There comes to mind the legend of Fra Angelico: that he wept continuously while he painted his pictures of Christ on the Cross. His personal realization of the agony of Jesus, of what he believed to be the supreme tragedy of mankind, was so poignant that he suffered and cried unashamedly as he created his pictorial re-expression of the event. Where among artists today is the comparable example?

Perhaps men feel as deeply. But where is the conviction, the faith, the passion to impel that self-outpouring? Not such is the feeling of the artist for his model, or for a landscape, or for the Republic, the Empire or the King. Artists are lost in individualism, with a plentiful measure of the purely personal emotion, but without the belief that permits a magnificent devotion, an impassioned impulse to express *through* oneself a lived truth.

Not one among us has failed to experience the incitement to expression of a feeling—which perhaps at the moment of flashing into our consciousness seemed clothed in the magnificence of universal truth. Painter, writer, theatre artist, sculptor: we have been afire with the flame of creation; but how often has the result been more than a reflection of limited personal emotion: turned out petty because our own understanding, desires and penetration were restricted and commonplace? Even when the content was less of our selves than of a "cause" or a group, we failed of a universal view, an inspired or epic love for our subject.

THE COMMUNIST VIEW

Insofar as there may be forming a main road of human or social expressiveness, based on a world view and an idealistic philosophy, I judge that it is being laid down by those radicals whom we may,

< 359 >

Thanksgiving 1884: One of the Haymarket series of drawings by Mitchell
Siporin. (By courtesy of the artist and *The Daily Worker*.)

in the looser significance, term Communists (this including—in our non-party sense—the Socialists). They are the only world-wide "community" of men and artists inspired by a shared conviction and a passionate devotion. Despite the frequent statements in earlier pages combating the idea—put forward by the most vociferous and extreme Communist artists—that art must serve the immediate proletarian struggle for power, I record my belief that insofar as a social consciousness is today stimulating artistic creation, and social conviction impelling personal expression, Communism is responsible. It is no accident that the theatre arts in the Soviet Union are incomparably more vigorous, vital and interesting than those of the rest of the world, or that in the United States the most stirring graphic art charged with social significance is in the far-left magazines and newspapers.

Communism as we know it, particularly in this country, from its day-by-day works—and more especially from the distorted "news" of it—may seem an imperfect vessel, and a faint promise upon which to pin hopes of a universally valid art of combined formal and human expressiveness. But in its world aspect and its essential idealism, beyond the immediate struggle and compromise and fear, it seems to me to exhibit the only unity to which millions of men are manifesting loyalty—even to that last earthly one of giving up their lives—internationally, as both a "religion" and a form of lay organization. No other ideal of the world reconstructed, no other vision of human-social order, affords the slightest promise of developing a comparable conviction and passion, strong enough to stir determining numbers of men to world action and a widely compelling art.

Perhaps I can re-state here my belief about the whole matter of art as abstract-mystic revealment and art eloquent of a social truth

< 361 >

or conviction. (I am conscious that I have left my position open to misinterpretation: perhaps myself open to the unpleasant charge of "straddling.") I believe the truth lies in these *two* statements:

First, Expressionism has gone far to prove, by progressively wide adoption of a new theory, and by a sizeable body of works, that a totally abstract or near-abstract art of painting can evoke a profound and enjoyable aesthetic response. This art will remain valid and accepted by reason of the intensity and reality of its formal-mystic crystallization of human-craved truths, regardless of lack of objective and social-stimulus content. It will survive as certainly as non-objective music has survived. It seems likely, moreover, that the evolution of man's aesthetic faculties is toward ever-greater sensitivity to the abstract element, so that artists may look forward to more rather than less absolute-abstract art; and to a greater measure of the abstract-formal element in all art.

Second, there is also an art of painting that adds to the formal abstract revelation, revealment of the artist's human feeling, and possibly stimulus to action, over the object or event. This sort of art takes on significance as it moves toward the unfoldment of truths important to group-man, as it partakes of the race-purpose and a common human spirit. In this field, the only achievement that even suggests a possible development of world-wide import is that foreshadowed in—using the term broadly—Communistic channels.

I argue the two opinions, doubtless, out of my own feeling and experience. I have enjoyed abstract art, and I have gained immensely in directness of approach since I learned to apprehend all works of art *first* as achievement of a characteristic formal completeness. Facing also a small body of contemporary art that combines the formally expressive element with subjective and social significance, evoking equally intense aesthetic response, I have found that

< 362 >

The Slaves: Mural by José Clemente Orozco, at the New School for Social Research, New York.

this oftener than not has connection with the only world-wide social-change current that I have been able to mark clearly in the confusion of the times. Both the abstract works, and the socially significant works with rich abstract core, therefore, appeal to me as phases of characteristically Modern painting. In example, I enjoy —seem to experience with typically modern intensity of feeling— Cezanne and Orozco, Marin and Siqueiros.

Ruling out the directly propagandist thing, frankly or craftily carrying a "lesson" to the beholder—(literature and the cinema, utilizing word and photograph, are better "teacher arts")—one may note that most objective or human-content painting or drawing is subtly propagandist for one social set-up or another. The endless conventional streams of portraits, nudes, sweethearts, landscapes,

< 363 >

Incumbent, by **William Gropper.** (By courtesy of the Associated
American Artists Galleries, New York.)

battle scenes, Venetian and Algerian travel bits, etc., etc., are really
eloquent of a way of living, and suggest by inference the superiority
or sufficiency of the life of which they are a part. The flattering

< 364 >

Bombardment of Workers in the Karl Marx Hof, Vienna: Illustration by
Marion Greenwood for *The New Masses*.

portraits of "important" people, the reminders of the delights of
the flesh, the romantic invitations to escape from familiar surroundings, the patriotic allegories—all these are indicative of the "society" that is: the tired, faithless, materialistic, divided world,
held together precariously, without a ground for common conviction
of artist and any large group of beholders. They "speak for" the
status quo.

If subject-painting must be eloquent of something in life, let it
be—say the social-stimulus advocates—a something worth being

< 365 >

Illustration by Phil Bard, for *The New Masses.*

passionate over, arising out of conviction, and communicating conviction. In other words, let us have Rivera, and those who go farther in that direction, rather than Sargent and Frieseke, and those nonentities who, largely, fill the walls on 57th Street today.

Where I part from the typical Communist critic is, first, in my willingness on occasion to accept as self-sufficient a type of art without the attributes of social meaning; and second—when I come to human-content art—in my insistence that there are sorts with universal values not directly *illustrating* the coming of a world-state and justice for the worker.

It is not surprising that when political dissentients are on the defensive, when every avowed radical is made keenly aware of

< 366 >

Illustration by Phil Bard, for *The New Masses*.

strife, injustice and opposition, the constituted spokesmen should claim that no art is good that does not directly further "the cause." The world is in an emergency; ergo, art must be drafted with all else, to the one political end. But any observer not blinded by the immediacy of the beginning struggle should see that art can serve better by developing to its own greatest intensity in its own primary terms, not distorted to message-bearing purposes; and if it has become truly Modern, it will then be found to link inevitably with the social Modernism that is of the coming age.

The test, I think, should be that this art will be worthy of the society that will *follow* the immediate inevitable struggle, not merely of service to the participants in that struggle. The very extreme

< 367 >

Haymarket 1934: One of the drawings by Mitchell Siporin commemo-
rating the "Haymarket Massacre." (By courtesy of the artist and
The Daily Worker.)

claim that no art is worth survival that does not promulgate the theses of radicalism—we might substitute Fascism for Communism here—is sufficiently answered, perhaps, by a counter-question: is music, a non-objective, message-free art, not to survive? The Expressionist is likely to claim that any painting as intensely expressive in its own terms as the music of Bach or Beethoven, is bound to override any temporal struggle or interlude of chaos.

The existence of a significant art of painting linked with the radical or leftist social movement, can best be illustrated from the works of those Mexican muralists who have so curiously come to pre-eminence in the United States. Despite the lack of sympathy in high places, Rivera, Orozco and Siqueiros, and their Northern imitators, have pushed forward until they afford the only instance of a group movement, of undoubted creative significance, in the American world of painting. If this were the sole evidence of linked formal-creative achievement and radical social consciousness, no inferences would be in order. But in the kindred field of black-and-white illustration there is nothing in the "regular" press to approach the vitality of the drawings appearing in such newspapers as *The Daily Worker* and such magazines as *The New Masses*. I speak not of the human content alone, but of that joint plastic-formal and human-feeling expressiveness which alone can make this sort of thing lastingly significant. I reproduce examples which the reader may analyse for himself.

Equally, I shall leave the reproductions of the murals of Orozco and Rivera to illustrate without comment the richly formal achievement, linked with socially significant "content," that places these Mexicans in the forefront of American Expressionists.

What I have said in this chapter on Feeling and Meaning might be set down in one-two-three order thus:

< 369 >

Division and Depression: Mural by Diego Rivera at the New Workers School, New York, depicting the unemployed, bread lines, and police rule. (By courtesy of Covici-Friede, publishers of *Portrait of America,* by Diego Rivera.)

All creative painting is expressive of the instrument and of the artist's feeling: of his mastery of the specialized plastic means of the art, and of his image-compelling emotion. The meaning carried over to the observer may be of three sorts: first, a mystic-abstract

< 370 >

meaning wholly free from images of the concrete world; second, a meaning both mystic and incidentally objective—as in much of Cezanne—in which case the abstract-formal core is the truer reason for the existence of the picture; and third, a combined formal-expressive and socially-valuable or humanly-stirring meaning—in the art of immediate subjective appeal, over a formally vital skeleton, as in Orozco, and (in black-and-white) Siporin, Gorelick, Gellert, Gropper, Burck, Del, and Bard.

Mural, by Diego Rivera. (Photo by courtesy of Weyhe Gallery, from original in Mexico City.)

< 371 >

The News Building, New York. Like the Rockefeller Center buildings, this illustrates the bare bones of a new architecture: structurally expressive, but without creative enrichment. (John Mead Howells and Raymond M. Hood, Architects.)

CHAPTER XIII

THE ARTS OTHER THAN PAINTING

HAVING attempted my answer to the unanswerable question, "Are Modern painters necessarily Reds?" I am relieved to reach the comparatively untroubled waters of the other arts. The streams of progress of the several arts flow parallel, and even mingle at some points; but, in general, there is not elsewhere the vexing question of the comparative degree of abstraction, subject-interest and meaning-stimulus.

The pictorial art, as noted in an early chapter, affords the neatest example of revolutionary change from 19th Century Realism to 20th Century Expressionism. The boundary line between an old art and a new is there most distinct: the about-face of theory most cleancut and decisive, the contrast of exhibited examples most unmistakable. I have, therefore, in setting out to illustrate the development of Expressionism, chosen to analyze from several viewpoints the advance in painting, as the type art.

It is of course impossible to treat all the arts in similar detail— in less than a seven-volume work. But it is part of my purpose, in outlining what has been learned of the nature of Expressionism, in its first half-century of development, to indicate briefly how the lines of advance, as illustrated in painting, are clearly traceable in several sister arts. It would be but poor support for my theory of the interlocking nature of the several Modernisms—in art, science, government, the spiritual realm—if I could not show a

< 373 >

common progress, nay revolution, in the several fields within the broad activity termed art. In practice and in theory, indeed, there are corresponding gains in the theatre, the dance, architecture, and on—though less patently—to the end of the list.

The broad shifts which may be expected to discover themselves throughout the range, if there is an all-embracing creative advance, may be summed up as these: negatively, an abandonment, in the graphic arts, of photographic, transcriptive and illusional aims, and in the near-abstract arts, a denial of historic-imitational limitations (such as existed in 19th Century "Eclectic" architecture, or the contemporary remnants of the dance art); and, positively or constructively, a leap forward to intensified expression, in the triple achievement of newly-compelling use of the medium, revelation of profounder implications of order, and subjective crystallization of the artist's feeling or insight. The sum of these gains might be described as the attainment, among the Expressionists, of a common element termed "expressive form," partaking of the three sorts of "revealment"—instrumental-formal, universal, and personal-responsive—but in each art conditioned by the nature of the medium, sculptural, theatrical, plastic, etc.

ARCHITECTURE, THE TIMES, AND EXPRESSIONISM

The art of architecture, next to painting, affords the clearest-cut example of utter revolution, in theory, and in widespread "radical" practice. If the main lines of change were obscured, for thirty years, after being laid down a half century ago, the sudden swing toward "the new architecture," throughout Europe and the United States, since the World War, has made the logic of Modernism in the building art patent to all, and the examples inescapable.

< 374 >

In the Victorian era, imitative, historic-echo architecture was as prevalent as Realistic painting. The Eclectics ruled the profession, the schools, and the channels of criticism and appreciation. The originator was scoffed at. Tradition was praised as something ended and sacrosanct. The "art" consisted in re-arranging bits adapted from past practice. The revolution from this sort of reflective and impotent building, to a truly expressive architecture, started when a few pioneers—most notably Sullivan and Wright in this country, Berlage in Holland, and Wagner in Austria—challenged the historic knickknack sort of thing, and set out upon a course of creative experiment with modern materials and machine-age methods of engineering.

Sullivan promulgated a motto for the "radicals" the world over: "Form must follow function." It is worth while to pause a little over the ways in which functional—or expressive-organic—architecture had been lost to Europe and America in his time.

Architects throughout the Western world had become mere choosers and adapters, in the mid-19th Century. They had decided that all possible styles had been invented. They chose their style and their motifs from the buildings of the past. They taught students that any structure, even railway terminal or hangar, could be properly sheathed within one of the stylistic envelopes hallowed by age.

Even with new inventions in structural methods, and the development of new building materials, steel and poured concrete, the architects covered over the engineering with veneers echoing the old methods and materials—remained faithfully mediaeval or tastefully Renaissance. They masked the steel-frame structures with temple façades and cathedral fronts. They even tortured concrete into forms simulating cut stone. You can see this sort of

< 375 >

architectural falsification in almost any concrete structure in your own town. And surely you will find there banks hiding behind Greek temple porticos, and vegetable markets in Italian palace loggias. A lot of us used to believe that a building with a row of Greek columns on the front was *ipso facto* artistic.

Those 19th Century architects hung up useless cornices on flat-top buildings, attached functionless columns where they cut off light from the windows, and did a dozen other architecturally-dishonest things. They were forgetting the organism that lies at the heart of every true work of art. They were dealing in antiquarian trifles, thinking in terms of unrelated façades, of pretty arrangements of surface ornament. Their structures were generally inexpressive of the engineering within, of the materials employed, and of the spirit of their own time. Their art was a hangover from the courtly age, totally unrelated to any of the deeper social drifts of the era, democracy, industrialism, scientific advance. Architecture had become a museum art—reflective and illustrative, not expressive.

Even during that 19th Century when architectural falsification was almost universal, a few radical artists were laying the foundation of a new sort of building. Today there emerge, in all the countries of Europe, and in every town of our own land, the beginnings of an expressive building art. It is unmistakably new, unmistakably of the machine age; and certainly it is the first great creative advance in the art since the Gothic. Renaissance was just what its name implies, the rebirth of an old architecture. Today the building is new in every phase, engineering, use, design, appearance.

Looking at the styles and motifs, the columns and cornices and ornaments, of the Eclectics and the Beaux-Arts men, the Modernists

< 376 >

A House in Illinois, by Frank Lloyd Wright. An early work that exhibits many of the idioms later incorporated into European-American expressive Modernism.

say, "sweep it all out." Strip off every vestige of ornament, every column, pilaster, cornice or window frame that has been divorced from its original function, every meaningless escutcheon and cupid and regally decorated ceiling. Shear off every merely "picturesque" addition, every flourish, every atrophied member. Thus the first phase of the new building sometimes seems like a "stripped architecture."

< 377 >

Some people, of course, don't like the stripped look. To them the new architecture seems bare, almost hospital-like. They miss the cushioning, the regal softness, and the Victorian luxuriousness. But enrichment will come, in idioms that belong to our own time— particularly in a greater fullness of color. But in "decoration" too. Only that decoration, the Expressionists insist, must grow out of the characteristics of the type of building men are now doing, and out of the materials they are using. Some critics believe that the stripped look is proper expression of a machine-age directness and mathematical precision. Certainly a great deal of the new architecture so far, whether in the American skyscraper or the functional houses of Germany and Russia, exhibits long, hard edges, surfaces kept smooth and sanitarily clean, and massive proportions. Some of the sense of irresistible power, of mechanical efficiency, belonging to our era, is here objectified.

Beyond the basic simplicity, directness, massiveness, there is, of course, a form appropriate to the skyscraper and another appropriate to the house, and still another appropriate to library or market or gymnasium. But from all, if the architect is true to his materials and his time, the old decorative motives have been sheared away.

The new architecture is Expressionistic in exactly the way of the new painting.. The first characteristic is—let me repeat—that it expresses, rather than imitates. There is, first of all—and this is the easiest characteristic to mark—genuine and clear expression of the materials and methods of the art. There is also expression of the life of today: men's ways of living, their activities and thought, and their highest aspirations. Finally, there is—in a small fraction of cases—expression of the subjective, personal, creative genius of the designer.

< 378 >

Karl Marx Hof: Modern workingmen's apartments in Vienna.
Karl Ehn, Architect.

The Expressionist architect more than any other artist gains in having at his disposal an enlarged range of physical materials. Instead of the immemorial building by means of stone laid on stone, he is released for new sorts of compositional design, in having steel (and other metals just now being tried), concrete, and glass in large areas and new forms not dreamed possible by earlier generations. The skyscrapers, now that the Classic and Gothic veneers are generally omitted, assert the cage-like steel frame—towering upright, and repeated cross-member; factories, warehouses and stations are eloquent of the heavy block of poured concrete; and not a few houses tell the story of new possibilities of concrete blocks, of stucco, and of wood used for typically wood-like effect.

All these materials are utilized by the Moderns with scrupulous regard for their own natural effects when functionally placed. The

< 379 >

Model for a Functionalist House, by Norman Bel Geddes.

aesthetics of the building art begins here: in the organic truth of member-parts, and the undisguised attributes and peculiarities of the materials. It was Louis Sullivan—engineer as well as architect —who summed this up, back in the 'Eighties, with that now-famous challenge to the Eclectics, which can hardly be repeated too often: "Form must follow function." Only thus can the organic unity be manifested.

Frank Lloyd Wright was instrumental in spreading the "slogan" to cover the idea not only of material-and-member function but of

< 380 >

use-function—as also he was to provide the first example of out-standing personal creativeness linked with functional design.

Perhaps I can best indicate by example the change in thought on the matter of use-honesty. When I was outlining this book I was living in New Haven and one of my diversions was walking out among that strange collection of buildings which is, physically, Yale University. Day after day I passed what I took to be the Divinity School: a massive truncated Gothic tower, blocks of mediaeval monks' cells with thin infrequent windows, mortuary chapels, and sculpture direct from some ancient Notre Dame. Then something prompted me to step inside, and I found encased in those ecclesiastic walls—the new Yale gymnasium. That is what the Expressionist calls "falsification of use-expression." It is a form of architectural dishonesty that became well-nigh universal in the Victorian era, surviving still in such strongholds of tradition as universities, museums and women's clubs.

The Modernists insist upon an appropriateness of design to occupancy, to use-function. One reason for the stripped and bare "look" of early functional architecture is to be discovered in this: the orthodox architects relinquished to the radicals first such difficult-to-ornament structures as factories, hangars, and warehouses, where use determined sanitarily sheer walls and a generally simple effect. As the modern home, now a functioning machine for pleasant housekeeping, becomes more efficient, the machine-idioms of simple lines and clean surfaces creep also into expressive-functional house-design: where, in the Eclectic era, planning began with choice of the Spanish style or the Italian, or English-cottage or Dutch Colonial. In the later examples the richness and ease of living are expressed also in a greater colorfulness, reposefulness and terraced openness.

< 381 >

Functional Houses, by Edward Stone and Donald Deskey, at Mt. Kisco, New York (above); and **Walter Gropius**, at Stuttgart, Germany (below).

Let no one suppose, incidentally, that the true Expressionist will own the current "Century of Progress" Exposition in Chicago as other than a travesty on Modernist architecture. It illustrates practically every violation of creative-expressive principles: every fault of the old Eclectic architecture except the return to borrowed antiquarian surface-motifs. It utterly lacks unity, an organic creative relatedness. The surface forms, instead of growing out of structural methods, material and uses, are in general borrowings from the outward "effects" of recent European exposition buildings. The collection as a whole is a perfect example of the imitative designer's failure to attain to the spirit of creative Modernism. The Exposition, of course, was "done" by Eclectics, who thought they were being creatively Modern because they incorporated the surface idioms of some "early Modern" buildings, as easily as they had previously borrowed Greek, Gothic or Renaissance façades. Expressionism goes deeper than that. It must be organic. It must be expressive. It must be from within.

Of the Moderns who express, over and above those other formal values, a deeply creative personality, the foremost is Frank Lloyd Wright. Through nearly forty years Wright has used the materials of architecture in expressions unmistakably original, compelling and rich. Almost invariably the building can be recognized as Wright's; and yet Wright has no recognizable "style"—because he varies his creative touch with the conditions of materials, use, site, and owner-personality. I am illustrating two of Wright's creations, to suggest that Modernism can be varied in effect, even while true to its own materials and the times. Wright has said that the problem is not to create a "modern style," but to put style into whatever you design—varied by the conditioning purpose of the building, structural characteristics, etc.

< 383 >

Attempts have been made to define a typical style of the machine-age, especially as something termed "the International Style." But only up to a point is this a possibility: the new materials afford certain typical outward effects, and contemporary machined life dictates a frank simplification, a cleanness of aspect—and an openness. It might be argued—regarding the "open" aspect—that architecture has marched fairly straight from dugout, windowless temple and fortress to the openness possible with steel-and-concrete frame and movable glass areas. But no matter how these fundamentals may dictate the negative change of abandoning ancient stylistic detail, and the positive one of building on a frankly age-of-steel framework, the fact remains that the final determining element, the subjective-creative emotional contribution of the architect, is only slightly expressed as yet. In other words, the world has recognized the theory and early basic manifestations of an Expressionist art of building, but the larger part of the creative outpouring, even the fixing of idiomatic enrichment and accent, is yet to come. Masters have been among us already, Wright, Hoffmann, Mies van der Rohe, and a very few others, but the practice is only a beginning of the flowering we shall see in the second half of the 20th Century.

If there is in architecture an analogue to the newly-stated expressive-formal theory of painting—the theory of plastic orchestration—it is to be found in the talk about the "space conception" of the building art. That space enclosed, space used, and spatial proportions are nearer basic than wall-building—even the pioneer Modernists were too thoughtful of walls, perhaps—might be considered the beginning point of a new architectural philosophy: developed first by Wright in his notably "open" buildings, and expressed in varying forms by Oud, Gropius, Mies van der Rohe,

< 384 >

Falling Water House, Bear Run, Pennsylvania, by Frank Lloyd Wright. (By courtesy of Edgar J. Kaufmann, Jr., and the Museum of Modern Art, New York.)

Dudok, Le Corbusier, Kiesler, Neutra, and Geddes. After the façade-adapting during the centuries of Renaissance theorizing and neo-historic practice, this conception of spatial design, of plastic-organic parts, and of machine-efficient functioning, comes as a revolutionary basis, for an epochally new expressive architecture. The crag-like skyscrapers of New York, the functional houses of Ger-

< 385 >

man suburbs, the Soviet factories, the schools of progressive Dutch towns, and the houses by Wright in Illinois and California, are examples, variously creative, of that expressiveness—and by that token truly Expressionistic.

THE DANCE: BALLET, DUNCAN, WIGMAN

In the dance again, there is the perfect parallel: an art expressive in historic times, but brought within strict imitative limitations in the 18th-19th Centuries; then a revolutionary figure appearing, followed immediately by other innovators, challenging conventional practice and orthodox theory, and initiating an epochally different —and richly expressive—manifestation.

The ballet is the immediate background: a type of dance bound up in a strict code of technical regulations, designed exclusively for a small class-audience, restricted to a minor place in another art, opera. Today it is difficult to realize that this court plaything, embedded in an operatic mélange, constituted all there was to the art of the dance, through several generations. Yet the literature of the subject will attest that there was no other dancing "art"—barring sporadic "folk" activity—through centuries.

The revolutionary practice initiated by Isadora Duncan, and then developed in many lands under an assortment of labels—the free dance, aesthetic dancing, abstract dance, etc.—is seen now as a parallel to the painting of Cezanne and the architecture of Sullivan and Wright. There is first the stripping from the art of old aims, old rules, and the accumulation of borrowed features. In this case Duncan swept out not only the tight-binding regulations about steps and patterning, but the tight-binding costume—a heritage from the masquerade-like court ballets. She liberated the body for self-expression, for expression of the prime instrument of the art. In

Head, by Wilhelm Lehmbruck.   (By courtesy of the Downtown Gallery, New York.)

another gesture she exactly paralleled the Expressionists of the pictorial art: she wrenched dancing free from its literary aims, from the story-telling which had been an inseparable part of the ballet.

In all of this Duncan was travelling the high road from imitationalism to Expressionism.   She is the pivotal figure, opening the world's eyes to the way in which an art had been narrowed till

< 387 >

opportunity for creativeness had been all but squeezed out of it; then offering examples of a free art, capitalizing anew the typical medium of expression, offering at the same time an outpouring of herself. With her the *self*-expression element was strong; the grasp of abstract-formal means more intuitive than studied. Her essays on the dance are full of references to nature as an inspiration, offering not ready-made patterns for interpretation, but a mystic urge to further personal revelation of rhythmic order. Duncan, like Cezanne and Sullivan, is ranged with those who seek a realization of unseen overtones, of a unity and a purpose beyond surface nature.

Some critics feel that Isadora failed to divest herself of the last vestiges of Impressionism, even of Romanticism. While granting her the position of the pioneer Secessionist from the rule-encumbered ballet, they think of her as only imperfectly expressive of a new abstract-formal understanding and a contemporary machine-age meaning. They point to the German "abstract" dancers as evidence of an advance beyond anything exhibited or forecast by her. The question is perhaps unimportant, at the point now reached by dance practice and dance criticism. Here there is, I believe, no such clarifying body of theory, on the instrumental side, as the theory of plastic design in the pictorial field. It is easy to mark the epochal shift into new ways of expression. But there are no landmarks, no generally accepted theoretical guide, no authority for ranking the several contributive figures.

All one can record confidently is that Duncan came at a time when the art had crystallized, that she turned the attention of the world to a different sort of dance, by the example of her own self-expression, and that she released new energies in countless directions: sometimes through frank imitators, sometimes by inspiring "schools"—Dalcroze, etc.—sometimes by galvanizing traditionally

< 388 >

Young Pegasus, by William Zorach.

trained troupes into richer expression, as in the offerings of Diag-
hileff's Russian Ballet, Pavlowa, and Fokine's groups. The
"spread" of her influence and inspiration were truly amazing;
though she herself may have failed to escape wholly from emotional-
interpretive limitations.

Certainly Mary Wigman carries her audience into a realm where
abstract-formal means count for more. Both dancers attained to
an organic unity, in this case a flow, a revealed rhythmic order.
One was subjective, expressed life as she felt it, perhaps a bit pic-
turesquely still; the other delights to sink herself in expression of

< 389 >

Seated Nude, by Aristide Maillol. (By courtesy of Pierre Matisse Gallery.)

abstractions—machine-age mathematical abstractions. She carries the dance one step farther from Realism, and she affords millions of people an aesthetic stimulus, in terms true to the dance art. She too is a great Expressionist, the greatest in the field today—as Isadora Duncan was in the pioneer days.

Expressive form in this art, as I have noted, has been but confusedly debated by the dancers and critics, and it remains for some future student to formulate the theory of dance Modernism, as helpfully as the new painting and architecture and theatre have been interpreted. But this much is easy to see: the art has returned, substantially, to intensified expressiveness of the means—movement and the human body—of the artist's emotion or understanding, and of life today.*

EXPRESSIONISM IN SCULPTURE

In reviewing the several arts, in this way, I find the revolutions so alike that I am at a loss for words not already overused. And indeed, when I arrive at scultpure, I know that again the revolution is to be explained in only one way: a return, essentially, to expression, from imitation. Again it is a threefold expressiveness that is attained, of the materials and methods particular to the art—resulting in unmistakably *sculptural* form; of a deeper order and structure in the object; and of the artist's feeling.

In this art there is a fairly well-defined theory of formal organization. It not only parallels the theory of plastic orchestration in painting; with allowances for the difference of materials in the two arts, it partakes of the same nature of plastic elements ordered in space. A theory first set forth by Adolph Hildebrand posits that

* Martha Graham, a rare artist and a creative leader in the art of the dance, has taken first place in the Modern tradition in this country, since this book was first written.

< 391 >

Camels: Early Chinese Sculptures. Richly expressive of a deeper "realization" of the object, and of the potentialities of the medium. (By courtesy of Richard E. Fuller and the Seattle Art Museum.)

a sculptural field is established by the farthest projections or total "relief" of the statue—establishing understood limits or a frame similar to that of the spatial field in painting—and that the sculptural order is created by manipulation of volume and plane with relation to this field. It remained for others to clarify this theory by reference to modern physical law: showing that relation of volume to volume, with felt tensions between axes, is the basic structural factor in the art. This is the art of related mass, of rhythmic-voluminous organization.

Linked with this theory of an instrumental unity, a plastic structure, is the insistence upon a return to essentially sculptural materials. All the early pioneers of Modernism denied validity to modelling as the method of the art, and demanded a return to stone-cutting. The first principles arise from the massiveness of the stone block, the resistance of the stone to the tool, and the glyptic process. The light painty effects possible to modelling belong, the Expressionists believe, to a minor branch of the art, not truly sculptural. They claim that nothing but confusion can result from transferring the modelled figure into stone. There are processes which fix the modelled volumes and planes appropriately—as terra cotta. The clay figure can also be built up with regard to an ultimate casting in metal—the effect of the metal surface being remembered at every step along the way. But the truest sculpture deals with stone, expresses stone-quality, is massive with the density and heaviness of this material. It is partly the return to stone as a conditioning factor that puts Expressionist sculpture into obvious accord with the Primitives of many nations, and with certain periods of Chinese and Egyptian art.

But while there is the usual background of Expressionist achievement, in the far past, the 17th-19th Centuries were even more

< 393 >

Bird, by Constantin Brancusi. An example of near-abstraction in **sculpture.**
(From copyright photo by F. S. Lincoln.)

innocent of creative figures here than in painting. Michael Angelo is the sole great Renaissance artist claimed by the Expressionists. After him there was ornamental and naturalistic and selectively Realistic sculpture. In the latter half of the 19th Century, Realism culminated in Rodin, the master-Impressionist. He fixed in clay or stone the arrested gesture, the picturesque pose, the fleeting natural aspect. He also played with light effects, by rippling or stippling his surfaces. A very few times he gave himself over to an expression beyond nature—but in general he is the great Realist.

After Impressionism, Maillol came, to bring back a forgotten largeness, and a sense of solid organizational order. Lehmbruck, however, was nearer to the type Expressionist: distorting nature for the sake of intensified sculptural expression, gaining a sense of fourth-dimensional order, pouring out his own feeling so unmistakably that his statues could never be mistaken for another's. He will rank, perhaps, as the greatest sculptor since Michael Angelo. But then one has to add that the expressive-stone quality is more intensively achieved in the work of Gill or Lachaise; and that Epstein reveals the hidden character of a sitter the more compellingly. William Zorach returns the art nearer to the architectural reposefulness of Maillol, seldom distorting the outward detail of nature, but always subordinating the "natural effect" to the search for sculptural order. In this country, in Germany and France, even in England—a land without a known sculptor in all its history up to 1920—there are creative young artists fired with a new vision of manifestations of order to be characteristically revealed by the sculptural process.

Thus another art, once upon a time expressive in the language of its own materials and methods, declined into Realism, was given up to photographic and lightly ornamental aims, with hardly a

< 395 >

Woman Looking Up, by Georg Kolbe.

trace of Expressionistic achievement through three centuries; but now is brought back to intensified expression, through a revived devotion to the medium, and a new understanding of formal order and art's expressive purpose.

EXPRESSION IN THE THEATRE

The story of the revolution in the theatre art is of another sort, in that the actual shift to Expressionistic practice has been delayed. Realism still rules the day-by-day stage, although the theory of the art has been utterly remade, and certain features of production have been obviously revolutionized.

In other words, the change from Realism to Expressionism is only partial or fragmentary. The reason may lie in the fact that the machinery of the art is very expensive—both the actual machinery of getting a play staged and an audience comfortably seated, and the business framework by which plays are bought, actors hired, rehearsals paid for, etc. In other words, the theatre is owned, administered, and exploited for a profit, by others than the artists concerned. The newly creative figure, the tangent thinker, the visionary prophet, tend to be excluded from the actual theatres. More practical progress has been made in "little theatres"—considered by the "regulars" unprofessional and negligible—than in the fully accredited and fully equipped commercial playhouses; and the two pioneer prophet-theorists of Modernism were all but exiled from the stages of their own time.

Despite the halting progress in actual production, the revolution in accepted theory is, I believe, as near complete as any radical could ask. Even the universities recognize that there is a theatre art, and offer courses of instruction that begin with a consideration

< 397 >

of the relationship of stage forms, settings, acting and play. In 1900 no college or school in the country took cognizance of an art of the theatre. Drama was considered, historically, as a minor branch of literature. Outside the respectable institutions of learning there were to be found a few schools of acting, considered rather "shady"; and a still more distant activity called "scene painting" could be learned by apprenticeship in a commercial studio—a studio that purveyed, usually, a sign-painter's notion of Realistically artistic play settings, to a businessman's order.

Nothing could better illustrate the utter change in theory, the return to a conception of the theatre art as a unity, an organic-expressive medium, than the correction of this separation. Today there are numberless schools of the theatre art, and the universities and colleges build laboratory-theatres, within which courses on the drama, acting and setting—and production—are secondary to a consideration of the stage art *as a whole*.

The separation of functions, of activities, was, of course, characteristic of the actual producing stages of forty years ago. The first great Expressionist rebel, Gordon Craig, cried out against the disunity of the theatre production of the Century-end. In a passage of an essay published in 1905—and since become as famous as Sullivan's dictum about architecture, "form must follow function"— Craig underscored this disunity as the one great weakness of the current production, and demanded that staging be given over to a new figure: the artist of the theatre—or the artist-director. It is largely through the entry of the *regisseur,* in the years since, that European and American stages have seen a return to theatrically expressive production, in examples numerous enough to warrant prediction of a typically Expressionistic stage-art in place of the present average Realism.

< 398 >

Setting for *Electra*, by Gordon Craig. An early landmark in the modern movement toward simplification and abandonment of the "picture" setting. (From *Towards a New Theatre*, by Edward Gordon Craig.)

Two drawings for productions, by Adolphe Appia. Above, formalized setting for Glück's *Iphigenia in Tauris;* below, a platform stage for *Orpheus.* (From *Adolphe Appia,* a portfolio privately printed in Zurich.)

Stanislavsky, Reinhardt, Jessner, Meyerhold, and a few other world-known figures, have brought back the lost unity, have restored the theatre to an expressive rôle, in terms natural to the theatre, and in a few cases they have turned the medium to the expression of typically machine-age social meanings. They capitalized the elements—largely lost in the Realistic era—of movement, color, light, with a new intensification out of modern mechanical invention. They brought production as a craft to a degree of theatrical effectiveness unknown in the Realistic centuries. Unfortunately they advanced without carrying with them playwrights of similar vision and mastery.

What we have essentially, today, is a new theatre without contemporary dramatists. Competent playwrights have been drafted to the commercial stage, to repeat the formulas of journalistic Realism. The great regisseurs have been driven, for adequately theatrical-poetic-expressive texts, to the Greeks and Shakespeare. They have achieved productions beautifully Expressionistic—except in contemporary-social meaning. The Russians alone, I believe, are offering, commonly, works in which the new formal unity is linked with an emotionally-significant content out of the life of today.

The theory of a theatric organism, in the nature of a flow, has been built up in the writings of a dozen artists, most notably perhaps by Craig, Appia, Evreinoff and Meyerhold. It remained for Roy Mitchell to sum up—in a book entitled *Creative Theatre*, which seems to me the best single work on the theory of the art—the importance of the artist-director in achieving the synthesis:

"Once we have recognized the miraculous power of the theatre to initiate, and have seen how such a recognition can bring order into the relation of its many parts, we have our first understanding of the function of an initiator who stands nearer to its mystery than

< 401 >

the playwright can and nearer than the actor himself. He is the director.

"Whatever we have achieved these last few years towards a finer ideal and better unified practice has been exactly in the measure of our recognition of the director as nearest the theatre's heart. He can be master of things a thousand playwrights have never troubled themselves to learn, and a hundred thousand actors have despised. We have had playwright's theatre and our miracle has been smothered in turgid debate. We have had actor's theatre and it has been killed by strife or diffused in shabby vanities. Not for a long time have we had director's theatre but we are getting it and at last we seem to be going somewhere. . . .

"This new director is an ordainer of volumes, of massive shapes, of spatial relation, of the cumulative power of motion, of swirl, of interlude, of farandole. He found the theatre doing appropriate things; already he has made it do vital things. I can fancy him making it do divine things."

While the achieving of the synthesis has been the first considera tion of the Moderns—all credos begin with attestation of the importance of the rhythmic organism, the theatric unity—it is possible to examine the parts separately for signs of advance. Contemporary playwriting, as I have implied, has failed to develop co-ordinately with the craft of production. There is no master-dramatist to be named.* There have been stirrings of new life—as in the experiments of the Expressionist playwrights of Germany and

* In early 1948, looking back over the theatre of the last fifteen years, I feel that the most heartening gain has been the emergence of Thornton Wilder as an Expressionist playwright. His plays *Our Town* and *The Skin of Our Teeth* are anti-realistic, creative and deeply significant. One other "new" playwright deserves mention: Tennessee Williams. For the rest, the little and college theatres have continued to make experimntal progress, while the professional theatre, whether on Broadway or "the road," has sunk to shameful depths of commercialism and infantilism. The American theatre is owned by those who have the taste of the realist, the sensationalist, the half-educated; to expect important progress before repertory theatres and other institutional playhouses are founded seems futile.

< 402 >

Two sketches for a production of *King Lear*, by Norman Bel Geddes.

America, Toller, Kaiser, Lawson, and a few others, and in the body of recent Russian social drama. But the directors and actors and designers still await the texts which should be the inspirational beginning-point for their organized presentations. Nor is there reason to pause over acting, for signs of revolutionary change. What is to be Modern acting will be recognized largely as a return from naturalistic representation to creative presentation: the actor no longer merely a variation of himself, as natural as your umbrella or your grocer, but expressing overtones of feeling, within the special beauty of words, movement, theatric flow.

In the one "department" of scene design, of physical stage background—or stage space made theatrically living—there has been complete revolution. The disappearance of the old detailed picture-setting, whether artificially painty or naturalistically photographic, is one of the easiest-marked phenomena of the Expressionist advance. The "scene" has been simplified, ordered, made beautiful, with a beauty that furthers the expressiveness of the total production. Not only the progressive theatres but the commercial have benefited immensely in this particular. The Realistic play, as well as the Modernistic experiment, is adequately "set." Craig was the pioneer instigator to this change, though Adolphe Appia had as early made designs which today are recognized as beautiful and prophetic. Both men wrote treatises which still stand among the few books indispensable to the student of the art.

But if scene has been reformed, made expressive in truly theatrical terms, that is perhaps merely incidental to the emergence of the craft of "production" as an organic, vitalizing process. The true Expressionist advance has been in the denial of the Realistic story, naturalistic acting, and romantic or naturalistic "scenery"— a negation of all the merely imitative elements—and the develop-

< 404 >

Stage Design by Louis Jouvet, for *Dr. Knock*. An example of the abandonment of picture background or "scenery" for organization of stage space.

ment, in one flow, under one visioning direction, of all the factors that make the play live theatrically.

If I summarize, in a few paragraphs, the parallels in two other arts, it is not because I am less convinced that they are moving forward in a revolutionary change, which can be marked as essentially Expressionistic. In the one—literature—the shifts have been more gradual and inconclusive than elsewhere, and the roots of anti-Realism are hidden much farther back, beyond the half-century range of study that tells the story of a new painting and a new

< 405 >

architecture; and it is a question of suggesting a few main lines of growth, or embarking upon explorations impossible within the compass of this summarizing chapter. In the case of the other art, music, I am frank to say that my knowledge is inadequate: that I will not undertake an exposition because I do not know. It happens that I have studied somewhat in every other art, even compositionally in a small way; but I have no such "inside" insight into music.

I feel that there are analogies between the thing we have been studying and the rising opposition to Impressionistic and other program music; and the continuing growth of Bach's popularity seems to me not unlike the emergence of El Greco as an Expressionist master, rich in formal-abstract realization. There are negative indications too: vociferous challenge of the coded laws, constant quarreling between conservatives and "wild" radicals, and—nearest to the painting case—a decrying of composition that leans heavily on the stimulus of ephemeral natural phenomena. This last leads us back to the constructive: instead of what is taken from nature, impressionistically or emotionally, a greater capitalization of formal values. With that so-brief paragraph, I will end all discussion of music.

If we try to test recent changes in literature by the Expressionist principles, we first run into the confusion of the division into poetry, fiction, etc. Perhaps poetry, by reason of being more rigidly ordered, is always Expressionist to some degree; whereas fiction leans more naturally to the Realistic. And yet in both divisions there is today a welter of experiment; and some critics would say that, on the one hand, there was a master-Modernist seventy years ago, in the figure of Whitman, while, on the other, the first great Expressionist novelist appears in a contemporary, Joyce.

< 406 >

Certain it is that in the art of poetry, which especially capitalizes formal-expressive elements, Whitman two generations ago challenged the academic rules and the orthodox "authorities"—a perfect parallel to Isadora Duncan denying the coded patterns of the ballet-masters, and setting out to express herself in free dance, or Sullivan striking off the shackles of neo-historic architectural practice. I believe that any study of Expressionism in literature would have to go back to Walt Whitman as the pioneer of expression in free verse, intensifying his emotions in new ways, distorting what had been known as normal verse forms, mystically enlarging the art. Of his followers the Imagists were most suggestive of the Expressionist painters: seeking a new concentrated, ordered movement, banishing the dead spots, achieving a typically modern precision and exactness. Their self-discipline to this end often resulted in self-consciousness, but I think no student can overlook them as furtherers of Expressionist-formal ideals. But it is necessary to add that the greatest Imagist lived and wrote and died before the name was invented: Emily Dickinson. She exhibited the directness and concentration and order, with a personal accent of her own, and, like Whitman, an independence from the rules of orthodox rhythm and rhyme; and over it all an imaginative and mystic attitude toward common things. I think there has been no such Expressionistic poet since; but there is an extraordinary range of experiment between her and the latest works of Kreymborg, Cummings, Pound, Sandburg, Jeffers, and H. D.

The fiction writers have advanced in a more oblique direction, perhaps because they move into verse the moment they obviously adopt a formal order as conditioning. The greater advance has been in the abandonment of surface recording of life for reproduction of the total "stream of consciousness"—and this is new, if

< 407 >

hardly more a Modern advance than are the dream pictures and somnambulistic reporting of the Sur-Realists. Joyce may well be the first important artist of a beginning Expressionist era, and certainly Virginia Woolf is breaking new trails. I think, though, that a crystallization of the actualities of the stream of consciousness is not enough; the attainment of a new ordered movement, a freshly expressive orchestration of the elements that go into the "story"— content, words considered sensuously as well as literally, musical rhythms and intervals, etc.—will be the larger part of the gain. In regard to words, one cannot overlook the experiments of Gertrude Stein, aiming at the attainment of abstract but emotionally compelling effects, by arrangement of these prime materials of the art outside their usual significance. It seems likely that a purely abstract literary art is a will-o'-the-wisp, because words came into existence as intellectual symbols for things and ideas. But so sincere an effort to widen their usefulness cannot but add grist to the mill of the literary composers.

In all of this we are studying efforts to widen expressiveness, within the limits of the medium particular to the art. In other words, we are tracing one more parallel to the Expressionism of the painters, who have abandoned imitativeness of older practitioners, and imitativeness of nature, to seek intensified *Expression.*

< 408 >

CONCLUSION

THAT the work of art shall *live* for me, with its own sort of vitality, is my deepest wish. There is a knowing about art, which is secondary, intellectual. Criticism too often concerns itself with developing a talent and a vocabulary for that knowing. It should lend itself rather to clearing the way to an immediate response, to a living with art. The justification for this book, if any, will lie in its efficacy in bringing the reader to the realization, the actual experience, of Modern works of art.

When I have talked to students about these matters, I have urged on them three injunctions, as protection against the critic's tendency to pose as an authority, to codify, and to intellectualize. It is well to warn the reader, in similar danger.

1. *Don't believe a word I say.* That is, unless you have come to the conclusion yourself, after I have afforded you a clue, or have cleared the way to seeing, don't accept the offered idea. Hold it open, pending further experiment, and personal experience. If I have said, "There is in the canvas a plastic organization, a mystic-rhythmic movement, which is more precious than any other formal element in the painting," don't believe me until you have experienced that beautiful hidden thing. If I have said, "Mankind is accomplishing an epochal revolution in ways of living, of which the revolution in art is an integral part," don't believe me—until you too can image the old world that is passing, the civilization dying, and the new world that is being born, with its changed patterns of living, institutions, philosophies, art. Accept my ideas here,

< 409 >

tentatively; for you will know by this time that I have studied into these matters, and that art has come to dwell in my everyday life with an unaccustomed immediacy, as constant enrichment of experience. But make your life a reflection of no man's thinking or teaching. Don't accept any interpreter as a permanent crutch. Be independent, even to that last childish confession, "I know what I like"—rather than like blindly what someone else knows.

2. *Strive for direct response, immediate experience.* Let the fact-finding mind be stilled. Don't intellectualize over Modern art except as preparation for feeling and enjoyment. For most people a period of self-conscious study and judgment is inevitable, due to early mis-education, as a means to dislodge prejudice and open the way to intuitive acceptance. But the objective is to free the vision, to prepare the eye and the inner faculties for the single response. While studying go continually to the works of art themselves, for the aesthetic experience. Better still, practice widely in the arts, not primarily for the works you will produce, but for broadened and intensified creative appreciation.*

3. *Accept art not as a refuge from life, but as an intensification of living.* As such, it will be related to man's environment and associations and spiritual discernment in this machine age. Go occasionally to the art of long ago and far away, not as escape from

---

* You might be surprised if one brought to your attention the multiplicity of ways in which art already enters creatively into your intimate life. If you are a woman, your personal "make-up," and dress, and the graces you cultivate in your housekeeping —laying the table, arranging harmonious furniture, etc.—are essentially arts. You may be practicing them with none but a Realistic-imitative intelligence, modelling your make-up and your dress on something seen shallowly, from the outside; or you may be creative, taking expression of your inmost self as the beginning point—Expressionistically. But I would advocate that you go farther, if only for the deeper insight it will afford you in regard to these intensely personal arts: I would have everyone draw and paint, practice in the handicrafts, and develop a basic sense of *design in living*, which will extend from the spiritual-creative center to every outward expression of personality.

< 410 >

City **of Lights,** by Umberto Romano. (By courtesy of the **Associated** American Artists Galleries, New York.)

existence as it is today, but because some artist, **far removed** in **time** or space, achieved expression that lives for us, when he recorded and revealed something of himself and of social living in his age, in universally valid plastic and mystic values. Modernist art offers a like creative experience, and one closer to our desires, because the artist reveals his emotions or imagination intensified through his feel for life in our times. This is the art that will be nearest to you if you are living fully.

Remember that true creative art has a vitality of its own, is a separate living thing in the world, offers, in the meeting with it, an experience different from any to be had from nature, or from the secondary, **imitative** art which affords the **illusion of** nature. To

< 411 >

find that experience continually is to lift living from the plane of commonplace reality to the plane of the reality of the Spirit.

As the artist is concerned with creation, expression—no longer with illusion, transfer, photography—so the beholder prepares himself for experience, aesthetic response, giving himself to art; not for judgment, thought or diversion. The appreciation of art becomes a spiritual rather than a mental activity. It seems to me that Expressionism returns art to livingness, to aesthetic evocation, to revealment of those values that feed the Spirit.

< 412 >

INDEX

Abstraction, 58, 82, 313, 317-, 362
Adams-Danysh Gallery, San Francisco, ix
Albinson, Dewey, 198
Allen, Mary-Cecil, 72
Appia, Adolphe, 85, 400, 404
Architecture, 39, 320, 374-
Armfield, Maxwell, 134
Art, *Definition*, 49, 55
Art History, 23, 26
Art Institute, Chicago, ix
Arthur, Revington, 344
Austin, Darrel, 51

Bard, Phil, 366, 367
Barnes, Albert C, ix, 48, 111, 113, 329
Barnes, Matthew, 7, 62, 121
Barye, 37
Beckmann, Max, 2, 29, 123, 231
Bell, Clive, vii, 48, 97, 110, 113
Bellows, George, 101, 221
Benton, Thomas, 186, 241, 296
Bergson, Henri, 48
Besnard, Albert, 294
Biddle, George, 355
Binyon, Laurence, 122, 124, 332
Blake, Vernon, 124, 170
Blaue Reiter Group, 76
Bonnard, Pierre, 309
Booth, Cameron, 133
Braque, Georges, 94, 177
Bragdon, Claude, 329
Brancusi, Constantin, 394
Brücke, Die, 76
Bulliet, C. J., 72
Burck, Jacob, 288, 346
Burnet, John, 233

California Palace of the Legion of Honor, ix
Callahan, Kenneth, 326
Campendonk, Heinrich, 139, 187
Candler, Martha, x

Carroll, John, 103
Cezanne, Paul, 10, 14, 29, 36, 37, 53, 66, 69, 85, 90, 95, 99, 110, 111, 116, 132, 139, 141, 146, 158, 167, 175, 183-, 197, 217, 225-, 243, 250, 251, 254, 264, 353
Chauvannes, Puvis de, 291, 293
Cheney, Warren, ix
Chiaroscuro, 232
Chinese Art, 107, 108, 122, 125, 174, 392
Chirico, Giorgio di, 345
Classicism, 31
Color, 175, 183, 243-, 254-, 262
Communist Art, 63, 359
Composition, 115-, 142, 225, 228
Courbet, Gustave, 218
Cox, Kenyon, 233
Craig, Gordon, 42, 85, 398, 399
Craven, Thomas, 61, 67, 97, 102, 226, 334
Croce, Benedetto, 45-, 48
Cubism, 71, 82, 92, 95, 151, 176, 179-, 227, 337
"Curtain Theory," 276-

Daddi, Bernardo, 180, 181
Dance, The, 42, 85, 320, 386-
Dasburg, Andrew, 151
Daumier, Honoré, 28, 38, 118, 140, 165, 215
David, 32
Davidson, Morris, 113
Davies, A. B., 248, 336
Decorative Painting, 273-, 289-, 298-
Degas, Edgar, 138
Del, 371
Delacroix, 30, 32
Derain, André, 68
Deskey, Donald, 382
Dove, Arthur G., 329
Dow, Arthur W., 116
Dreier, Katherine S., 339
Downtown Gallery, New York City, ix
Duncan, Isadora, 42, 85, 386-
Duccio, 273
Dynamic Symmetry, 159, 223

< 413 >

El Greco, *Frontispiece*, 13, 24, 26, 91, 96, 99, 107, 116, 122, 139, 143, 153, 154, 162, 166, 172, 173, 205, 208, 220, 221, 235, 261, 281, 284, 406
Evergood, Philip, 352
Expressionism, viii, 8, 11, 15, 52-, 69-, 75-, 84-, 257, 262, 274, 292, 310, 318-, 362, 374, 391-, 397-, 408

Feeling, 347-, 369-
Florentine Salver, 301
Forain, Jean Louis, 202
Form, 73, 97-, 163, 199, 212, 391-
Fortess, Karl, 342
Fresnaye, Roger de la, 255
Futurism, 65, 70, 193

Gallatin, A. E., ix, 337
Gardner, Helen, 72
Gaudier-Brzeska, Henri, 85
Gauguin, Paul, 36, 95, 242, 274, 275, 280, 285, 287, 303, 304
Geddes, Norman Bel, 380, 403
Gellert, Hugo, 371
Giorgione, 172
Gill, Eric, 395
Giotto, 107, 122, 148, 149, 181, 205, 208, 266, 276, 277, 296, 297, 310
Giusto, Andrea di, 147
Gleizes, Albert, ix, 132, 160, 176
Gorelick, Boris, 370
Graham, Martha, 391
Greenwood, Marion, 365
Gromaire, Marcel, 150
Gropius, Walter, 382
Gropper, William, 364, 371

Hambidge, Jay, 115-, 224
Heckel, Erich, 75
Helion, Jean, 337, 338
Hildebrand, Adolph, 176, 273, 391
Hodler, Ferdinand, 76
Hofmann, Hans, ix, 113, 156, 159, 160, 176, 186, 212

Impressionism, 34, 76, 257
Ikons, 301

Johnson, Eastman, 33
Jonson, Raymond, 312, 315, 319
Jouvet, Louis, 406

Kandinsky, Vasily, 66, 75, 78, 92, 93, 139, 149, 155, 176, 199, 205, 222, 330, 335

Kantor, Morris, 259
Karfiol, Bernard, 228, 230, 232
Kaus, Max, 237
Kirschner, Ludwig E., 75
Kiesler, Frederic, 385
Klee, Paul, 41, 66, 75, 307, 345
Kleinholz, Frank, 127
Knaths, Karl, 71
Kolbe, George, 396
Kokoschka, Oskar, 2, 193
Kopman, Ben, 357
Kuniyoshi, Yasuo, 105
Kuhn, Walt, 240

Lachaise, Gaston, 395
Laurencin, Marie, 307, 308
Leger, Fernand, 179
Lehmbruck, Wilhelm, 29, 39, 387, 395
Lewisohn, Adolph, ix
Literature, 318, 406

Maillol, Aristide, 390, 395
Marc, Franz, 83, 207, 208
Margules, de Hirsch, 225
Marin, John, vii, 13, 35, 59, 66, 79, 131, 139, 191, 192
Martini, Joseph de, 19, 171
Mather, Frank Jewett, 72, 104
Matisse, Henri, 66, 95, 137, 205, 246-, 265, 268, 274, 303
Matisse, Pierre, ix
Mattson, Henry, 200
Meaning, 347-, 353-, 369-
Metropolitan Museum, New York, ix
Mitchell, Roy, 401
Modernism, 12, 20, 27, 45, 57, 64, 66, 69, 381
Modersohn-Becker, Paula, 238
Modigliani, Amadeo, 74
Moholy-Nagy, 337
Movement in the Canvas, 58, 120-, 130-, 136-, 189-, 212-, 214-
Munch, Edvard, 75, 76
Mural Painting, 289-
Museum of Modern Art, New York, ix
Museums, 20-23
Music, 318, 320
Mystic Element, 100, 117, 315-, 321-, 331

Naturalism, 29, 64, 70
Neumann, J. B., ix, 76, 89
New Objectivism, The, 66
News Building, New York, 372
Nolde, Emil, 75

< 414 >

O'Keeffe, Georgia, 169, 209, 210, 340, 341
Oriental Painting, 298-
Orozco, José Clemente, 188, 216, 292, 363, 369
Osver, Arthur, 322

Pascin, Jules, 189, 190, 191
Pearson, Ralph, 191
Pechstein, Max, 75
Perspective, 168
Pfister, Dr. Oskar, 77-
Phillips, Duncan, 83
Picasso, Pablo, 66, 91, 139, 181, 182, 267, 331, 333, 336
Pietro, Sano di, 260
Plane, Focal, 278-
Plane, Picture, 86, 132, 134, 278, 283
Plane, Surface, 132, 201
Planes, 163, 175, 177, 182, 184, 189, 196, 199, 205, 274-
Planetary Movement, 203
Poore, H. Rankin, 115, 126
Plastic, *Definition*, 130, 393
Plastic Organization, 58, 61, 104, 121, 130, 143, 163-, 170, 195, 223, 228, 244, 276, 278, 307, 310, 311, 321, 384
Post-Impressionism, 70
Poussin, Nicholas, 196, 197
Proportion, 223
Purism, 72, 254

Raphael, 116, 224
Read, Herbert, 48, 106, 113
Realism, 14, 29, 30, 31, 64, 69, 76, 82, 92, 327
Rembrandt, 232, 233, 234, 270
Rivera, Diego, 16, 286, 290, 358, 369, 370
Robinson, Boardman, 43
Rodin, August, 39
Roerich, Nicholas, 149, 159, 335
Romano, Umberto, 411
Romanticism, 31, 64
Ross, Denman, 115
Rouault, Georges, 44, 65, 66, 139, 145, 191, 193, 206, 208, 209, 230
Rousseau, Henri, 88, 95, 261, 274, 283, 305-
Ryder, Albert, 114, 157, 219, 351

Saint Gaudens, Augustus, 37
Santos, 295, 300, 302
Schmidt-Rotluff, Karl, 75, 139, 193
Sculpture, 391-
Seurat, Georges, 95, 149, 152, 154, 191, 193, 194, 195, 206

Schaeffer, Rudolph, 256
Sheridan, Joseph, ix, 158, 263, 264, 330, 331, 342
Siporin, Mitchell, 360, 368
Siqueiros, David, 369
Social Significance, 63, 353
Stieglitz, Alfred, vii
Stein, Leo, 46, 48
Sterne, Maurice, 167
Stone, Edward, 382
Strindberg, August, 75
Structure, 243
Subject, 348-
Sullivan, Louis, 14, 29, 40, 69, 375
Sur-Realism, 65, 342-
Synchromism, 257-
Sweeney, James Johnson, 337

Tensions, 58, 142-, 177, 183, 211, 231, 236
Texture, 58, 175, 237, 246-, 264-
Theatre, 85, 397-
Theotokopulos, *see* El Greco
Tintoretto, 107, 172, 206, 213
Troward, Thomas, 330, 332

van Gogh, Vincent, 36, 66, 76, 85, 87, 95, 249, 279
Vaughan, Keith, 342
Vlaminck, Maurice de, 47
Volume, 154, 163, 175, 182, 201-, 211, 227, 231, 236, 275
Volume-space organization, 58, 203-, 214-, 227-, 230, 235, 250
von Marées, Hans, 76, 302
von Sydow, Eckart, 76
Vytlacil, Vaclav, 160

Walden, Herwarth, 76
Walkowitz, Abraham, 239
Weber, Max, 229
Wessels, Glen, ix, 129, 135, 151, 176, 186, 204, 214
Weyhe Gallery, New York City, ix
Whistler, James McNeill, 302
Wigman, Mary, 42, 389
Wilder, Thornton, 402
Wilenski, R. H., vii, 48, 72, 113
Williams, Tennessee, 402
Wright, Frank Lloyd, 41, 375, 377, 381, 383, 385
Wright, Willard Huntington, 257-8

Zorach, Marguerite, 230, 233
Zorach, William, 54, 389, 395

< 415 >

TABLE 2 SQUARES AND SQUARE ROOTS

n	n²	√n	√10n	n	n²	√n	√10n
1	1	1.000	3.162	51	2601	7.141	22.583
2	4	1.414	4.472	52	2704	7.211	22.804
3	9	1.732	5.477	53	2809	7.280	23.022
4	16	2.000	6.325	54	2916	7.348	23.238
5	25	2.236	7.071	55	3025	7.416	23.452
6	36	2.449	7.746	56	3136	7.483	23.664
7	49	2.646	8.367	57	3249	7.550	23.875
8	64	2.828	8.944	58	3364	7.616	24.083
9	81	3.000	9.487	59	3481	7.681	24.290
10	100	3.162	10.000	60	3600	7.746	24.495
11	121	3.317	10.488	61	3721	7.810	24.698
12	144	3.464	10.954	62	3844	7.874	24.900
13	169	3.606	11.402	63	3969	7.937	25.100
14	196	3.742	11.832	64	4096	8.000	25.298
15	225	3.873	12.247	65	4225	8.062	25.495
16	256	4.000	12.649	66	4356	8.124	25.690
17	289	4.123	13.038	67	4489	8.185	25.884
18	324	4.243	13.416	68	4624	8.246	26.077
19	361	4.359	13.784	69	4761	8.307	26.268
20	400	4.472	14.142	70	4900	8.367	26.458
21	441	4.583	14.491	71	5041	8.426	26.646
22	484	4.690	14.832	72	5184	8.485	26.833
23	529	4.796	15.166	73	5329	8.544	27.019
24	576	4.899	15.492	74	5476	8.602	27.203
25	625	5.000	15.811	75	5625	8.660	27.386
26	676	5.099	16.125	76	5776	8.718	27.568
27	729	5.196	16.432	77	5929	8.775	27.749
28	784	5.292	16.733	78	6084	8.832	27.928
29	841	5.385	17.029	79	6241	8.888	28.107
30	900	5.477	17.321	80	6400	8.944	28.284
31	961	5.568	17.607	81	6561	9.000	28.460
32	1024	5.657	17.889	82	6724	9.055	28.636
33	1089	5.745	18.166	83	6889	9.110	28.810
34	1156	5.831	18.439	84	7056	9.165	28.983
35	1225	5.916	18.708	85	7225	9.220	29.155
36	1296	6.000	18.974	86	7396	9.274	29.326
37	1369	6.083	19.235	87	7569	9.327	29.496
38	1444	6.164	19.494	88	7744	9.381	29.665
39	1521	6.245	19.748	89	7921	9.434	29.833
40	1600	6.325	20.000	90	8100	9.487	30.000
41	1681	6.403	20.248	91	8281	9.539	30.166
42	1764	6.481	20.494	92	8464	9.592	30.332
43	1849	6.557	20.736	93	8649	9.644	30.496
44	1936	6.633	20.976	94	8836	9.695	30.659
45	2025	6.708	21.213	95	9025	9.747	30.822
46	2116	6.782	21.448	96	9216	9.798	30.984
47	2209	6.856	21.679	97	9409	9.849	31.145
48	2304	6.928	21.909	98	9604	9.899	31.305
49	2401	7.000	22.136	99	9801	9.950	31.464
50	2500	7.071	22.361	100	10000	10.000	31.623

Beginning Algebra

Fourth Edition

Margaret L. Lial

Charles D. Miller
American River College

Scott, Foresman and Company

Glenview, Illinois

Dallas, Texas
Oakland, New Jersey
Palo Alto, California
Tucker, Georgia
London, England

To the Student

The *Study Guide: Beginning Algebra,* Fourth Edition, and the *Student Solutions Manual* are available from your local college bookstore. These books can help you study and review the course material.

Photo Acknowledgments

Cover: *Totem,* 1981, by McCrystle Wood. Collection of Deloitte, Haskins & Sells, Cincinnati. © McCrystle Wood.

1, 306, Scott, Foresman & Co. staff; 52, 109, Jean-Claude Lejeune; 148, NASA; 187, Bohdan Hrynewych/Southern Light; 229, André Sima/NFB Photothèque; 273, U.S. Air Force Photo; 341, Ray Jenkins/Stockphotos, Inc.

Library of Congress Cataloging in Publication Data

Lial, Margaret L.
    Beginning algebra.

    Includes index.
    1. Algebra. I. Miller, Charles David.
II. Title.
QA152.2.L5   1984   512.9   83-14042
ISBN 0-673-15890-X

3 4 5 6-RRC-89 88 87 86 85 84

Preface

Ever since the first edition of *Beginning Algebra,* we have tried to produce a book that is both *useful* to the student and *helpful* for the instructor. For the student, we have written a book with explanations and examples that are clear, direct, and to the point. The exercise sets are carefully graded in difficulty, with examples corresponding to exercises. For the instructor, we have produced a complete instructional package. The text is carefully laid out to match standard courses, with the sections including only what an instructor would normally expect to find in each section. The supplemental package offers those items we have found useful in our own classes: tests, complete solutions to 75 percent of the exercises, additional exercises keyed to objectives, a *Study Guide,* audiotapes, and videotapes.

KEY FEATURES

Word Problems   A problem-solving approach gives students early and repeated experience in solving applied problems. A list of steps for solving word problems is first presented in Chapter 2, yet even Chapter 1 has some simple word problems. Throughout the text students are given practice translating English words into algebraic symbols. In this way, students see word problems early and gradually improve their problem-solving skills.

Examples   More than 350 worked-out examples clearly illustrate concepts and techniques. Second color is used to identify pertinent steps within examples, as well as to highlight explanatory side comments.

Keyed Objectives   Each section opens with a list of skills that students should learn in that section. These objectives are keyed to the appropriate portions of each section with symbols such as ▮ or ▯.

Graded Exercises The range of difficulty in the exercise sets affords students ample practice with drill problems. Then they are eased gradually through problems of increasing difficulty to problems that will challenge outstanding students. More than 4000 drill exercises and 300 word problems, keyed to examples, are included.

Calculator Exercises Calculator exercises have been included throughout the book. These optional exercises are identified with the symbol ▦.

Review Exercises Beginning in Chapter 2, most exercise sets end with a few problems that help prepare students for the following section. For example, at the end of the section preceding the discussion of solving quadratic equations by factoring, students review the solution of equations such as $2x + 3 = 0$.

Chapter Review Exercises Extensive review exercises at the end of each chapter, nearly 650 in all, provide further opportunity for mastery of the material before students take an examination. These exercises are keyed to appropriate sections in the text.

Chapter Tests Sample tests, of a length comparable to that of actual classroom tests, have been made somewhat more difficult in this edition of the book. More than 250 test questions give additional practice to students.

Second color is used pedagogically in the following ways.
- Screens set off key definitions, formulas, and procedures, helping students review.
- Color side comments within examples explain the structure of the problem.
- For clarity, the end of each example is indicated with a color symbol, ●.
- Warnings about common student errors are included in color when appropriate.

Beginning Algebra, Fourth Edition, has an extensive supplemental package that includes testing materials, solutions, and electronic media.

The **Instructor's Guide** features five tests for each chapter. One version is a multiple-choice test. In addition to the chapter tests, two forms of a final examination are given, as well as a diagnostic pretest. Answers to all tests are provided in columns that can be lined up with the answer blanks of the student tests. Answers to even-numbered exercises in the text are given in this guide.

Additional Exercises, keyed to objectives, are also available. Ten to 20 exercises for each objective in the book help students review exactly where their difficulties are.

A **Solutions Manual,** featuring complete solutions to all even-numbered exercises, is available to adopters.

A **Student Solutions Manual** has solutions to one half of the odd-numbered exercises in the text. Some students use this volume as an additional source of examples.

A **Study Guide,** in a semiprogrammed format, provides additional practice and reinforcement for students.

Professional-quality **videotapes** are available at low cost to users of this text. The tapes amplify the ideas in the book that cause students the most difficulty.

Audiotapes that cover all topics in the text are available at no charge to users of the book. Students who need help with a particular topic or who have missed class find these tapes help them master the material.

We thank the many users of the previous editions of this book who were kind enough to share their experiences with us. This revision has benefited from their comments and suggestions. (See the list of acknowledgments that follows this Preface.)

We also thank the people who reviewed all or part of the revised manuscript and gave us many helpful suggestions: Ron Beeler, East Central College; Arthur Dull, Diablo Valley College; K. Elayn Gay, University of New Orleans; John H. Gray, University of North Alabama; George Grisham, Illinois Central College; Daniel A. Hogan, Hinds Junior College; Myrna L. Mitchell, Pima Community College; William C. Monnin, University of Southwestern Louisiana; John Monroe, University of Akron; David W. Sicks, Olympic College; Mary Jo Steig, Mesa Community College; George T. Wales, Ferris State College; Hettie M. Williams, Broward Community College; and Cynthia Yang, Miami University.

Our appreciation also goes to the staff at Scott, Foresman and Company, who did an excellent job in working with us toward publication.

Margaret L. Lial
Charles D. Miller

ACKNOWLEDGMENTS

Lynda L. Allen, *Hinds Junior College*

Robert B. Ambrose, *Methodist College*

Roger A. Avelsgaard, *Bemidji State University*

Chris Avery, *De Anza College*

Ronald G. Bates, *Hartnell College*

Charles M. Beals, *Hartnell College*

Oscar Beck, *University of North Alabama*

Charles D. Bedal, *Maricopa Technical Community College*

C. Leary Bell, *Columbus College*

David J. Bender, *Green River Community College*

Carole Bergen, *Mercy College*

Dale E. Boye, *Schoolcraft College*

Brent A. Bradberry, *National University*

Frank Caldwell, *York Technical College*

Thomas Calhoun, *Southwest Mississippi Junior College*

Robert Coombs, *Santa Rosa Junior College*

Norman Edward Coulson, *National University*

William D. Crim, *Penn Valley Community College*

Elwyn D. Cutler, *Ferris State College*

Ronald L. Dabbs, *Mitchell Community College*

George DeMers, *Modesto Junior College*

Tony DiJulio, *Ohlone College*

Larry Dilley, *Central Missouri State University*

Patsy Dinkins, *Pitt Community College*

Sandy Eastway, *Alpena Community College*

Louis M. Edwards, *Valencia Community College*

Robert Eicken, *Illinois Central College*

Merritt Elmore, *San Jose City College*

Michael S. Emerick, *Parkland College*

George A. Emerson, *National University*

Harriett E. Emery, *Schoolcraft College*

Lee E. Evinger, *Missouri Western State College*

Dorothy Fisher, *Casper College*

Donna Foss, *University of Central Arkansas*

Patricia A. Frantz, *Community College of Delaware County*

Brian Garman, *University of Tampa*

Elayn Gay, *University of New Orleans*

Mary E. Graham, *Skyline College*

John H. Gray, *University of North Alabama*

George Grisham, *Illinois Central College*

R. G. Hammond, *Utah State University*

Stuart Hansen, *University of Wisconsin–Stevens Point*

Sammye Sue Harrill, *University of Central Arkansas*

William N. Harter, *San Diego Mesa College*

Larry Hayman, *Mount San Antonio College*

Fried Heyn, *Orange Coast College*

Daniel A. Hogan, *Hinds Junior College*

Teresa Huether, *St. Louis Community College at Florissant Valley*

Marcia K. James, *Pitt Community College*

P. A. Jenkins, *South Carolina State College*

John Kennedy, *Santa Monica College*

Charles L. Kerner, Jr., *Community College of Delaware County*

Georgianna T. Klein, *Grand Valley State College*

Dorothy E. Koniges, *San Diego Mesa College*

Cony M. Lau, *Saginaw Valley State College*

Phung Lecong, *San Diego Mesa College*

Louise M. Lewald, *State Technical Institute of Knoxville*

Fred Lyon, *National University*

Robert L. McDonald, *Columbia College*

Jimmie J. McKim, *University of Central Arkansas*

Philip Metz, *Passaic County Community College*

Myrna L. Mitchell, *Pima Community College*

Ann Moskol, *Rhode Island College*

Susan C. Myers, *Sinclair Community College*

Norma Neal, *Arkansas State University*

Eleanor H. Ninestein, *Fayetteville Technical Institute*

Michael Ortell, *Orange Coast College*

Henry J. Osner, *Modesto Junior College*

Don Paulson, *Mesa Community College*

Treva Payne, *Casper College*

David R. Peterson, *University of Central Arkansas*

Richard L. Reese, *Pensacola Junior College*

Ruby E. Reeves, *York Technical College*

Constance L. Rhem, *Pitt Community College*

Doug Richey, *Henderson County Junior College*

Lavar Rigby, *Ventura College*

Elaine B. Roberts, *York Technical College*
William H. Robinson, *Ventura College*
Patricia Roden, *University of North Alabama*
John M. Samoylo, *Community College of Delaware County*
Sam Sargis, *Modesto Junior College*
Alan L. Sawyer, *Orange Coast College*
Leo H. Schmitz, *Missouri Western State College*
Ernest L. Smith, *Sayre Junior College*
Gaston Smith, *William Carey College*
Jo Karen Smith, *Arkansas State University*
John Snyder, *Sinclair Community College*
Edwin M. Specht, *San Diego Mesa College*
Ronald Staszkow, *Ohlone College*
Mary Jo Steig, *Mesa Community College*
Amber Steinmetz, *Santa Rosa Junior College*
Umesh Swami, *South Carolina State College*

Jim Swink, *Southwest Texas Junior College*
G. A. Tagliarini, *Montreat–Anderson College*
Virginia Tebelskis, *Ohlone College*
Barbara L. Thacker, *Southwest Virginia Community College*
George T. Wales, *Ferris State College*
Andrew L. Walker, *North Seattle Community College*
Lary Wasserman, *Passaic County Community College*
David Wettstein, *Olympic College*
Jerry M. Wilkerson, *Missouri Western State College*
Ronald Wisdom, *Arkansas State University*
Jack Woy, *Fullerton College*
Eleanor Young, *Community College of Delaware County*
Rich Yurman, *Skyline College*

Contents

1

Number Systems

1

1.1 Fractions *1*
1.2 Symbols *7*
1.3 Exponents and Order of Operations *9*
1.4 Variables and Equations *14*
1.5 Real Numbers and the Number Line *19*
1.6 Addition of Real Numbers *25*
1.7 Subtraction of Real Numbers *30*
1.8 Multiplication of Real Numbers *33*
1.9 Division of Real Numbers *38*
1.10 Properties of Addition and Multiplication *42*

Chapter 1 Review Exercises *48*
Chapter 1 Test *50*

2

Solving Equations and Inequalities

52

2.1 Simplifying Expressions *52*
2.2 The Addition Property of Equality *56*
2.3 The Multiplication Property of Equality *60*
2.4 Solving Linear Equations *65*
2.5 Word Problems *71*
2.6 Ratios and Proportions *80*
2.7 Further Word Problems (Optional) *84*
2.8 The Addition Property of Inequality *92*
2.9 The Multiplication Property of Inequality *97*

Chapter 2 Review Exercises *104*
Chapter 2 Test *107*

3

Exponents and Polynomials

3.1 Exponents *109*

3.2 Further Rules for Exponents *115*

3.3 An Application of Exponents: Scientific Notation *119*

3.4 Polynomials *122*

3.5 Multiplication of Polynomials *129*

3.6 Products of Binomials *132*

3.7 Dividing a Polynomial by a Monomial *137*

3.8 The Quotient of Two Polynomials *141*

Chapter 3 Review Exercises *145*

Chapter 3 Test *146*

4

Factoring and Applications

4.1 Factors; The Greatest Common Factor *148*

4.2 Factoring Trinomials *154*

4.3 More on Factoring Trinomials *158*

4.4 Special Factorizations *163*

Miscellaneous Factoring Exercises *167*

4.5 Solving Quadratic Equations *169*

4.6 Applications of Quadratic Equations *174*

4.7 Solving Quadratic Inequalities (Optional) *181*

Chapter 4 Review Exercises *184*

Chapter 4 Test *186*

5

Rational Expressions

5.1 The Fundamental Property of Rational Expressions *187*

5.2 Multiplication and Division of Rational Expressions *192*

5.3 The Least Common Denominator *196*

5.4 Addition and Subtraction of Rational Expressions *200*

5.5 Complex Fractions *205*

5.6 Equations Involving Rational Expressions *210*

Miscellaneous Exercises *216*

5.7 Applications of Rational Expressions *217*

Chapter 5 Review Exercises *225*

Chapter 5 Test *227*

6

Graphing Linear Equations
229

6.1 Linear Equations in Two Variables *229*

6.2 Graphing Linear Equations *237*

6.3 The Slope of a Line *246*

6.4 The Equation of a Line *252*

6.5 Graphing Linear Inequalities *258*

6.6 Functions *264*

Chapter 6 Review Exercises *269*

Chapter 6 Test *271*

7

Linear Systems
273

7.1 Solving Systems of Linear Equations by Graphing *273*

7.2 Solving Systems of Linear Equations by Addition *279*

7.3 Solving Systems of Linear Equations by Substitution *286*

7.4 Applications of Linear Systems *291*

7.5 Solving Systems of Linear Inequalities *299*

Chapter 7 Review Exercises *302*

Chapter 7 Test *304*

8

Roots and Radicals 306

8.1 Finding Roots *306*
8.2 Products and Quotients of Radicals *312*
8.3 Rationalizing the Denominator *316*
8.4 Addition and Subtraction of Radicals *320*
8.5 Simplifying Radicals *322*
8.6 Equations with Radicals *327*
8.7 Fractional Exponents *333*

Chapter 8 Review Exercises *337*
Chapter 8 Test *339*

9

Quadratic Equations 341

9.1 Solving Quadratic Equations by the Square Root Method *341*
9.2 Solving Quadratic Equations by Completing the Square *344*
9.3 Solving Quadratic Equations by the Quadratic Formula *349*
Miscellaneous Quadratic Equations *355*
9.4 Complex Solutions of Quadratic Equations *356*
9.5 Graphing Quadratic Equations *360*

Chapter 9 Review Exercises *366*
Chapter 9 Test *368*

Appendices 369

Appendix A Review of Decimals and Percents *369*
Appendix B Sets *372*
Appendix C The Metric System *374*

Answers to Selected Exercises *376*

Index *402*

Number Systems

These carpenters are using a ruler, which is based on the same idea as a number line.

1.1 Fractions

1. Write fractions in lowest terms.
2. Multiply fractions.
3. Divide fractions.
4. Write a fraction as an equal fraction having a given denominator.
5. Add fractions.
6. Subtract fractions.

To prepare for the study of algebra, we begin with a brief review of arithmetic. In everyday life, the numbers seen most often are the **whole numbers,**

$$0, \quad 1, \quad 2, \quad 3, \quad 4, \quad 5, \quad . \quad . \quad . \quad ,$$

and the **fractions,** such as

$$\frac{1}{2}, \quad \frac{2}{3}, \quad \frac{11}{12}, \quad \text{and so on.}$$

In a fraction, the top number is called the **numerator** and the bottom number is called the **denominator.**

1   A fraction is in **lowest terms** when the numerator and the denominator cannot both be divided by the same number other than 1 (without remainder). Use the following steps to write a fraction in lowest terms.

Writing a Fraction in Lowest Terms

> *Step 1*   Find the largest number that will divide into both the numerator and the denominator. This number is called the **greatest common factor.**
>
> *Step 2*   Divide both the numerator and the denominator by the greatest common factor.

EXAMPLE 1

Write each fraction in lowest terms.

(a) $\dfrac{10}{15} = \dfrac{10 \div 5}{15 \div 5} = \dfrac{2}{3}$

Since the largest number that can be divided without remainder into both 10 and 15 is 5, the number 5 is the greatest common factor of 10 and 15. Both numerator and denominator are divided by 5 to write the fraction in lowest terms.

(b) $\dfrac{15}{45} = \dfrac{15 \div 15}{45 \div 15} = \dfrac{1}{3}$

Both 15 and 45 can be divided by 3, 5, and 15. The largest of these three numbers, 15, is the greatest common factor, so use 15 to divide both the numerator and denominator.   ●

2   The basic operations on whole numbers are addition, subtraction, multiplication, and division. These same operations apply to fractions. To *multiply* two fractions, multiply their numerators and then multiply their denominators. In symbols, if *a/b* and *c/d* are fractions, then

Multiplying Fractions

$$\frac{a}{b} \cdot \frac{c}{d} = \frac{a \cdot c}{b \cdot d}.$$

The dot indicates multiplication. For example,

$$3 \cdot 5 = 15 \qquad \text{and} \qquad 7 \cdot 8 = 56.$$

The answer to a multiplication problem is called the **product.**

EXAMPLE 2

Find the product of 3/8 and 4/9, and write it in lowest terms.
First, multiply 3/8 and 4/9.

$$\frac{3}{8} \cdot \frac{4}{9} = \frac{3 \cdot 4}{8 \cdot 9} = \frac{12}{72}$$

Write the product in lowest terms.

$$\frac{12}{72} = \frac{12 \div 12}{72 \div 12} = \frac{1}{6} \quad \bullet$$

3   Two fractions are **reciprocals** of each other if their product is 1. For example, 3/4 and 4/3 are reciprocals since

$$\frac{3}{4} \cdot \frac{4}{3} = 1.$$

Also, 7/11 and 11/7 are reciprocals of each other. The reciprocal is used to divide fractions. To *divide* two fractions, multiply the first and the reciprocal of the second, or

Dividing Fractions

$$\frac{a}{b} \div \frac{c}{d} = \frac{a}{b} \cdot \frac{d}{c}.$$

The reason this method works will be explained in a later chapter. The answer to a division problem is called a **quotient.** For example, the quotient of 20 and 10 is 2, since $20 \div 10 = 2$.

EXAMPLE 3   Find the following quotients, and write them in lowest terms.

(a) $\dfrac{3}{4} \div \dfrac{8}{5} = \dfrac{3}{4} \cdot \dfrac{5}{8} = \dfrac{3 \cdot 5}{4 \cdot 8} = \dfrac{15}{32}$

(b) $\dfrac{3}{4} \div \dfrac{5}{8} = \dfrac{3}{4} \cdot \dfrac{8}{5} = \dfrac{3 \cdot 8}{4 \cdot 5} = \dfrac{24}{20} = \dfrac{6}{5} \quad \bullet$

4   All the fractions in an addition or subtraction problem must have the same denominator. If they do not, rewrite the fractions with a new common denominator. For example, to rewrite 3/4 as a fraction with a denominator of 32,

$$\frac{3}{4} = \frac{\blacksquare}{32},$$

we need to find the number that can be multiplied by 4 to give 32. Since $4 \cdot 8 = 32$, use the number 8. We want the value of the original fraction, 3/4, to stay the same, so multiply 3/4 by the fraction 8/8, which equals 1.

$$\frac{3}{4} = \frac{3}{4} \cdot \frac{8}{8} = \frac{3 \cdot 8}{4 \cdot 8} = \frac{24}{32}$$

EXAMPLE 4   Write 5/8 as a fraction with a denominator of 72.
   Since the quotient of 72 and 8 is 9, multiply 5/8 by 9/9.

$$\frac{5}{8} = \frac{5}{8} \cdot \frac{9}{9} = \frac{5 \cdot 9}{8 \cdot 9} = \frac{45}{72} \quad \bullet$$

5   The **sum** of two fractions having the same denominator is found by adding the numerators. If a/b and c/b are fractions with the same denominator, then

Adding Fractions

$$\frac{a}{b} + \frac{c}{b} = \frac{a+c}{b}.$$

EXAMPLE 5   Add.

(a) $\dfrac{3}{7} + \dfrac{2}{7} = \dfrac{3+2}{7} = \dfrac{5}{7}$

(b) $\dfrac{2}{10} + \dfrac{5}{10} = \dfrac{2+5}{10} = \dfrac{7}{10}$ ●

If two fractions to be added do not have the same denominators, the rule above can still be used, but only after the fractions are rewritten with a common denominator.

EXAMPLE 6   Add.

(a) $\dfrac{1}{2} + \dfrac{1}{3}$

We cannot add until the fractions have the same denominator. Use 6 as a common denominator, since both 2 and 3 divide into 6. Write 1/2 and 1/3 as fractions with a denominator of 6.

$$\frac{1}{2} = \frac{1}{2} \cdot \frac{3}{3} = \frac{1\cdot 3}{2\cdot 3} = \frac{3}{6} \quad \text{and} \quad \frac{1}{3} = \frac{1}{3} \cdot \frac{2}{2} = \frac{1\cdot 2}{3\cdot 2} = \frac{2}{6}$$

Now add.

$$\frac{1}{2} + \frac{1}{3} = \frac{3}{6} + \frac{2}{6} = \frac{3+2}{6} = \frac{5}{6}$$

(b) $3\dfrac{1}{2} + 2\dfrac{3}{4}$

Change both numbers to fractions, as follows.

$$3\frac{1}{2} = 3 + \frac{1}{2} = \frac{3}{1} + \frac{1}{2} = \frac{6}{2} + \frac{1}{2} = \frac{6+1}{2} = \frac{7}{2}$$

Also, $2\dfrac{3}{4} = 2 + \dfrac{3}{4} = \dfrac{8}{4} + \dfrac{3}{4} = \dfrac{8+3}{4} = \dfrac{11}{4}.$

Now add.

$$3\frac{1}{2} + 2\frac{3}{4} = \frac{7}{2} + \frac{11}{4} = \frac{14}{4} + \frac{11}{4} = \frac{25}{4} \text{ or } 6\frac{1}{4}$$ ●

6   *Subtraction* of fractions is similar to addition. Just subtract the numerators instead of adding them, according to the following definition.

Subtracting Fractions

$$\frac{a}{b} - \frac{c}{b} = \frac{a-c}{b}$$

EXAMPLE 7   Subtract.

(a) $\dfrac{5}{8} - \dfrac{3}{8} = \dfrac{5-3}{8} = \dfrac{2}{8} = \dfrac{1}{4}$

(b) $\dfrac{3}{4} - \dfrac{1}{3}$

A common denominator is 12.

$$\cdot \ \frac{3}{4} - \frac{1}{3} = \frac{9}{12} - \frac{4}{12} = \frac{9-4}{12} = \frac{5}{12} \quad \bullet$$

1.1   EXERCISES

Write each fraction in lowest terms. See Example 1.

1. $\dfrac{7}{14}$ 2. $\dfrac{3}{9}$ 3. $\dfrac{10}{12}$ 4. $\dfrac{8}{10}$

5. $\dfrac{16}{18}$ 6. $\dfrac{14}{20}$ 7. $\dfrac{50}{75}$ 8. $\dfrac{32}{48}$

9. $\dfrac{72}{108}$ 10. $\dfrac{96}{120}$ 11. $\dfrac{120}{144}$ 12. $\dfrac{77}{132}$

Find the products or quotients. Write answers in lowest terms. See Examples 2 and 3.

13. $\dfrac{3}{4} \cdot \dfrac{3}{5}$ 14. $\dfrac{3}{8} \cdot \dfrac{5}{7}$ 15. $\dfrac{1}{10} \cdot \dfrac{6}{5}$ 16. $\dfrac{6}{7} \cdot \dfrac{1}{3}$

17. $\dfrac{9}{4} \cdot \dfrac{8}{15}$ 18. $\dfrac{3}{5} \cdot \dfrac{20}{15}$ 19. $\dfrac{3}{8} \div \dfrac{5}{4}$ 20. $\dfrac{9}{16} \div \dfrac{3}{8}$

21. $\dfrac{5}{12} \div \dfrac{15}{4}$ 22. $\dfrac{15}{16} \div \dfrac{30}{8}$ 23. $\dfrac{15}{32} \div \dfrac{25}{8}$ 24. $\dfrac{24}{25} \div \dfrac{3}{50}$

25. $\dfrac{5}{9} \cdot \dfrac{7}{10}$ 26. $\dfrac{21}{30} \cdot \dfrac{5}{7}$ 27. $\dfrac{13}{10} \cdot \dfrac{5}{3}$ 28. $\dfrac{21}{16} \cdot \dfrac{8}{7}$

29. $\dfrac{28}{3} \cdot \dfrac{6}{7}$ 30. $\dfrac{121}{9} \cdot \dfrac{18}{11}$ 31. $\dfrac{28}{15} \div \dfrac{14}{5}$ 32. $\dfrac{120}{7} \div \dfrac{45}{3}$

Add or subtract. Write answers in lowest terms. Work from left to right in Exercises 51–56. See Examples 4–7.

33. $\dfrac{1}{12} + \dfrac{5}{12}$

34. $\dfrac{2}{5} + \dfrac{1}{5}$

35. $\dfrac{1}{10} + \dfrac{7}{10}$

36. $\dfrac{3}{8} + \dfrac{1}{8}$

37. $\dfrac{4}{9} + \dfrac{2}{3}$

38. $\dfrac{3}{5} + \dfrac{2}{15}$

39. $\dfrac{8}{11} + \dfrac{3}{22}$

40. $\dfrac{9}{10} + \dfrac{3}{5}$

41. $\dfrac{2}{3} - \dfrac{3}{5}$

42. $\dfrac{7}{12} - \dfrac{5}{9}$

43. $\dfrac{5}{6} - \dfrac{3}{10}$

44. $\dfrac{11}{4} - \dfrac{5}{8}$

45. $3\dfrac{1}{4} + \dfrac{1}{8}$

46. $5\dfrac{2}{3} + \dfrac{1}{4}$

47. $4\dfrac{1}{2} + 3\dfrac{2}{3}$

48. $7\dfrac{5}{8} + 3\dfrac{3}{4}$

49. $6\dfrac{2}{3} - 5\dfrac{1}{4}$

50. $8\dfrac{8}{9} - 7\dfrac{4}{5}$

51. $\dfrac{2}{5} + \dfrac{1}{3} + \dfrac{9}{10}$

52. $\dfrac{3}{8} + \dfrac{5}{6} + \dfrac{2}{3}$

53. $\dfrac{5}{7} + \dfrac{1}{4} - \dfrac{1}{2}$

54. $\dfrac{2}{3} + \dfrac{1}{6} - \dfrac{1}{2}$

55. $\dfrac{3}{4} + \dfrac{1}{8} - \dfrac{2}{3}$

56. $\dfrac{7}{10} + \dfrac{3}{5} - \dfrac{5}{8}$

Work each word problem.

57. John Rizzo paid 1/8 of a debt in January, 1/3 in February, and 1/4 in March. What portion of the debt was paid in these three months?

58. A rectangle is 5/16 yard on each of two sides, and 7/12 yard on each of the other two sides. Find the total distance around the rectangle.

59. Last month the Eastside Wholesale Market sold 3 1/4 tons of broccoli, 2 3/8 tons of spinach, 7 1/2 tons of corn, and 1 5/16 tons of turnips. Find the total number of tons of vegetables sold by the firm during the month.

60. Sharkey's Resort decided to expand by buying a piece of property next to the resort. The property has an irregular shape, with five sides. The lengths of the five sides are 146 1/2 feet, 98 3/4 feet, 196 feet, 76 5/8 feet, and 100 7/8 feet. Find the total distance around the piece of property.

61. Joann Kaufmann worked 40 hours during a certain week. She worked 8 1/4 hours on Monday, 6 3/8 hours on Tuesday, 7 2/3 hours on Wednesday, and 8 3/4 hours on Thursday. How many hours did she work on Friday?

62. A concrete truck is loaded with 9 7/8 cubic yards of concrete. The driver delivers 1 1/2 cubic yards at the first stop and 2 3/4 cubic yards at the second stop. At the third stop, the customer receives 3 5/12 cubic yards. How much concrete is left in the truck?

63. Rosario wants to make 16 dresses to sell at the company bazaar. Each dress needs 2 1/4 yards of material. How many yards should be bought?

64. Lindsay allows 1 3/5 bottles of beverage for each guest at a party. If he expects 35 guests, how many bottles of beverage will he need?

1.2   Symbols

■ Know the meaning of < and >.

② Translate word phrases to symbols.

❸ Know the meaning of ≤ and ≥.

④ Write statements that change the direction of inequality symbols.

So far we have seen the symbols of arithmetic, such as $+$, $-$, $\times$, and $\div$. We also have seen a dot used for multiplication. Another common symbol is the one for equality, $=$, which says that two numbers are equal. This symbol with a slash through it, $\neq$, means "is *not* equal to." For example,

$$7 \neq 8$$

says that 7 is not equal to 8.

■   If two numbers are not equal, then one of the numbers must be smaller than the other. The symbol < represents "is less than," so that "7 is less than 8" is written

$$7 < 8.$$

Also, "6 is less than 9" is written $6 < 9$.

The symbol > means "is greater than." Write "8 is greater than 2" as

$$8 > 2.$$

The statement "17 is greater than 11" becomes $17 > 11$.

To keep the symbols < and > straight, remember that the symbol always points to the smaller number. To write "8 is less than 15," point the symbol toward the 8, or $8 < 15$.

②   In algebra, it is often necessary to convert word phrases to symbols. The next example shows this.

EXAMPLE 1   Write each word statement in symbols.

(a) Twelve equals ten plus two.

$$12 = 10 + 2$$

(b) Nine is less than ten.

$$9 < 10$$

(c) Fifteen is not equal to eighteen.

$$15 \neq 18$$

(d) Seven is greater than four.

$$7 > 4 \quad \bullet$$

❸   Two other symbols, ≤ and ≥, also represent the idea of inequality. The symbol ≤ means "is less than or equal to," so that

$$5 \leq 9$$

means "5 is less than or equal to 9." This statement is true, since $5 < 9$ is true. If either the < part or the $=$ part is true, then the inequality ≤ is true.

The symbol $\geq$ means "is greater than or equal to." Again,

$$9 \geq 5$$

is true because $9 > 5$ is true. Also, $8 \leq 8$ is true since $8 = 8$ is true. But it is not true that $13 \leq 9$ because neither $13 < 9$ nor $13 = 9$ is true.

EXAMPLE 2   Tell whether or not each statement is true.

(a) $15 \leq 20$

Since $15 < 20$, the statement $15 \leq 20$ is true.

(b) $25 \geq 30$

Both $25 > 30$ and $25 = 30$ are false. Because of this, $25 \geq 30$ is false.

(c) $12 \geq 12$

Since $12 = 12$, this statement is true.   ●

4   Any statement with $<$ can be converted to one with $>$, and any statement with $>$ can be converted to one with $<$. Do this by reversing the order of the numbers and the direction of the symbol. For example, the statement $6 < 10$ can be written with $>$ as $10 > 6$. Also, any statement containing $\leq$ can be changed to one with $\geq$, and any statement with $\geq$ can be changed to one with $\leq$. For example, the statement $4 \leq 10$ can be changed to $10 \geq 4$.

EXAMPLE 3   The following list shows the same statement written in two equally correct ways.

(a) $9 < 16$ $16 > 9$ (b) $5 > 2$ $2 < 5$

(c) $3 \leq 8$ $8 \geq 3$ (d) $12 \geq 5$ $5 \leq 12$ ●

Here is a summary of the symbols discussed in this section.

List of Symbols

$=$	is equal to	$\neq$	is not equal to
$<$	is less than	$>$	is greater than
$\leq$	is less than or equal to	$\geq$	is greater than or equal to

1.2 EXERCISES

Insert $<$ or $>$ to make the following statements true.

1. 6____9 **2.** 5____3 **3.** 12____15 **4.** 8____10

5. 25____12 **6.** 17____9 **7.** 32____50 **8.** 41____72

9. $\dfrac{3}{4}$____1 **10.** $\dfrac{2}{3}$____0 **11.** $1\dfrac{5}{8}$____1 **12.** $3\dfrac{7}{9}$____2

Insert $\leq$ *or* $\geq$ *to make the following statements true.*

13. 12 _____ 17   **14.** 28 _____ 42   **15.** 16 _____ 14   **16.** 39 _____ 17

17. 8 _____ 28   **18.** 10 _____ 15   **19.** 35 _____ 42   **20.** 51 _____ 62

Which of the symbols $<$, $>$, $\leq$, *and* $\geq$ *make the following statements true?*
Give all possible correct answers.

21. 6 _____ 9   **22.** 18 _____ 12   **23.** 51 _____ 50   **24.** 0 _____ 12

25. 5 _____ 5   **26.** 10 _____ 10   **27.** 48 _____ 0   **28.** 100 _____ 1000

29. 16 _____ 10   **30.** 5 _____ 3   **31.** $\dfrac{1}{4}$ _____ $\dfrac{2}{5}$ **32.** $\dfrac{2}{3}$ _____ $\dfrac{5}{8}$

33. .609 _____ .61   **34.** .5 _____ .499   **35.** $3\dfrac{1}{2}$ _____ 4   **36.** $5\dfrac{7}{8}$ _____ 6

Write the following word statements in symbols. See Example 1.

37. Seven equals five plus two.

38. Nine is greater than the product of four and two.

39. Three is less than the quotient of fifty and five.

40. Five equals ten minus five.

41. Twelve is not equal to five.

42. Fifteen does not equal sixteen.

43. Zero is greater than or equal to zero.

44. Six is less than or equal to six.

Tell whether each statement is true or false. See Example 2.

45. $8 + 2 = 10$ **46.** $8 \neq 9 - 1$ **47.** $12 \geq 10$ **48.** $45 < 45$

49. $0 < 15$ **50.** $16 \geq 10$ **51.** $9 + 12 = 21$ **52.** $9 < 12$

53. $25 \geq 19$ **54.** $18 < 5$ **55.** $9 < 0$ **56.** $15 \leq 32$

57. $6 \neq 5 + 1$ **58.** $15 < 21$ **59.** $11 < 11$ **60.** $29 \geq 30$

61. $8 \leq 0$ **62.** $26 \geq 50$ **63.** $12 \geq 12$ **64.** $5 \leq 5$

Rewrite the following statements so the inequality symbol points in the opposite direction. See Example 3.

65. $6 < 14$ **66.** $8 \leq 9$ **67.** $15 \geq 3$ **68.** $29 > 4$

69. $9 > 8$ **70.** $12 < 17$ **71.** $0 \leq 6$ **72.** $7 \leq 12$

73. $18 \geq 15$ **74.** $25 \geq 1$ **75.** $.481 \geq .439$ **76.** $.762 < .763$

1.3   Exponents and Order of Operations

1   Identify factors.
2   Use exponents.
3   Use the order of operations.
4   Use brackets.
5   Insert parentheses.

1 The product of the numbers 3 and 4 is 12. For this reason, both 3 and 4 are **factors** of 12. Other factors of 12 are 6 and 2, and 1 and 12. (Factors are usually restricted to whole numbers.)

EXAMPLE 1 The list shows several numbers and the whole number factors of each.

Number	Factors
2	1, 2
10	1, 2, 5, 10
25	1, 5, 25
29	1, 29
36	1, 2, 3, 4, 6, 9, 12, 18, 36 ●

2 It is common for a multiplication problem to have the same factor appearing several times. For example,

$$3 \cdot 3 \cdot 3 \cdot 3 = 81$$

has the factor 3 appearing four times. To save space, repeated factors can be written with an *exponent*. For example, in $3 \cdot 3 \cdot 3 \cdot 3$, the number 3 appears as a factor four times, with the product written as 3^4.

$$3 \cdot 3 \cdot 3 \cdot 3 = 3^4$$

The number 4 is the **exponent** and 3 is the **base.** An exponent, then, tells how many times the base is used as a multiplier.

EXAMPLE 2 Find the values of the following.

(a) 5^2

$$5 \cdot 5 = 25$$

————— 5 is used as a factor 2 times

Read 5^2 as "5 squared."

(b) 6^3

$$6 \cdot 6 \cdot 6 = 216$$

————— 6 is used as a factor 3 times

Read 6^3 as "6 cubed."

(c) $2^5 = 2 \cdot 2 \cdot 2 \cdot 2 \cdot 2 = 32$ 2 is used as a factor 5 times

Read 2^5 as "2 to the fifth power."

(d) $\left(\dfrac{2}{3}\right)^3 = \dfrac{2}{3} \cdot \dfrac{2}{3} \cdot \dfrac{2}{3} = \dfrac{8}{27}$ $\dfrac{2}{3}$ is used as a factor 3 times ●

3   Many problems involve more than one operation of arithmetic. For example, to find the value of

$$5 + 2 \cdot 3,$$

should we add first, or should we multiply first? It turns out that the most useful way to work problems with more than one operation is to use the following **order of operations.**

Order of
Operations

> *If parentheses or fraction bars are present,* simplify within parentheses, innermost first, and above and below fraction bars separately, in the following order.
>
> 1. Apply all exponents.
> 2. Do any multiplications or divisions in the order in which they occur, working from left to right.
> 3. Do any additions or subtractions in the order in which they occur, working from left to right.
>
> *If no parentheses or fraction bars are present,* start with Step 1.

EXAMPLE 3   Find the value of $5 + 2 \cdot 3$.

Using the order of operations given above, first multiply 2 and 3, to get 6, and then add to 5.

$$5 + 2 \cdot 3 = 5 + 6 = 11$$

Therefore, $5 + 2 \cdot 3 = 11$.   ●

We have used a dot to show multiplication; another way to show multiplication is with parentheses. For example, $3(7)$, $(3)7$, and $(3)(7)$ each mean $3 \cdot 7$ or 21. The next example shows the use of parentheses for multiplication.

EXAMPLE 4   Find the following.

(a) $9(6 + 11)$

Work first inside the parentheses.

$$\begin{aligned} 9(6 + 11) &= 9(17) &&\text{Work inside parentheses} \\ &= 153 &&\text{Multiply} \end{aligned}$$

(b) $6 \cdot 8 + 5 \cdot 2$

Do any multiplications, working from left to right, and then add.

$$\begin{aligned} 6 \cdot 8 + 5 \cdot 2 &= 48 + 10 &&\text{Multiply} \\ &= 58 &&\text{Add} \end{aligned}$$

(c) $2(5 + 6) + 7 \cdot 3 = 2(11) + 7 \cdot 3$ Work inside parentheses

$= 22 + 21$ Multiply

$= 43$ Add

(d) $\dfrac{4(5 + 3) + 3}{2(3) - 1}$

Simplify the numerator and denominator separately.

$$\frac{4(5 + 3) + 3}{2(3) - 1} = \frac{4(8) + 3}{2(3) - 1} \quad \text{Work inside parentheses}$$

$$= \frac{32 + 3}{6 - 1} \quad \text{Multiply}$$

$$= \frac{35}{5} \quad \text{Add or subtract}$$

$$= 7 \quad \text{Simplify}$$

(e) $9 + 2^3 - 5$

First, find 2^3.

$$9 + 2^3 - 5 = 9 + 8 - 5 \quad \text{Apply the exponent}$$

$$= 12 \quad \text{Add or subtract} \quad \bullet$$

4   An expression with double parentheses, such as $2(8 + 3(6 + 5))$, can be confusing. To eliminate this, square brackets, [ ], can be used instead of one of the pairs of parentheses.

EXAMPLE 5   Simplify $2[8 + 3(6 + 5)]$.

Work first within the parentheses, and then simplify until a single number is found inside the brackets.

$$2[8 + 3(6 + 5)] = 2[8 + 3(11)]$$

$$= 2[8 + 33]$$

$$= 2[41]$$

$$= 82 \quad \bullet$$

5   Some problems are not true as written, but become true when parentheses are inserted in the proper place.

EXAMPLE 6   Insert parentheses so that the following are true.

(a) $9 - 3 - 2 = 8$

This statement would be true if parentheses were inserted around $3 - 2$.

$$9 - (3 - 2) = 8$$

It is not true that $(9 - 3) - 2 = 8$, since $6 - 2 \neq 8$.

(b) $9 \cdot 2 - 4 \cdot 3 = 6$

Since $9 \cdot 2 - 4 \cdot 3 = 18 - 12 = 6$, no parentheses are needed here. If desired, parentheses may be placed as follows.

$$(9 \cdot 2) - (4 \cdot 3) = 6 \quad \bullet$$

1.3 EXERCISES

Find all whole number factors of each number. See Example 1.

1. 30   **2.** 40   **3.** 50   **4.** 72

5. 65   **6.** 85   **7.** 100   **8.** 110

9. 17   **10.** 13   **11.** 29   **12.** 37

Find the values of the following. In Exercises 33–36, round to the nearest thousandth. See Example 2.

13. 6^2 **14.** 9^2 **15.** 8^2 **16.** 10^2

17. 17^2 **18.** 22^2 **19.** 5^3 **20.** 7^3

21. 6^4 **22.** 3^4 **23.** 2^5 **24.** 4^5

25. 3^6 **26.** 2^6 **27.** $\left(\dfrac{1}{2}\right)^2$ **28.** $\left(\dfrac{3}{4}\right)^2$

29. $\left(\dfrac{2}{5}\right)^3$ **30.** $\left(\dfrac{3}{7}\right)^3$ **31.** $\left(\dfrac{4}{5}\right)^3$ **32.** $\left(\dfrac{2}{3}\right)^5$

*** 33.** $(.83)^4$ **34.** $(.712)^2$ **35.** $(1.46)^3$ **36.** $(2.85)^4$

First simplify the left side of each inequality. Then tell whether the given statement is true or false. See Examples 3–5.

37. $9 \cdot 3 - 11 \le 16$ **38.** $6 \cdot 5 - 12 \le 18$

39. $3 \cdot 8 - 4 \cdot 6 \le 0$ **40.** $2 \cdot 20 - 8 \cdot 5 \ge 0$

41. $5 \cdot 11 + 2 \cdot 3 \le 60$ **42.** $9 \cdot 3 + 4 \cdot 5 \ge 48$

43. $12 \cdot 3 - 6 \cdot 6 \le 0$ **44.** $13 \cdot 2 - 15 \cdot 1 \ge 10$

45. $6 \cdot 5 + 3 \cdot 10 \le 0$ **46.** $5 \cdot 8 + 10 \cdot 4 \ge 0$

47. $5[8 + (2 + 3)] > 60$ **48.** $9[(14 + 5) - 10] > 80$

49. $2[2 + 3(2 + 5)] \le 45$ **50.** $3[4 + 3(4 + 1)] \le 55$

51. $[3 \cdot 4 + 5(2)] \cdot 3 > 72$ **52.** $2 \cdot [7 \cdot 5 - 3(2)] \le 58$

53. $\dfrac{5(4 - 1) + 3}{2 \cdot 4 + 1} \ge 3$ **54.** $\dfrac{7(3 + 1) - 2}{5 \cdot 2 + 3} \le 2$

55. $\dfrac{2(5 + 3) + 2 \cdot 2}{2(4 - 1)} > 4$ **56.** $\dfrac{9(7 - 1) - 8 \cdot 2}{4(6 - 1)} > 2$

---

*This symbol indicates problems where a calculator would be helpful.

57. $\dfrac{2(5 + 1) - 3(1 + 1)}{5(8 - 6) - 4 \cdot 2} \le 3$

58. $\dfrac{3(8 - 3) + 2(4 - 1)}{9(6 - 2) - 11(5 - 2)} \ge 7$

59. $8^2 + 2 \ge 63$

60. $4^2 - 8 \ge 9$

61. $5^2 + 2^2 \ge 30$

62. $6^2 - 3^2 > 25$

63. $7.43^2 - 5.77^2 \ge 21.92$

64. $(.841)^3 - (.58)^4 < .479$

Insert parentheses in each expression so that the resulting statement is true.
Some problems require no parentheses. See Example 6.

65. $10 - 7 - 3 = 6$

66. $16 - 4 - 3 = 15$

67. $3 \cdot 5 + 7 = 22$

68. $3 \cdot 5 + 7 = 36$

69. $3 \cdot 5 - 4 = 3$

70. $3 \cdot 5 - 4 = 11$

71. $3 \cdot 5 + 2 \cdot 4 = 23$

72. $3 \cdot 5 + 2 \cdot 4 = 84$

73. $3 \cdot 5 + 2 \cdot 4 = 68$

74. $3 \cdot 5 - 2 \cdot 4 = 36$

75. $3 \cdot 5 - 2 \cdot 4 = 7$

76. $7 \cdot 8 - 4 \cdot 3 = 84$

77. $100 \div 20 \div 5 = 1$

78. $360 \div 18 \div 4 = 5$

79. $100 \div 20 \div 5 = 25$

80. $4096 \div 256 \div 4 = 4$

81. $2^2 + 4 \cdot 2 = 16$

82. $6 + 5 \cdot 3^2 = 99$

83. $3^3 - 2 \cdot 4 = 100$

84. $8 - 2^2 \cdot 2 = 8$

85. $6^2 - 2 \cdot 5 = 170$

Write the information given in the following problems using numerical symbols
and parentheses.

86. Marjorie Jensen invested $600. After one year, her investment had tripled.
She then took $150 and paid a car payment.

87. John Wilson had 5 decks of cards, each containing 52 cards. He removed
all 4 aces from one deck.

88. A bus has 63 passengers. At one stop, 23 people get off and 17 new
people get on.

1.4 Variables and Equations

1 Define *variable.*

2 Find the value of algebraic expressions.

3 Convert words to algebraic expressions.

4 Identify solutions of equations.

5 Define *set* and *domain.*

1 A **variable** is a symbol, usually a letter, such as x, y, or z, used to represent
any unknown number. An **algebraic expression** is a collection of numbers, variables, symbols for operations, and symbols for grouping (such as parentheses). For
example,

$$x + 5, \qquad 2m - 9, \qquad \text{and} \qquad 8p^2 + 6p + 2$$

are all algebraic expressions. In the algebraic expression $2m - 9$, the expression $2m$
indicates the product of 2 and m, just as $8p^2$ shows the product of 8 and p^2.

2   An algebraic expression takes on different numerical values as the variables take on different values.

EXAMPLE 1   Find the values of the following algebraic expressions when $m = 5$.

(a) $8m$

Replace m with 5, to get

$$8m = 8 \cdot 5 = 40.$$

(b) $3m^2$

For $m = 5$,

$$3m^2 = 3 \cdot 5^2 = 3 \cdot 25 = 75. \quad \bullet$$

In Example 1(b), it is important to notice that $3m^2$ means $3 \cdot m^2$; it *does not* mean $3m \cdot 3m$.

EXAMPLE 2   Find the value of each expression when $x = 5$ and $y = 3$.

(a) $2x + 7y$

Replace x with 5 and y with 3. Do the multiplications first, and then add.

$$
\begin{aligned}
2x + 7y &= 2 \cdot 5 + 7 \cdot 3 && \text{Let } x = 5 \text{ and } y = 3 \\
&= 10 + 21 && \text{Multiply} \\
&= 31 && \text{Add}
\end{aligned}
$$

(b) $\dfrac{9x - 8y}{2x - y}$

Replace x with 5 and y with 3.

$$
\begin{aligned}
\frac{9x - 8y}{2x - y} &= \frac{9 \cdot 5 - 8 \cdot 3}{2 \cdot 5 - 3} && \text{Let } x = 5 \text{ and } y = 3 \\
&= \frac{45 - 24}{10 - 3} && \text{Multiply} \\
&= \frac{21}{7} && \text{Subtract} \\
&= 3 && \text{Simplify}
\end{aligned}
$$

(c)
$$
\begin{aligned}
x^2 - 2y^2 &= 5^2 - 2 \cdot 3^2 && \text{Let } x = 5 \text{ and } y = 3 \\
&= 25 - 2 \cdot 9 && \text{Apply the exponents} \\
&= 25 - 18 && \text{Multiply} \\
&= 7 && \text{Subtract} \quad \bullet
\end{aligned}
$$

3   Variables are used in changing word phrases into algebraic expressions. The next example shows how to do this.

EXAMPLE 3   Change the following word phrases to algebraic expressions. Use x as the variable.

(a) The sum of a number and 9

"Sum" is the answer to an addition problem. This phrase translates as

$$x + 9 \quad \text{or} \quad 9 + x.$$

(b) 7 minus a number

"Minus" indicates subtraction, so the answer is

$$7 - x.$$

(Note: $x - 7$ would *not* be correct.)

(c) 7 taken from a number

Since 7 is taken *from* a number, write

$$x - 7.$$

(Here $7 - x$ would not be correct.)

(d) The product of 11 and a number

$$11 \cdot x \quad \text{or} \quad 11x$$

(e) 5 divided by a number

$$\frac{5}{x}$$

(f) The product of 2, and the sum of a number and 8

$$2(x + 8) \quad \bullet$$

4   An **equation** is a statement that says two algebraic expressions are equal. Examples of equations are

$$x + 4 = 11, \quad 2y = 16, \quad \text{and} \quad 4p + 1 = 25 - p.$$

To **solve** an equation means to find all the values of the variable that make the equation true. The values of the variable that make the equation true are called the **solutions** of the equation.

EXAMPLE 4   Decide whether the given number is a solution of the equation.

(a) $5p + 1 = 36;$ 7

Replace p with 7.

$$
\begin{aligned}
5p + 1 &= 36 \\
5 \cdot 7 + 1 &= 36 \qquad \text{Let } p = 7 \\
35 + 1 &= 36 \\
36 &= 36 \qquad \text{True}
\end{aligned}
$$

The number 7 is a solution of the equation.

(b) $9m - 6 = 32$;   4

$$9m - 6 = 32$$
$$9 \cdot 4 - 6 = 32 \qquad \text{Let } m = 4$$
$$36 - 6 = 32$$
$$30 = 32 \qquad \text{False}$$

The number 4 is not a solution of the equation.   ●

5   Sometimes the solutions of an equation must come from a certain list of numbers. This list of numbers is often written as a **set;** for example, the set containing the numbers 1, 2, 3, 4, and 5 is written with **set braces** as

$$\{1, 2, 3, 4, 5\}.$$

A set is a collection of objects. For more information on sets, see Appendix B at the back of this book.

The set of numbers from which the solutions of an equation must be chosen is called the **domain** of the equation.

EXAMPLE 5   Change each word statement to an equation. Use x as the variable. Then find all solutions for the equation from the domain

$$\{0, 2, 4, 6, 8, 10\}.$$

(a) The sum of a number and four is six.

The word "is" suggests "equals." If x represents the unknown number, then translate as follows.

$$\begin{array}{ccc} \text{The sum of} & & \\ \text{a number and four} & \text{is} & \text{six.} \\ \downarrow & \downarrow & \downarrow \\ x + 4 & = & 6 \end{array}$$

Try each number from the given domain $\{0, 2, 4, 6, 8, 10\}$, in turn, to see that 2 is the only solution of $x + 4 = 6$.

(b) 9 more than five times a number is 49.

Use x to represent the unknown number.

$$\begin{array}{ccccc} 9 & \text{more than} & \text{five times a number} & \text{is} & 49. \\ \downarrow & \downarrow & \downarrow & \downarrow & \downarrow \\ 9 & + & 5x & = & 49 \end{array}$$

Try each number from the domain $\{0, 2, 4, 6, 8, 10\}$. The solution is 8, since $9 + 5 \cdot 8 = 49$.   ●

1.4 EXERCISES

Find the numerical values of the following when (a) x = 3 and (b) x = 15. See Examples 1 and 2.

1. $x + 9$

2. $x - 1$

3. $5x$

4. $7x$

5. $2x + 8$

6. $9x - 5$

7. $\dfrac{x + 1}{3}$

8. $\dfrac{x - 2}{5}$

9. $\dfrac{3x - 5}{2x}$

10. $\dfrac{x + 2}{x - 1}$

11. $3x^2 + x$

12. $2x + x^2$

13. $6.459x$

14. $.74x^2$

15. $.0745(x^2 + 2)$

16. $.204(3 + x)$

Find the numerical values of the following when (a) x = 4 and y = 2 and (b) x = 1 and y = 5. Round to the nearest thousandth in Exercises 35 and 36. See Example 2.

17. $8x + 3y + 5$

18. $4x + 2y + 7$

19. $3(x + 2y)$

20. $2(2x + y)$

21. $x + \dfrac{4}{y}$

22. $y + \dfrac{8}{x}$

23. $\dfrac{x}{3} + \dfrac{5}{y}$

24. $\dfrac{x}{5} + \dfrac{y}{4}$

25. $5(4x + 7y)$

26. $8(5x + 9y)$

27. $\dfrac{2x + 3y}{x + y + 1}$

28. $\dfrac{5x + 3y + 1}{2x}$

29. $\dfrac{2x + 4y - 6}{5y + 2}$

30. $\dfrac{4x + 3y - 1}{x}$

31. $2y^2 + 5x$

32. $6x^2 + 4y$

33. $\dfrac{x^2 + y^2}{x + y}$

34. $\dfrac{9x^2 + 4y^2}{3x^2 + 2y}$

35. $.841x^2 + .32y^2$

36. $\dfrac{3.4x + 2.59y}{0.8x + 0.3y^2}$

Change the word phrases to algebraic expressions. Use x to represent the variable. See Example 3.

37. Eight times a number

38. 15 times a number

39. Five times a number

40. 6 added to a number

41. 4 added to a number

42. A number subtracted from eight

43. Nine subtracted from a number

44. Eight added to three times a number

45. 6 subtracted from 5 times a number

46. 8 times a number, added to 52

Decide whether the given number is a solution of the equation. See Example 4.

47. $p - 5 = 12$;   17

48. $x + 6 = 15$;   9

49. $5m + 2 = 7$;   2

50. $3r + 5 = 8$;   2

51. $2y + 3(y - 2) = 14$;   4

52. $6a + 2(a + 3) = 14$;   1

53. $6p + 4p - 9 = 11$;   2

54. $2x + 3x + 8 = 38$;   6

55. $3r^2 - 2 = 46$;   4

56. $2x^2 + 1 = 19$;   3   **57.** $\dfrac{z + 4}{z - 2} = 2$;   8   **58.** $\dfrac{x + 6}{x - 2} = 9$;   3

59. $9.54x + 3.811 = 0.4273x + 16.57718$;   1.4

60. $0.935(y + 6.1) + 0.0142 = 7.83y + .2017$;   .8

Change the word statements to equations. Use x as the variable. Find the solutions from the domain {0, 2, 4, 6, 8, 10}. See Example 5.

61. The sum of a number and 8 is 12.

62. A number minus three equals seven.

63. The sum of a number and two is ten.

64. The sum of twice a number and 6 is 18.

65. Five more than twice a number is 13.

66. The product of a number and 3 is 24.

67. Three times a number is equal to two more than twice the number.

68. Twelve divided by a number equals three times that number.

69. Twenty divided by five times a number is 2.

70. A number divided by 2 is 0.

1.5   Real Numbers and the Number Line

1️⃣ Set up number lines.

2️⃣ Identify whole numbers, integers, rational numbers, irrational numbers, and real numbers.

3️⃣ Tell which of two real numbers is smaller.

4️⃣ Find additive inverses.

5️⃣ Find absolute values of real numbers.

1️⃣ When studying numbers in algebra, it is often helpful to draw graphs. This is done with a **number line,** such as the one in Figure 1.1.

Figure 1.1

To set up a number line, locate any point on a line and call it 0. Choose any point to the right of 0 and call it 1. The distance between 0 and 1 gives a unit of measure used to locate other points, as shown in Figure 1.1. The points labeled in Figure 1.1 correspond to the set of **whole numbers.**

Whole numbers $\{0, 1, 2, 3, 4, 5, \cdots\}$

The three dots show that the list of numbers continues in the same way indefinitely.

All the whole numbers starting with 1 are located to the right of 0 on the number line. But numbers may also be placed to the left of 0. These numbers, written $-1, -2, -3$, and so on, are shown in Figure 1.2. (The minus sign is used to show that the numbers are located to the *left* of 0.)

Figure 1.2

The numbers to the *left* of 0 are **negative numbers.** The numbers to the *right* of 0 are **positive numbers.** The number 0 itself is neither positive nor negative. Positive numbers and negative numbers are called **signed numbers.**

There are many practical applications of negative numbers. For example, a temperature on a cold January day might be $-10°$, or 10 degrees below zero. A business that spends more than it takes in has a negative "profit."

2   The set of numbers (including positive and negative numbers and zero) marked on the number line in Figure 1.2 is called the set of **integers.**

Integers $\{\cdots, -3, -2, -1, 0, 1, 2, 3, \cdots\}$

Not all numbers are integers. For example, 1/2 is not; it is a number halfway between the integers 0 and 1. Also, 3 1/4 is not an integer. Several numbers that are not integers are shown in Figure 1.3.

Figure 1.3

All the numbers in Figure 1.3 can be written as quotients of integers. All such numbers make up the **rational numbers.**

Rational numbers   {quotient of two integers, with denominator not 0}

Since any integer can be written as the quotient of itself and 1, all integers are also rational numbers.

Although a great many numbers are rational, not all are. For example, a floor tile one foot on a side has a diagonal whose length is the square root of 2 (written $\sqrt{2}$). It can be shown that $\sqrt{2}$ cannot be written as a quotient of integers. Because of this, $\sqrt{2}$ is not rational; it is **irrational.**

Irrational numbers   {numbers represented by points on the number line that are not rational}

Examples of irrational numbers include $\sqrt{3}$, $\sqrt{7}$, $-\sqrt{10}$, and π, which is the ratio of the distance around a circle to the distance across it.

Finally, *all* numbers that can be represented by points on the number line are called **real numbers.**

Real numbers   {all numbers that can be represented on the number line}

All the numbers mentioned above are real numbers. The relationships between the various types of numbers are shown in Figure 1.4. (An example of a number that is *not* a real number is the square root of a negative number, as discussed in the last chapter of this book.)

Figure 1.4

EXAMPLE 1   List the numbers in the set

$$\left\{-5, -\frac{2}{3}, 0, \sqrt{2}, 3\frac{1}{4}, 5, 5.8\right\}$$

that are

(a) integers;

The integers in the set are -5, 0, and 5.

(b) rational numbers;

The rational numbers are -5, $-2/3$, 0, $3\ 1/4$, 5, 5.8.

(c) real numbers.

All the numbers in the set are real numbers.   ●

3   Given any two whole numbers, you probably can tell which number is smaller. But what happens with negative numbers, such as those in the set of integers? Positive numbers decrease as the corresponding points on the number line go to the left. For example, $8 < 12$, and 8 is to the left of 12 on the number line. We can extend this idea to all real numbers.

The smaller of any two different real numbers is the one farther to the left on the number line.

Because of this definition, any negative number is smaller than 0, and any negative number is smaller than any positive number. Also, 0 is smaller than any positive number.

EXAMPLE 2   Is it true that $-3 < -1$?

To decide whether the statement $-3 < -1$ is true, locate both numbers, -3 and -1, on a number line, as shown in Figure 1.5. Since -3 is to the left of -1 on the number line, -3 is smaller than -1. The statement $-3 < -1$ is true.   ●

Figure 1.5

4   One property of the real numbers says that if we select any real number x (except 0), we can find exactly one number on the number line the same distance from 0 as x but on the opposite side of 0.

For example, Figure 1.6 shows that the numbers 3 and -3 are each the same distance from 0 but are on opposite sides of 0. The numbers 3 and -3 are called **additive inverses,** or **opposites,** of each other.

Figure 1.6

Additive Inverse

> The **additive inverse** of a number x is the number that is the same distance from 0 on the number line as x, but on the opposite side of 0.

The additive inverse of the number 0 is 0 itself. This makes 0 the only real number that is its own additive inverse. Other additive inverses occur in pairs. For example, 4 and -4, and 5 and -5, are additive inverses of each other. Several pairs of additive inverses are shown in Figure 1.7.

Figure 1.7

The additive inverse of a number can be indicated by writing the symbol $-$ in front of the number. With this symbol, the additive inverse of 7 is written -7. The additive inverse of -3 can be written $-(-3)$. We know that 3 is an additive inverse of -3. Since a number can have only one additive inverse, the symbols 3 and $-(-3)$ must represent the same number, which means that

$$-(-3) = 3.$$

Generalizing,

for any real number x, $-(-x) = x.$

EXAMPLE 3   Find the additive inverse of each number.

Number	Additive inverse
-4	$-(-4)$, or 4
0	0
-2	$-(-2)$, or 2
19	-19 ●

As Example 3 suggests,

to find the additive inverse of a number, change the sign of the number.

5   As we said, additive inverses are numbers that are the same distance from 0 on the number line. To express this, we say that a number and its additive inverse have the same absolute value. The **absolute value** of a real number is defined as the distance between 0 and the number on the number line.

The symbol for the absolute value of the number x is $|x|$, read "the absolute value of x." For example, the distance between 2 and 0 on the number line is 2 units, so that

$$|2| = 2.$$

Also, the distance between -2 and 0 on the number line is 2 units, so that

$$|-2| = 2.$$

Since distance is a physical measurement, which is never negative,

---

the absolute value of a number is never negative.

For example, $|12| = 12$ and $|-12| = 12$, since both 12 and -12 lie at a distance of 12 units from 0 on the number line. Since 0 is a distance 0 units from 0, we have $|0| = 0$.

EXAMPLE 4   Simplify by removing absolute value symbols.

(a) $|5| = 5$ (b) $|-5| = 5$

(c) $-|5| = -(5) = -5$ (d) $-|-14| = -(14) = -14$

(e) $|8 - 2| = |6| = 6$ ●

1.5   EXERCISES

Find the additive inverse of each number. For the exercises with absolute value, simplify first before deciding on the additive inverse. See Examples 3 and 4.

1. 8   **2.** 12   **3.** −9   **4.** −11
5. −2   **6.** −3   **7.** $|15|$ **8.** $|5|$
9. $|8|$ **10.** $|0|$ **11.** $|-12|$ **12.** $|-3|$

Select the smaller of the two given numbers. See Examples 2 and 4.

13. −12, −4   **14.** −9, −14   **15.** −8, −1   **16.** −15, −16
17. 3, $|-4|$ **18.** 5, $|-2|$ **19.** $|-3|$, $|-4|$ **20.** $|-8|$, $|-9|$
21. $-|-6|$, $-|-4|$ **22.** $-|-2|$, $-|-3|$ **23.** $|5-3|$, $|6-2|$ **24.** $|7-2|$, $|8-1|$

Write true *or* false *for each statement. See Examples 2 and 4.*

25. $-2 < -1$ **26.** $-8 < -4$ **27.** $-3 \geq -7$
28. $-9 \geq -12$ **29.** $-15 \leq -20$ **30.** $-21 \leq -27$
31. $-8 \leq -(-4)$ **32.** $-9 \leq -(-6)$ **33.** $0 \leq -(-4)$
34. $0 \geq -(-6)$ **35.** $-9 \leq -(-6)$ **36.** $8 \leq -(-4)$
37. $6 > -(-2)$ **38.** $-8 > -(-2)$ **39.** $-4 < -(-5)$
40. $-6 \leq -0$ **41.** $|-6| < |-9|$ **42.** $|-12| < |-20|$
43. $-|8| > |-9|$ **44.** $-|12| > |-15|$ **45.** $-|-5| \geq -|-9|$
46. $-|-12| \leq -|-15|$ **47.** $|6-5| \geq |6-2|$ **48.** $|13-8| \leq |7-4|$

49. List all numbers from the set

$$\left\{ -9, -\sqrt{7}, -1\frac{1}{4}, -\frac{3}{5}, 0, \sqrt{5}, 3, 5.9, 7 \right\}$$

that are
(a) whole numbers;   (b) integers;   (c) rational numbers;
(d) irrational numbers;   (e) real numbers.

50. List all numbers from the set

$$\left\{ -5.3, -5, -\sqrt{3}, -1, -\frac{1}{9}, 0, 1.2, 1.8, 3, \sqrt{11} \right\}$$

that are
(a) whole numbers;   (b) integers;   (c) rational numbers;
(d) irrational numbers;   (e) real numbers.

Graph each group of numbers on a number line.

51. 0, 3, −5, −6   **52.** 2, 6, −2, −1
53. −2, −6, $|-4|$, 3, $-|4|$ **54.** −5, −3, $-|-2|$, −0, $|-4|$

55. $\dfrac{1}{4}$, $2\dfrac{1}{2}$, $-3\dfrac{4}{5}$, -4, $-1\dfrac{5}{8}$

56. $5\dfrac{1}{4}$, $4\dfrac{5}{9}$, $-2\dfrac{1}{3}$, 0, $-3\dfrac{2}{5}$

57. $|3|$, $-|3|$, $-|-4|$, $-|-2|$

58. $|6|$, $-|6|$, $-|-8|$, $-|-3|$

In Exercises 59–64, give three examples of numbers that satisfy the given condition.

59. Positive real numbers but not integers

60. Real numbers but not positive numbers

61. Real numbers but not whole numbers

62. Rational numbers but not integers

63. Real numbers but not rational numbers

64. Rational numbers but not negative numbers

In Exercises 65–74, answer true *or* false *for each statement.*

65. Every rational number is a real number.

66. Every integer is a rational number.

67. Some integers are not real numbers.

68. Every integer is positive.

69. Every whole number is positive.

70. Some irrational numbers are negative.

71. Some real numbers are not rational.

72. Not every rational number is positive.

73. Some whole numbers are not integers.

74. The number 0 is irrational.

1.6   Addition of Real Numbers

1 Add two numbers with the same sign on a number line.

2 Add positive and negative numbers.

3 Use the order of operations with real numbers.

1   The number line can be used to show the addition of real numbers, as in the following examples.

EXAMPLE 1   Use the number line to find the sum $2 + 3$.

To add the positive numbers 2 and 3 on the number line, start at 0 and draw an arrow two units to the *right,* as shown in Figure 1.8. This arrow represents the number 2 in the sum $2 + 3$. Then, from the right end of this arrow draw another arrow three units to the right. The number below the end of this second arrow is 5, so $2 + 3 = 5$.   ●

Figure 1.8

EXAMPLE 2   Use the number line to find the sum $-2 + (-4)$. (We placed parentheses around the -4 to avoid the confusing use of $+$ and $-$ next to each other.)

To add the negative numbers -2 and -4 on the number line, again start at 0 and draw an arrow two units to the *left,* as shown in Figure 1.9. The arrow is drawn to the left to represent the addition of a *negative* number. From the left end of this first arrow, draw a second arrow four units to the left. The number below the end of this second arrow is -6, so $-2 + (-4) = -6$. •

Figure 1.9

In Example 2, the sum of the two negative numbers -2 and -4 is a negative number whose distance from 0 is the sum of the distance of -2 from 0 and the distance of -4 from 0. That is, *the sum of two negative numbers is the negative of the sum of their absolute values.*

$$-2 + (-4) = -(|-2| + |-4|) = -(2 + 4) = -6$$

To add two numbers having the same signs, add the absolute values of the numbers. The result has the same sign as the numbers being added.

EXAMPLE 3   Find the sums.

(a) $-2 + (-9) = -11$

(b) $-8 + (-12) = -20$

(c) $-15 + (-3) = -18$ •

2   To find the sum of a positive number and a negative number, use the number line again.

EXAMPLE 4   Use the number line to find the sum $-2 + 5$.

To find the sum $-2 + 5$ on the number line, start at 0 and draw an arrow two units to the left. From the left end of this arrow, draw a second arrow five units to the right, as shown in Figure 1.10. The number below the end of the second arrow is 3, so $-2 + 5 = 3$. •

Figure 1.10

While a number line is useful in showing the rules for addition, it is important to be able to do the problems mentally.

EXAMPLE 5   Check each answer, trying to work the addition mentally. If you get stuck, use a number line.

(a) $7 + (-4) = 3$

(b) $-8 + 12 = 4$

(c) $-\dfrac{1}{2} + \dfrac{1}{8} = -\dfrac{4}{8} + \dfrac{1}{8} = -\dfrac{3}{8}$ Remember to get a common denominator first

(d) $\dfrac{5}{6} + \left(-\dfrac{4}{3}\right) = -\dfrac{1}{2}$

(e) $-4.6 + 8.1 = 3.5$ ●

Addition of numbers with different signs can also be defined using absolute value.

To add numbers with different signs, find the difference of the absolute values of the numbers. The answer is given the sign of the number with the larger absolute value.

For example, to add -12 and 5, find their absolute values: $|-12| = 12$ and $|5| = 5$. Then find the difference of these absolute values: $12 - 5 = 7$. Since $|-12| > |5|$, the sum will be negative, so that the final answer is $-12 + 5 = -7$.

Let us now summarize the rules for adding signed numbers.

Adding Signed Numbers

> *Like signs*   Add the absolute values of the numbers. The sum has the same sign as the given numbers.
>
> *Unlike signs*   Find the difference of the larger absolute value and the smaller. Give the answer the sign of the number having the larger absolute value.

3   Sometimes a problem involves square brackets, [ ]. As mentioned earlier, brackets are treated just like parentheses. Do the calculations inside the brackets until a single number is obtained. Remember to use the order of operations given in Section 1.3 when adding more than two numbers.

EXAMPLE 6   Find the sums.

(a) $-3 + [4 + (-8)]$

First work inside the brackets. Follow the rules for the order of operations given in Section 1.3.

$$-3 + [4 + (-8)] = -3 + (-4) = -7$$

(b) $8 + [(-2 + 6) + (-3)] = 8 + [4 + (-3)] = 8 + 1 = 9$ ●

1.6   EXERCISES

Find the sums. See Examples 1–6.

1. $5 + (-3)$ **2.** $11 + (-8)$ **3.** $6 + (-8)$

4. $3 + (-7)$ **5.** $-6 + (-2)$ **6.** $-8 + (-3)$

7. $-3 + (-9)$ **8.** $-11 + (-5)$ **9.** $12 + (-8)$

10. $10 + (-2)$ **11.** $4 + [13 + (-5)]$ **12.** $6 + [2 + (-13)]$

13. $8 + [-2 + (-1)]$ **14.** $12 + [-3 + (-4)]$ **15.** $-2 + [5 + (-1)]$

16. $-8 + [9 + (-2)]$ **17.** $-6 + [6 + (-9)]$ **18.** $-3 + [4 + (-8)]$

19. $[(-9) + (-14)] + 12$ **20.** $[(-8) + (-6)] + 10$ **21.** $-\dfrac{1}{6} + \dfrac{2}{3}$

22. $\dfrac{9}{10} + \left(-\dfrac{3}{5}\right)$ **23.** $\dfrac{5}{8} + \left(-\dfrac{17}{12}\right)$ **24.** $-\dfrac{6}{25} + \dfrac{19}{20}$

25. $2\dfrac{1}{2} + \left(-3\dfrac{1}{4}\right)$ **26.** $-4\dfrac{3}{8} + 6\dfrac{1}{2}$ **27.** $-6.1 + [3.2 + (-4.8)]$

28. $-9.4 + [-5.8 + (-1.4)]$ **29.** $[-3 + (-4)] + [5 + (-6)]$ **30.** $[-8 + (-3)] + [-7 + (-6)]$

31. $[-4 + (-3)] + [8 + (-1)]$

32. $[-5 + (-9)] + [16 + (-21)]$

33. $[-4 + (-6)] + [(-3) + (-8)] + [12 + (-11)]$

34. $[-2 + (-11)] + [12 + (-2)] + [18 + (-6)]$

35. $(-9.648 + 11.237) + [(-4.9123 + 1.8769) + 3.1589]$

36. $[-3.851 + (-2.4691)] + [11.809 + (-1.735)] + (-1.409)$

Write true *or* false *for each statement.*

37. $-9 + 5 + 6 = -2$ **38.** $-6 + (8 - 5) = -3$

39. $-3 + 5 = 5 + (-3)$ **40.** $11 + (-6) = -6 + 11$

41. $|-8 + 3| = 8 + 3$ **42.** $|-4 + 2| = 4 + 2$

43. $|12 - 3| = 12 - 3$ **44.** $|-6 + 10| = 6 + 10$

45. $[4 + (-6)] + 6 = 4 + (-6 + 6)$ **46.** $[(-2) + (-3)] + (-6) = 12 + (-1)$

47. $-7 + [-5 + (-3)] = [(-7) + (-5)] + 3$ **48.** $6 + [-2 + (-5)] = [(-4) + (-2)] + 5$

49. $-5 + (-|-5|) = -10$ **50.** $|-3| + (-5) = -2$

51. $-2 + |-5| + 3 = 8 + (-2)$

Find all solutions for the following equations from the domain $\{-3, -2, -1, 0, 1, 2, 3\}$.

52. $x + 3 = 0$ **53.** $x + 1 = -2$ **54.** $x + 2 = -1$

55. $14 + x = 12$ **56.** $x + 8 = 7$ **57.** $x + (-4) = -6$

58. $x + (-2) = -5$ **59.** $-8 + x = -6$ **60.** $-2 + x = -1$

The word "sum" indicates addition. Write a numerical expression for each statement and simplify.

61. The sum of -9 and 2 and 6

62. The sum of 4 and -7 and -3

63. 12 added to the sum of -17 and -6

64. -3 added to the sum of 15 and -1

65. The sum of -11 and -4 increased by -5

66. The sum of -8 and -15 increased by -3

Solve the word problems.

67. Joann has $15. She then spends $6. How much is left?

68. An airplane is flying at an altitude of 6000 feet. It then descends 4000 feet. What is its final altitude?

69. Chuck is standing 15 feet below sea level in Death Valley. He then goes down another 120 feet. Find his final altitude.

70. Donna has $11 and spends $19. What is her final balance? (Write the answer with a negative number.)

71. One number of Nancy's blood pressure was 120, but then it changed by -30. Find her present blood pressure.

72. The temperature was $-14°$, but then it went down 12°. Find the new temperature.

73. The temperature at 4 A.M. was $-22°$, but it went up 35° by noon. What was the temperature at noon?

74. A man owes $94 to a credit card company. He makes a payment of $60. What amount does he still owe?

75. Joann Post owes $983.72 on her Visa credit card. She returns items costing $74.18 and $12.53. She makes two purchases of $11.79 each and further purchases of $106.58, $29.81, and $73.24. She makes a payment of $186.50. Find the amount that she then owes.

76. A welder working with stainless steel must use precise measurements. Suppose a welder attaches two pieces of steel that are each 3.589 inches in length, then attaches an additional three pieces that are each 9.089 inches long, and finally cuts off a piece that is 7.612 inches long. Find the length of the welded piece of steel.

77. What number must be added to -9 to get 8?

78. What number must be added to -15 to get 3?

79. The sum of what number and 5 is -11?

80. The sum of what number and -6 is -9?

1.7   Subtraction of Real Numbers

■ Find a difference on the number line.

② Use the definition of subtraction.

③ Work subtraction problems that involve brackets.

■   Recall that the answer to a subtraction problem is a **difference.** Differences can be found by using a number line. Since addition of a positive number on the number line is shown by drawing an arrow to the *right,* subtraction of a positive number is shown by drawing an arrow to the *left.*

EXAMPLE 1   Use the number line to find the difference $7 - 4$.

To find the difference $7 - 4$ on the number line, begin at 0 and draw an arrow seven units to the right. From the right end of this arrow, draw an arrow four units to the left, as shown in Figure 1.11. The number at the end of the second arrow shows that $7 - 4 = 3$.   ●

Figure 1.11

The procedure used in Example 1 to find $7 - 4$ is exactly the same procedure that would be used to find $7 + (-4)$, so that

$$7 - 4 = 7 + (-4).$$

②   Based on this, it seems that subtraction of a positive number from a larger positive number is the same as adding the additive inverse of the smaller number to the larger. This result can be extended as the definition of subtraction for all real numbers.

Definition of Subtraction

> For any real numbers x and y, $x - y = x + (-y)$.

That is, to subtract y from x, add the additive inverse (or opposite) of y to x. This definition gives the following procedure for subtracting signed numbers.

Subtracting Signed Numbers

> 1. Change the subtraction symbol to addition.
> 2. Change the sign of the number being subtracted.
> 3. Add, as in the previous section.

EXAMPLE 2   Subtract.

┌─Change − to +
No change─┐   │   ┌─Additive inverse of 3
(a) $12 - 3 = 12 + (-3) = 9$

(b) $5 - 7 = 5 + (-7) = -2$

┌─Change − to +
No change─┐   │   ┌─Additive inverse of −5
(c) $-3 - (-5) = -3 + (5) = 2$

(d) $-6 - (-9) = -6 + (9) = 3$ ●

The operation of subtraction is the inverse of the operation of addition, since subtraction can be used to reverse the result of an addition problem. For example, if 4 is added to a number and then subtracted from the sum, the original number is the result.

We now have used the symbol − for a variety of purposes. One use is to represent subtraction, as in $9 - 5$. The symbol − is also used to represent negative numbers, such as -10, -2, -3, and so on. Finally, the symbol − is used to represent the additive inverse of a number (the additive inverse of 9 is -9, for example). More than one use may appear in the same problem, such as $-6 - (-9)$, where -9 is subtracted from -6. The meaning of the symbol depends on its position in the algebraic expression.

3   As before, with problems that have both parentheses and brackets, first do any operations inside the parentheses and brackets. Work from the inside out.

EXAMPLE 3   Work each problem.

(a) $-6 - [2 - (8 + 3)] = -6 - [2 - 11]$
$$= -6 - (-9)$$
$$= -6 + (9) = 3$$

(b) $5 - [(-3 - 2) - (4 - 1)] = 5 - [(-3 + (-2)) - 3]$
$$= 5 - [(-5) - 3]$$
$$= 5 - [(-5) + (-3)]$$
$$= 5 - (-8)$$
$$= 5 + 8$$
$$= 13$$ ●

1.7 EXERCISES

Subtract. See Examples 1–2.

1. $3 - 6$ **2.** $7 - 12$ **3.** $5 - 9$ **4.** $8 - 13$

5. $-6 - 2$ **6.** $-11 - 4$ **7.** $-9 - 5$ **8.** $-12 - 15$

9. $6 - (-3)$ **10.** $8 - (-5)$ **11.** $5 - (-12)$ **12.** $12 - (-2)$

13. $-6 - (-2)$ **14.** $-7 - (-5)$ **15.** $2 - (3 - 5)$ **16.** $5 - (6 - 13)$

17. $-2 - (5 - 8)$ **18.** $-3 - (4 - 11)$ **19.** $\dfrac{1}{2} - \left(-\dfrac{1}{4}\right)$ **20.** $\dfrac{1}{3} - \left(-\dfrac{4}{3}\right)$

21. $-\dfrac{3}{4} - \dfrac{5}{8}$ **22.** $-\dfrac{5}{6} - \dfrac{1}{2}$ **23.** $\dfrac{5}{8} - \left(-\dfrac{1}{2} - \dfrac{3}{4}\right)$ **24.** $\dfrac{9}{10} - \left(\dfrac{1}{8} - \dfrac{3}{10}\right)$

25. $3.4 - (-8.2)$ **26.** $5.7 - (-11.6)$ **27.** $-6.4 - 3.5$ **28.** $-4.4 - 8.6$

29. $-4.1128 - (7.418 - 9.80632)$ **30.** $(-1.8142 - 3.7256) - (-9.8025)$

31. $[-7.6892 - (-3.2512)] - (-8.1243)$

32. $[(-2.1463 - 1.8374) - .28174] - [-3.258 - (-1.0926)]$

Work each problem. See Example 3.

33. $(4 - 6) + 12$ **34.** $(3 - 7) + 4$

35. $(8 - 1) - 12$ **36.** $(9 - 3) - 15$

37. $6 - (-8 + 3)$ **38.** $8 - (-9 + 5)$

39. $2 + (-4 - 8)$ **40.** $6 + (-9 - 2)$

41. $(-5 - 6) - (9 - 2)$ **42.** $(-4 - 8) - (6 - 1)$

43. $(-8 - 2) - (-9 - 3)$ **44.** $(-4 - 2) - (-8 - 1)$

45. $-9 - [(3 - 2) - (-4 - 2)]$ **46.** $-8 - [(-4 - 1) - (9 - 2)]$

47. $-3 + [(-5 - 8) - (-6 + 2)]$ **48.** $-4 + [(-12 + 1) - (-1 - 9)]$

49. $-9.1237 + [(-4.8099 - 3.2516) + 11.27903]$

50. $-7.6247 - [(-3.9928 + 1.42773) - (-2.80981)]$

51. $[-12.1035 - (8.11725 + 3.83122)] - 17.40963$

52. $[-34.9122 + (6.45378 - 12.14273)] - 8.46922$

Write the given problem in symbols (no variables are needed). Then solve.

53. Subtract -6 from 12.   **54.** Subtract -8 from 15.

55. From -25, subtract -4.   **56.** What number is 6 less than -9?

57. -24 is how much greater than -27?   **58.** How much greater is 8 than -5?

59. How much greater is -7.3 than -8.4?   **60.** -12.4 is how much greater than -14.3?

The word ''difference'' indicates subtraction. Write a numerical expression for each statement and simplify.

61. Find the difference of 8 and -2.   **62.** Find the difference of 3 and -7.

63. Add -11 to the difference of -4 and 2.   **64.** Add 8 to the difference of 1 and -3.

65. From the sum of -12 and -3, subtract 4.   **66.** From the sum of 8 and -13, subtract -2.

Solve the word problems.

67. The temperature dropped 10° below the previous temperature of −5°. Find the new temperature.

68. Bill owed his brother $10. He repaid $6 and later borrowed $7. What positive or negative number represents his present financial status?

69. The bottom of Death Valley is 282 feet below sea level. The top of Mt. Whitney, visible from Death Valley, has an altitude of 14,494 feet above sea level. Using zero as sea level, find the difference between these two elevations.

70. Harriet has $15, and Joann is $12 in debt. Find the difference between these amounts.

71. A chemist is running an experiment at a temperature of −174.6°. She then raises the temperature by 2.3°. Find the new temperature.

72. One year a company had a "profit" of −$25,000. The next year, the profit decreased by $7200. Find the profit the next year.

73. One company made a profit of $76,000, and another company lost $29,000. Find the difference between these.

74. One reading of a dial was 7.904. A second reading was −3.291. By how much had the reading declined?

1.8   Multiplication of Real Numbers

1 Find the product of a positive and a negative number.

2 Find the product of two negative numbers.

3 Use the order of operations in multiplication with signed numbers.

4 Evaluate expressions.

We already know the rules for multiplying positive numbers. For example,

the product of two positive numbers is positive.

But what about multiplying other real numbers? Any rules that we develop for multiplication of real numbers ought to be consistent with the rules for multiplication of positive numbers. For example, we would want the product of 0 and any real number (positive or negative) to be 0.

Multiplication by Zero

> For any real number x, $x \cdot 0 = 0.$

1   In order to define the product of a positive and a negative number so that the result is consistent with our definition of multiplying two positive numbers, look at the following pattern.

$$3 \cdot 5 = 15$$
$$3 \cdot 4 = 12$$
$$3 \cdot 3 = 9$$
$$3 \cdot 2 = 6$$
$$3 \cdot 1 = 3$$
$$3 \cdot 0 = 0$$
$$3 \cdot (-1) = ?$$

Numbers decrease by 3

What number should we assign to the product $3(-1)$ so that the pattern is maintained? The numbers on the left of the equals sign shown in color decrease by 1 as we go down the list. The products on the right decrease by 3 as we go down the list. To maintain this pattern, the number on the right in the bottom row must be 3 less than 0, or -3. Therefore, we must have

$$3(-1) = -3$$
$$3(-2) = -6$$
$$3(-3) = -9,$$

and so on.

Based on this,

for any positive real numbers x and y,

$$x(-y) = -(xy) \qquad \text{and} \qquad (-x)y = -(xy).$$

That is,

the product of two numbers with opposite signs is negative.

EXAMPLE 1   Find the products using the multiplication rule given above.

(a) $8(-5) = -(8 \cdot 5) = -40$

(b) $5(-4) = -(5 \cdot 4) = -20$

(c) $(-7)(2) = -(7 \cdot 2) = -14$

(d) $(-9)(3) = -(9 \cdot 3) = -27$ ●

2   The product of two positive numbers is positive, and the product of a positive and a negative number is negative. What about the product of two negative numbers? Look at another pattern.

$$(-5)(4) = -20$$
$$(-5)(3) = -15$$
$$(-5)(2) = -10$$
$$(-5)(1) = -5$$
$$(-5)(0) = 0$$
$$(-5)(-1) = ?$$

Numbers increase by 5

The numbers on the left of the equals sign shown in color decrease by 1 as we go down the list. The products on the right increase by 5 as we go down the list. To maintain this pattern, we will have to agree that $(-5)(-1)$ is 5 more than $(-5)(0)$, or 5 more than 0. Therefore, we must have

$$(-5)(-1) = 5.$$

The pattern continues with

$$(-5)(-2) = 10$$
$$(-5)(-3) = 15$$
$$(-5)(-4) = 20$$
$$(-5)(-5) = 25,$$

and so on. Thus,

for any positive real numbers x and y,

$$(-x)(-y) = xy.$$

In words,

the product of two negative numbers is positive.

EXAMPLE 2   Find the products using the multiplication rule given above.

(a) $(-9)(-2) = 9 \cdot 2 = 18$ (b) $(-6)(-12) = 6 \cdot 12 = 72$

(c) $(-8)(-1) = 8 \cdot 1 = 8$ (d) $(-15)(-2) = 15 \cdot 2 = 30$ ●

Now we can summarize our results for multiplying signed numbers.

Multiplying Signed Numbers

> The product of two numbers having the *same* signs is *positive*, and the product of two numbers having *different* signs is *negative*.

3   The next example shows the order of operations discussed earlier used with the multiplication of positive and negative numbers.

EXAMPLE 3   Simplify.

(a) $(-9)(2) - (-3)(2)$

First find all products, working from left to right.

$$(-9)(2) - (-3)(2) = -18 - (-6)$$

Now perform the subtraction.

$$-18 - (-6) = -18 + 6 = -12$$

(b) $(-6)(-2) - (3)(-4) = 12 - (-12) = 12 + 12 = 24$

(c) $-5(-2 - 3) = -5(-5) = 25$ •

4 The last example shows how numbers may be substituted for variables.

EXAMPLE 4 Evaluate the expression

$$(3x + 4y)(-2m)$$

given:

(a) $x = -1, \quad y = -2, \quad m = -3;$

First substitute the given values for the variables. Then find the value of the expression.

$(3x + 4y)(-2m) = [3(-1) + 4(-2)][-2(-3)]$ Put parentheses around the number for each variable

$\qquad = [-3 + (-8)][6]$ Find the products

$\qquad = (-11)(6)$ Use order of operations

$\qquad = -66$

(b) $x = 7, \quad y = -9, \quad m = 5.$

Substitute.

$(3x + 4y)(-2m) = [3 \cdot 7 + 4(-9)](-2 \cdot 5)$ Use parentheses around -9

$\qquad = [21 + (-36)](-10)$ Find the products

$\qquad = (-15)(-10)$

$\qquad = 150$ •

1.8 EXERCISES

Find the products. In Exercises 27–30, round to the nearest thousandth. See Examples 1 and 2.

1. $(-3)(-4)$ **2.** $(-3)(4)$ **3.** $3(-4)$ **4.** $-2(-8)$

5. $(-10)(-12)$ **6.** $9(-5)$ **7.** $(8)(-6)$ **8.** $(13)(-2)$

9. $(-9)(0)$ **10.** $(13)(-5)$ **11.** $0(-11)$ **12.** $3(-15)$

13. $(15)(-11)$ **14.** $(-9)(-4)$ **15.** $-\dfrac{3}{8} \cdot \left(-\dfrac{10}{9}\right)$ **16.** $-\dfrac{5}{4} \cdot \left(-\dfrac{5}{8}\right)$

17. $\left(-\dfrac{5}{4}\right)\left(\dfrac{2}{15}\right)$ **18.** $\left(\dfrac{3}{7}\right)\left(-\dfrac{14}{9}\right)$ **19.** $(-8)\left(-\dfrac{3}{4}\right)$ **20.** $(-6)\left(-\dfrac{5}{3}\right)$

21. $(-5.1)(.02)$ **22.** $(-3.7)(-2.1)$ **23.** $(1.8)(-7.2)$ **24.** $(-4.7)(-6.8)$

25. $(3.4)(-3.5)$ **26.** $(-5.2)(-7.4)$ ▣ **27.** $(-12.804)(4.12)$ **28.** $(3.871)(-5.463)$

29. $(-8.91)(-4.725)$ **30.** $(-6.4972)(-13.8015)$

Perform the indicated operations. See Example 3.

31. $6 - 4 \cdot 5$ **32.** $3 - 2 \cdot 9$ **33.** $-9 - (-2) \cdot 3$

34. $-11 - (-7) \cdot 4$ **35.** $9(6 - 10)$ **36.** $5(12 - 15)$

37. $-6(2 - 4)$ **38.** $-9(5 - 8)$ **39.** $(4 - 9)(2 - 3)$

40. $(6 - 11)(3 - 6)$ **41.** $(2 - 5)(3 - 7)$ **42.** $(5 - 12)(2 - 6)$

43. $(-4 - 3)(-2) + 4$ **44.** $(-5 - 2)(-3) + 6$ **45.** $5(-2) - 4$

46. $9(-6) - 8$ **47.** $3(-4) - (-2)$ **48.** $5(-2) - (-9)$

49. $(-8 - 2)(-4) - (-5)$ **50.** $(-9 - 1)(-2) - (-6)$ **51.** $|-4(-2)| + |-4|$

52. $|8(-5)| + |-2|$ **53.** $|2|(-4) + |6| \cdot |-4|$ **54.** $|-3|(-2) + |-8| \cdot |5|$

Evaluate the following expressions, given $x = -2$, $y = 3$, and $a = -4$. See Example 4.

55. $5x - 2y + 3a$ **56.** $6x - 5y + 4a$ **57.** $(2x + y)(3a)$

58. $(5x - 2y)(-2a)$ **59.** $(3x - 4y)(-5a)$ **60.** $(6x + 2y)(-3a)$

61. $(-5 + x)(-3 + y)(2 - a)$ **62.** $(6 - x)(5 + y)(3 + a)$ **63.** $-2y^2 + 3a$

64. $5x - 4a^2$ **65.** $3a^2 - x^2$ **66.** $4y^2 - 2x^2$

Find the solution for the following equations from the domain $\{-3, -2, -1, 0, 1, 2, 3\}$.

67. $2x = -4$ **68.** $-4m = 0$ **69.** $-9y = 0$

70. $-8p = 16$ **71.** $-9r = 27$ **72.** $2x + 1 = -3$

73. $3w + 3 = -3$ **74.** $-4a + 2 = 10$ **75.** $-5t + 6 = 11$

The word "product" indicates multiplication. Write a numerical expression for each statement and simplify.

76. The product of -9 and 2 is added to 6.

77. The product of 4 and -7 is added to -9.

78. After the product of -1 and 6 is found, the result is subtracted from -9.

79. Twice the product of -8 and 2 is subtracted from -4.

80. Nine is subtracted from the product of 7 and -6.

81. Three is subtracted from the product of -2 and 3.

1.9   Division of Real Numbers

▢1   Find the reciprocal, or multiplicative inverse, of a number.
▢2   Divide positive and negative numbers.
▢3   Simplify numerical expressions.

▢1   The difference of two numbers is found by adding the additive inverse of the second number to the first. Division is related to multiplication in a similar way. To subtract, use the additive inverse; to divide, use the multiplicative inverse. Since

$$8 \cdot \frac{1}{8} = \frac{8}{8} = 1 \quad \text{and} \quad \frac{5}{4} \cdot \frac{4}{5} = \frac{20}{20} = 1,$$

the multiplicative inverse of 8 is 1/8, and of 5/4 is 4/5.

Multiplicative Inverse

> Pairs of numbers whose product is 1 are **multiplicative inverses,** or **reciprocals,** of each other.

EXAMPLE 1   Find the multiplicative inverse of each number.

Number	Multiplicative inverse (Reciprocal)
4	$\frac{1}{4}$
-5	$\frac{1}{-5}$ or $-\frac{1}{5}$
$-\frac{5}{8}$	$-\frac{8}{5}$
0	None ●

Why is there no multiplicative inverse for the number 0? Suppose that k is to be the multiplicative inverse of 0. Then $k \cdot 0$ should equal 1. But $k \cdot 0 = 0$ for any number k. There is no value of k that is a solution of the equation $k \cdot 0 = 1$, and so 0 has no multiplicative inverse.

▢2   By definition, the quotient of x and y is the product of x and the multiplicative inverse of y. That is,

Definition of Division

> for any real numbers x and y, with $y \neq 0$, $\dfrac{x}{y} = x \cdot \dfrac{1}{y}$.

In the definition above, y, the number we divide by, cannot be 0. The reason is that 0 has no multiplicative inverse, so that 1/0 is not a number. For this reason

division by 0 is meaningless

and is never permitted. If a division problem turns out to involve division by 0, write "meaningless."

Since division is defined in terms of multiplication, all the rules for multiplication of signed numbers also apply to division.

EXAMPLE 2 Find the quotients using the definition of division.

(a) $\dfrac{12}{3} = 12 \cdot \dfrac{1}{3} = 4$ (b) $\dfrac{-10}{2} = -10 \cdot \dfrac{1}{2} = -5$

(c) $\dfrac{-14}{-7} = -14\left(\dfrac{1}{-7}\right) = 2$ (d) $\dfrac{-10}{0}$ meaningless ●

In practice,

Dividing Signed Numbers

> to divide with signed numbers, divide the absolute values of the numbers. The quotient will be positive if both of the original numbers have like signs, and negative if the numbers have unlike signs.

EXAMPLE 3 Find the quotients.

(a) $\dfrac{8}{-2} = -4$

(b) $\dfrac{-45}{-9} = 5$

(c) $-\dfrac{1}{8} \div \left(-\dfrac{3}{4}\right) = -\dfrac{1}{8} \cdot \left(-\dfrac{4}{3}\right) = \dfrac{1}{6}$ ●

From the definitions of multiplication and division of real numbers,

$$\frac{-40}{8} = -40 \cdot \frac{1}{8} = -5,$$

and

$$\frac{40}{-8} = 40\left(\frac{1}{-8}\right) = -5,$$

so that

$$\frac{-40}{8} = \frac{40}{-8}.$$

Based on this example, we can express the quotient of a positive and a negative number in three forms.

For any positive real numbers x and y, $\dfrac{-x}{y} = \dfrac{x}{-y} = -\dfrac{x}{y}$.

The form $x/-y$ is seldom used.

We also can express the quotient of two negative numbers as a quotient of two positive numbers.

For any positive real numbers x and y, $\dfrac{-x}{-y} = \dfrac{x}{y}$.

3 The next example shows how to simplify numerical expressions involving quotients.

EXAMPLE 4 Simplify $\dfrac{5(-2) - (3)(4)}{2(1 - 6)}$.

Simplify the numerator and denominator separately. Then divide.

$$\frac{5(-2) - (3)(4)}{2(1 - 6)} = \frac{-10 - 12}{2(-5)} = \frac{-22}{-10} = \frac{11}{5} \quad \bullet$$

Let us now summarize the rules for operating with signed numbers.

Operations with Signed Numbers

Addition
Like signs   Add the absolute values of the numbers. The result has the same sign as the numbers.
Unlike signs   Subtract the number with the smaller absolute value from the one with the larger. Give the result the sign of the number having the larger absolute value.

Subtraction
Add the additive inverse, or opposite number.

Multiplication and Division
Like signs   The product or quotient of two numbers with like signs is positive.
Unlike signs   The product or quotient of two numbers with unlike signs is negative.
Division by 0 is not permitted.

1.9 EXERCISES

Find the multiplicative inverse where one exists. Round to the nearest thousandth in Exercises 11 and 12. See Example 1.

1. 9

2. 8

3. -4

4. -10

5. $\dfrac{2}{3}$

6. $\dfrac{3}{4}$

7. $\dfrac{-9}{10}$

8. $\dfrac{-4}{5}$

9. 0

10. $\dfrac{0}{5}$

🔳 **11.** .8697

12. 1.4385

Find the quotients. Round to the nearest thousandth in Exercises 41 and 42.
See Examples 2 and 3.

13. $\dfrac{-10}{5}$

14. $\dfrac{-12}{3}$

15. $\dfrac{-15}{5}$

16. $\dfrac{-20}{2}$

17. $\dfrac{18}{-3}$

18. $\dfrac{24}{-6}$

19. $\dfrac{-150}{-10}$

20. $\dfrac{-280}{-20}$

21. $\dfrac{-180}{-5}$

22. $\dfrac{-350}{-7}$

23. $\dfrac{0}{-2}$

24. $\dfrac{0}{12}$

25. $-\dfrac{1}{2} \div \left(-\dfrac{3}{4}\right)$

26. $-\dfrac{5}{8} \div \left(-\dfrac{3}{16}\right)$

27. $(-4.2) \div (-2)$

28. $(-9.8) \div (-7)$

29. $\dfrac{4}{-.8}$

30. $\dfrac{-6}{.3}$

31. $\dfrac{12}{2-5}$

32. $\dfrac{15}{3-8}$

33. $\dfrac{50}{2-7}$

34. $\dfrac{30}{5-8}$

35. $\dfrac{-40}{8-(-2)}$

36. $\dfrac{-72}{6-(-2)}$

37. $\dfrac{-120}{-3-(-5)}$

38. $\dfrac{-200}{-6-(-4)}$

39. $\dfrac{-30-(-8)}{-11}$

40. $\dfrac{-17-(-12)}{5}$

🔳 **41.** $\dfrac{-6.42-(-3.891)}{-.05}$

42. $\dfrac{11.096-(-8.1151)}{.8-.05}$

Simplify the numerators and denominators separately. Then find the quotients.
Round to the nearest thousandth in Exercises 56 and 57. See Example 4.

43. $\dfrac{-8(-2)}{3-(-1)}$

44. $\dfrac{-12(-3)}{-15-(-3)}$

45. $\dfrac{-15(2)}{-7-3}$

46. $\dfrac{-20(6)}{-5-1}$

47. $\dfrac{-2(6)+3}{2-(-1)}$

48. $\dfrac{3(-8)+4}{-6+1}$

49. $\dfrac{-5(2)+3(-2)}{-3-(-1)}$

50. $\dfrac{4(-1)+3(-2)}{-2-3}$

51. $\dfrac{-9(-2)-(-4)(-2)}{-2(3)-2(2)}$

52. $\dfrac{4^2-5^2}{3(6-9+2)}$

53. $\dfrac{6^2+4^2}{5(2+13)}$

54. $\dfrac{3^2+5^2}{4^2+1^2}$

55. $\dfrac{10^2-5^2}{8^2+3^2+2}$

🔳 **56.** $\dfrac{(.86)^2+(2.5)^2}{(-1.43)^3-(-3.76)}$

57. $\dfrac{(-.49)^2-(.21)^2}{3.58-(-1.12)^3}$

Find the solution of each equation from the domain
$\{-8, -6, -4, -2, 0, 2, 4, 6, 8\}$.

58. $\dfrac{x}{4} = -2$

59. $\dfrac{x}{2} = -1$

60. $\dfrac{n}{-2} = 3$

61. $\dfrac{t}{-2} = -2$

62. $\dfrac{q}{-3} = 0$ **63.** $\dfrac{p}{5} = 0$ **64.** $\dfrac{m}{-2} = -4$ **65.** $\dfrac{y}{-1} = 2$

Write each statement in symbols and find the solution. The domain is the set of integers between −12 and 12, inclusive.

66. Six times a number is −42.

67. Four times a number is −32.

68. When a number is divided by 3, the result is −3.

69. When a number is divided by −3, the answer is −4.

70. The quotient of a number and 2 is −6. $\left(\text{Write the quotient as }\dfrac{x}{2}.\right)$

71. The quotient of a number and 5 is −2.

72. The quotient of 6 and one more than a number is 3.

73. When the square of a number is divided by 3, the result is 12.

Write a numerical expression for each statement and simplify.

74. Add −9 to the quotient of 15 and −3.

75. Add 4 to the quotient of −28 and 4.

76. Subtract 3 from the quotient of 8 and −2.

77. Subtract 3 from the quotient of −16 and 4.

78. Find the product of −10 and 2. Then find the quotient of this product and 5.

1.10 Properties of Addition and Multiplication

Identify the use of the following properties:

1. commutative;
2. associative;
3. identity;
4. inverse;
5. distributive.

In this section we list some of the properties of addition and multiplication of real numbers. In the following statements, *x, y,* and *z* are all real numbers.

1 **Commutative properties** By the commutative properties, two numbers can be added or multiplied in any order.

$$x + y = y + x$$

$$xy = yx$$

EXAMPLE 1   Use a commutative property to complete each statement.

(a) $-8 + 5 = 5 +$ _____

By the commutative property for addition, the missing number is -8, since $-8 + 5 = 5 + (-8)$.

(b) $(-2)(7) =$ _____ (-2)

By the commutative property for multiplication, the missing number is 7, since $(-2)(7) = (7)(-2)$.   ●

■2   **Associative properties**   The associative properties say that when three numbers are added or multiplied, the first two may be grouped together, or the last two may be grouped together, without affecting the answer.

$$(x + y) + z = x + (y + z)$$

$$(xy)z = x(yz)$$

EXAMPLE 2   Use an associative property to complete each statement.

(a) $8 + (-1 + 4) = (8 +$ _____ $) + 4$

The missing number is -1.

(b) $[2 \cdot (-7)] \cdot 6 = 2 \cdot$ _____

The completed expression on the right should be $2 \cdot [(-7) \cdot 6]$.   ●

By the associative property of addition, the sum of three numbers will be the same however the numbers are "associated" in groups. For this reason, parentheses can be left out in many addition problems. For example, either

$$(-1 + 2) + 3 \qquad \text{or} \qquad -1 + (2 + 3)$$

can be written as just

$$-1 + 2 + 3.$$

In the same way, parentheses can also be left out of many multiplication problems.

EXAMPLE 3   (a) Is $(2 + 4) + 5 = 2 + (4 + 5)$ an example of the associative property?

The order of the three numbers is the same on both sides of the equals sign. The only change is in the grouping of the numbers. Therefore, this is an example of the associative property.

(b) Is $6(3 \cdot 10) = 6(10 \cdot 3)$ an example of the associative property or the commutative property?

The same numbers, 3 and 10, are grouped on both sides of the equals sign. On the left, however, the 3 appears first in $(3 \cdot 10)$. On the right, the 10 appears first. Since the change involves the order of the numbers, this is an example of the commutative property.

(c) Is $(8 + 1) + 7 = 8 + (7 + 1)$ an example of the associative property or the commutative property?

In this statement, both the order and the grouping are changed. On the left the order of the three numbers is 8, 1, and 7. On the right it is 8, 7, and 1. On the left the 8 and 1 are grouped, and on the right the 7 and 1 are grouped. Therefore, both the associative and the commutative properties were used.   ●

3 **Identity properties**   The identity properties say that we can add 0 to any number and get the same number, and we can multiply any number by 1 and get the same number.

$$x + 0 = x \quad \text{and} \quad 0 + x = x$$

$$x \cdot 1 = x \quad \text{and} \quad 1 \cdot x = x$$

The number 0 leaves the identity, or value, of any real number unchanged by addition. For this reason, 0 is called the **identity element for addition.** In a similar way, multiplication by 1 leaves any real number unchanged, so 1 is the **identity element for multiplication.**

EXAMPLE 4   These statements are examples of the identity properties.

(a) $-3 + 0 = -3$

(b) $0 + \dfrac{1}{2} = \dfrac{1}{2}$

(c) $-\dfrac{3}{4} \cdot 1 = -\dfrac{3}{4}$

(d) $1 \cdot 25 = 25$ ●

4 **Inverse properties**   By the inverse properties, the sum of the numbers x and $-x$ is 0, and the product of the nonzero numbers x and $1/x$ is 1.

$$x + (-x) = 0 \quad \text{and} \quad -x + x = 0$$

$$x \cdot \frac{1}{x} = 1 \quad \text{and} \quad \frac{1}{x} \cdot x = 1 \quad (x \neq 0)$$

As we know, the number $-x$ is the **additive inverse** of x and $1/x$ is the **multiplicative inverse** of the nonzero number x.

EXAMPLE 5   These statements are examples of the inverse properties.

(a) $\dfrac{2}{3} \cdot \dfrac{3}{2} = 1$

(b) $(-5)\left(-\dfrac{1}{5}\right) = 1$

(c) $-\dfrac{1}{2} + \dfrac{1}{2} = 0$

(d) $4 + (-4) = 0$ ●

5   The final property of real numbers, the distributive property, is one that relates addition and multiplication. Using the distributive property, a product can be changed to a sum.

Distributive property   By the distributive property, we can multiply a number x by a sum of numbers $y + z$ by multiplying x by y and x by z and then adding the resulting products.

$$x(\overbrace{y + z}) = xy + xz \qquad \text{and} \qquad (\overbrace{y + z})x = yx + zx$$

As the arrows show, the x outside the parentheses is "distributed" over the y and z inside. Another form of the distributive property is valid for subtraction.

$$x(y - z) = xy - xz \qquad \text{and} \qquad (y - z)x = yx - zx$$

The distributive property also can be extended to more than two numbers.

$$x(y + z + w) = xy + xz + xw$$

EXAMPLE 6   Simplify using the distributive property.

(a) $5(9 + 6) = 5 \cdot 9 + 5 \cdot 6$ Multiply both terms by 5
$$= 45 + 30$$
$$= 75$$

(b) $4(x + 5 + y) = 4x + 4 \cdot 5 + 4y = 4x + 20 + 4y$

(c) $-2(x + 3) = -2x + (-2)(3) = -2x - 6$

(d) $3(k - 9) = 3k - 3 \cdot 9 = 3k - 27$

(e) $6 \cdot 8 + 6 \cdot 2 = 6(8 + 2) = 6(10) = 60$

(f) $8(3r + 11t + 5z) = 8(3r) + 8(11t) + 8(5z)$
$$= (8 \cdot 3)r + (8 \cdot 11)t + (8 \cdot 5)z \qquad \text{Associative property}$$
$$= 24r + 88t + 40z \quad \bullet$$

The distributive property is used to simplify expressions such as $-(2y + 3)$. Do this by writing $-(2y + 3)$ as $-1 \cdot (2y + 3)$.

$$-(2y + 3) = -1 \cdot (2y + 3)$$
$$= -1 \cdot (2y) + (-1) \cdot (3)$$
$$= -2y - 3$$

EXAMPLE 7   Simplify.

(a) $-(7r - 8) = -1(7r) + (-1)(-8) = -7r + 8$

(b) $-(-9w + 2) = 9w - 2 \quad \bullet$

We now can summarize the properties of addition and multiplication.

Properties of Addition and Multiplication

For all real numbers x, y, and z:

	Addition	*Multiplication*
Commutative	$x + y = y + x$	$xy = yx$
Associative	$(x + y) + z = x + (y + z)$	$(xy)z = x(yz)$
Identity	$x + 0 = x$ and $0 + x = x$	$x \cdot 1 = x$ and $1 \cdot x = x$
Inverse	$x + (-x) = 0$ and $-x + x = 0$	$x \cdot \dfrac{1}{x} = 1$ and $\dfrac{1}{x} \cdot x = 1$ $(x \neq 0)$
Distributive	$x(y + z) = xy + xz$ and $(y + z)x = yx + zx$	

1.10 EXERCISES

Label each statement as an example of the commutative, associative, identity, inverse, or distributive property. See Examples 1–6.

1. $6 + 15 = 15 + 6$

2. $9 + (11 + 4) = (9 + 11) + 4$

3. $5(15 \cdot 8) = (5 \cdot 15)8$

4. $(23)(9) = (9)(23)$

5. $12(-8) = (-8)(12)$

6. $(-9)[6(-2)] = [-9(6)](-2)$

7. $2 + (p + r) = (p + r) + 2$

8. $(m + n) + 4 = (n + m) + 4$

9. $-6 + 12 = 12 + (-6)$

10. $(-9)(-11) = (-11)(-9)$

11. $6 + (-6) = 0$

12. $-8 + 8 = 0$

13. $-4 + 0 = -4$

14. $0 + (-9) = -9$

15. $3\left(\dfrac{1}{3}\right) = 1$

16. $-7\left(-\dfrac{1}{7}\right) = 1$

17. $\dfrac{2}{3} \cdot 1 = \dfrac{2}{3}$

18. $-\dfrac{9}{4} \cdot 1 = -\dfrac{9}{4}$

19. $6(5 - 2x) = 6 \cdot 5 - 6(2x)$

20. $5(2m) + 5(7n) = 5(2m + 7n)$

Use the indicated property to write a new expression that is equal to the given expression. Simplify the new expression if possible. See Examples 1, 2, and 4–6.

21. $9 + k$;   commutative

22. $z + 5$;   commutative

23. $m + 0$;   identity

24. $(-9) + 0$;   identity

25. $3(r + m)$;   distributive

26. $11(k + z)$;   distributive

27. $8 \cdot \dfrac{1}{8}$;   inverse

28. $\dfrac{1}{6} \cdot 6$;   inverse

29. $12 + (-12)$;   inverse

30. $-8 + 8$;   inverse

31. $5 + (-5)$;   commutative

32. $-9 + 9$;   commutative

33. $-3(r + 2)$;   distributive

34. $4(k - 5)$;   distributive

35. $9 \cdot 1$;   identity

36. $1(-4)$;   identity

37. $(k + 5) + (-6)$;   associative

38. $(m + 4) + (-2)$;   associative

39. $(4z + 2r) + 3k$;   associative

40. $(6m + 2n) + 5r$;   associative

Use the distributive property to rewrite each expression. See Example 6.

41. $5(m + 2)$

42. $6(k + 5)$

43. $-4(r + 2)$

44. $-3(m + 5)$

45. $-8(k - 2)$

46. $-4(z - 5)$

47. $-9(a + 3)$

48. $-3(p + 5)$

49. $(r + 8)4$

50. $(m + 12)6$

51. $(8 - k)(-2)$

52. $(9 - r)(-3)$

53. $2(5r + 6m)$

54. $5(2a + 4b)$

55. $-4(3x - 4y)$

56. $-9(5k - 12m)$

57. $5 \cdot 8 + 5 \cdot 9$

58. $4 \cdot 3 + 4 \cdot 9$

59. $7 \cdot 2 + 7 \cdot 8$

60. $6x + 6m$

61. $9p + 9q$

62. $8(2x) + 8(3p)$

63. $5(7z) + 5(8w)$

64. $11(2r) + 11(3s)$

Use the distributive property to simplify each expression. See Example 7.

65. $-(3k + 5)$

66. $-(2z + 12)$

67. $-(4y - 8)$

68. $-(3r - 15)$

69. $-(-4 + p)$

70. $-(-12 + 3a)$

71. $-(-1 - 15r)$

72. $-(-14 - 6y)$

Decide whether or not the following events are commutative.

73. Getting out of bed and taking a shower

74. Putting on your right shoe or your left shoe first

75. Taking English or taking history

76. Putting on your shoe or putting on your sock

77. Evaluate $25 - (6 - 2)$ and evaluate $(25 - 6) - 2$. Do you think subtraction is associative?

78. Evaluate $180 \div (15 \div 3)$ and evaluate $(180 \div 15) \div 3$. Do you think division is associative?

Chapter 1 Review Exercises

If you have trouble with any of these exercises, look in the section given in brackets.

[1.1] *Write each fraction in lowest terms.*

1. $\dfrac{18}{54}$ **2.** $\dfrac{60}{72}$ **3.** $\dfrac{22}{110}$ **4.** $\dfrac{120}{150}$

Find the products or quotients. Write the answers in lowest terms.

5. $\dfrac{7}{10} \cdot \dfrac{1}{5}$ **6.** $\dfrac{3}{7} \cdot \dfrac{5}{6}$ **7.** $\dfrac{8}{5} \div \dfrac{32}{15}$ **8.** $\dfrac{32}{15} \div \dfrac{8}{5}$

Add or subtract. Write the answers in lowest terms.

9. $\dfrac{3}{8} + \dfrac{1}{2}$ **10.** $\dfrac{7}{10} - \dfrac{1}{4}$ **11.** $2\dfrac{3}{4} + 5\dfrac{5}{12}$ **12.** $6\dfrac{1}{4} - 5\dfrac{3}{4}$

Work the following word problems.

13. John painted 1/4 of a room on Monday and 1/3 of the room on Tuesday. What portion was then painted?

14. A contractor installs toolsheds. Each requires 1 1/4 cubic yards of concrete. How much concrete would be needed for 25 sheds?

[1.2] *Which of the symbols $<$, $\leq$, $>$, and $\geq$ make the following statements true? Give all possible correct answers.*

15. .87 _____ .865   **16.** .94 _____ .904   **17.** $\dfrac{2}{3}$ _____ .7   **18.** $\dfrac{3}{4}$ _____ .8

[1.3] *Find the following.*

19. 4^3 **20.** 6^3 **21.** $\left(\dfrac{5}{8}\right)^2$ **22.** $\left(\dfrac{7}{3}\right)^3$

Simplify on the left, and then decide whether the statement is true or false.

23. $9 \cdot (6 + 2) - 4 > 70$ **24.** $5 \cdot (4 + 8) + 2 \cdot 3 \leq 68$ **25.** $\dfrac{2(1 + 3)}{3(2 + 1)} < 1$

26. $6^2 - 4^2 \geq 5$ **27.** $5^2 + 4^2 \leq 40$

[1.4] *Find the numerical value of the given expression when $x = 2$ and $y = 5$.*

28. $\dfrac{3x - y}{2x}$ **29.** $\dfrac{2x}{y + 1}$ **30.** $x^2 + y^2$ **31.** $\dfrac{3x^2 + 5y^2}{7x^2 - y^2}$

Write each word phrase using algebraic expressions. Use x as the variable.

32. Six subtracted from three times a number   **33.** The difference of 4 and a number

34. The sum of a number and 4, divided by 8   **35.** The product of a number and one more than the number

[1.5] *Select the smaller of the two given numbers.*

36. $5, |-8|$ **37.** $9, |-7|$ **38.** $-|-2|, -|-9|$ **39.** $-|-7|, -|-4|$

Decide whether each statement is true or false.

40. $3 \leq -(-5)$ **41.** $9 \geq -(-10)$ **42.** $-3 > -2$ **43.** $-5 < -4$

44. $-|7| \leq -|-2|$ **45.** $-|4| > -|-3|$ **46.** $|-(-2)| > -|-2|$ **47.** $|-5| < |5|$

Graph each group of numbers on a number line.

48. $-1, -3, |-4|, |-1|$ **49.** $3\dfrac{1}{4}, -2\dfrac{4}{5}, -1\dfrac{1}{8}, \dfrac{2}{3}$ **50.** $|-2|, -|-5|, -|3|, -|0|$

[1.6] *Find the sums.*

51. $(-9 + 6) + (-10)$ **52.** $[-3 + (-5)] + (-8)$ **53.** $\dfrac{7}{8} + \left(-\dfrac{3}{10}\right)$

54. $\dfrac{7}{12} + \left(-\dfrac{2}{9}\right)$ **55.** $14.2 + (-8.6)$ **56.** $-11.3 + (-2.9)$

57. $[(-4) + 6 + (-9)] + [-3 + (-5)]$ **58.** $[(-6) + (-7) + 8] + [8 + (-15)]$

Solve the word problems.

59. Tom has \$9. He spends \$11. Find his new balance.

60. The temperature is $15°$. It goes down $22°$. Find the new temperature.

61. One year a company spent \$28,000 on advertising. The next year it changed the amount spent on advertising by $-\$7000$. How much was spent on advertising the second year?

62. On a cold day, the temperature was $-17°$. It then increased by $19°$. Find the new temperature.

[1.7] *Find any sums or differences.*

63. $15 - (-3)$ **64.** $-8 - 9$ **65.** $\dfrac{3}{4} - \left(-\dfrac{2}{3}\right)$

66. $-\dfrac{1}{5} - \left(-\dfrac{7}{10}\right)$

67. $(-9 + 6) - (-3)$

68. $(-15 - 7) - (-9)$

69. $(-8 - 2) - [(-1 - 4) - (-1)]$

70. $-3 + [(-12 + 15) - (-4 - 5)]$

[1.8] *Simplify.*

71. $-\dfrac{4}{5}\left(-\dfrac{10}{7}\right)$

72. $-\dfrac{3}{8}\left(-\dfrac{16}{15}\right)$

73. $(-11.3)(2.5)$

74. $(-9.4)(-2.8)$

75. $8(-9) - (6)(-2)$

76. $-6(-2) - (-4)(3)$

77. $-11(-4) - (3)(-7)$

78. $|6(-8)| - |-3|$

79. $-|(-9)(4)| - |-2|$

Evaluate the following expressions, given $x = -5$, $y = 4$, and $z = -3$.

80. $y^2 - 2z^2$

81. $(2x - 8y)(z^2)$

82. $3z^2 - 4x^2$

[1.9] *Find the quotients.*

83. $\dfrac{-8 - (-9)}{10}$

84. $\dfrac{-7 - (-21)}{8}$

85. $\dfrac{8 - 4(-2)}{-5(3) - 1}$

86. $\dfrac{5(-3) - 8(3)}{(-5)(-4) + (-7)}$

87. $\dfrac{7^2 - 3^2}{2^2 + 4^2}$

88. $\dfrac{11^2 - 5^2 + 2}{5^2 + 5^2 - 1^2}$

[1.10] *Decide whether each statement is an example of the commutative, associative, identity, inverse, or distributive property.*

89. $8.974 \cdot 1 = 8.974$

90. $-\dfrac{2}{3} + \dfrac{2}{3} = 0$

91. $7 + 4m = 4m + 7$

92. $8(4 \cdot 3) = (8 \cdot 4)3$

93. $\dfrac{5}{8} \cdot \dfrac{8}{5} = 1$

94. $9p + 0 = 9p$

Simplify using the distributive property.

95. $6(3k + 5r)$

96. $-3(2m - 7k)$

Chapter 1   Test

1. Write $\dfrac{84}{132}$ in lowest terms.

2. Add: $\dfrac{3}{8} + \dfrac{7}{12} + \dfrac{11}{15}$.

3. Divide: $\dfrac{6}{5} \div \dfrac{19}{15}$.

Answer true *or* false *for the following.*

4. $6 - |-4| \geq 10$

5. $4[5(-4) + 7(-2)] \leq 135$

6. $\dfrac{9(-4) - 3(-6)}{(-2)(-4) - (-1)} \leq -2$

7. $\dfrac{8(7 - 3) + 4(1 + 5)}{6(3 - 5) - (5 - 9)(2)} > -14$

8. $(-3)^2 + 2^2 = 5^2$

Find the numerical value of the given expression when m = 6 and p = 2.

9. $5m + 2p^3$

10. $\dfrac{7m^2 - p^2}{m + 4}$

Select the smaller number from each pair.

11. $6, -|-8|$

12. $.742, .705$

Write each word phrase as an algebraic expression. Use x as the variable.

13. Twice a number subtracted from 11

14. The quotient of 9 and the difference of a number and 8

Decide whether the given number is a solution for the equation.

15. $6m + m + 2 = 37; \quad 5$

16. $8(y - 3) + 2y = 18; \quad 4$

Perform the indicated operations wherever possible.

17. $-9 - (4 - 11) + (-5)$

18. $-2\dfrac{1}{5} + 5\dfrac{1}{4}$

19. $-6 - [-5 + (8 - 9)]$

20. $3^2 + (-7) - (2^3 - 5)$

21. $|-6| \cdot (-5) + 2 \cdot |8|$

22. $\dfrac{-7 - (-5 + 1)}{-4 - (-3)}$

23. $\dfrac{-6[5 - (-1 + 4)]}{-9[2 - (-1)] - 6(-4)}$

24. $\dfrac{15(-4 - 2)}{16(-2) + (-7 - 1)(-3 - 1)}$

Find the solution for each equation. Choose solutions from the domain $\{-9, -5, -4, -3, -2, -1, 3, 9\}$.

25. $\dfrac{p}{-3} = 3$

26. $2x + 1 = -7$

27. $-4x - 7 = 5$

Match the property in Column I with all examples of it from Column II.

Column I	Column II
28. Commutative	**A.** $12 + (-12) = -12 + 12$
29. Associative	**B.** $\dfrac{6}{5}\left(\dfrac{5}{6}\right) = 1$
30. Identity	
31. Inverse	**C.** $1(-9) = -9$
32. Distributive	**D.** $2(5) + 2(9) = 2(5 + 9)$
	E. $8x = x \cdot 8$
	F. $-(2 - p) = -2 + p$
	G. $-7 + 7 = 0$
	H. $9 + (2 + y) = (9 + 2) + y$
	I. $-12 + 0 = -12$

33. Use the distributive property to simplify $-(3 - 4m)$.

2

Solving Equations
and Inequalities

*Learning to solve equations
is basic to algebra.*

2.1 Simplifying Expressions

1. Simplify expressions.
2. Identify terms and numerical coefficients.
3. Identify like terms.
4. Combine like terms.
5. Simplify expressions obtained from word problems.

1 To solve equations, it is often necessary to simplify the equation as the first step in solving it. This section shows how to simplify expressions, and the next section starts the process of solving equations.

EXAMPLE 1 Simplify the following expressions.

(a) $4x + 8 + 9$

Since $8 + 9 = 17$,

$$4x + 8 + 9 = 4x + 17.$$

(b) $4(3m - 2n)$

Use the distributive property.

$$4(3m - 2n) = 4(3m) - 4(2n) = 12m - 8n$$

(c) $6 + 3(4k + 5) = 6 + 3(4k) + 3(5)$
$$= 6 + 12k + 15$$
$$= 21 + 12k$$

(d) $5 - (2y - 8) = 5 - 1 \cdot (2y - 8)$
$$= 5 - 2y + 8$$
$$= 13 - 2y \quad \bullet$$

2   A **term** is a single number, or a product of a number and one or more variables raised to powers. Examples of terms include

$$-9x^2, \qquad 15y, \qquad -3, \qquad 8m^2n, \qquad \text{and} \qquad k.$$

The **numerical coefficient** of the term $9m$ is 9, the numerical coefficient of $-15x^3y^2$ is -15, the numerical coefficient of x is 1, and the numerical coefficient of 8 is 8.

EXAMPLE 2   Give the numerical coefficient of the following terms.

Term	Numerical coefficient
$-7y$	-7
$8p$	8
$34r^3$	34
$-26x^5yz^4$	-26
$-k$	-1 $\bullet$

3   Terms with exactly the same variable (including the same exponent) are called **like terms.** For example, $9m$ and $4m$ have the same variables and are like terms. Also, $6x^3$ and $-5x^3$ are like terms. The terms $-4y^3$ and $4y^2$ have different exponents and are **unlike terms.**

Like terms may be added or subtracted by using the distributive property. For example,

$$3x + 5x = (3 + 5)x = 8x.$$

EXAMPLE 3   Simplify the following expressions.

(a) $9m + 5m$

Use the distributive property to add the like terms.

$$9m + 5m = (9 + 5)m = 14m$$

(b) $6r + 3r + 2r = (6 + 3 + 2)r = 11r$

(c) $4x + x = 4x + 1x = 5x$ (Note: $x = 1x$.)

(d) $16y^2 - 9y^2 = (16 - 9)y^2 = 7y^2$

(e) $32y + 10y^2$ cannot be simplified because $32y$ and $10y^2$ are unlike terms. $\bullet$

4 Carrying out the addition or subtraction of like terms is called **combining like terms.** Remember that

---

only *like terms* may be added or subtracted.

EXAMPLE 4 Simplify the following expressions by combining terms.

(a) $14y + 2(6 + 3y) = 14y + 2(6) + 2(3y)$ Distributive property

$= 14y + 12 + 6y$ Multiply

$= 20y + 12$ Add like terms

(b) $9k - 6 - 3(2 - 5k) = 9k - 6 - 3(2) - 3(-5k)$ Distributive property

$= 9k - 6 - 6 + 15k$ Multiply

$= 24k - 12$ Combine like terms

(c) $-(2 - r) + 10r = -1(2 - r) + 10r$

$= -1(2) - 1(-r) + 10r$ Distributive property

$= -2 + r + 10r$ Multiply

$= -2 + 11r$ Combine like terms

(d) $5(2a - 6) - 3(4a - 9) = 10a - 30 - 12a + 27$ Distributive property

$= -2a - 3$ Combine like terms ●

5 The next example shows how to simplify the result of converting a word phrase to a mathematical expression.

EXAMPLE 5 Five times a number, four times a number, and six times a number are added to 9.

$5x + 4x + 6x + 9$ Write as a mathematical expression

$= 15x + 9$ Simplify ●

2.1 EXERCISES

Give the numerical coefficient of the following terms. See Example 2.

1. $15y$	**2.** $7z$	**3.** $-22m^4$	**4.** $-2k^7$
5. $35a^4b^2$	**6.** $12m^5n^4$	**7.** -9	**8.** 21
9. y^2	**10.** x^4	**11.** $-r$	**12.** $-z$

Write like *or* unlike *for the following groups of terms.*

13. $6m, -14m$	**14.** $-2a, 5a$	**15.** $7z^3, 7z^2$	**16.** $10m^5, 10m^6$
17. $25y, -14y, 8y$	**18.** $-11x, 5x, 7x$	**19.** $2, 5, -2$	**20.** $-8, 3, 9$
21. $p, -5p, 12p$	**22.** $15k, 7k, k$	**23.** $5, -5r$	**24.** $10, -10y$

Simplify the following expressions by combining terms. See Examples 1 and 3.

25. $9y + 8y$

26. $15m + 12m$

27. $-4a - 2a$

28. $-3z - 9z$

29. $12b + b$

30. $30x + x$

31. $2k + 9 + 5k + 6$

32. $2 + 17z + 1 + 2z$

33. $m + 1 - m + 2 + m - 4$

34. $12 - 13x - 27 + 2x - x$

35. $-5y + 3 - 1 + 5 + y - 7$

36. $2k - 7 - 5k + 7k - 3 - k$

37. $-2x + 3 + 4x - 17 + 20$

38. $r - 6 - 12r - 4 + 6r$

39. $16 - 5m - 4m - 2 + 2m$

40. $6 - 3z - 2z - 5 + z - 3z$

41. $-3z + 7 - 3z + 7z + 31$

42. $15 - 2 + 4 - 5k + 7k - k$

43. $-10 + x + 4x - 7 - 4x$

44. $-p + 10p - 3p - 4 - 5p$

45. $1 + 7x + 11x - 1 + 5x$

46. $-r + 2 - 5r + 3 + 4r$

47. $6y^2 + 11y^2 - 8y^2$

48. $-9m^3 + 3m^3 - 7m^3$

49. $2p^2 + 3p^2 - 8p^3 - 6p^3$

50. $5y^3 + 6y^3 - 3y^2 - 4y^2$

51. $-7.913q^2 + 2.804q - 11.723 + 5.069q^2 - 8.124q - 6.977$

52. $8.271m^3 - 3.722m^2 + 5.006 - 3.994m^3 + 4.129m^2 - 1.728$

Use the distributive property to simplify the following expressions. See Example 4.

53. $6(5t + 11)$

54. $2(3x + 4)$

55. $-3(n + 5)$

56. $-4(y - 8)$

57. $-3(2r - 3) + 2(5r + 3)$

58. $-4(5y - 7) + 3(2y - 5)$

59. $8(2k - 1) - (4k - 3)$

60. $6(3p - 2) - (5p + 1)$

61. $-2(-3k + 2) - (5k - 6) - 3k - 5$

62. $-2(3r - 4) - (6 - r) + 2r - 5$

63. $-7.916(3y - 2.8) - 4.72(9.1 - 5y)$

64. $4.873(8.2q - 7.3) + 1.29(3.9 - .42q)$

Convert the following word phrases into mathematical expressions. Use x as the variable. Combine terms whenever possible. See Example 5.

65. Two times a number is subtracted from the sum of a number and 2.

66. Four times a number is added to the sum of the number and -15.

67. Three times a number is subtracted from twice the number. This result is subtracted from 9 times the number.

68. A number is subtracted from 4 times the number, with this result subtracted from the sum of 6 and five times the number.

69. Nine is multiplied times the sum of five times a number and 4, with the result subtracted from the difference of 4 and twice the number.

70. Seven times a number is added to -9. This result is subtracted from four times the sum of three times the number and 5.

Review Exercises *Most of the exercise sets in the rest of the book end with brief sets of review exercises. These exercises are designed to help you review ideas needed for the next few sections in the chapter. If you need help with these review exercises, look in the sections indicated each time.*

Find the additive inverse of each number. For help see Section 1.5.

71. 6 **72.** 15 **73.** −4 **74.** −8

Add a number to each expression so that the result is just x.

75. $x - 7$ **76.** $x + 10$ **77.** $x + 6$ **78.** $x - 3$

2.2 The Addition Property of Equality

■ Identify linear equations.

■ Use the addition property of equality.

■ Simplify equations, and then use the addition property of equality.

■   In this section we begin to study the methods of solving a linear equation. A **linear equation** has the form

Linear Equation

$$ax + b = c, \quad \text{for real numbers } a, b, \text{ and } c, \text{ with } a \neq 0.$$

To solve such an equation, we go through a series of steps, ending up with a simpler equation of the form

$$x = \text{a number.}$$

■   Let us see how to solve the equation

$$x - 5 = 2.$$

Both "$x - 5$" and "2" represent the same number, since this is the meaning of the equals sign. We want to change the left side from $x - 5$ to just x. We can do this if 5 is added to $x - 5$. The equals sign can be maintained, however, only if 5 is also added on the right side.

$$x - 5 = 2 \qquad \text{Given equation}$$
$$x - 5 + 5 = 2 + 5 \qquad \text{Add 5 on both sides}$$

Here 5 was added on both sides of the equation. Now simplify each side separately to get

$$x = 7.$$

The solution of the given equation is 7. To check this, replace x with 7 in the given equation.

$$x - 5 = 2 \quad \text{Given equation}$$
$$7 - 5 = 2 \quad \text{Let } x = 7$$
$$2 = 2 \quad \text{True}$$

Since this final result is true, 7 checks as the solution.

To solve the equation above, the same number was added to both sides. This is justified by the **addition property of equality.**

Addition Property of Equality

> If A, B, and C are algebraic expressions, then the equations
> $$A = B \quad \text{and} \quad A + C = B + C$$
> have exactly the same solution. In words, the same number may be added to both sides of an equation.

EXAMPLE 1

Solve the equation $x - 16 = 7$.

If the left side of this equation was just x, we would have the solution. To get just x, use the addition property of equality and add 16 on both sides.

$$x - 16 = 7$$
$$(x - 16) + 16 = 7 + 16 \quad \text{Add 16 on both sides}$$
$$x = 23$$

To check, substitute 23 for x in the original equation.

$$x - 16 = 7 \quad \text{Given equation}$$
$$23 - 16 = 7 \quad \text{Let } x = 23$$
$$7 = 7 \quad \text{True}$$

Since the check results in a true statement, 23 is the correct solution.   ●

In this example, how did we know that 16 should be added on both sides of the equation $x - 16 = 7$? We know that we want one side of the equation to contain only the variable and the other side to contain only a number. Since $x + 0 = x$, we need to get $x + 0$ on one side of the equation. What number must be added to $x - 16$ to get $x + 0$? Since the sum of any number and its additive inverse is 0, we must add the additive inverse of -16, which is 16, on both sides of the equation.

The addition property of equality says that the same number may be *added* to both sides of an equation. As we saw in Chapter 1, subtraction is defined in terms of addition. Because of the way subtraction is defined, the addition property also permits us to *subtract* the same number on both sides of an equation.

EXAMPLE 2

Solve the equation $3k + 17 = 4k$.

To find the solution, get all terms that contain variables on the same side of the equation. One way to do this is to subtract $3k$ from each side.

$$3k + 17 = 4k$$
$$3k + 17 - 3k = 4k - 3k \qquad \text{Subtract } 3k \text{ from both sides}$$
$$17 = k$$

The solution is 17. The equation $3k + 17 = 4k$ could also be solved by first subtracting $4k$ from each side, as follows.

$$3k + 17 = 4k$$
$$3k + 17 - 4k = 4k - 4k \qquad \text{Subtract } 4k$$
$$17 - k = 0$$

Now subtract 17 from both sides.

$$17 - k - 17 = 0 - 17 \qquad \text{Subtract } 17$$
$$-k = -17$$

This result gives the value of $-k$, but not of k itself. However, this result does say that the additive inverse of k is -17, which means that k must be 17.

$$-k = -17$$
$$k = 17$$

This solution agrees with the first one. ●

3 Sometimes an equation must be simplified as a first step in its solution.

EXAMPLE 3

Solve the equation $4r + 5r - 3 + 8 - 3r - 5r = 12 + 8$.

First, simplify the equation by combining like terms.

$$4r + 5r - 3r - 5r - 3 + 8 = 12 + 8$$
$$r + 5 = 20$$

Subtract 5 from both sides of this equation.

$$r + 5 - 5 = 20 - 5 \qquad \text{Subtract } 5$$
$$r = 15$$

The solution of the given equation is 15. (Check this.) ●

EXAMPLE 4

Solve the equation $3(2 + 5x) - (1 + 14x) = 6$.

Use the distributive property to simplify the equation.

$$3(2 + 5x) - (1 + 14x) = 6$$
$$3(2) + 3(5x) - 1(1) - 1(14x) = 6 \qquad \text{Distributive property}$$
$$6 + 15x - 1 - 14x = 6 \qquad \text{Multiply}$$
$$x + 5 = 6 \qquad \text{Combine terms}$$

Subtract 5 from both sides of the equation to end up with

$$x = 1.$$

Check this answer by substituting 1 for x in the original equation. ●

2.2 EXERCISES

Solve each equation by using the addition property of equality. Check each solution. See Examples 1 and 2.

1. $x - 3 = 7$

2. $x + 5 = 13$

3. $7 + k = 5$

4. $9 + m = 4$

5. $3r - 10 = 2r$

6. $2p = p + 3$

7. $7z = -8 + 6z$

8. $4y = 3y - 5$

9. $m + 5 = 0$

10. $k - 7 = 0$

11. $2 + 3x = 2x$

12. $10 + r = 2r$

13. $2p + 6 = 10 + p$

14. $5r + 2 = -1 + 4r$

15. $2k + 2 = -3 + k$

16. $6 + 7x = 6x + 3$

17. $x - 5 = 2x + 6$

18. $-3r + 7 = -4r - 19$

19. $6z + 3 = 5z - 3$

20. $6t + 5 = 5t + 7$

21. $2p = p + \dfrac{1}{2}$

22. $5m = 4m + \dfrac{2}{3}$

23. $\dfrac{4}{3}z = \dfrac{1}{3}z - 5$

24. $\dfrac{9}{5}m = \dfrac{4}{5}m + 6$

25. $-2 - \dfrac{3}{4}y = \dfrac{1}{4}y$

26. $-11 - \dfrac{7}{9}p = \dfrac{2}{9}p$

27. $\dfrac{11}{4}r - \dfrac{1}{2} = \dfrac{7}{4}r + \dfrac{2}{3}$

28. $\dfrac{9}{2}y - \dfrac{3}{4} = \dfrac{7}{2}y + \dfrac{5}{8}$

29. $2.7a + 5 = 1.7a$

30. $4.7p - 3 = 3.7p$

Solve the following equations. First simplify each side of the equation as much as possible. Check each solution. See Example 3.

31. $4x + 3 + 2x - 5x = 2 + 8$

32. $3x + 2x - 6 + x - 5x = 9 + 4$

33. $9r + 4r + 6 - 8 = 10r + 6 + 2r$

34. $-3t + 5t - 6t + 4 - 3 = -3t + 2$

35. $11z + 2 + 4z - 3z = 5z - 8 + 6z$

36. $2k + 8k + 6k - 4k - 8 + 2 = 3k + 2 + 10k$

37. $4m + 8m - 9m + 2 - 5 = 4m + 6$

38. $15y - 4y + 8 - 2 + 7 - 4 = 4y + 2 + 8y$

39. $-9p + 4p - 3p + 2p - 6 = -5p - 6$

40. $5x - 2x + 3x - 4x + 8 - 2 + 4 = x + 10$

Solve the following equations. Check each solution. See Example 4.

41. $5(m - 1) - 6m = -8$

42. $2(k + 5) - 3k = 8$

43. $-4(3y + 2) = -13y - 10$

44. $-5(2q - 3) = -11q + 19$

45. $(11y + 10) - 3(3 + 4y) = 2$

46. $(15p - 3) - 2(7p + 1) = -3$

47. $2(r + 5) - (9 + r) = -1$

48. $4(y - 6) - (3y + 2) = 8$

49. $-6(2a + 1) + (13a - 7) = 4$

50. $-5(3k - 3) + (1 + 16k) = 2$

51. $4(7x - 1) + 3(2 - 5x) = 4(3x + 5)$

52. $9(2m - 3) - 4(5 + 3m) = 5(4 + m)$

53. $-2(8p + 7) - 3(4 - 7p) = 2(3 + 2p) - 6$

54. $-5(8 - 2z) + 4(7 - z) = 7(8 + z) - 3$

Write an equation using the following information. Then solve the equation.

55. Three times a number is 17 more than twice the number. Find the number.

56. If six times a number is subtracted from seven times a number, the result is -9. Find the number.

57. If five times a number is added to three times the number, the result is the sum of seven times the number and 9. Find the number.

58. If nine times a number is subtracted from eleven times the number, the result is -4 more than three times the number. Find the number.

59. The sum of twice a number and 5 is multiplied by 6. The result is 8 less than 13 times the number. Find the number.

60. Four times a number is subtracted from 7. The result is multiplied by 5, giving 3 more than -19 times the number. Find the number.

Review Exercises *Use the associative and inverse properties to simplify. See Section 1.10.*

61. $3\left(\dfrac{1}{3}m\right)$

62. $5\left(\dfrac{1}{5}q\right)$

63. $\dfrac{1}{7}(7y)$

64. $\dfrac{1}{12}(12z)$

65. $-\dfrac{1}{9}(-9q)$

66. $-\dfrac{1}{4}(-4m)$

67. $-\dfrac{5}{8}\left(-\dfrac{8}{5}r\right)$

68. $-\dfrac{9}{10}\left(-\dfrac{10}{9}x\right)$

2.3 The Multiplication Property of Equality

1 Use the multiplication property of equality.

2 Simplify equations, and then use the multiplication property of equality.

3 Solve equations such as $-r = a$.

The addition property of equality by itself is not enough to solve an equation like $3x + 2 = 17$.

$$3x + 2 = 17$$
$$3x + 2 - 2 = 17 - 2 \qquad \text{Subtract 2 from both sides}$$
$$3x = 15 \qquad \text{Simplify}$$

The variable x is not alone on one side of the equation; we have $3x$ instead. To go from $3x = 15$ to $x =$ a number, we need another property similar to the addition property.

1   If $3x = 15$, then $3x$ and 15 both represent the same number. Multiplying both $3x$ and 15 by the same number will also result in an equality. The **multiplication property of equality** states that both sides of an equation can be multiplied by the same term.

Multiplication Property of Equality

> If A, B, and C are algebraic expressions, then the equations
>
> $$A = B \quad \text{and} \quad AC = BC$$
>
> have exactly the same solution. (Assume that $C \neq 0$.) In words, both sides of an equation may be multiplied by the same nonzero number.

Now we can solve $3x = 15$. The $3x$ on the left must be changed to $1x$, or x, instead of $3x$. To get x, multiply both sides of the equation by $1/3$. (Use $1/3$ since it is the reciprocal of the coefficient of x.) This works because $3 \cdot 1/3 = 3/3 = 1$.

$$3x = 15$$

$$\frac{1}{3}(3x) = \frac{1}{3} \cdot 15 \qquad \text{Multiply both sides by } \frac{1}{3}$$

$$\left(\frac{1}{3} \cdot 3\right)x = \frac{1}{3} \cdot 15 \qquad \text{Associative property}$$

$$1x = 5 \qquad \text{Simplify}$$

$$x = 5$$

The solution of the equation is 5. Check this by substituting 5 for x in the given equation.

Just as the addition property of equality permits us to *subtract* the same number from both sides of an equation, the multiplication property of equality permits us to *divide* both sides of an equation by the same nonzero number. For example, the equation $3x = 15$, solved above by multiplication, could also be solved by dividing both sides by 3, as follows.

$$3x = 15$$

$$\frac{3x}{3} = \frac{15}{3} \qquad \text{Divide by 3}$$

$$x = 5 \qquad \text{Simplify}$$

EXAMPLE 1   Solve the equation $5p = 30$.

To get p on the left (instead of $5p$), use the multiplication property of equality and divide both sides of the equation by 5, the coefficient of p.

$$5p = 30$$

$$\frac{5p}{5} = \frac{30}{5} \qquad \text{Divide by 5}$$

$$p = 6 \qquad \text{Simplify}$$

The solution is 6.   ●

In the next two examples, multiplication produces the solution more quickly than division would.

EXAMPLE 2   Solve the equation $\dfrac{a}{4} = 3$.

We can replace $\dfrac{a}{4}$ by $\dfrac{1}{4}a$, since division by 4 is the same as multiplication by $\dfrac{1}{4}$. To get a on the left, multiply both sides by 4, the reciprocal of the coefficient of a.

$$\frac{a}{4} = 3$$

$$\frac{1}{4}a = 3 \qquad \text{Change } \frac{a}{4} \text{ to } \frac{1}{4}a$$

$$4 \cdot \frac{1}{4}a = 4 \cdot 3 \qquad \text{Multiply by 4}$$

$$1a = 12$$

$$a = 12$$

We multiplied by 4 since $4 \cdot \dfrac{1}{4} = 1$ and we want $1a$ on the left, not $\dfrac{1}{4}a$. Check the answer.

$$\frac{a}{4} = 3 \qquad \text{Given equation}$$

$$\frac{12}{4} = 3 \qquad \text{Let } a = 12$$

$$3 = 3 \qquad \text{True}$$

The solution 12 is correct.   ●

EXAMPLE 3   Solve the equation $\frac{3}{4}h = 6$.

To get h on the left, multiply both sides of the equation by $\frac{4}{3}$. Use $\frac{4}{3}$ because

$$\frac{4}{3} \cdot \frac{3}{4}h = 1 \cdot h = h.$$

$$\frac{3}{4}h = 6$$

$$\frac{4}{3}\left(\frac{3}{4}h\right) = \frac{4}{3} \cdot 6 \qquad \text{Multiply by } \frac{4}{3}$$

$$1 \cdot h = \frac{4}{3} \cdot \frac{6}{1}$$

$$h = 8$$

The solution is 8. Check the answer by substitution in the given equation.   •

2   In the next example, it is necessary to simplify the equation first before finding its solution.

EXAMPLE 4   Solve the equation $5m + 6m = 33$.

Simplify the equation by using the distributive property to combine terms.

$$5m + 6m = 33$$

$$11m = 33 \qquad \text{Distributive property}$$

Now divide both sides by 11.

$$\frac{11m}{11} = \frac{33}{11} \qquad \text{Divide by 11}$$

$$m = 3 \qquad \text{Simplify}$$

The solution is 3. Check this solution.   •

3   The following example shows how to use the multiplication property of equality to solve equations such as $-r = 4$.

EXAMPLE 5   Solve the equation $-r = 4$.

To solve this equation, we need r, and not $-r$, on the left. To do this, first write $-r$ as $-1 \cdot r$.

$$-r = 4$$

$$-1 \cdot r = 4 \qquad\qquad -r = -1 \cdot r$$

Now multiply both sides of this equation by -1.

$$-1(-1 \cdot r) = -1 \cdot 4 \qquad \text{Multiply by } -1$$
$$(-1)(-1) \cdot r = -4 \qquad \text{Associative property}$$
$$1 \cdot r = -4 \qquad \text{Simplify}$$
$$r = -4$$

The solution of the equation $-r = 4$ is thus -4. Check this solution.

$$-r = 4 \qquad \text{Given equation}$$
$$-(-4) = 4 \qquad \text{Let } r = -4$$
$$4 = 4$$

The solution, -4, checks. ●

2.3 EXERCISES

Solve each equation. See Examples 1–5.

1. $5x = 25$ **2.** $7x = 28$ **3.** $2m = 50$ **4.** $6y = 72$

5. $3a = -24$ **6.** $5k = -60$ **7.** $8s = -56$ **8.** $9t = -36$

9. $-4x = 16$ **10.** $-6x = 24$ **11.** $-12z = 108$ **12.** $-11p = 77$

13. $5r = 0$ **14.** $2x = 0$ **15.** $-y = 6$ **16.** $-m = 2$

17. $-n = -4$ **18.** $-p = -8$ **19.** $2x + 3x = 20$ **20.** $3k + 4k = 14$

21. $5m + 6m - 2m = 72$ **22.** $11r - 5r + 6r = 84$

23. $k + k + 2k = 80$ **24.** $4z + z + 2z = 28$

25. $3r - 5r = 6$ **26.** $9p - 13p = 12$

27. $7r - 13r = -24$ **28.** $12a - 18a = -36$

29. $6y + 8y - 17y = 9$ **30.** $14a - 19a + 2a = 15$

31. $-7y + 8y - 9y = -56$ **32.** $-11b + 7b + 2b = -100$

33. $\dfrac{m}{2} = 16$ **34.** $\dfrac{p}{5} = 3$ **35.** $\dfrac{x}{7} = 7$ **36.** $\dfrac{k}{8} = 2$

37. $\dfrac{2}{3}t = 6$ **38.** $\dfrac{3}{4}m = 18$ **39.** $\dfrac{5}{2}z = 20$ **40.** $\dfrac{9}{5}r = 18$

41. $\dfrac{3}{4}p = -60$ **42.** $\dfrac{5}{8}z = -40$ **43.** $\dfrac{2}{3}k = 5$ **44.** $\dfrac{5}{3}m = 6$

45. $\dfrac{-2}{7}p = -7$ **46.** $-\dfrac{3}{11}y = -2$ **47.** $1.7p = 5.1$ **48.** $2.3k = 11.5$

49. $-4.2m = 25.2$ **50.** $-3.9a = -15.6$ **51.** $8.974z = 6.2818$ **52.** $11.506y = 3.4518$

53. $-9.273k = 10.2003$ **54.** $-1.565r = 3.9125$

55. $.9123p = -5.20011$ **56.** $.8761a = -3.32918$

Write an equation for each problem. Then solve the equation.

57. When a number is divided by 4, the result is 6. Find the number.

58. When a number is divided by -5, the result is 2. Find the number.

59. Chuck decided to divide a sum of money equally among four relatives, Dennis, Mike, Ed, and Joyce. Each relative received $62. Find the sum that was originally divided.

60. If twice a number is divided by 5, the result is 4. Find the number.

61. Twice a number is divided by 1.74, producing -8.38 as a quotient. Find the number.

62. A number is multiplied by 12 and then divided by 54.96. The result is -3.1. Find the number.

Review Exercises   *Simplify each expression. See Section 2.1.*

63. $9(2q + 7)$ **64.** $4(3m - 5)$ **65.** $-4(5p - 1) + 6$ **66.** $-3(2y + 7) - 9$

67. $-(2 - 5r) + 6r$ **68.** $-(12 - 3y) - 2$ **69.** $6 - 3(4a + 3)$ **70.** $9 - 5(7 - 8p)$

2.4 Solving Linear Equations

1. Learn the four steps for solving a linear equation and how to use them.
2. Write verbal phrases as mathematical phrases.

1. We now combine our previous methods in order to solve more complicated equations.

Solving a Linear Equation

Step 1	Combine like terms to simplify. Use the commutative, associative, and distributive properties as needed.
Step 2	If necessary, use the addition property of equality to simplify further, so that the variable is on one side of the equals sign and the number is on the other.
Step 3	If necessary, use the multiplication property of equality to simplify further. This gives an equation of the form $x = $ a number.
Step 4	Check the solution by substituting into the original equation. (Do *not* substitute into an intermediate step.)

EXAMPLE 1 Solve the equation $2x + 3x + 3 = 38$.

Follow the four steps summarized above.

Step 1 Combine like terms.

$$2x + 3x + 3 = 38$$
$$5x + 3 = 38 \qquad \text{Combine like terms}$$

Step 2 Use the addition property of equality. Subtract 3 from both sides.

$$5x + 3 - 3 = 38 - 3 \qquad \text{Subtract 3}$$
$$5x = 35$$

Step 3 Use the multiplication property of equality. Divide both sides by 5.

$$\frac{5x}{5} = \frac{35}{5} \qquad \text{Divide by 5}$$
$$x = 7$$

Step 4 Check the solution. Substitute 7 for x in the given equation.

$$2x + 3x + 3 = 38$$
$$2(7) + 3(7) + 3 = 38 \qquad \text{Let } x = 7$$
$$14 + 21 + 3 = 38$$
$$38 = 38 \qquad \text{True}$$

Since the final statement is true, 7 is the solution. ●

EXAMPLE 2 Solve the equation $3r + 4 - 2r - 7 = 4r + 3$.

Step 1 $3r + 4 - 2r - 7 = 4r + 3$

$$r - 3 = 4r + 3 \qquad \text{Combine like terms}$$

Step 2 $\quad r - 3 + 3 = 4r + 3 + 3 \qquad \text{Add 3}$

$$r = 4r + 6$$
$$r - 4r = 4r + 6 - 4r \qquad \text{Subtract } 4r$$
$$-3r = 6$$

Step 3 $\qquad \dfrac{-3r}{-3} = \dfrac{6}{-3} \qquad \text{Divide by } -3$

$$r = -2$$

Step 4 Substitute -2 for r in the original equation.

$$3r + 4 - 2r - 7 = 4r + 3$$
$$3(-2) + 4 - 2(-2) - 7 = 4(-2) + 3$$
$$-6 + 4 + 4 - 7 = -8 + 3$$
$$-5 = -5 \qquad \text{True}$$

The solution of the equation is -2. ●

EXAMPLE 3 Solve the equation $4(k - 3) - k = k - 6$.

Step 1 Before combining like terms, use the distributive property to simplify $4(k - 3)$.

$$4(k - 3) = 4k - 4 \cdot 3 = 4k - 12$$

Now combine like terms.

$$4k - 12 - k = k - 6$$
$$3k - 12 = k - 6$$

Step 2

$$3k - 12 + 12 = k - 6 + 12 \qquad \text{Add 12}$$
$$3k = k + 6$$
$$3k - k = k + 6 - k \qquad \text{Subtract } k$$
$$2k = 6$$

Step 3

$$\frac{2k}{2} = \frac{6}{2} \qquad \text{Divide by 2}$$
$$k = 3$$

Step 4 Check your answer by substituting 3 for k in the given equation. Remember to do all the work inside the parentheses first.

$$4(k - 3) - k = k - 6$$
$$4(3 - 3) - 3 = 3 - 6$$
$$4(0) - 3 = 3 - 6$$
$$0 - 3 = 3 - 6$$
$$-3 = -3 \qquad \text{True}$$

The solution of the equation is 3. ●

EXAMPLE 4 Solve the equation $6a - (3 + 2a) = 3a + 1$.

Step 1 Simplify.

$$6a - (3 + 2a) = 3a + 1$$
$$6a - 1 \cdot (3 + 2a) = 3a + 1$$
$$6a - 3 - 2a = 3a + 1$$
$$4a - 3 = 3a + 1$$

Step 2 First, add 3 to both sides; then subtract $3a$.

$$4a - 3 + 3 = 3a + 1 + 3 \qquad \text{Add 3}$$
$$4a = 3a + 4$$
$$4a - 3a = 3a + 4 - 3a \qquad \text{Subtract } 3a$$
$$a = 4$$

Step 3 is not needed. Check that the solution is 4. ●

EXAMPLE 5   Solve the equation $4(8 - 3t) = 32 - 8(t + 2)$.

Step 1   Simplify.

$$4(8 - 3t) = 32 - 8(t + 2)$$
$$32 - 12t = 32 - 8t - 16$$
$$32 - 12t = 16 - 8t$$

Step 2   Subtract 32 from both sides, and then add $8t$ to both sides.

$$32 - 12t - 32 = 16 - 8t - 32 \qquad \text{Subtract 32}$$
$$-12t = -16 - 8t$$
$$-12t + 8t = -16 - 8t + 8t \qquad \text{Add } 8t$$
$$-4t = -16$$

Step 3   Divide both sides by -4.

$$\frac{-4t}{-4} = \frac{-16}{-4} \qquad \text{Divide by } -4$$
$$t = 4$$

Step 4   Check this solution in the given equation.

$$4(8 - 3t) = 32 - 8(t + 2)$$
$$4(8 - 3 \cdot 4) = 32 - 8(4 + 2) \qquad \text{Let } t = 4$$
$$4(8 - 12) = 32 - 8(6)$$
$$4(-4) = 32 - 48$$
$$-16 = -16 \qquad \text{True}$$

The solution, 4, checks.   ●

2   In the next section we begin a detailed discussion of the methods of solving word problems. One of the main steps in solving word problems is converting the phrases in the word problem into mathematical equations. In making this translation, we will see some of the same words again and again. The next few examples show how to make this translation.

EXAMPLE 6   Write the following phrases as mathematical expressions. Use x to represent the unknown. (We could use other letters to represent this unknown quantity.)

(a) 5 plus a number

The word *plus* indicates addition. If x represents the unknown number, then "5 plus a number" can be written as either

$$5 + x \qquad \text{or} \qquad x + 5.$$

(b) Add 20 to a number.

If x represents the unknown number, then "add 20 to a number" becomes

$$x + 20.$$

(c) "The sum of a number and 12" is $x + 12$ or $12 + x$.

(d) "7 more than a number" is $7 + x$ or $x + 7$. ●

EXAMPLE 7 Write each phrase as a mathematical expression. Use x as the variable.

(a) 3 less than a number

The words *less than* indicate subtraction, so "3 less than a number" is

$$x - 3.$$

(Note: $3 - x$ would *not* be correct.)

(b) "A number decreased by 14" is $x - 14$.

(c) "Ten fewer than x" is $x - 10$. ●

EXAMPLE 8 Write the following as mathematical expressions. Use x as the variable.

(a) "The product of a number and 3" is written $3 \cdot x$ or just $3x$, since *product* indicates multiplication.

(b) "Three times a number" is also $3x$.

(c) "Two thirds of a number" is $\frac{2}{3}x$.

(d) "The quotient of a number and 2" is $\frac{x}{2}$. (The word *quotient* indicates division; use a fraction bar instead of $\div$.)

(e) "The reciprocal of a number" is $\frac{1}{x}$. ●

Some word problems must be translated with a combination of symbols, as the next example shows.

EXAMPLE 9 Write the following as mathematical expressions. Use x as the variable.

(a) "7 subtracted from 4 times a number" is written $4x - 7$.

(b) "A number plus its reciprocal" is $x + \frac{1}{x}$.

(c) "The sum of a number and 2, multiplied by 5" is $(x + 2) \cdot 5$, or the preferred form, $5(x + 2)$.

(d) "The quotient of a number, and 4 plus the number" is $\frac{x}{4 + x}$. ●

2.4 EXERCISES

Solve each equation. Check your solutions. See Examples 1–5.

1. $4h + 8 = 16$

2. $3x - 15 = 9$

3. $6k + 12 = -12 + 7k$

4. $2m - 6 = 6 + 3m$

5. $12p + 18 = 14p$

6. $10m - 15 = 7m$

7. $3x + 9 = -3(2x + 3)$

8. $4z + 2 = -2(z + 2)$

9. $2(2r - 1) = -3(r + 3)$

10. $3(3k + 5) = 2(5k + 5)$

11. $2(3x + 4) = 8(2 + x)$

12. $4(3p + 3) = 3(3p - 1)$

13. $3(5 + 1.4x) = 3x$

14. $2(-3 + 2.1x) = 2x + x$

15. $7.492y - 3.86 = 5.562y$

16. $4.813q + 1.769 = 5.25525q$

17. $.291z + 3.715 = -.874z + 1.9675$

18. $1.043k - 2.816 = .359k - 4.2524$

Combine terms as necessary. Then solve the equations. See Examples 3–5.

19. $-4 - 3(2x + 1) = 11$

20. $8 - 2(3x - 4) = 2x$

21. $-5k - 8 = 2(k + 6) + 1$

22. $4a - 7 = 3(2a + 5) - 2$

23. $5(2m - 1) = 4(2m + 1) + 7$

24. $3(3k - 5) = 4(3k - 1) - 17$

25. $5(4t + 3) = 6(3t + 2) - 1$

26. $7(2y + 6) = 9(y + 3) + 5$

27. $5(x - 3) + 2 = 5(2x - 8) - 3$

28. $6(2v - 1) - 5 = 7(3v - 2) - 24$

29. $-2(3s + 9) - 6 = -3(3s + 11) - 6$

30. $-3(5z + 24) + 2 = 2(3 - 2z) - 10$

31. $6(2p - 8) + 24 = 3(5p - 6) - 6$

32. $2(5x + 3) - 3 = 6(2x - 3) + 15$

33. $3(m - 4) - (4m - 11) = -5$

34. $4(2a + 6) - (a + 1) = 2$

35. $-(4m + 2) - (-3m - 5) = 3$

36. $-(6k - 5) - (-5k + 8) = -4$

37. $2x + 2(3x + 2) - 9 = 3x - 9 + 3$

38. $3(z - 2) + 4z = 8 + z + 1 - z$

39. $2(r - 3) + 5(r + 4) = 9$

40. $-4(m - 8) + 3(2m + 1) = 6$

41. $1.2(x + 5) = 3(2x - 8) + 23.28$

42. $4.7(m - 1) = 2(3m + 5) - 17.69$

43. $5.1(p + 6) - 3.8p = 4.9(p + 3) + 34.62$

44. $2.7(k - 3) + 1.1k = 3.4(k + 1) - 10.54$

45. $-3.2(1.4k + .8) - (2.97k - .3) = 1.32(2k - 1.8) - 16.028$

46. $1.53(4y - 3) - 2.8(3y + 1) = .74(5y + 6) - 6.448$

Write each phrase as a mathematical expression. Use x as the variable. See Examples 6–9.

47. 8 plus a number

48. A number added to -6

49. -1 added to a number

50. The sum of a number and 12

51. A quantity increased by -18

52. The total of x and 12

53. 5 less than a number

54. A number decreased by 6

55. Subtract 9 from a number

56. 16 fewer than a number

57. The product of a number and 9

58. Double a number

59. Triple a number

60. Three fifths of a number

61. The quotient of a number and 6

62. The quotient of −9 and a number

63. A number divided by −4

64. 7 divided by a number

65. The product of 8 and the sum of a number and 3

66. A number added to twice the number

67. A number subtracted from its reciprocal

68. Three times the quotient of a number and 2

69. Eight times the difference of a number and 8

70. The difference of a number and 2, multiplied by −7

Use an algebraic expression to answer each of the following questions.

71. Two numbers have a sum of 11. One of the numbers is q. Find the other number.

72. The product of two numbers is 9. One of the numbers is k. What is the other number?

73. Yesterday Walt bought x apples. Today he bought 7 apples. How many apples did he buy altogether?

74. Joann has 15 books. She donated p books to the library. How many books does she have left?

75. Mary is a years old. How old will she be in 12 years?

76. Tom has r quarters. Find the value of the quarters in cents.

77. A bank teller has t dollars, all in five-dollar bills. How many five-dollar bills does the teller have?

78. A plane ticket costs b dollars for an adult and d dollars for a child. Find the total cost for 3 adults and 2 children.

79. Suppose n represents an even integer. Find the next higher even integer.

80. Let x represent the first of three consecutive integers. Find the next two integers.

2.5   Word Problems

■   Translate phrases into equations and solve the equations.

■   Use a formula to write an equation.

■   Solve a formula for a specified variable.

In this section we see how to solve many common types of word problems. To get the solution to a word problem, first read the problem carefully and determine what facts are given and what must be found. Then go through the five steps given on the next page.

Solving a Word Problem

Step 1	Choose a variable to represent the numerical value that you are asked to find—the unknown number.
Step 2	Translate the problem into an equation.
Step 3	Solve the equation.
Step 4	Answer the question asked in the problem.
Step 5	Check your solution by using the original words of the problem.

1 The second step, to translate the words into an equation, is often the hardest. To do this, write the given facts as mathematical expressions. We saw in the previous section how to translate word phrases into mathematical expressions. In this section we translate word statements into equations. To get an equation we need two equal mathematical expressions, so translate any words that mean *equals* or *same* as "=." The = sign gives the equation that is to be solved.

EXAMPLE 1

Translate "the product of 4, and a number decreased by 7 is 100" into an equation. Use x as the variable. Solve the equation.

Translate as follows.

$$\begin{array}{cccccc}
\text{The product} & \text{and a} & \text{decreased} & & & \\
\text{of 4,} & \text{number} & \text{by} & 7 & \text{is} & 100. \\
\downarrow & \downarrow & \downarrow & \downarrow & \downarrow & \downarrow \\
4\cdot & (x & - & 7) & = & 100
\end{array}$$

Solve the equation, using the steps given in the last section.

$$\begin{array}{ll}
4\cdot(x-7)=100 & \\
4x-28=100 & \text{Distributive property} \\
4x=128 & \text{Add 28 to both sides} \\
x=32 & \text{Divide by 4}
\end{array}$$

Now check the answer by substituting 32 for x in the original problem.

$$\begin{array}{ll}
4(\mathbf{32}-7)=100 & \text{Let } x=32 \\
4(25)=100 & \\
100=100 &
\end{array}$$

Since the last statement is true, 32 is the correct answer.   ●

Notice how the five steps given in the box above are used in the solution of the next few word problems.

EXAMPLE 2   At a concert, there were 25 more women than men. The total number of people at the concert was 139. Find the number of men.

Let x represent the number of men. Then the number of women is $x + 25$. Now write an equation.

The		the number		the number
total	is	of men	plus	of women.
↓	↓	↓	↓	↓
139	=	x	+	$x + 25$

Solve the equation.

$$139 = 2x + 25$$
$$139 - 25 = 2x + 25 - 25 \qquad \text{Subtract 25}$$
$$114 = 2x \qquad \text{Simplify}$$
$$57 = x \qquad \text{Divide by 2}$$

There were 57 men at the concert.   ●

The next example uses **consecutive odd integers,** which are odd integers in a row, such as 5 and 7, or 31 and 33.

EXAMPLE 3   If the smaller of two consecutive odd integers is doubled, the result is 7 more than the larger of the two integers. Find the smaller integer.

Let x be the smaller integer. Since the two numbers are consecutive *odd* integers, $x + 2$ is the larger. Now write an equation from the statement of the problem.

If the smaller			more	the
is doubled	the result is	7	than	larger.
↓	↓	↓	↓	↓
$2x$	=	7	+	$x + 2$

Solve the equation.

$$2x = 7 + x + 2$$
$$2x = 9 + x \qquad \text{Combine terms}$$
$$2x - x = 9 + x - x \qquad \text{Subtract } x$$
$$x = 9 \qquad \text{Combine terms}$$

The smaller integer is 9. The larger integer would be $9 + 2 = 11$. Check that twice the smaller is 7 more than the larger.   ●

When you work with consecutive integers, the following information may be helpful.

Two consecutive:	*Variables*
integers	$x, \quad x + 1$
odd integers	$x, \quad x + 2$
even integers	$x, \quad x + 2$

2   Many word problems can be solved with a formula. Formulas exist for geometric figures such as squares and circles, for distance, for money earned on bank savings, and for converting English measurements to metric measurements, for example. A list of the formulas you will need in this book is given inside the back cover. As the next examples show, formulas are often used to write equations.

EXAMPLE 4   The perimeter of a rectangle is 80 meters, and the length is 25 meters.* (See Figure 2.1.) Find the width of the rectangle.

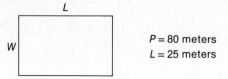

Figure 2.1

The distance around a rectangle is called the **perimeter** of the rectangle. The formula for perimeter is

$$P = 2L + 2W.$$

In this formula, P stands for the perimeter, L stands for the length (the long side), and W stands for the width (the short side).

To find the width, substitute 80 for P and 25 for L in the formula $P = 2L + 2W$.

$$P = 2L + 2W$$
$$80 = 2(25) + 2W \qquad P = 80, \; L = 25$$

To solve this equation to find W, first simplify it.

$$80 = 50 + 2W$$

Subtract 50 from both sides.

$$80 - 50 = 50 + 2W - 50 \qquad \text{Subtract 50}$$
$$30 = 2W$$

Divide both sides by 2.

$$15 = W \qquad \qquad \text{Divide by 2}$$

The width of the rectangle is 15 meters. Check this in the words of the original problem.   ●

---

*A meter is a unit of length in the metric system, which is explained in Appendix C in the back of the book. No knowledge of the metric system is required for this example.

EXAMPLE 5   The area of a triangle is 126 square meters. The base of the triangle is 21 meters. Find the height.

　　　The formula for the area of a triangle is $A = (1/2)bh$, where A is area, b is the base, and h is the height. Substitute 126 for A and 21 for b in the formula.

$$A = \frac{1}{2}bh$$

$$126 = \frac{1}{2}(21)h \qquad A = 126,\ b = 21$$

$$126 = \frac{21}{2}h$$

To find h, multiply both sides by 2/21.

$$\frac{2}{21}(126) = \frac{2}{21} \cdot \frac{21}{2}h$$

$$12 = h$$

The height of the triangle is 12 meters.　●

3　Sometimes it is necessary to solve a large number of problems that use the same formula. For example, a surveying class might need to solve several problems that involve the formula for the area of a rectangle, $A = LW$. Suppose that in each problem we are given the area, A, and the length, L, of a rectangle and want to find the width, W. We can save time by rewriting the formula $A = LW$ so that the unknown value, W, is alone on one side of the equals sign. The next example shows how to do this. The process of isolating one letter from a formula is called **solving for a specified variable.** As the examples show, solve for a specified variable by using the same steps used to solve an equation.

EXAMPLE 6   Solve $A = LW$ for W.

　　　We need to get W alone on one side of the equals sign. To do this, divide both sides of $A = LW$ by L.

$$A = LW$$

$$\frac{A}{L} = \frac{LW}{L} \qquad \text{Divide by } L$$

$$\frac{A}{L} = W$$

The formula is now solved for W.　●

The formula for converting temperatures given in degrees Celsius to degrees Fahrenheit is

$$F = \frac{9}{5}C + 32.$$

In the next example we see how to solve this formula for C.

EXAMPLE 7

Solve $F = \frac{9}{5}C + 32$ for C.

First, get $(9/5)C$ alone on one side of the equals sign. Do this by subtracting 32 from both sides.

$$F = \frac{9}{5}C + 32$$

$$F - 32 = \frac{9}{5}C + 32 - 32 \qquad \text{Subtract 32}$$

$$F - 32 = \frac{9}{5}C$$

Now multiply both sides by 5/9. Use parentheses on the left.

$$\frac{5}{9}(F - 32) = \frac{5}{9} \cdot \frac{9}{5}C \qquad \text{Multiply by } \frac{5}{9}$$

$$\frac{5}{9}(F - 32) = C$$

This last result is the formula for converting temperatures from Fahrenheit to Celsius. ●

2.5 EXERCISES

In the following exercises a formula is given, along with the values of all but one of the variables in the formula. Find the value of the variable that is not given. See Examples 4 and 5.

1. $V = \frac{1}{3}Bh$; $B = 20, h = 9$

2. $V = \frac{1}{3}Bh$; $B = 82, h = 12$

3. $d = rt$; $d = 8, r = 2$

4. $d = rt$; $d = 100, t = 5$

5. $A = \frac{1}{2}bh$; $A = 20, b = 5$

6. $A = \frac{1}{2}bh$; $A = 30, b = 6$

7. $P = 2L + 2W$; $P = 40, W = 6$

8. $P = 2L + 2W$; $P = 180, L = 50$

9. $V = \frac{1}{3}Bh$; $V = 80, B = 24$

10. $V = \frac{1}{3}Bh$; $V = 52, h = 13$

11. $A = \dfrac{1}{2}(b + B)h$; $b = 6$, $B = 8$, $h = 3$

12. $A = \dfrac{1}{2}(b + B)h$; $b = 10$, $B = 12$, $h = 3$

13. $C = 2\pi r$; $C = 9.42$, $\pi = 3.14*$

14. $C = 2\pi r$; $C = 25.12$, $\pi = 3.14$

15. $A = \pi r^2$; $r = 9$, $\pi = 3.14$

16. $A = \pi r^2$; $r = 15$, $\pi = 3.14$

17. $V = \dfrac{4}{3}\pi r^3$; $r = 3$, $\pi = 3.14$

18. $V = \dfrac{4}{3}\pi r^3$; $r = 6$, $\pi = 3.14$

19. $I = prt$; $I = 100$, $p = 500$, $r = .10$

20. $I = prt$; $I = 60$, $p = 150$, $r = .08$

21. $V = LWH$; $V = 150$, $L = 10$, $W = 5$

22. $V = LWH$; $V = 800$, $L = 40$, $W = 10$

23. $A = \dfrac{1}{2}(b + B)h$; $A = 42$, $b = 5$, $B = 7$

24. $A = \dfrac{1}{2}(b + B)h$; $A = 70$, $b = 15$, $B = 20$

25. $V = \dfrac{1}{3}\pi r^2 h$; $V = 9.42$, $\pi = 3.14$, $r = 3$

26. $V = \dfrac{1}{3}\pi r^2 h$; $V = 37.68$, $\pi = 3.14$, $r = 6$

Solve the given formulas for the indicated variables. See Examples 6 and 7.

27. $A = LW$;   for L

28. $d = rt$;   for t

29. $V = LWH$;   for H

30. $I = prt$;   for t

31. $C = 2\pi r$;   for r

32. $A = \dfrac{1}{2}bh$;   for b

33. $P = 2L + 2W$;   for W

34. $a + b + c = P$;   for b

35. $A = \dfrac{1}{2}(b + B)h$;   for b

36. $C = \dfrac{5}{9}(F - 32)$;   for F

37. $S = 2\pi rh + 2\pi r^2$;   for h

38. $A = p + prt$;   for r

39. $A = 4\pi r^2$;   for r^2

40. $c^2 = a^2 + b^2$;   for a^2

41. $V = \dfrac{1}{3}\pi r^2 h$;   for r^2

Write an equation for each word problem and then solve it. Check the solution in the words of the original problem. The necessary formulas are given inside the back cover of the book. Use 3.14 as an approximation for π.*

42. The area of a rectangle is 60 square meters, and the width is 6 meters. Find the length.

43. The perimeter of a square is 80 centimeters. Find the length of a side.

44. The radius of a circle is 6 feet. Find the circumference (the distance around the circle).

45. The length of a rectangle is 15 inches, and the perimeter is 50 inches. Find the width.

46. The perimeter of a triangle is 72 meters. One side is 16 meters, and another side is 32 meters. Find the third side.

---

*Actually, π is *approximately* equal to 3.14, not *exactly* equal to 3.14.

47. The shorter base of a trapezoid is 16 centimeters, and the longer base is 20 centimeters. The height is 6 centimeters. Find the area.

48. The circumference of a circle is 13.12 centimeters more than three times the radius. Find the radius of the circle.

49. Find the radius of a circle if the circumference is 1.96 centimeters more than six times the radius.

Solve the following word problems. Follow Steps 1–5. See Example 1.

(1) Choose a variable to represent the unknown quantity.
(2) Translate the problem into an equation.
(3) Solve the equation.
(4) Answer the question asked in the problem.
(5) Check your solution by using the original words of the problem.

50. When 6 is added to four times a number, the result is 42. Find the number.

51. The sum of a number and 3 is multiplied by 4, giving 36 as a result. Find the number.

52. The sum of a number and 8 is multiplied by 5, giving 60 as the answer. Find the number.

53. Twice a number is added to the number, giving 90. Find the number.

54. If the sum of a number and 8 is multiplied by −2, the result is −8. Find the number.

55. When 6 is subtracted from a number, the result is seven times the number. Find the number.

56. If 4 is subtracted from twice a number, the result is 4 less than the number. Find the number.

Solve the following word problems. See Example 2.

57. Tony has a board 44 inches long. He wishes to cut it into two pieces so that one piece will be 6 inches longer than the other. How long should the shorter piece be?

58. Nevarez and Smith were opposing candidates in the school board election. Nevarez received 30 more votes than did Smith, with 516 total votes cast. How many votes did Smith receive?

59. On an algebra test, the highest grade was 42 points more than the lowest grade. The sum of the two grades was 138. Find the lowest grade.

60. In a physical fitness test, Rolfe did 25 more push-ups than Chuck did. The total number of push-ups for both men was 173. Find the number of push-ups that Chuck did.

61. A pharmacist found that at the end of the day she had 12 more prescriptions for antibiotics than she had for tranquilizers. She had 84 prescriptions altogether for these two types of drugs. How many did she have for tranquilizers?

62. Mark White gives glass-bottom boat rides in the Bahama Islands. One day he noticed that the boat contained 17 more men (counting himself) than women, with a total of 165 people on the boat. How many women were on the boat?

63. Joann McKillip runs a dairy farm. Last year, her cow Bessie gave 238 more gallons of milk than one of her other cows, Bossie. Between them, the two cows gave 1464 gallons of milk. How many gallons of milk did Bossie give?

64. Kevin is 8 years older than Bob. The sum of their ages is 46 years. How old is each now?

Solve the following word problems. See Example 3.

65. When the smaller of two consecutive integers is added to three times the larger, the result is 43. Find the smaller integer.

66. If five times the smaller of two consecutive integers is added to three times the larger, the result is 59. Find the smaller integer.

67. The smallest of three consecutive integers is added to twice the largest, producing a result 15 less than four times the middle integer. Find the smallest integer.

68. If the middle of three consecutive integers is added to 100, the result is 1 less than the sum of the third integer and twice the smallest. Find the smallest integer.

The following two problems are real "head-scratchers."

69. A store has 39 quarts of milk, some in pint cartons and some in quart cartons. There are six times as many quart cartons as pint cartons. How many quart cartons are there? (Hint: 1 quart = 2 pints.)

70. A table is three times as long as it is wide. If it were 3 feet shorter and 3 feet wider, it would be square (with all sides equal). How long and how wide is it?

Review Exercises   *Solve each equation. See Section 2.3.*

71. $6x = 12$

72. $9y = 36$

73. $3p = 8$

74. $2q = 11$

75. $-7z = 15$

76. $-5m = 3$

77. $-\dfrac{3}{5}x = 12$

78. $-\dfrac{2}{3}m = 4$

2.6 Ratios and Proportions

1 Write ratios.
2 Decide whether proportions are true.
3 Solve proportions.
4 Solve word problems using proportions.

1 Ratios provide a way of comparing two numbers or quantities. A **ratio** is a quotient of two quantities. The ratio of the number a to the number b is written

Ratio

$$a \text{ to } b, \qquad a:b, \qquad \text{or} \qquad \frac{a}{b}.$$

This last way of writing a ratio is the most common in algebra.

EXAMPLE 1   Write a ratio for each word phrase.

(a) The ratio of 5 hours to 3 hours is

$$\frac{5}{3}.$$

(b) To find the ratio of 5 hours to 3 days, first convert 3 days to hours.

$$3 \text{ days} = 3 \cdot 24 = 72 \text{ hours}$$

The ratio of 5 hours to 3 days is thus

$$\frac{5}{72}. \quad \bullet$$

2 A ratio is used to compare two numbers or amounts. A **proportion** says that two ratios are equal. For example,

$$\frac{3}{4} = \frac{15}{20}$$

is a proportion that says that the ratios 3/4 and 15/20 are equal. In the proportion

$$\frac{a}{b} = \frac{c}{d},$$

a, b, c, and d are the **terms** of the proportion. If we begin with the proportion

$$\frac{a}{b} = \frac{c}{d}$$

and multiply both sides by the common denominator, bd, we get

$$bd \cdot \frac{a}{b} = bd \cdot \frac{c}{d}$$
$$ad = bc.$$

The products ad and bc are found by multiplying diagonally.

For this reason, ad and bc are called **cross products.**

> In a proportion, the cross products are equal.

EXAMPLE 2   Decide whether the following proportions are true.

(a) $\dfrac{3}{4} = \dfrac{15}{20}$

Check to see whether the cross products are equal.

The cross products are equal, so the proportion is true.

(b) $\dfrac{6}{7} = \dfrac{30}{32}$

The cross products are $6 \cdot 32 = 192$ and $7 \cdot 30 = 210$. The cross products are different, so the proportion is false.   ●

3   Four numbers are used in a proportion. If we know any three of these numbers, we can find the fourth.

EXAMPLE 3   (a) Find x in the proportion

$$\frac{5}{9} = \frac{x}{63}.$$

The cross products must be equal, or

$$5 \cdot 63 = 9 \cdot x$$
$$315 = 9x.$$

Divide both sides by 9 to get

$$35 = x.$$

(b) Find r in the proportion $\dfrac{8}{5} = \dfrac{12}{r}$.

Set the cross products equal to each other.

$$8r = 5 \cdot 12$$
$$8r = 60$$
$$r = \frac{60}{8} = \frac{15}{2} \quad \bullet$$

EXAMPLE 4   Find m in the proportion

$$\frac{m-2}{m+1} = \frac{5}{3}.$$

Find the cross products, and set them equal to each other.

$$3(m-2) = 5(m+1)$$
$$3m - 6 = 5m + 5$$
$$3m = 5m + 11 \qquad \text{Add 6}$$
$$-2m = 11 \qquad \text{Subtract } 5m$$
$$m = -\frac{11}{2} \qquad \text{Divide by } -2 \quad \bullet$$

■4   Proportions occur in many practical applications, as the next example shows.

EXAMPLE 5   A hospital charges a patient \$7.80 for 12 capsules. How much should it charge for 18 capsules?

Let x be the cost of 18 capsules. Set up a proportion; one ratio in the proportion can involve the number of capsules, and the other ratio can use the costs. Make sure that corresponding numbers appear in the numerator and the denominator.

$$\begin{array}{cc} \text{Cost} & \text{Number} \\ \downarrow & \downarrow \end{array}$$

$$\begin{array}{l} x \text{ is cost of } 18 \rightarrow \\ \$7.80 \text{ is cost of } 12 \rightarrow \end{array} \quad \frac{x}{7.80} = \frac{18}{12}$$

Solve the proportion. Find the cross products, and set them equal to each other.

$$12x = 18(7.80)$$
$$12x = 140.40$$
$$x = 11.70 \qquad \text{Divide by } 12$$

The 18 capsules should cost \$11.70. $\bullet$

2.6   EXERCISES

Write the following ratios. Write each ratio in lowest terms. See Example 1.

1. 30 miles to 20 miles

2. 50 feet to 90 feet

3. 72 dollars to 110 dollars

4. 120 people to 80 people

5. 6 feet to 5 yards

6. 10 yards to 8 feet

7. 30 inches to 4 feet

8. 100 inches to 5 yards

9. 12 minutes to 2 hours

10. 8 quarts to 5 pints

11. 4 dollars to 10 quarters

12. 35 dimes to 6 dollars

13. 20 hours to 5 days

14. 6 days to 9 hours

15. 80¢ to $3

Decide whether the following proportions are true. See Example 2.

16. $\dfrac{5}{8} = \dfrac{35}{56}$

17. $\dfrac{4}{7} = \dfrac{12}{21}$

18. $\dfrac{9}{10} = \dfrac{18}{20}$

19. $\dfrac{6}{8} = \dfrac{15}{20}$

20. $\dfrac{12}{18} = \dfrac{8}{12}$

21. $\dfrac{7}{10} = \dfrac{82}{120}$

22. $\dfrac{18}{20} = \dfrac{56}{60}$

23. $\dfrac{16}{40} = \dfrac{22}{55}$

24. $\dfrac{19}{30} = \dfrac{57}{90}$

25. $\dfrac{110}{18} = \dfrac{160}{27}$

26. $\dfrac{420}{600} = \dfrac{14}{20}$

27. $\dfrac{315}{78} = \dfrac{7875}{1950}$

28. $\dfrac{12.39}{8.91} = \dfrac{4.13}{2.97}$

29. $\dfrac{.612}{1.05} = \dfrac{1.0404}{1.785}$

30. $\dfrac{6.354}{7.823} = \dfrac{3.987}{4.096}$

31. $\dfrac{3.827}{2.4513} = \dfrac{8.0946}{5.7619}$

Solve the following proportions. See Examples 3 and 4.

32. $\dfrac{7}{12} = \dfrac{a}{24}$

33. $\dfrac{35}{4} = \dfrac{k}{20}$

34. $\dfrac{z}{56} = \dfrac{7}{8}$

35. $\dfrac{m}{32} = \dfrac{3}{24}$

36. $\dfrac{6}{x} = \dfrac{4}{18}$

37. $\dfrac{z}{80} = \dfrac{20}{100}$

38. $\dfrac{25}{100} = \dfrac{8}{m}$

39. $\dfrac{2}{3} = \dfrac{y}{7}$

40. $\dfrac{5}{8} = \dfrac{m}{5}$

41. $\dfrac{5}{9} = \dfrac{z}{15}$

42. $\dfrac{3}{4} = \dfrac{r}{10}$

43. $\dfrac{7}{k} = \dfrac{8}{5}$

44. $\dfrac{5}{p} = \dfrac{3}{4}$

45. $\dfrac{m}{m-3} = \dfrac{5}{3}$

46. $\dfrac{r+1}{r} = \dfrac{1}{3}$

47. $\dfrac{3k-1}{k} = \dfrac{6}{7}$

48. $\dfrac{y}{6y-5} = \dfrac{5}{11}$

49. $\dfrac{p+7}{p-1} = \dfrac{3}{4}$

50. $\dfrac{r+8}{r-9} = \dfrac{7}{3}$

51. $\dfrac{a+2}{a-1} = \dfrac{3}{4}$

Solve the following word problems involving proportions. See Example 5.

52. A certain lawn mower uses 3 tanks of gas to cut 10 acres of lawn. How many tanks of gas would be needed for 30 acres?

53. A Hershey bar contains 200 calories. How many bars would you need to eat to get 500 calories?

54. José can assemble 12 car parts in 40 minutes. How many minutes would he need to assemble 15 car parts?

55. If 2 pounds of fertilizer will cover 50 square feet of garden, how many pounds would be needed for 225 square feet?

56. The tax on a $20 item is $1. Find the tax on a $110 item.

57. On a road map, 3 inches represents 8 miles. How many inches would represent a distance of 24 miles?

58. A garden service charges $30 to install 50 square feet of sod. Find the charge to install 125 square feet.

59. If 9 pairs of jeans cost $121.50, find the cost of 5 pairs.

60. Suppose that 7 sacks of fertilizer cover 3325 square feet of lawn. Find the number of sacks needed for 7125 square feet.

61. The distance between two cities on a road map is 11 inches. Actually, the cities are 308 miles apart. The distance between two other cities is 15 inches. How far apart are these cities?

62. Twelve yards of material is needed for 5 dresses. How much material would be needed for 8 dresses?

63. The charge to move a load of freight 750 miles is $90. Find the charge to move the freight 1200 miles.

64. To ride a bus 80 miles cost $5. Find the charge to ride 180 miles.

Review Exercises *Solve the following problems by choosing the proper formula. See Section 2.5.*

65. Tom travels 520 miles in 13 hours. How fast does he travel?

66. Joann goes 49 miles per hour, and covers 367.5 miles. How many hours did she travel?

67. Seamus earned $5700 in interest on a deposit of $19,000 at 12%. For how long was the money deposited?

68. Linda deposited $12,000 at 14% interest for 3 years. How much interest did she earn?

2.7 Further Word Problems (Optional)

Learn to solve word problems about

1. geometric figures;
2. money;
3. interest;
4. distance;
5. mixtures.

In this section, we look at further types of word problems. As you read through these examples, pay careful attention to the way we start each solution by stating what the variable represents.

1 The first example shows how word problems result from discussions of geometric figures.

EXAMPLE 1   The length of a rectangle is 2 meters more than the width. The perimeter is 40 meters. (See Figure 2.2.) Find the width and length of the rectangle.

Figure 2.2

Let x represent the width of the rectangle. Since the length is 2 meters more than the width, $x + 2$ represents the length. The formula for the perimeter of a rectangle is $P = 2L + 2W$. Substitute x for W, $x + 2$ for L, and 40 for P.

$$P = 2L + 2W$$

$40 = 2(x + 2) + 2x$	$P = 40, L = x + 2, W = x$
$40 = 2x + 4 + 2x$	Distributive property
$40 = 4x + 4$	Simplify
$36 = 4x$	Subtract 4 from both sides
$9 = x$	Divide by 4

The width of the rectangle is 9 meters, and the length is $9 + 2 = 11$ meters.   ●

2 The next example shows a word problem involving money.

EXAMPLE 2   A bank teller has 25 more five-dollar bills than ten-dollar bills. The total value of the money is $200. How many of each type of bill does he have?

Let x be the number of ten-dollar bills; then $x + 25$ is the number of fives. The value of all the tens is given by the product of the number of tens (x) and the value per bill (10), or

$$\text{value of tens} = 10x.$$

In the same way,

$$\text{value of fives} = 5(x + 25).$$

The total value of all the money is $200.

$$
\begin{array}{ccccc}
\text{value of} & & \text{value of} & & \\
\text{fives} & \text{plus} & \text{tens} & \text{is} & \text{\$200} \\
\downarrow & \downarrow & \downarrow & \downarrow & \downarrow \\
5(x + 25) & + & 10x & = & 200
\end{array}
$$

Solve this equation.

$$
\begin{array}{ll}
5x + 125 + 10x = 200 & \text{Distributive property} \\
15x + 125 = 200 & \text{Simplify} \\
15x = 75 & \text{Subtract 125} \\
x = 5 & \text{Divide by 15}
\end{array}
$$

Since x represents the number of tens, the teller has 5 tens and $5 + 25 = 30$ fives. Check that the value of this money is $5(\$10) + 30(\$5) = \$200$.   •

3   The next example uses the formula for interest, $I = prt$.

EXAMPLE 3   Elizabeth Thornton receives an inheritance. She invests part of it at 9% and $2000 more than this amount at 10%. Altogether, she makes $1150 per year in interest. How much does she have invested at each rate?

Let x be the amount invested at 9%, and $x + 2000$ the amount invested at 10%. The formula for simple interest is $I = prt$. For the money at 9%, we have $p = x$, $r = 9\% = .09$, and $t = 1$, so that

$$\text{interest at } 9\% = x(.09)(1) = .09x.$$

Also, $\quad\quad\quad$ interest at $10\% = .10(x + 2000)$.

The total interest is $1150.

$$
\begin{array}{ccccc}
\text{interest} & & \text{interest} & & \text{total} \\
\text{at 9\%} & \text{plus} & \text{at 10\%} & \text{is} & \text{interest} \\
\downarrow & \downarrow & \downarrow & \downarrow & \downarrow \\
.09x & + & .10(x + 2000) & = & 1150
\end{array}
$$

Solve.

$$
\begin{array}{ll}
.09x + .10x + 200 = 1150 & \text{Distributive property} \\
.19x + 200 = 1150 & \text{Simplify} \\
.19x = 950 & \text{Subtract 200} \\
x = 5000 & \text{Divide by .19}
\end{array}
$$

She has $5000 invested at 9% and $5000 + $2000 = $7000 invested at 10%.   •

4   The next example uses the formula for distance, $d = rt$, where d represents distance, r is the rate or speed, and t is the time. The information given in this example is summarized in a chart. Making a chart is often a useful technique in problem solving.

EXAMPLE 4   Two cars start from the same point at the same time and travel in the same direction at constant speeds of 34 and 45 miles per hour, respectively. In how many hours will they be 33 miles apart? (See Figure 2.3.)

Figure 2.3

Let t represent the unknown number of hours. The distance traveled by the slower car is its rate multiplied by its time, or $34t$. The distance traveled by the faster car is $45t$. Summarize this information in a chart.

Car	r	t	d	$r \times t = d$
Faster	45	t	$45t$	⌐ Difference
Slower	34	t	$34t$	⌐ is 33

The quantities $45t$ and $34t$ represent different distances. We need to find the number of hours it will take for the cars to be 33 miles apart, or

$$45t - 34t = 33.$$

Solve.

$$11t = 33$$
$$t = 3$$

The two cars will be 33 miles apart in 3 hours.   ●

5   Our last example shows how algebra can be used to solve a word problem about mixing chemicals. Problems like this occur in science and medicine. In the solution of this example, a chart is used to help keep track of all the information.

EXAMPLE 5   A chemist needs to mix 20 liters of 40% salt solution with some 70% solution to get a mixture that is 50% salt. How many liters of the 70% solution should be used?

Let x represent the number of liters of 70% solution that are needed. The amount of pure salt in this solution will be given by the product of the percent of strength and the number of liters of solution, or

$$\text{liters of pure salt in } 70\% = .70x.$$

The amount of pure salt in the 20 liters of 40% solution is

$$\text{liters of pure salt in } 40\% = .40(20) = \mathbf{8}.$$

The new solution will contain $20 + x$ liters of 50% solution. The amount of pure salt in this solution is

$$\text{liters of pure salt in } 50\% = .50(20 + x).$$

The following chart shows all this information.

Strength	Liters of solution	Liters of pure salt
40%	20	.40(20)
70%	x	.70x
50%	$20 + x$	.50(20 + x)

Sum must equal

As the chart shows, the amount of pure salt before and after mixing the solutions must be equal, so our equation is

pure salt in 70%	plus	pure salt in 40%	is	pure salt in 50%
↓	↓	↓	↓	↓
.70x	+	.40(20)	=	.50(20 + x).

Solve.

$$.70x + 8 = 10 + .50x \qquad \text{Distributive property}$$
$$.20x + 8 = 10 \qquad \text{Subtract } .50x$$
$$.20x = 2 \qquad \text{Subtract } 8$$
$$x = 10 \qquad \text{Divide by } .20$$

The chemist needs to use 10 liters of the 70% salt solution.   ●

2.7 EXERCISES

Work the following word problems. See Example 1.

1. The perimeter of a certain square is seven times the length of a side, decreased by 12. Find the length of a side.

2. The perimeter of a certain rectangle is 16 times the width. The length is 12 centimeters more than the width. Find the width of the rectangle.

3. The width of a certain rectangle is 1 less than the length. The perimeter is five times the length, decreased by 5. Find the length of the rectangle.

4. The length of a certain rectangle is 8 more than the width. The perimeter of the rectangle is 6 more than five times the width. Find the width of the rectangle.

5. The longest side of a triangle is 5 meters longer than the shortest side, and the medium side is 2 meters longer than the shortest side. The perimeter of the triangle is 55 meters. Find the length of the shortest side of the triangle.

6. One side of a triangle is 10 centimeters longer than the shortest side. A third side is 20 centimeters longer than the shortest side. The perimeter of the triangle is 120 centimeters. Find the length of the shortest side of the triangle.

7. If the radius of a certain circle is tripled, with 8.2 centimeters then added, the result is the circumference of the circle. Find the radius of the circle. (Use 3.14 as an approximation for π.)

8. The circumference of a certain circle is five times the radius, increased by 2.56 meters. Find the radius of the circle. (Use 3.14 as an approximation for π.)

Work the following word problems. See Example 2.

9. A bank teller has some five-dollar bills and some twenty-dollar bills. The teller has 5 more of the twenties. The total value of the money is $725. Find the number of five-dollar bills that the teller has.

10. A woman has $1.70 in dimes and nickels; she has 2 more dimes than nickels. How many nickels does she have?

11. A stamp collector buys some 16¢ stamps and some 29¢ stamps, paying $8.68 for them. He buys 2 more 29¢ stamps than 16¢ stamps. How many 16¢ stamps does he buy?

12. For a retirement party, a person buys some 32¢ favors and some 50¢ favors, paying $46 in total. If she buys 10 more of the 50¢ favors, how many of the 32¢ favors were bought?

13. A cashier has a total of 126 bills, made up of fives and tens. The total value of the money is $840. How many ten-dollar bills does he have?

14. A convention manager finds that she has $1290, made up of twenties and fifties. She has a total of 42 bills. How many fifty-dollar bills does the manager have?

Work the following word problems. See Example 3.

15. Dorothy Raymond inherited a sum of money from a relative. She deposits some of the money at 16%, and $4000 more than this amount at 12%. She earns $3840 in interest per year. Find the amount she has invested at 16%.

16. Adda McDowell invested some money at 18%, and $3000 less than that amount at 20%. The two investments produce a total of $3200 per year interest. How much is deposited at 18%?

17. Two investments produce an annual interest income of $4200. The amount invested at 14% is $6000 less than the amount invested at 10%. Find the amount invested at 14%.

18. Carol Foresman invested some money at 10%, and invested $5000 more than this at 14%. Her total annual income from these investments is $3100. How much does she have invested at 10%?

19. With income earned by selling a patent, an engineer invests some money at 16%, and $3000 more than twice as much at 20%. The total annual income from the investments is $5080. Find the amount invested at 16%.

20. An actor invests his earnings in two ways: some goes into a 10% tax-free bond, and $5000 more than twice as much goes into an apartment house paying 20%. His total annual income from the investments is $9200. Find the amount he has invested at 10%.

Work the following word problems. See Example 4.

21. Two trains leave a city at the same time. One travels north at 60 miles per hour, and the other travels south at 80 miles per hour. In how many hours will they be 280 miles apart?

Train	r	t	d
Northbound	60	t	
Southbound	80	t	

22. Two planes leave an airport at the same time. One flies east at 300 miles per hour, and the other flies west at 450 miles per hour. In how many hours will they be 2250 miles apart?

Plane	r	t	d
Eastbound	300	t	
Westbound	450	t	

23. From a point on a straight road, John and Fred ride bicycles in opposite directions. John rides 10 miles per hour and Fred rides 12 miles per hour. In how many hours will they be 55 miles apart?

John (10 mph)
55 miles
Fred (12 mph)

24. Two cars are 400 miles apart. Both start at the same time and travel toward one another. They meet 4 hours later. If the speed of one car is 20 miles per hour faster than the other, what is the speed of each car?

Slower car
400 miles
Faster car

25. Two runners start from the same point and run in the same direction. One runner goes at 8 miles per hour, and the other runs at 11 miles per hour. In how many hours will the runners be 9 miles apart?

26. At a given hour, two steamboats leave a city in the same direction on a straight canal. One travels at 18 miles per hour, and the other travels at 25 miles per hour. In how many hours will the boats be 35 miles apart?

Work the following word problems. See Example 5.

27. How many gallons of 50% antifreeze must be mixed with 80 gallons of 20% antifreeze to get a mixture that is 40% antifreeze?

Strength	Gallons of solution	Gallons of pure antifreeze
50%	x	$.50x$
20%	80	
40%		

28. How many liters of 25% salt solution must be added to 80 liters of 40% solution to get a solution that is 30% salt?

Strength	Liters of solution	Liters of pure salt
25%	x	
40%	80	$.40(80)$
30%		

29. A certain metal is 40% tin. How many kilograms of this metal must be mixed with 80 kilograms of a metal that is 70% tin to get a metal that is 50% tin?

30. A pharmacist has 20 liters of a 10% drug solution. How many liters of 5% solution must be added to get a mixture that is 8%?

31. A merchant wishes to mix candy worth $5 per pound with 40 pounds of candy worth $2 per pound to get a mixture that can be sold for $3 per pound. How many pounds of $5 candy should be used?

32. Ink worth $100 per barrel will be mixed with 30 barrels of ink worth $60 per barrel to get a mixture worth $75 per barrel. How many barrels of $100 ink should be used?

Work the following miscellaneous word problems.

33. Ann has saved $281 for a trip to Disneyland. Transportation will cost $56, tickets for park entrance and rides will cost $15 per day, and lodging and meals will cost $60 per day. How many days can she spend there?

34. At Irv's Burgerville, hamburgers cost 90 cents each, and a bag of french fries costs 40 cents. How many hamburgers and how many bags of french fries can Ted buy with $8.80 if he wants twice as many hamburgers as bags of french fries?

35. A boat travels upstream for 3 hours. The return trip requires 2 hours. If the speed of the current is 5 miles per hour, find the speed of the boat in still water.

36. In an automobile race, a driver was 120 miles from the finish line after 5 hours. Another driver, who was in a later race, traveled at the same speed as the first driver. After 3 hours, the second driver was 250 miles from the finish. Find the speed of each driver.

Review Exercises *Place < or > in each blank to make a true statement. See Section 1.5.*

37. -7 ____ 3 **38.** -9 ____ 6 **39.** -11 ____ -4 **40.** -10 ____ -12

41. -8 ____ -10 **42.** -5 ____ -3 **43.** 5 ____ -9 **44.** 8 ____ -1

2.8 The Addition Property of Inequality

1 Graph intervals on a number line.

2 Learn the addition property of inequality.

3 Solve inequalities.

4 Write verbal phrases as inequalities.

5 Solve inequalities about numbers between other numbers.

Inequalities are statements with algebraic expressions related by

$<$ "is less than"

$\leq$ "is less than or equal to"

$>$ "is greater than"

$\geq$ "is greater than or equal to."

An inequality is solved by finding all real number solutions for it. For example, the solution of $x \leq 2$ is made up of all real numbers that are less than or equal to 2, and not just the integers less than or equal to 2.

1   A good way to show the solution of an inequality is by graphing. To graph all real numbers satisfying $x \leq 2$, place a dot at 2 on a number line and draw an arrow extending from the dot to the left (to represent the fact that all numbers less than 2 are also part of the graph). The graph is shown in Figure 2.4.

Figure 2.4

EXAMPLE 1   Graph $x > -5$.
    The statement $x > -5$ says that x can represent any number greater than -5, but x cannot equal -5 itself. To show this on a graph, place an open circle at -5 and draw an arrow to the right, as in Figure 2.5. The open circle at -5 shows that -5 is not part of the graph.   ●

Figure 2.5

EXAMPLE 2   Graph $3 > x$.
    The statement $3 > x$ means the same as $x < 3$. The graph of $x < 3$ is shown in Figure 2.6.   ●

Figure 2.6

EXAMPLE 3   Graph $-3 \leq x < 2$.
    The statement $-3 \leq x < 2$ is read "-3 is less than or equal to x *and* x is less than 2." To graph this inequality, place a solid dot at -3 (because -3 is part of the graph) and an open circle at 2 (because 2 is not part of the graph). Then draw a line segment between the two circles, as in Figure 2.7.   ●

Figure 2.7

2   Inequalities such as $x + 4 \leq 9$ can be solved in much the same way that we solved equations. First use the **addition property of inequality,** which states that the same term can be added on both sides of an inequality.

Addition
Property of
Inequality

> For any expressions A, B, and C, the inequalities
>
> $$A < B \qquad \text{and} \qquad A + C < B + C$$
>
> have exactly the same solutions. In words, the same number may be added on both sides of an inequality.

The addition property of inequality also works with $>$, $\leq$, or $\geq$. Just as with the addition property of equality, we also may use the addition property of inequality to *subtract* the same term on both sides of an inequality.

3   The following examples show how the addition property is used to solve inequalities.

EXAMPLE 4   Solve the inequality $7 + 3k > 2k - 5$.

Use the addition property of inequality twice, once to get the terms containing k on one side of the inequality and a second time to get the integers together on the other side.

$$7 + 3k > 2k - 5$$
$$7 + 3k - 2k > 2k - 5 - 2k \qquad \text{Subtract } 2k$$
$$7 + k > -5 \qquad \text{Simplify}$$
$$7 + k - 7 > -5 - 7 \qquad \text{Subtract } 7$$
$$k > -12$$

The graph of the solution $k > -12$ is shown in Figure 2.8.   ●

Figure 2.8

EXAMPLE 5   Solve $6 + 3y \geq 4y - 5$.

First subtract $3y$ from both sides.

$$6 + 3y - 3y \geq 4y - 5 - 3y$$
$$6 \geq y - 5$$

Then add 5 to both sides.

$$6 + 5 \geq y - 5 + 5$$
$$11 \geq y$$

This solution is correct, but it is customary to write the solution to an inequality with the variable on the left. The statement $11 \geq y$ says that 11 is greater than or equal to y. We can say the same thing in another way by saying that y is less than or equal to 11, or

$$y \leq 11.$$

The graph of the solution $y \leq 11$ is shown in Figure 2.9.   ●

Figure 2.9

If the inequality $6 + 3y \geq 4y - 5$ in Example 5 is solved by first subtracting $4y$ from both sides, we get

$$6 + 3y - 4y \geq 4y - 5 - 4y$$
$$6 - y \geq -5$$
$$6 - y - 6 \geq -5 - 6 \qquad \text{Subtract 6}$$
$$-y \geq -11.$$

To complete the solution, add y and 11 on both sides.

$$-y \geq -11$$
$$-y + y \geq -11 + y \qquad \text{Add } y$$
$$0 \geq -11 + y$$
$$0 + 11 \geq -11 + y + 11 \qquad \text{Add 11}$$
$$11 \geq y$$

This solution can be rewritten as $y \leq 11$ if desired, as above.

4   The next example shows how inequalities can be used in the solution of a word problem.

EXAMPLE 6   If 2 is added to five times a number, the result is greater than or equal to 5 more than four times the number. Find the number.

First translate this word problem into an inequality. Let x represent the number you want to find. The "2 is added to five times a number" is expressed as $5x + 2$. And "5 more than four times the number" is $4x + 5$. The two expressions are related by "is greater than or equal to."

$$5x + 2 \geq 4x + 5$$

To solve the inequality $5x + 2 \geq 4x + 5$, first subtract $4x$ from both sides.

$$5x + 2 - 4x \geq 4x + 5 - 4x \qquad \text{Subtract } 4x$$
$$x + 2 \geq 5$$

Then subtract 2 from both sides.

$$x + 2 - 2 \geq 5 - 2 \qquad \text{Subtract 2}$$
$$x \geq 3$$

The solution is any number greater than or equal to 3.   ●

5   Inequalities that say that one number is between two other numbers can also be solved by using the addition property of inequality.

EXAMPLE 7   Solve each inequality.

(a) $4 \leq x + 5 \leq 15$

Subtract 5 from each part of the inequality.

$$4 \leq x + 5 \leq 15$$
$$4 - 5 \leq x + 5 - 5 \leq 15 - 5 \qquad \text{Subtract 5}$$
$$-1 \leq x \leq 10$$

A graph of this result is shown in Figure 2.10.

Figure 2.10

(b) $24 < y - 5 < 32$

Add 5 throughout.

$$24 + 5 < y - 5 + 5 < 32 + 5 \qquad \text{Add 5}$$
$$29 < y < 37$$

The graph is shown in Figure 2.11.   ●

Figure 2.11

2.8 EXERCISES

Graph each inequality on a number line. See Examples 1–3.

1. $x \leq 4$ **2.** $k \geq -5$ **3.** $a < 3$ **4.** $p > 4$

5. $-2 \leq x \leq 5$ **6.** $8 \leq m \leq 10$ **7.** $3 \leq y < 5$ **8.** $0 < y \leq 10$

Solve each inequality. See Examples 4 and 5.

9. $a + 6 < 8$ **10.** $k - 4 < 2$ **11.** $z - 3 \geq -2$ **12.** $p + 2 \geq -6$

13. $p - 8 \leq 4$ **14.** $2 + m \geq 5$ **15.** $-3 + k \geq 2$ **16.** $-8 + y < -10$

17. $x + 6 \leq 6$ **18.** $x + 5 > 5$ **19.** $4x < 3x + 6$ **20.** $5x \leq 4x - 8$

Solve each inequality and graph the solution. See Examples 4 and 5.

21. $3n + 5 \leq 2n - 6$ **22.** $5x - 2 < 4x - 5$

23. $2z - 8 > z - 3$ **24.** $4x + 6 \leq 3x - 5$

25. $3(y - 5) + 2 < 2(y - 4)$ **26.** $4(x + 6) - 5 > 3(x + 1)$

27. $-6(k + 2) + 3 \geq -7(k - 5)$ **28.** $-3(m - 5) + 8 < -4(m + 2)$

29. $5(2k + 3) - 2(k - 8) > 3(2k + 4) + k - 2$

30. $2(3z - 5) + 4(z + 6) \geq 2(3z + 2) + 3(z - 5)$

Solve each inequality and graph the solution. See Example 7.

31. $8 \leq p + 2 \leq 15$ **32.** $4 \leq k - 1 \leq 10$ **33.** $-3 < y - 8 < 4$

34. $-6 < r - 1 < -2$ **35.** $-10 \leq p + 11 \leq -2$ **36.** $0 \leq x + 7 \leq 8$

In Exercises 37–42, write an inequality using the information given in the problem and then solve it. See Example 6.

37. If four times a number is added to 8, the result is less than three times the number added to 5. Find all possible values of the number.

38. The product of 7 and a number is added to 4, giving a result that is greater than or equal to six times the number. Find all possible values of the number.

39. If the length of a rectangle is to be twice the width, and the difference between the two dimensions is to be less than or equal to 7 meters, what is the largest possible value for the width?

40. The perimeter of a triangle must be no more than 55 centimeters. One side of the triangle is 18 centimeters, and a second side is 13 centimeters. Find the largest possible length for the third side.

41. The length of a rectangle is four times the width. If three times the width is subtracted from the length, the result is at least 15. Find the smallest possible values for the length and width of the rectangle.

42. The perimeter of a triangle cannot be more than 25 meters. One side is 7 meters. A second side is 9 meters. Find the longest possible length of the third side.

Review Exercises *Multiply both sides of each statement first by 4 and then by -2. Decide whether each result is true or false. See Section 1.8.*

43. $6 < 8$ **44.** $9 < 10$ **45.** $4 \geq -9$ **46.** $3 \geq -6$

47. $-5 < -3$ **48.** $-12 \leq -8$ **49.** $-10 \geq -13$ **50.** $-7 \geq -11$

2.9 The Multiplication Property of Inequality

  1 Learn the multiplication property of inequality.

  2 Solve inequalities.

  3 Solve inequalities about numbers between other numbers.

  1 The addition property of inequality alone cannot be used to solve inequalities such as $4y \geq 28$. We need the *multiplication property of inequality*. To see how this property works, look at some examples.

First, start with the inequality $3 < 7$ and multiply both sides by the positive number 2.

$$3 < 7$$
$$2(3) < 2(7) \qquad \text{Multiply both sides by 2}$$
$$6 < 14 \qquad \text{True}$$

Now multiply both sides of $3 < 7$ by the negative number -5.

$$3 < 7$$
$$-5(3) < -5(7) \qquad \text{Multiply both sides by } -5$$
$$-15 < -35 \qquad \text{False}$$

To get a true statement when we multiply both sides by -5, we would have to reverse the direction of the inequality symbol.

$$3 < 7$$
$$-5(3) > -5(7) \qquad \text{Multiply by } -5; \text{ reverse the symbol}$$
$$-15 > -35 \qquad \text{True}$$

Take the inequality $-6 < 2$ as another example. Multiply both sides by the positive number 4.

$$-6 < 2$$
$$4(-6) < 4(2) \qquad \text{Multiply by 4}$$
$$-24 < 8 \qquad \text{True}$$

If we multiply both sides of $-6 < 2$ by -5 *and at the same time reverse the direction of the inequality symbol,* we get

$$-6 < 2$$
$$(-5)(-6) > (-5)(2) \qquad \text{Multiply by } -5$$
$$30 > -10. \qquad \text{True}$$

In summary, the two parts of the **multiplication property of inequality** are stated below.

Multiplication Property of Inequality

For any expressions A, B, and C,

(1) if C is *positive,* then the inequalities

$$A < B \qquad \text{and} \qquad AC < BC$$

have exactly the same solutions;

(2) if C is *negative,* then the inequalities

$$A < B \qquad \text{and} \qquad AC > BC$$

have exactly the same solutions. (Assume that $C \neq 0$.) In words, both sides of an inequality may be multiplied by the same nonzero number. When you multiply by a negative number, reverse the inequality symbol.

The multiplication property of inequality works with $>$, $\leq$, or $\geq$, as well. The multiplication property of inequality also permits *division* of both sides of an inequality by the same nonzero number.

> **Important:** (1) When both sides of an inequality are multiplied or divided by a positive number, the direction of the inequality symbol *does not change*. Adding or subtracting terms on both sides also does not change the symbol.
>
> (2) When both sides of an inequality are multiplied or divided by a negative number, the direction of the symbol does change. **Reverse the symbol of inequality only when you multiply or divide both sides by a negative number.**

2 The next examples show how to solve inequalities with the multiplication property.

EXAMPLE 1

Solve the inequality $3r < 18$.

To simplify this inequality, use the multiplication property of inequality and divide both sides by 3. Since 3 is a positive number, the direction of the inequality symbol *does not* change.

$$3r < 18$$

$$\frac{3r}{3} < \frac{18}{3} \qquad \text{Divide by 3}$$

$$r < 6$$

The graph of this solution is shown in Figure 2.12. ●

Figure 2.12

EXAMPLE 2

Solve the inequality $-4t \geq 8$.

Here we need to divide both sides of the inequality by -4, a negative number. This *does* change the direction of the inequality symbol.

$$-4t \geq 8$$

$$\frac{-4t}{-4} \leq \frac{8}{-4} \qquad \text{Divide by } -4; \text{ symbol reversed}$$

$$t \leq -2$$

The solution is graphed in Figure 2.13. ●

Figure 2.13

EXAMPLE 3   Solve the inequality $-y \le -11$.

In the previous section we solved this inequality by using the addition property. It can be solved more quickly by using the multiplication property of inequality. Multiply both sides by -1; since -1 is negative, change the direction of the inequality symbol.

$$-y \le -11$$

$$(-1)(-y) \ge (-1)(-11) \quad \text{Multiply by } -1$$

$$y \ge 11$$

The solution is graphed in Figure 2.14.   ●

Figure 2.14

We now can summarize the steps taken to solve an inequality. (Remember that $<$ can be replaced with $>$, $\le$, or $\ge$ in this summary.)

Solving an Inequality

> *Step 1*   Use the associative, commutative, and distributive properties to combine like terms on each side of the inequality.
>
> *Step 2*   Use the addition property of inequality to simplify the inequality to one of the form $ax < b$, where a and b are real numbers.
>
> *Step 3*   Use the multiplication property of inequality to simplify further to an inequality of the form $x < c$ or $x > c$, where c is a real number.

EXAMPLE 4   Solve the inequality $3z + 2 - 5 > -z + 7 + 2z$.

Step 1   Combine like terms and simplify.

$$3z + 2 - 5 > -z + 7 + 2z$$

$$3z - 3 > z + 7$$

Step 2   Use the addition property of inequality.

$$3z - 3 + 3 > z + 7 + 3 \qquad \text{Add 3}$$

$$3z > z + 10$$

$$3z - z > z + 10 - z \qquad \text{Subtract } z$$

$$2z > 10$$

Step 3   Use the multiplication property of inequality.

$$\frac{2z}{2} > \frac{10}{2} \qquad\qquad \text{Divide by 2}$$

$$z > 5$$

Since 2 is positive, the direction of the inequality symbol was not changed in the third step. A graph of the solution is shown in Figure 2.15.   ●

Figure 2.15

EXAMPLE 5   Solve $5(k - 3) - 7k \geq 4(k - 3) + 9$.

Step 1   Combine like terms.

$$5(k - 3) - 7k \geq 4(k - 3) + 9$$
$$5k - 15 - 7k \geq 4k - 12 + 9 \qquad \text{Distributive property}$$
$$-2k - 15 \geq 4k - 3 \qquad \text{Combine like terms}$$

Step 2   Use the addition property.

$$-2k - 15 - 4k \geq 4k - 3 - 4k \qquad \text{Subtract } 4k$$
$$-6k - 15 \geq -3$$
$$-6k - 15 + 15 \geq -3 + 15 \qquad \text{Add 15}$$
$$-6k \geq 12$$

Step 3   Divide both sides by -6, a negative number. Change the direction of the inequality symbol.

$$\frac{-6k}{-6} \leq \frac{12}{-6} \qquad \text{Divide by } -6$$
$$k \leq -2$$

A graph of the solution is shown in Figure 2.16.   ●

Figure 2.16

3   Our final example shows how to solve inequalities in which the variable expression is between two numbers.

EXAMPLE 6   (a) Solve $4 \leq 3x - 5 < 6$.

First add 5 to each part.

$$4 \leq 3x - 5 < 6$$
$$4 + 5 \leq 3x - 5 + 5 < 6 + 5 \qquad \text{Add 5}$$
$$9 \leq 3x < 11$$

Now divide each part by the positive number 3.

$$\frac{9}{3} \le \frac{3x}{3} < \frac{11}{3} \qquad \text{Divide by 3}$$

$$3 \le x < \frac{11}{3}$$

A graph of the solution is shown in Figure 2.17.

Figure 2.17

(b) Solve $-4 \le \frac{2}{3}m - 1 < 8$.

First add 1 to each part.

$$-4 \le \frac{2}{3}m - 1 < 8$$

$$-4 + 1 \le \frac{2}{3}m - 1 + 1 < 8 + 1 \qquad \text{Add 1}$$

$$-3 \le \frac{2}{3}m < 9$$

Multiply each part by 3/2, a positive number.

$$\frac{3}{2}(-3) \le \frac{3}{2} \cdot \frac{2}{3}m < \frac{3}{2} \cdot 9 \qquad \text{Multiply by } \frac{3}{2}$$

$$-\frac{9}{2} \le m < \frac{27}{2}$$

A graph of the solution is shown in Figure 2.18. ●

Figure 2.18

2.9 EXERCISES

Solve each inequality and graph the solution. See Examples 1–5.

1. $3x < 27$ **2.** $5h \ge 20$ **3.** $4r \ge -12$ **4.** $6a < -18$

5. $-2k \le 12$ **6.** $-3v > 6$ **7.** $-8y > 72$ **8.** $-5z \le 40$

9. $-5m > -35$ **10.** $-8x \le -16$ **11.** $-6r < -16$ **12.** $-9a \ge -63$

13. $4k + 1 \geq 2k - 9$

14. $5y + 3 < 2y + 12$

15. $3 + 2r > 5r - 27$

16. $8 + 6t \leq 8t + 12$

17. $4q + 1 - 5 < 8q + 4$

18. $5x - 2 \leq 2x + 6 - x$

19. $10p + 20 - p > p + 3 - 23$

20. $-3v + 6 + 3 - 2 > -5v - 19$

21. $-k + 4 + 5k \leq -1 + 3k + 5$

22. $6y - 2y - 4 + 7y > 3y - 4 + 7y$

23. $2(x - 5) + 3x < 4(x - 6) + 3$

24. $5(t + 3) - 6t \leq 3(2t + 1) - 4t$

25. $5 - (2 - r) \leq 3r + 5$

26. $-9 + (8 + y) > 7y - 4$

27. $3(p + 1) - 2(p - 4) \geq 5(2p - 3) + 2$

28. $-5(m - 3) + 4(m + 6) < 2(m - 3) + 4$

Solve each inequality. Graph your solution. See Example 6.

29. $-5 \leq 2x - 3 \leq 9$

30. $-7 \leq 3x - 4 \leq 8$

31. $5 < 6m - 1 < 12$

32. $10 < 7p + 3 < 24$

33. $-1 \leq 5q - 1 \leq 16$

34. $-8 \leq 3r - 1 \leq -1$

35. $-12 \leq \frac{1}{2}z + 1 \leq 4$

36. $-6 \leq \frac{1}{3}a - 3 \leq 5$

37. $1 \leq 3 + \frac{2}{3}p \leq 7$

38. $2 < 6 + \frac{3}{4}y < 12$

39. $-7 \leq \frac{5}{4}r - 1 \leq -1$

40. $-12 \leq \frac{3}{7}a + 2 \leq -4$

Solve each word problem.

41. A student has test grades of 75 and 82. What must he score on a third test to have an average of 80 or higher?

42. In Exercise 41, if 100 is the highest score possible on the third test, how high an average (to the nearest tenth) can the student make? What is the lowest average possible for the three tests?

43. Twice a number added to three times the sum of the number and 2 is more than 17. Find the numbers that satisfy this condition.

44. Mr. Odjakjian earned $200 at odd jobs during July, $300 during August, and $225 during September. If his average salary for the four months from July through October is to be at least $250, how much must he earn during October?

45. The perimeter of a rectangle must be no greater than 120 meters. The width of the rectangle must be 22 meters. Find the longest possible value for the length of the rectangle.

46. One side of a triangle is twice as long as a second side. The third side of the triangle is 17 feet long. The perimeter of the triangle cannot be more than 50 feet. Find the longest possible values for the other two sides of the triangle.

47. In order to qualify for a company pension plan, an employee must average at least $1000 per month in earnings. During the first four months of the year, an employee made $900, $1200, $1040, and $760. What amount of earnings during the fifth month will qualify the employee?

48. When four times a number is subtracted from 8, the result is less than 15. Find all numbers that satisfy this condition.

49. If half a number is added to 5, the result is greater than or equal to -3. Find all such numbers.

50. If two thirds of a number is added to -3, the result is no more than 2. Find all such numbers.

51. One side of a rectangle is 8 meters long. The area of the rectangle must be at least 240 square meters. Find the shortest possible length for the rectangle.

52. A triangle has a height of 20 meters. The area of the triangle must be less than or equal to 40 square meters. Find the longest possible length for the base of the triangle.

Review Exercises *Evaluate each expression. See Section 1.3.*

53. $2 \cdot 2 \cdot 2 \cdot 2 \cdot 2$

54. $3 \cdot 3 \cdot 3$

55. $5 \cdot 5 \cdot 5 \cdot 5$

56. $4 \cdot 4 \cdot 4 \cdot 4$

57. $\dfrac{2}{3} \cdot \dfrac{2}{3} \cdot \dfrac{2}{3}$

58. $\dfrac{5}{8} \cdot \dfrac{5}{8}$

59. $(2 \cdot 2 \cdot 2)(2 \cdot 2 \cdot 2 \cdot 2)$

60. $(3 \cdot 3) \cdot (3 \cdot 3 \cdot 3)$

Simplify. See Sections 1.6 and 1.7.

61. $8 + (-5)$

62. $9 + (-12)$

63. $3 - (-2)$

64. $5 - (-7)$

65. $8 - 4 - (-9)$

66. $-6 - (-8)$

67. $-2 - [-4 - (3 - 2)]$

68. $1 - [-(8 - 9) - 2]$

Chapter 2   Review Exercises

[2.1] *Combine terms whenever possible.*

1. $2m + 9m$

2. $15p^2 - 7p^2 + 8p^2$

3. $5p^2 - 4p + 6p + 11p^2$

4. $-2(3k - 5) + 2(k + 1)$

5. $7(2m + 3) - 2(8m - 4)$

6. $-(2k + 8) - (3k - 7)$

[2.2–2.4] *Solve each equation.*

7. $m - 5 = 1$

8. $y + 8 = -4$

9. $3k + 1 = 2k + 8$

10. $5k = 4k + \dfrac{2}{3}$

11. $(4r - 2) - (3r + 1) = 8$

12. $3(2y - 5) = 2 + 5y$

13. $7k = 35$

14. $12r = -48$

15. $2p - 7p + 8p = 15$

16. $\dfrac{m}{12} = -1$

17. $\dfrac{5}{8}k = 8$

18. $12m + 11 = 59$

19. $2k - 5 = 4k + 7$

20. $2 - 3(y - 5) = 4 + y$

21. $-(m + 2) = -3m - 11$

[2.5] *Solve the word problems.*

22. If 7 is added to six times a number, the result is 22. Find the number.

23. If 4 is subtracted from twice a number, the result is 8. Find the number.

24. The sum of a number and 5 is multiplied by 6, giving 72 as a result. Find the number.

25. If three times the smaller of two consecutive odd integers is added to twice the larger, the result is 99. Find the smaller integer.

26. On a test in geometry, the highest grade was 35 points more than the lowest. The sum of the highest and lowest grades was 157. Find the lowest score.

27. In a race, Susan ran 6 miles more than Steve. In all, the two people ran 30 miles. How many miles did Susan run?

28. Charles has 15 more college units than Tom. Altogether, the two men have 95 units. How many units does Tom have?

A formula is given in the following exercises, along with the values of some of the variables. Find the value of the variable that is not given.

29. $A = \dfrac{1}{2}bh$; $A = 22, b = 4$

30. $A = \dfrac{1}{2}(b + B)h$; $b = 9, B = 12, h = 8$

31. $C = 2\pi r$; $C = 12.56, \pi = 3.14$

32. $V = \dfrac{4}{3}\pi r^3$; $\pi = 3.14, r = 1$

Solve each formula for the specified variable.

33. $A = LW$;   for W

34. $I = prt$;   for r

35. $a + b + c = P$;   for a

36. $A = \dfrac{1}{2}(b + B)h$;   for h

Solve the word problems.

37. The area of a triangle is 25 square meters. The base is 10 meters in length. Find the height.

38. The shorter base of a trapezoid is 42 centimeters long, and the longer base is 48 centimeters long. The height of the trapezoid is 8 centimeters. Find the area of the trapezoid.

[2.6] *Write the following ratios and reduce them to lowest terms.*

39. 50 centimeters to 30 centimeters

40. 6 days to 1 week

41. 45 inches to 5 feet

42. 2 months to 3 years

Decide whether or not the following proportions are true.

43. $\dfrac{15}{18} = \dfrac{45}{54}$

44. $\dfrac{11}{19} = \dfrac{55}{105}$

45. $\dfrac{38}{51} = \dfrac{722}{1020}$

46. $\dfrac{29}{72} = \dfrac{899}{2232}$

Solve each proportion.

47. $\dfrac{p}{5} = \dfrac{21}{30}$ **48.** $\dfrac{3}{5} = \dfrac{k}{12}$ **49.** $\dfrac{y}{y-5} = \dfrac{7}{2}$ **50.** $\dfrac{2+m}{2-m} = \dfrac{3}{4}$

Solve the word problems.

51. If 1 quart of oil must be mixed with 24 quarts of gasoline, how much oil would be needed for 192 quarts of gasoline?

52. The distance between two cities on a road map is 16 centimeters. The two cities are actually 150 kilometers apart. The distance on the map between two other cities is 40 centimeters. How far apart are these cities?

[2.7] Solve the word problems.

53. The perimeter of a rectangle is ten times the short side. The length is 9 meters more than the width. Find the width of the rectangle.

54. The longest side of a triangle is 11 meters longer than the shortest side. The medium side is 15 meters long. The perimeter of the triangle is 46 meters. Find the length of the shortest side of the triangle.

55. A person has $250 in fives and tens. He has twice as many tens as fives. How many fives does he have?

56. For a party, Joann bought some 15¢ candy and some 30¢ candy, paying $15 in all. If there are 25 more pieces of 15¢ candy, how many pieces of 30¢ did she buy?

57. An inheritance is invested two ways—some at 5% and $6000 more at 10%. The total annual income from interest is $2100. Find the amount invested at each rate.

58. Two trains are 390 miles apart. They start at the same time and travel toward one another, meeting 3 hours later. If the speed of one train is 30 miles per hour faster than the speed of the other train, find the speed of each train.

59. How many liters of 40% salt solution should be added to 72 liters of 80% salt solution to get a 70% mixture?

60. A nurse must mix 15 liters of a 10% solution of a drug with some 60% solution to get a 20% mixture. How many liters of the 60% solution would be needed?

[2.8–2.9] Graph each inequality on a number line.

61. $m \geq -2$ **62.** $a < -3$ **63.** $-5 \leq p < 6$ **64.** $1 \leq m < 4$

Solve each inequality.

65. $y + 5 \geq 2$ **66.** $5y > 4y + 8$

67. $9(k - 5) - (3 + 8k) \geq 5$

68. $3(2z + 5) + 4(8 + 3z) \leq 5(3z + 2) + 2z$

69. $-6 \leq x + 2 \leq 0$

70. $3 < y - 4 < 5$

71. $6k \geq -18$

72. $-11y < 22$

73. $-z > -4$

74. $7m + 3 \leq 5m - 9$

75. $2 - 4p + 7p + 8 < 6p - 5p$

76. $-(y + 2) + 3(2y - 7) \leq 4 - 5y$

77. $-3 \leq 2m + 1 \leq 4$

78. $9 < 3m + 5 \leq 20$

Solve each word problem.

79. The perimeter of a square cannot be greater than 200 meters. Find the longest possible value for the length of a side.

80. One side of a triangle is 3 centimeters longer than the shortest side. The third side is twice as long as the shortest side. If the perimeter of the triangle cannot exceed 39 centimeters, find the maximum possible length for the shortest side.

Chapter 2   Test

Simplify by combining like terms.

1. $9r + 3r - 4r - r - 8r$

2. $3z - 7z + 8 - 9 - (-5) + 4z$

3. $4(2m - 1) - (m + 5) - 3(m - 5)$

Solve each equation.

4. $3(a + 12) = 1 - 2(a - 5)$

5. $4k - 6k + 8(k - 3) = -2(k + 12)$

6. $\dfrac{5}{4}m = -3$

7. $\dfrac{1}{2}p + \dfrac{1}{3} = \dfrac{5}{2}p - \dfrac{4}{3}$

8. $-(y + 3) + 2y - 5 = 4 - 3y$

9. Three times a number is subtracted from 4, giving a result 20 more than the number. Find the number.

10. Vern paid $57 more to tune up his Bronco than his Oldsmobile. He paid $257 in all. How much did it cost for the tune-up on the Oldsmobile?

11. Solve the formula $I = prt$ for p.

12. Solve the formula $A = \dfrac{1}{2}(b + B)h$ for h.

13. Is the proportion $\dfrac{15}{79} = \dfrac{465}{2449}$ true or not?

Solve each proportion.

14. $\dfrac{z}{16} = \dfrac{3}{48}$ **15.** $\dfrac{y+5}{y-2} = \dfrac{1}{4}$

16. If 11 hamburgers cost $6.05, find the cost of 32 hamburgers.

Write an equation for each problem, and then solve it.

17. Sam has some ten-dollar bills and some twenty-dollar bills. He has 10 more twenties than tens. The money has a total value of $800. Find the number of ten-dollar bills that he has.

18. Trains A and B leave the same station at the same time, traveling in opposite directions. Train A travels at 50 miles per hour, and Train B travels at 70 miles per hour. After how many hours will the trains be 360 miles apart?

19. A woman invests some money at 12%, with $6000 more than this amount invested at 15%. Her total annual income from interest is $3870. How much is invested at 12%?

20. How many liters of a 20% chemical solution must be mixed with 30 liters of a 60% solution to get a 50% mixture?

Solve each inequality. Graph each solution.

21. $-2m < -14$

22. $5(k-2) + 3 \le 2(k-3) + 2k$

23. $-4r + 2(r-3) \ge 5r - (3+6r) - 7$

24. $-8 < 3k - 2 \le 12$

3

Exponents and Polynomials

Scientists use exponents in scientific notation, for small and large measurements.

3.1 Exponents

▪ Use exponents.
▪ Learn the product rule for exponents.
▪ Use zero as an exponent.
▪ Use negative numbers as exponents.
▪ Learn the quotient rule for exponents.

▪ In Chapter 1 we used exponents to write products of repeated factors:

$$5^2 = 5 \cdot 5 = 25,$$
$$4^3 = 4 \cdot 4 \cdot 4 = 64,$$
$$9^1 = 9,$$

and so on. In the expression 5^2, the number 5 is the **base** and 2 is the **exponent.** The expression 5^2 is called an **exponential expression.**

EXAMPLE 1   Evaluate each exponential expression. Name the base and the exponent.

	Base	Exponent
(a) $5^4 = 5 \cdot 5 \cdot 5 \cdot 5 = 625$	5	4
(b) $-5^4 = -1 \cdot 5^4 = -1 \cdot (5 \cdot 5 \cdot 5 \cdot 5) = -625$	5	4
(c) $(-5)^4 = (-5)(-5)(-5)(-5) = 625$	−5	4 ●

It is important to understand the differences between parts (b) and (c) of Example 1. In -5^4 the lack of parentheses shows that the exponent 4 refers only to the base 5, and not -5; in $(-5)^4$ the parentheses show that the exponent 4 refers to the base -5. In summary,

$-a^n$ and $(-a)^n$ are not necessarily the same.			
Expression	*Base*	*Exponent*	*Example*
$-a^n$	a	n	$-3^2 = -(3 \cdot 3) = -9$
$(-a)^n$	$-a$	n	$(-3)^2 = (-3)(-3) = 9$

2 By the definition of exponents,

$$2^4 \cdot 2^3 = (2 \cdot 2 \cdot 2 \cdot 2)(2 \cdot 2 \cdot 2)$$
$$= 2 \cdot 2 \cdot 2 \cdot 2 \cdot 2 \cdot 2 \cdot 2$$
$$= 2^7.$$

Generalizing from this example, $2^4 \cdot 2^3 = 2^{4+3} = 2^7$, gives the **product rule for exponents.**

For any positive integers m and n, $a^m \cdot a^n = a^{m+n}$.

The bases must be the same before the product rule for exponents can be applied. (A summary of all the rules for exponents is given at the end of the section.)

EXAMPLE 2 Use the product rule for exponents to find each product.

(a) $6^3 \cdot 6^5 = 6^{3+5} = 6^8$ by the product rule.

(b) $(-4)^5(-4)^3 = (-4)^{5+3} = (-4)^8$

(c) There is no shortcut for finding the product $2^3 \cdot 3^2$, since the bases are different. ●

EXAMPLE 3 Multiply $2x^3$ and $3x^7$.

Since $2x^3$ means $2 \cdot x^3$ and $3x^7$ means $3 \cdot x^7$, use the associative and commutative properties to get

$$2x^3 \cdot 3x^7 = 2 \cdot 3 \cdot x^3 \cdot x^7 = 6x^{10}. ●$$

Be careful to understand the difference between *adding* and *multiplying* terms. For example,

$$8x^3 + 5x^3 = 13x^3, \quad \text{but} \quad (8x^3)(5x^3) = 8 \cdot 5x^{3+3} = 40x^6.$$

3 The rule for division with exponents is similar to the product rule for exponents. For example,

$$\frac{6^5}{6^2} = \frac{6 \cdot 6 \cdot 6 \cdot 6 \cdot 6}{6 \cdot 6} = 6 \cdot 6 \cdot 6 = 6^3.$$

The difference of the exponents, $5 - 2$, gives the exponent of the answer, 3.

If the exponents in the numerator and denominator are equal, we have, for example,

$$\frac{6^5}{6^5} = \frac{6 \cdot 6 \cdot 6 \cdot 6 \cdot 6}{6 \cdot 6 \cdot 6 \cdot 6 \cdot 6} = 1.$$

If, however, the exponents are subtracted as above,

$$\frac{6^5}{6^5} = 6^{5-5} = 6^0.$$

This means that $6^0 = 1$. Based on this,

for any real number a, $a^0 = 1$ $(a \neq 0)$.

EXAMPLE 4   Evaluate each exponential expression.

(a) $60^0 = 1$

(b) $(-60)^0 = 1$

(c) $-(60^0) = -(1) = -1$ ●

Notice the difference between parts (b) and (c) of Example 4. In Example 4(b) the base is -60 and the exponent is 0. Any nonzero base raised to a zero exponent is 1. But in Example 4(c), the base is 60. Then $60^0 = 1$, so that $-60^0 = -1$.

◢ In the discussion above, we found that

$$\frac{6^5}{6^2} = 6^3,$$

where the bottom exponent was subtracted from the top exponent. If the bottom exponent were larger than the top exponent, we would end up with a negative exponent. **Negative exponents** are defined as follows.

For any real number a and any integer n,

$$a^{-n} = \frac{1}{a^n} \qquad (a \neq 0).$$

EXAMPLE 5   Simplify by using the definition of negative exponents.

(a) $3^{-2} = \dfrac{1}{3^2} = \dfrac{1}{9}$

(b) $5^{-3} = \dfrac{1}{5^3} = \dfrac{1}{125}$

(c) $\left(\dfrac{1}{2}\right)^{-3} = \dfrac{1}{\left(\dfrac{1}{2}\right)^3} = \dfrac{1}{\dfrac{1}{8}} = 1 \cdot \dfrac{8}{1} = 8$

(d) $4^{-1} - 2^{-1} = \dfrac{1}{4} - \dfrac{1}{2} = \dfrac{1}{4} - \dfrac{2}{4} = -\dfrac{1}{4}$ ●

Be careful:

> a negative exponent does not indicate a negative number; negative exponents lead to reciprocals.
>
> | *Expression* | *Example* | |
> |:---:|:---:|:---|
> | a^{-n} | $3^{-2} = \dfrac{1}{3^2} = \dfrac{1}{9}$ | Not negative |
> | $-a^{-n}$ | $-3^{-2} = -\dfrac{1}{3^2} = -\dfrac{1}{9}$ | Negative |

5 Using the definition of negative exponents, we now can give the **quotient rule for exponents.**

For any real number a and any integers m and n,

$$\frac{a^m}{a^n} = a^{m-n} \qquad (a \neq 0).$$

EXAMPLE 6 Simplify by using the quotient rule for exponents.

(a) $\dfrac{5^8}{5^6} = 5^{8-6} = 5^2$

(b) $\dfrac{4^2}{4^9} = 4^{2-9} = 4^{-7} = \dfrac{1}{4^7}$

(c) $\dfrac{5^{-3}}{5^{-7}} = 5^{-3-(-7)} = 5^4$

(d) $\dfrac{3^2 x^5}{3^4 x^3} = 3^{2-4} x^{5-3} = 3^{-2} x^2 = \dfrac{1}{3^2} \cdot x^2 = \dfrac{x^2}{3^2}$

Sometimes numerical expressions with small exponents, such as 3^2, are evaluated. Doing that would give the result as $x^2/9$. ●

By the definition of negative exponents, the product rule for exponents is also true for negative integer exponents. We now can summarize the rules for exponents.

Rules for Exponents

Product rule	$a^m \cdot a^n = a^{m+n}$	
Zero exponent	$a^0 = 1$	$(a \neq 0)$
Negative exponent	$a^{-n} = \dfrac{1}{a^n}$	$(a \neq 0)$
Quotient rule	$\dfrac{a^m}{a^n} = a^{m-n}$	$(a \neq 0)$

EXAMPLE 7   Simplify by using the rules for exponents. Assume that no variables are zero.

(a) $5^{-4} \cdot 5^7 = 5^{-4+7} = 5^3$

(b) $x^{-8} \cdot x^7 \cdot x^{-3} = x^{-8+7+(-3)} = x^{-4} = \dfrac{1}{x^4}$

(c) $\dfrac{m^{-2}}{m^{-5}} = m^{-2-(-5)} = m^3$ ●

3.1 EXERCISES

Identify the base and exponent for each exponential expression. See Example 1.

1. 5^{12} **2.** $(3m)^4$ **3.** -2^4 **4.** -125^3

5. $(-24)^2$ **6.** $-(-3)^5$ **7.** $-r^5$ **8.** $5y^3$

Write each expression using exponents.

9. $3 \cdot 3 \cdot 3 \cdot 3 \cdot 3$ **10.** $4 \cdot 4 \cdot 4$ **11.** $(-2)(-2)(-2)(-2)(-2)$

12. $(-1)(-1)(-1)(-1)$ **13.** $\dfrac{1}{(-2)(-2)(-2)}$ **14.** $\dfrac{1}{2 \cdot 2 \cdot 2 \cdot 2 \cdot 2}$

15. $p \cdot p \cdot p \cdot p \cdot p$ **16.** $k \cdot k \cdot k$ **17.** $\dfrac{1}{y \cdot y \cdot y \cdot y}$

18. $\dfrac{1}{a \cdot a \cdot a \cdot a \cdot a}$ **19.** $(-2z)(-2z)(-2z)$ **20.** $(-3m)(-3m)(-3m)(-3m)$

Evaluate each expression. For example, $5^2 + 5^3 = 25 + 125 = 150$. In Exercises 45–48, round to the nearest thousandth.

21. $3^2 + 3^4$ **22.** $2^8 - 2^6$ **23.** $4^2 + 4^3$ **24.** $3^3 + 3^4$

25. $2^2 + 2^5$

26. $4^2 + 4^1$

27. $4^0 + 5^0$

28. $3^0 + 8^0$

29. $(-9)^0 + 9^0$

30. $(-8)^0 + (-8)^0$

31. 3^{-3}

32. 2^{-5}

33. $(-12)^{-1}$

34. $(-6)^{-2}$

35. $\left(\dfrac{1}{2}\right)^{-5}$

36. $\left(\dfrac{1}{5}\right)^{-2}$

37. $\left(\dfrac{1}{2}\right)^{-1}$

38. $\left(\dfrac{3}{4}\right)^{-1}$

39. $\left(\dfrac{2}{3}\right)^{-3}$

40. $\left(\dfrac{5}{4}\right)^{-2}$

41. $2^{-1} + 3^{-1}$

42. $3^{-1} - 4^{-1}$

43. $5^{-1} + 4^{-1}$

44. $3^{-1} + 6^{-1}$

45. $(.98)^{-2}$

46. $(1.76)^{-2}$

47. $(3.918)^{-3}$

48. $(.162)^{-3}$

Use the product or quotient rule to simplify each expression. Write each answer in exponential form. Assume that all variables represent nonzero real numbers. See Examples 2, 3, and 5–7.

49. $4^2 \cdot 4^3$

50. $3^5 \cdot 3^4$

51. $3^4 \cdot 3^{-7}$

52. $2^{-5} \cdot 2^{15}$

53. $4^3 \cdot 4^5 \cdot 4^{-10}$

54. $2^3 \cdot 2^4 \cdot 2^{-6}$

55. $(-3)^3(-3)^2$

56. $(-4)^5(-4)^3$

57. $y^3 \cdot y^4 \cdot y^7$

58. $a^8 \cdot a^5 \cdot a^2$

59. $r \cdot r^5 \cdot r^4 \cdot r^7$

60. $m^9 \cdot m \cdot m^5 \cdot m^8$

61. $k^{-6} \cdot k^8 \cdot k^{-3}$

62. $p^{-2} \cdot p^{-7} \cdot p^5$

63. $(2p^4)(5p^9)$

64. $(3q^8)(7q^5)$

65. $(-9r^{-3})(7r^6)$

66. $(8a^{-9})(-3a^{14})$

67. $\dfrac{4^7}{4^2}$

68. $\dfrac{11^5}{11^3}$

69. $\dfrac{8^3}{8^9}$

70. $\dfrac{5^4}{5^{10}}$

71. $\dfrac{6^{-4}}{6^2}$

72. $\dfrac{7^{-5}}{7^3}$

73. $\dfrac{14^{-2}}{14^{-5}}$

74. $\dfrac{6^{-3}}{6^{-8}}$

75. $\dfrac{x^6}{x^{-9}}$

76. $\dfrac{y^2}{y^{-5}}$

77. $\dfrac{z}{z^{-1}}$

78. $\dfrac{r^{-1}}{r}$

79. $\dfrac{1}{2^{-5}}$

80. $\dfrac{1}{4^{-3}}$

81. $\dfrac{3^{-1}a^{-2}}{3^2 a^{-4}}$

82. $\dfrac{2^{-5}p^{-3}}{2^{-7}p^5}$

83. $\dfrac{4k^{-3}m^5}{4^{-1}k^{-7}m^{-3}}$

84. $\dfrac{6^{-1}y^{-2}z^5}{6^2 y^{-1}z^{-2}}$

In each of the following exercises, first add the given terms; then start over and multiply them.

85. $4m^3, 9m^3$

86. $8y^2, 7y^2$

87. $-12p, 11p$

88. $3q^4, 5q^4$

89. $7r, 3r, 5r$

90. $9a^3, 2a^3, 3a^3$

91. $-5a^{-2}, 3a^{-2}$

92. $6r^{-4}, -8r^{-4}$

Review Exercises *Evaluate each expression when (a) $x = 2$ and (b) $x = -3$. See Sections 1.6–1.8.*

93. $-x^2 + 4x - 7$

94. $-x^2 - 6x + 2$

95. $-x^3 + x^2 - 4$

96. $8 - 6x - x^3$

3.2   **Further Rules for Exponents**

1️⃣ Learn the power rule for exponents.

2️⃣ Use $(ab)^m = a^m b^m$.

3️⃣ Use $\left(\dfrac{a}{b}\right)^m = \dfrac{a^m}{b^m}$.

4️⃣ Use combinations of rules.

5️⃣ Use variables as exponents.

1️⃣   In this section we shall develop further rules for exponents to go with the product rule and quotient rule of the previous section.

To simplify an expression such as $(8^3)^2$, use the definition of an exponent.

$$(8^3)^2 = (8^3)(8^3)$$
$$= (8 \cdot 8 \cdot 8)(8 \cdot 8 \cdot 8)$$
$$= 8^6$$

Looking at just the exponents of the expression $(8^3)^2 = 8^6$, we see that $3 \cdot 2 = 6$. To find $(a^m)^n$, use the **power rule for exponents.**

For any integers m and n, $(a^m)^n = a^{mn}$.

EXAMPLE 1   Use the power rule for exponents to simplify each expression.

(a) $(2^5)^3 = 2^{5 \cdot 3} = 2^{15}$

(b) $(5^7)^{-2} = 5^{7(-2)} = 5^{-14} = \dfrac{1}{5^{14}}$

(c) $(8^{-2})^{-5} = 8^{(-2)(-5)} = 8^{10}$ ●

2️⃣   We can use the properties studied in Chapter 1 to develop two more rules for exponents. By definition and by the commutative and associative properties,

$$(4 \cdot 8)^3 = (4 \cdot 8)(4 \cdot 8)(4 \cdot 8)$$
$$= 4 \cdot 4 \cdot 4 \cdot 8 \cdot 8 \cdot 8$$
$$= 4^3 \cdot 8^3.$$

This example suggests the following rule.

For any integer m, $(ab)^m = a^m b^m$.

EXAMPLE 2   Use the rule given above to simplify each expression.

(a) $5(pq)^2 = 5(p^2 q^2) = 5p^2 q^2$

(b) $(2m^2 p^3)^4 = 2^4 (m^2)^4 (p^3)^4 = 2^4 m^8 p^{12}$

(c) $(3k^{-2})^{-3} = 3^{-3} k^{(-2)(-3)} = 3^{-3} k^6 = \dfrac{k^6}{3^3}$ ●

3 Since the quotient a/b can be written as $a\left(\dfrac{1}{b}\right)$, the rule above, together with some of the properties of real numbers, gives the final rule for exponents.

For any integer m, $\left(\dfrac{a}{b}\right)^m = \dfrac{a^m}{b^m}$ $(b \neq 0)$.

EXAMPLE 3   Use the rule given above to simplify each expression.

(a) $\left(\dfrac{2}{3}\right)^5 = \dfrac{2^5}{3^5}$

(b) $\left(\dfrac{4}{5}\right)^{-2} = \dfrac{4^{-2}}{5^{-2}} = \dfrac{\dfrac{1}{4^2}}{\dfrac{1}{5^2}} = \dfrac{1}{4^2} \cdot \dfrac{5^2}{1} = \dfrac{5^2}{4^2}$ or $\dfrac{25}{16}$ ●

4   The next example shows that more than one rule may be needed to simplify an expression.

EXAMPLE 4   Use a combination of the rules for exponents to simplify each expression.

(a) $\dfrac{(4^2)^3}{4^5}$

Use the power rule and then the quotient rule.

$$\dfrac{(4^2)^3}{4^5} = \dfrac{4^6}{4^5} = 4^{6-5} = 4^1 = 4$$

(b) $(2x)^3(2x)^2$

Use the product rule first.

$$(2x)^3(2x)^2 = (2x)^5 = 2^5x^5 \quad \text{or} \quad 32x^5$$

(c) $\left(\dfrac{2x^3}{5}\right)^4$

By the last two rules given above,

$$\left(\dfrac{2x^3}{5}\right)^4 = \dfrac{(2x^3)^4}{5^4} = \dfrac{2^4x^{12}}{5^4} \quad \text{or} \quad \dfrac{16x^{12}}{625}.$$

(d) $\left(\dfrac{3x^{-2}}{4^{-1}y^3}\right)^{-3} = \dfrac{3^{-3}x^6}{4^3y^{-9}} = \dfrac{\dfrac{1}{3^3} \cdot x^6}{4^3 \cdot \dfrac{1}{y^9}} = \dfrac{\dfrac{x^6}{3^3}}{\dfrac{4^3}{y^9}}$

$$= \dfrac{x^6}{3^3} \cdot \dfrac{y^9}{4^3} = \dfrac{x^6y^9}{3^3 \cdot 4^3} \quad \text{or} \quad \dfrac{x^6y^9}{1728} \quad ●$$

We again summarize the rules for exponents, adding the three rules from this section.

Rules for Exponents

For any integers m and n:

Product rule $\qquad a^m \cdot a^n = a^{m+n}$

Zero exponent $\qquad a^0 = 1 \qquad\qquad (a \neq 0)$

Negative exponent $\qquad a^{-n} = \dfrac{1}{a^n} \qquad (a \neq 0)$

Quotient rule $\qquad \dfrac{a^m}{a^n} = a^{m-n} \qquad (a \neq 0)$

Power rules $\qquad (a^m)^n = a^{mn}$

$\qquad\qquad\qquad (ab)^m = a^m b^m$

$\qquad\qquad\qquad \left(\dfrac{a}{b}\right)^m = \dfrac{a^m}{b^m} \qquad (b \neq 0)$

5   All the rules given in the box also apply when variables are used as exponents, as long as the variables represent only integers, an assumption we shall make throughout this chapter.

EXAMPLE 5   Simplify.

(a) $3x^k \cdot (2x^5) = 3 \cdot 2 \cdot x^k \cdot x^5 = 6x^{k+5}$

(b) $\dfrac{y^{7z}}{y^{3z}} = y^{7z-3z} = y^{4z}$

(c) $(2a^4)^r = 2^r \cdot a^{4r}$

(d) $z^q \cdot z^{5q} \cdot z^{-4q} = z^{q+5q+(-4q)} = z^{2q}$ ●

3.2 EXERCISES

Use the rules for exponents to simplify each expression. Write each answer in exponential form using only positive exponents. Assume that all variables represent only nonzero real numbers. See Examples 1–4.

1. $(6^3)^2$

2. $(8^4)^6$

3. $(9^{-3})^2$

4. $(2^{-3})^4$

5. $(3^{-5})^{-2}$

6. $(8^{-4})^{-1}$

7. $\dfrac{(y^3)^3}{(y^2)^2}$

8. $\dfrac{(r^2)^4}{(r^3)^2}$

9. $\dfrac{a^6 \cdot a^5}{(a^2)^4}$

10. $\dfrac{s^7 \cdot s^9}{(s^5)^2}$

11. $\dfrac{(k^2)^4}{(k^6)^2}$

12. $\dfrac{(w^4)^2}{(w^7)^3}$

13. $\dfrac{4^3 \cdot 4^{-5}}{4^7}$

14. $\dfrac{2^5 \cdot 2^{-4}}{2^{-1}}$

15. $\dfrac{5^{-3} \cdot 5^{-2}}{5^4}$

16. $\dfrac{8^{-2} \cdot 8^5}{8^6}$

17. $\dfrac{m^4 \cdot m^{-5}}{m^{-6}}$

18. $\dfrac{p^3 \cdot p^{-5}}{p^5}$

19. $\dfrac{a^{11} \cdot a^{-7}}{a^5}$

20. $\dfrac{z^3 \cdot z^{-5}}{z^{10}}$

21. $\dfrac{r^5 \cdot r^{-8}}{r^{-6} \cdot r^4}$

22. $\dfrac{x^3 \cdot x^{-1}}{x^8 \cdot x^{-2}}$

23. $\dfrac{a^6 \cdot a^{-3}}{a^{-5} \cdot a}$

24. $\dfrac{b^{10} \cdot b^{-2}}{b^{-8} \cdot b^6}$

25. $(5m)^3$

26. $(2xy)^4$

27. $(-2pq)^4$

28. $(-3ab)^5$

29. $(-3x^5)^2$

30. $(4m^3n^2)^4$

31. $(5a^2b)^3$

32. $(2y^2z^4)^5$

33. $(3x^{-5})^2$

34. $(5p^{-4})^{-2}$

35. $(9^{-1}y^5)^{-2}$

36. $(4^{-2}m^{-3})^{-2}$

37. $\left(\dfrac{a}{5}\right)^3$

38. $\left(\dfrac{9}{x}\right)^2$

39. $\left(\dfrac{3mn}{2}\right)^5$

40. $\left(\dfrac{2x}{5y}\right)^4$

41. $\left(\dfrac{a}{b}\right)^{-1}$

42. $\left(\dfrac{2a}{3}\right)^{-2}$

43. $\left(\dfrac{5m^{-2}}{m^{-1}}\right)^2$

44. $\left(\dfrac{4x^3}{3^{-1}}\right)^{-1}$

45. $\dfrac{x^7x^8(x^3)^2}{(x^2)^8}$

46. $\dfrac{(m^3)^2(m^2)^4m^8}{(m^9)^3}$

47. $\dfrac{b^{11}(b^2)^4}{(b^3)^3(b^2)^6}$

48. $\dfrac{(8r^2)^3(8r^4)^2}{(8r^3)^4}$

49. $\dfrac{(3x^2)^{-2}(5x^{-1})^3}{3x^{-5}}$

50. $\dfrac{(2k^3)^{-1}(3k^{-2})^2}{2k^{-4}}$

51. $\dfrac{(4a^2b^3)^{-2}(2ab^{-1})^3}{(a^3b)^{-4}}$

52. $\dfrac{(m^6n)^{-2}(m^2n^{-2})^3}{m^{-1}n^{-2}}$

53. $\dfrac{(2y^{-1}z^2)^2(3y^{-2}z^{-3})^3}{(y^3z^2)^{-1}}$

54. $\dfrac{(3p^{-2}q^3)^2(5p^{-1}q^{-4})^{-1}}{(p^2q^{-2})^{-3}}$

55. $\dfrac{(9^{-1}z^{-2}x)^{-1}(4z^2x^4)^{-2}}{(5z^{-2}x^{-3})^2}$

56. $\dfrac{(4^{-1}a^{-1}b^{-2})^{-2}(5a^{-3}b^4)^{-2}}{(3a^{-3}b^{-5})^2}$

Simplify each expression. Assume that all variables represent integers and that no denominators are ever zero. See Example 5.

57. $5^r \cdot 5^{7r} \cdot 5^{-2r}$

58. $6^{5p} \cdot 6^p \cdot 6^{-2p}$

59. $x^{-a} \cdot x^{-3a} \cdot x^{-7a}$

60. $q^{4m} \cdot q^{-6m} \cdot q^{-3m}$

61. $\dfrac{a^{6y}}{a^{2y}}$

62. $\dfrac{p^{9m}}{p^{5m}}$

63. $\dfrac{q^{-3k}}{q^{-8k}}$

64. $\dfrac{z^{-7m}}{z^{-12m}}$

65. $(6 \cdot p^{-3})^{-y}$

66. $(2 \cdot a^{-p})^4$

67. $\left(\dfrac{3m^{-2}}{p^{-1}}\right)^{-q}$

68. $\left(\dfrac{7z^{-1}}{x^{-5}}\right)^{-m}$

Review Exercises   *Evaluate. See Section 3.1.*

69. 10^2

70. 10^3

71. 10^5

72. 10^7

73. 10^{-1}

74. 10^{-2}

75. 10^{-4}

76. 10^{-6}

3.3 An Application of Exponents: Scientific Notation

1️⃣ Express numbers in scientific notation.

2️⃣ Convert numbers in scientific notation to numbers without exponents.

3️⃣ Use scientific notation in calculations.

1️⃣ One example of the use of exponents comes from science. The numbers in science are often extremely large (such as the distance from the earth to the sun, which is 93,000,000 miles) or extremely small (the wavelength of yellow green light is approximately .0000006 meters). Because of the difficulty of working with many zeros, scientists often express such numbers with exponents. Each number is written as the product of a number a, where $1 \leq a < 10$, and some power of 10. This form is called **scientific notation.** There is always one nonzero integer before the decimal point. For example, 35 is written 3.5×10^1, or 3.5×10; 56,200 is written 5.62×10^4, since

$$56{,}200 = 5.62 \times \mathbf{10{,}000} = 5.62 \times 10^4.$$

The following box shows the steps involved in writing a number in scientific notation.

Writing a Number in Scientific Notation

1. Place a caret, ∧, to the right of the first nonzero digit.
2. Count the number of places from the caret to the actual decimal point.
3. The number of places in Step 2 is the absolute value of the exponent on 10.
4. The exponent on 10 is positive if you counted from left to right; the exponent is negative if you counted from right to left.

EXAMPLE 1 Write each number in scientific notation.

(a) 93,000,000

Place a caret after the first nonzero digit.

$$9{∧}3{,}000{,}000$$
└─Caret to right of first nonzero digit

Count from the caret to the decimal point.

$$9{∧}3{,}000{,}000 \qquad 7 \text{ places}$$

Since we counted from left to right, the exponent on 10 is positive, and $93{,}000{,}000 = 9.3 \times 10^7$.

(b) $63{,}200{,}000{,}000 = 6.32 \times 10^{10}$

(c) .00462

Place a caret to the right of the first nonzero digit.

$$.004_\wedge 62$$

Count from the right of the caret to the decimal point.

$$\underset{\sim}{.004}_\wedge 62 \qquad 3 \text{ places}$$

Since we are counting from right to left, the exponent will be negative.

$$.00462 = \mathbf{4.62 \times 10^{-3}}$$

(d) $.0000762 = 7.62 \times 10^{-5}$ ●

2   To convert a number from scientific notation to a number without exponents, use the steps given below.

Converting from Scientific Notation

> 1. Count from the decimal point the same number of places as the exponent on 10, attaching additional zeros as necessary.
> 2. Move to the right if the exponent on 10 is positive; move to the left if the exponent is negative.

EXAMPLE 2   Write each number without exponents.

(a) 6.2×10^3

Moving the decimal point 3 places to the right gives

$$6.2 \times 10^3 = 6.2 \times \mathbf{1000} = 6200.$$

(b) $4.283 \times 10^5 = 4.\underset{\sim}{28300} = 428,300 \qquad 5 \text{ places to the right}$

(c) $7.04 \times 10^{-3} = \underset{\sim}{.00704}$

Here the decimal point was moved 3 places left.   ●

3   The next example shows how scientific notation can be used with products and quotients.

EXAMPLE 3   Write each number without exponents.

(a) $(6 \times 10^3)(5 \times 10^{-4})$

First use the commutative and associative properties.

$$(6 \times 10^3)(5 \times 10^{-4}) = (6 \times 5)(10^3 \times 10^{-4})$$

Now use the rules for exponents.

$$(6 \times 5)(10^3 \times 10^{-4}) = 30 \times 10^{-1}$$

Then express the result without exponents, as 3.0.

(b) $\dfrac{4 \times 10^{-5}}{2 \times 10^3} = \dfrac{4}{2} \times \dfrac{10^{-5}}{10^3} = 2 \times 10^{-8} = .00000002$ ●

3.3 EXERCISES

Express each number in scientific notation. See Example 1.

1. 6,835,000,000   **2.** 321,000,000,000,000   **3.** 8,360,000,000,000

4. 6850   **5.** 215   **6.** 683

7. 25,000   **8.** 110,000,000   **9.** .035

10. .005   **11.** .0101   **12.** .0000006

13. .000012   **14.** .000000982

Write each number without exponents. See Examples 2 and 3.

15. 8.1×10^9

16. 3.5×10^2

17. 9.132×10^6

18. 2.14×10^0

19. 3.24×10^8

20. 4.35×10^4

21. 3.2×10^{-4}

22. 5.76×10^{-5}

23. 4.1×10^{-2}

24. 1.79×10^{-3}

25. $(2 \times 10^8) \times (4 \times 10^{-3})$

26. $(5 \times 10^4) \times (3 \times 10^{-2})$

27. $(4 \times 10^{-1}) \times (1 \times 10^{-5})$

28. $(6 \times 10^{-5}) \times (2 \times 10^4)$

29. $(7 \times 10^3) \times (2 \times 10^2) \times (3 \times 10^{-4})$

30. $(3 \times 10^{-5}) \times (3 \times 10^2) \times (5 \times 10^{-2})$

31. $(1.2 \times 10^2) \times (5 \times 10^{-3}) \times (2.4 \times 10^3)$

32. $(4.6 \times 10^{-3}) \times (2 \times 10^{-1}) \times (4 \times 10^5)$

33. $\dfrac{9 \times 10^5}{3 \times 10^{-1}}$

34. $\dfrac{12 \times 10^{-4}}{4 \times 10^4}$

35. $\dfrac{4 \times 10^{-3}}{2 \times 10^{-2}}$

36. $\dfrac{5 \times 10^{-1}}{1 \times 10^{-5}}$

37. $\dfrac{2.6 \times 10^5}{2 \times 10^2}$

38. $\dfrac{9.5 \times 10^{-1}}{5 \times 10^3}$

39. $\dfrac{7.2 \times 10^{-3} \times 1.6 \times 10^5}{4 \times 10^{-2} \times 3.6 \times 10^9}$

40. $\dfrac{8.7 \times 10^{-2} \times 1.2 \times 10^{-6}}{3 \times 10^{-4} \times 2.9 \times 10^{11}}$

Write the numbers in each statement in scientific notation.

41. Light visible to the human eye has a wavelength between .0004 millimeters and .0008 millimeters.

42. In the ocean, the amount of oxygen per cubic mile of water is 4,037,000,000 tons, and the amount of radium is .0003 tons.

43. Each tide in the Bay of Fundy carries more than 3,680,000,000,000,000 cubic feet of water into the bay.

44. The mean (average) diameter of the sun is about 865,000 miles.

Write the numbers in each statement without exponents.

45. Many ocean trenches have a depth of 3.5×10^4 feet.

46. The average life span of a human is 1×10^9 seconds.

47. There are 1×10^3 cubic millimeters in 6.102×10^{-2} cubic inches.

48. In the food chain that links the largest sea creature, the whale, to the smallest, the diatom, 4×10^{14} diatoms sustain a medium-sized whale for only a few hours.

Review Exercises *Simplify. See Section 2.1.*

49. $7m + 8m$ **50.** $9y + 11y$ **51.** $12p - 9p + p$

52. $8x - 9x + 10x$ **53.** $5(2m - 1) - 3m$ **54.** $-7 + 2(2x + 5)$

Evaluate each expression when $x = -4$. See Sections 1.6–1.8.

55. $2x - 5$ **56.** $3x + 7$ **57.** $x^2 + x^3$ **58.** $2x^2 + 4x$

3.4 Polynomials

1. Identify terms and coefficients.
2. Combine like terms.
3. Know the vocabulary for polynomials.
4. Evaluate polynomials.
5. Add polynomials.
6. Subtract polynomials.

1 Recall that in an expression such as

$$4x^3 + 6x^2 + 5x,$$

the quantities $4x^3$, $6x^2$, and $5x$ are called **terms.** In the term $4x^3$, the number 4 is called the **numerical coefficient** of x^3. We can generalize this definition of coefficient: In a term with two or more factors, the coefficient of one factor is the product of the other factors.

EXAMPLE 1   The list below shows several terms having a factor of x^2. The list also gives the coefficient of x^2.

Term	Coefficient of x^2	
$-5x^2$	-5	
x^2	1	(understood)
$-x^2$	-1	(understood)
$9x^2y^3$	$9y^3$	●

The numerical coefficient of a term is made up of all the numbers appearing as factors in the term. Since the numerical coefficient is the most important coefficient we use, whenever we say *coefficient of a term,* we mean the *numerical coefficient.*

EXAMPLE 2   Name the coefficient of each term in these expressions.

(a) $4x^3$

The (numerical) coefficient is 4.

(b) $5 - v^3$

The coefficient of the term 5 is 5 since $5 = 5v^0$. By writing $5 - v^3$ as a sum, $5 + (-v^3)$, or $5 + (-1v^3)$, the coefficient of v^3 can be identified as -1.   ●

2   Recall that **like terms** have exactly the same combination of variables with the same exponent. Only the coefficients may be different. Examples of like terms are

$$19m^5 \quad \text{and} \quad 14m^5,$$
$$6y^9, \quad -37y^9, \quad \text{and} \quad y^9,$$
$$3pq \quad \text{and} \quad -2pq.$$

To add like terms, use the distributive property.

EXAMPLE 3   Simplify each expression by using the distributive property.

(a) $-4x^3 + 6x^3 = (-4 + 6)x^3 = 2x^3$

(b) $9x^6 - 14x^6 + x^6 = (9 - 14 + 1)x^6 = -4x^6$

(c) $12m^2 + 5m + 4m^2 = (12 + 4)m^2 + 5m = 16m^2 + 5m$

(d) $3x^2y + 4x^2y - x^2y = (3 + 4 - 1)x^2y = 6x^2y$ ●

Example 3(c) shows that it is not possible to add $16m^2$ and $5m$. These two terms are unlike because the exponents on the variables are different. **Unlike terms** have different variables or different exponents on the same variables.

3   *Polynomials* are basic to algebra. A **polynomial in x** is an expression containing the sum of only a finite number of terms of the form ax^n, for any real number a and any whole number n. For example,

$$16x^8 - 7x^6 + 5x^4 - 3x^2 + 4$$

is a polynomial in x (the 4 can be written as $4x^0$). This polynomial is written in **descending powers** of the variable, since the exponents on x decrease from left to right. On the other hand,

$$2x^3 - x^2 + \frac{4}{x}$$

is not a polynomial in x, since $4/x$ is not a *product, ax^n,* for a *whole number n.* (Of course, we could define *polynomial* using any variable or variables, and not just x.)

The **degree** of a term with one variable is the exponent on the variable. For example, $3x^4$ has degree 4, while $6x^{17}$ has degree 17, the term $5x$ has degree 1, and -7 has degree 0 (since -7 can be written as $-7x^0$). The **degree of a polynomial** in one variable is the highest exponent found in any nonzero term of the polynomial.

For example, $3x^4 - 5x^2 + 6$ is of degree 4, the polynomial $5x + 7$ is of degree 1, and 3 (or $3x^0$) is of degree 0.

Three types of polynomials are very common and are given special names. A polynomial with exactly three terms is called a **trinomial.** (*Tri-* means "three," as in *tri*angle.) Examples are

$$9m^3 - 4m^2 + 6, \qquad 19y^2 + 8y + 5, \qquad \text{and} \qquad -3m^5 - 9m^2 + 2.$$

A polynomial with exactly two terms is called a **binomial.** (*Bi-* means "two," as in *bi*cycle.) Examples are

$$-9x^4 + 9x^3, \qquad 8m^2 + 6m, \qquad \text{and} \qquad 3m^5 - 9m^2.$$

A polynomial with only one term is called a **monomial.** (*Mon(o)-* means "one," as in *mono*rail.) Examples are

$$9m, \qquad -6y^5, \qquad a^2, \qquad \text{and} \qquad 6.$$

EXAMPLE 4   For each polynomial, first simplify if possible by combining like terms. Then give the degree and tell whether it is a monomial, a binomial, a trinomial, or none of these.

(a) $2x^3 + 5$

The polynomial cannot be simplified. The degree is 3. The polynomial is a binomial.

(b) $4x - 5x + 2x$

Add like terms to simplify: $4x - 5x + 2x = x$, a monomial of degree 1.   ●

4   A polynomial represents different numbers for different values of the variable, as shown in the next examples.

EXAMPLE 5   Find the value of $3x^4 + 5x^3 - 4x - 4$ when $x = -2$ and when $x = 3$.
First, substitute -2 for x.

$$\begin{aligned}
3x^4 + 5x^3 - 4x - 4 &= 3(-2)^4 + 5(-2)^3 - 4(-2) - 4 \\
&= 3 \cdot 16 + 5 \cdot (-8) + 8 - 4 \\
&= 48 - 40 + 8 - 4 \\
&= 12
\end{aligned}$$

Next, replace x with 3.

$$\begin{aligned}
3x^4 + 5x^3 - 4x - 4 &= 3 \cdot 3^4 + 5 \cdot 3^3 - 4 \cdot 3 - 4 \\
&= 3 \cdot 81 + 5 \cdot 27 - 12 - 4 \\
&= 362 \quad ●
\end{aligned}$$

⑤   Polynomials may be added, subtracted, multiplied, and divided. We see how to add and subtract polynomials in the rest of this section.

Adding Polynomials

> **To add two polynomials, add like terms.**

EXAMPLE 6   Add $6x^3 - 4x^2 + 3$ and $-2x^3 + 7x^2 - 5$.
  Write like terms in columns.

$$6x^3 - 4x^2 + 3$$
$$\underline{-2x^3 + 7x^2 - 5}$$

Now add, column by column.

$$\begin{array}{ccc} 6x^3 & -4x^2 & 3 \\ \underline{-2x^3} & \underline{7x^2} & \underline{-5} \\ 4x^3 & 3x^2 & -2 \end{array}$$

Add the three sums together.

$$4x^3 + 3x^2 + (-2) = 4x^3 + 3x^2 - 2 \quad \bullet$$

We also can add the polynomials in Example 6 when they are written horizontally, as shown below.

EXAMPLE 7   Add $6x^3 - 4x^2 + 3$ and $-2x^3 + 7x^2 - 5$.
  Write the sum.

$$(6x^3 - 4x^2 + 3) + (-2x^3 + 7x^2 - 5)$$

Use the associative and commutative properties to rewrite this sum with the parentheses removed and with the subtractions changed to additions of inverses.

$$6x^3 + (-4x^2) + 3 + (-2x^3) + 7x^2 + (-5)$$

Place like terms together.

$$6x^3 + (-2x^3) \quad + (-4x^2) + 7x^2 \quad + 3 + (-5)$$

Combine like terms to get

$$4x^3 + 3x^2 + (-2), \quad \text{or simply} \quad 4x^3 + 3x^2 - 2,$$

the same answer found in Example 6. $\bullet$

⑥   Earlier, we defined the difference $x - y$ as $x + (-y)$. (To find the difference $x - y$, add x and the opposite of y.) For example,

$$7 - 2 = 7 + (-2) = 5 \quad \text{and} \quad -8 - (-2) = -8 + 2 = -6.$$

The same method is used to subtract polynomials.

EXAMPLE 8

Subtract: $(5x - 2) - (3x - 8)$.
By the definition of subtraction,

$$(5x - 2) - (3x - 8) = (5x - 2) + [-(3x - 8)].$$

As in Chapter 1, the distributive property gives

$$-(3x - 8) = -\mathbf{1}(3x - 8) = -3x + 8.$$

Now

$$(5x - 2) - (3x - 8) = (5x - 2) + (-3x + 8) = 2x + 6. \quad \bullet$$

In summary, polynomials are subtracted as follows.

Subtracting Polynomials

> To subtract two polynomials, change all the signs on the second polynomial and add the two polynomials.

EXAMPLE 9

Subtract $6x^3 - 4x^2 + 2$ from $11x^3 + 2x^2 - 8$.
Write the problem.

$$(11x^3 + 2x^2 - 8) - (6x^3 - 4x^2 + 2)$$

Change all the signs on the second polynomial and add.

$$(11x^3 + 2x^2 - 8) + (-6x^3 + 4x^2 - 2) = 5x^3 + 6x^2 - 10$$

To check a subtraction problem, use the fact that if $a - b = c$, then $a = b + c$. For example, $6 - 2 = 4$. To check this, write $6 = 2 + 4$, which is correct. To check the subtraction of Example 9, add $6x^3 - 4x^2 + 2$ and $5x^3 + 6x^2 - 10$. Since the sum is $11x^3 + 2x^2 - 8$, the subtraction was performed correctly. $\quad \bullet$

Subtraction also can be done in columns.

EXAMPLE 10

Use the method of subtracting by columns to find $(14y^3 - 6y^2 + 2y - 5) - (2y^3 - 7y^2 - 4y + 6)$.
Arrange like terms in columns.

$$\begin{array}{r} 14y^3 - 6y^2 + 2y - 5 \\ 2y^3 - 7y^2 - 4y + 6 \\ \hline \end{array}$$

Change all signs in the second row, and then add.

$$\begin{array}{r} 14y^3 - 6y^2 + 2y - 5 \\ -2y^3 + 7y^2 + 4y - 6 \\ \hline 12y^3 + y^2 + 6y - 11 \end{array} \quad \begin{array}{l} \text{All signs changed} \\ \text{Add} \quad \bullet \end{array}$$

Either the horizontal or the vertical method may be used for adding and subtracting polynomials.

3.4 EXERCISES

In each polynomial, combine terms where possible. Write the results in descending powers of the variable. See Example 3.

1. $2r^5 + (-3r^5)$

2. $-19y^2 + 9y^2$

3. $3x^5 + 2x^5 - 4x^5$

4. $6x^3 - 8x^7 - 9x^3$

5. $-4p^7 + 8p^7 - 5p^7$

6. $-3a^8 + 4a^8 - 3a^8 + 2a^8$

7. $4y^2 + 3y^2 - 2y^2 + y^2$

8. $3r^5 - 8r^5 + r^5 - 2r^5$

9. $-5p^5 + 8p^5 - 2p^5 - p^5$

10. $6k^3 - 9k^3 + 8k^3 - 2k^3$

11. $y^4 + 8y^4 - 9y^2 + 6y^2 + 10y^2$

12. $11a^2 - 10a^2 + 2a^2 - a^6 + 2a^6$

13. $4z^5 - 9z^3 + 8z^2 + 10z^5$

14. $-9m^3 + 2m^3 - 11m^3 + 15m^2 - 9m$

15. $2p^7 - 8p^6 + 5p^4 - 9p$

16. $7y^3 - 8y^2 + 6y + 2$

17. $-.823q^2 + 1.725q - .374 + 1.994q^2 - .324q + .122$

18. $5.893r^3 - 2.776r^2 + 5.409r - 6.783r^3 + 1.437r - r^2$

For each polynomial, first simplify, if possible; then give the degree of the polynomial and tell whether it is (a) a monomial, (b) a binomial, (c) a trinomial, (d) none of these. See Example 4.

19. $5x^4 - 8x$

20. $4y - 8y$

21. $23x^9 - \dfrac{1}{2}x^2 + x$

22. $2m^7 - 3m^6 + 2m^5 + m$

23. $x^8 + 3x^7 - 5x^4$

24. $2x - 2x^2$

25. $\dfrac{3}{5}x^5 + \dfrac{2}{5}x^5$

26. $\dfrac{9}{11}x^2$

27. $2m^8 - 5m^9$

Tell whether each statement is true always, sometimes, *or* never.

28. A binomial is a polynomial.

29. A polynomial is a trinomial.

30. A trinomial is a binomial.

31. A monomial has no coefficient.

32. A binomial is a trinomial.

33. A polynomial of degree 4 has 4 terms.

Find the value of each polynomial when (a) $x = 2$ and when (b) $x = -1$. See Example 5.

34. $2x^2 - 4x$

35. $8x + 5x^2 + 2$

36. $2x^5 - 4x^4 + 5x^3 - x^2$

37. $2x^2 + 5x + 1$

38. $-3x^2 + 14x - 2$

39. $-2x^2 + 3$

40. $-5x^2 + 4x + 5$

41. $-x^2 - 8x$

42. $-x^2 + 7x + 2$

Add or subtract as indicated. See Examples 6 and 10.

43. Add.

$$3m^2 + 5m$$
$$\underline{2m^2 - 2m}$$

44. Add.

$$4a^3 - 4a^2$$
$$\underline{6a^3 + 5a^2}$$

45. Subtract.

$$12x^4 - x^2$$
$$\underline{8x^4 + 3x^2}$$

46. Subtract.

$$2a + 5d$$
$$\underline{3a - 6d}$$

47. Subtract.

$$2n^5 - 5n^3 + 6$$
$$\underline{3n^5 + 7n^3 + 8}$$

48. Subtract.

$$3r^2 - 4r + 2$$
$$\underline{7r^2 + 2r - 3}$$

49. Add.

$$9m^3 - 5m^2 + 4m - 8$$
$$\underline{3m^3 + 6m^2 + 8m - 6}$$

50. Add.

$$12r^5 + 11r^4 - 7r^3 - 2r^2 - 5r - 3$$
$$\underline{-8r^5 - 10r^4 + 3r^3 + 2r^2 - 5r + 7}$$

51. Add.

$$12m^2 - 8m + 6$$
$$\underline{3m^2 + 5m - 2}$$

52. Subtract.

$$5a^4 - 3a^3 + 2a^2$$
$$\underline{a^3 - a^2 + a - 1}$$

53. Add.

$$5b^2 + 6b + 2$$
$$\underline{3b^2 - 4b + 5}$$

54. Add.

$$3w^2 - 5w + 2$$
$$4w^2 + 6w - 5$$
$$\underline{8w^2 + 7w - 2}$$

Perform the indicated operations. See Examples 7–9.

55. $(3r^2 + 5r - 6) + (2r - 5r^2)$

56. $(8m^2 - 7m) - (3m^2 + 7m)$

57. $(x^2 + x) - (3x^2 + 2x - 1)$

58. $(3x^2 + 2x + 5) + (8x^2 - 5x - 4)$

59. $(16x^3 - x^2 + 3x) + (-12x^3 + 3x^2 + 2x)$

60. $(-2b^6 + 3b^4 - b^2) - (b^6 + 2b^4 + 2b^2)$

61. $(7y^4 + 3y^2 + 2y) - (18y^4 - 5y^2 - y)$

62. $(3x^2 + 2x + 5) + (-7x^2 - 8x + 2) + (3x^2 - 4x + 7)$

63. $[(8m^2 + 4m - 7) - (2m^2 - 5m + 2)] - (m^2 + m + 1)$

64. $[(9b^3 - 4b^2 + 3b + 2) - (-2b^3 - 3b^2 + b)] - (8b^3 + 6b + 4)$

65. $(3.127m^2 - 5.148m - 3.947) - (-.259m^2 + 7.125m - 8.9)$

66. $(-4.009k^2 + 3.176k + 4.1) - (1.795k^2 - .165k - .9935)$

Write each statement as an equation or an inequality. Do not solve.

67. When $4 + x^2$ is added to $-9x + 2$, the result is larger than 8.

68. When $6 + 3x$ is subtracted from $5 + 2x$, the difference is larger than $8x + x^2$.

69. The sum of $5 + x^2$ and $3 - 2x$ is not equal to 5.

70. The sum of $3 - 2x + x^2$ and $8 - 9x + 3x^2$ is negative.

Review Exercises   *Simplify. See Section 3.1.*

71. $p(2p)$

72. $3k(5k)$

73. $5x^2(2x)$

74. $9r^3(2r)$

75. $7m^3(8m^2)$

76. $4y^5(7y^2)$

77. $6p^5(5p^4)$

78. $2z^8(5z^3)$

3.5   Multiplication of Polynomials

1 Multiply a monomial and a polynomial.
2 Multiply two polynomials.

1   As we have seen, the product of two monomials is found by using the rules for exponents and the commutative and associative properties. For example,

$$(-8m^6)(-9m^4) = (-8)(-9)(m^6)(m^4) = 72m^{6+4} = 72m^{10}.$$

As mentioned earlier, it is important not to confuse the *addition* of terms with the *multiplication* of terms. For example,

$$7q^5 + 2q^5 = 9q^5, \quad \text{but} \quad (7q^5)(2q^5) = 7 \cdot 2q^{5+5} = 14q^{10}.$$

To use the method of finding the product of two monomials to find the product of a monomial and a polynomial with more than one term, use the distributive property, as shown in Example 1.

EXAMPLE 1   Use the distributive property to find each product.

(a) $4x^2(3x + 5)$

$$4x^2(3x + 5) = (4x^2)(3x) + (4x^2)(5) = 12x^3 + 20x^2$$

(b) $-8m^3(4m^3 + 3m^2 + 2m - 1)$

$$-8m^3(4m^3 + 3m^2 + 2m - 1)$$
$$= (-8m^3)(4m^3) + (-8m^3)(3m^2) + (-8m^3)(2m) + (-8m^3)(-1)$$
$$= -32m^6 - 24m^5 - 16m^4 + 8m^3 \quad \bullet$$

2   The distributive property is also used to find the product of any two polynomials. To find the product of the polynomials $x + 1$ and $x - 4$, think of $x + 1$ as a single quantity and use the distributive property as follows.

$$(x + 1)(x - 4) = (x + 1)x + (x + 1)(-4)$$

Now use the distributive property twice to find $(x + 1)x$ and $(x + 1)(-4)$.

$$(x + 1)x + (x + 1)(-4) = x(x) + 1(x) + x(-4) + 1(-4)$$
$$= x^2 + x + (-4x) + (-4)$$
$$= x^2 - 3x - 4$$

EXAMPLE 2   Find the product $(2x + 1)(3x + 5)$.
Use the distributive property.

$$(2x + 1)(3x + 5) = (2x + 1)(3x) + (2x + 1)(5)$$
$$= (2x)(3x) + (1)(3x) + (2x)(5) + (1)(5)$$
$$= 6x^2 + 3x + 10x + 5$$
$$= 6x^2 + 13x + 5 \quad \bullet$$

In Example 2 we found the product of $2x + 1$ and $3x + 5$. The work involved in such a multiplication often can be simplified by writing one polynomial above the other.

$$
\begin{array}{r}
2x + 1 \\
\underline{3x + 5}
\end{array}
$$

Do not worry about lining up the like terms in columns, because any terms may be multiplied (and not just like terms). To begin, multiply each of the terms in the top row by 5.

Step 1

$$
\begin{array}{r}
2x + 1 \\
\underline{3x + 5} \\
10x + 5
\end{array}
$$

Notice how similar this is to ordinary multiplication. Then multiply each term in the top row by $3x$. Now be careful to place the like terms in columns, since the final step will involve addition (as in multiplying two whole numbers).

Step 2

$$
\begin{array}{r}
2x + 1 \\
\underline{3x + 5} \\
10x + 5 \\
6x^2 + 3x
\end{array}
$$

Step 3   Add like terms.

$$
\begin{array}{r}
2x + 1 \\
\underline{3x + 5} \\
10x + 5 \\
\underline{6x^2 + 3x} \\
6x^2 + 13x + 5
\end{array}
$$

Finally, $(2x + 1)(3x + 5) = 6x^2 + 13x + 5$.

The next example shows how to find the product of polynomials having more than one variable.

EXAMPLE 3

Find the product of $3p - 5q$ and $2p + 7q$.

$$
\begin{array}{r}
3p - 5q \\
\underline{2p + 7q} \\
21pq - 35q^2 \quad \leftarrow 7q(3p - 5q) \\
\underline{6p^2 - 10pq \quad \leftarrow 2p(3p - 5q)} \\
6p^2 + 11pq - 35q^2 \quad \bullet
\end{array}
$$

EXAMPLE 4

Find the product of $4m^3 - 2m^2 + 4m$ and $m^2 + 5$.

$$
\begin{array}{r}
4m^3 - 2m^2 + 4m \\
\underline{m^2 + 5} \\
20m^3 - 10m^2 + 20m \quad \leftarrow \text{Terms of top row multiplied by 5} \\
\underline{4m^5 - 2m^4 + 4m^3 \quad \leftarrow \text{Terms of top row multiplied by } m^2} \\
4m^5 - 2m^4 + 24m^3 - 10m^2 + 20m \quad \bullet
\end{array}
$$

EXAMPLE 5   Find $(n + 2)^2$.

We know $(n + 2)^2 = (n + 2)(n + 2)$. Use the vertical method of multiplication to find the product.

$$
\begin{array}{r}
n + 2 \\
n + 2 \\
\hline
2n + 4 \\
n^2 + 2n \\
\hline
n^2 + 4n + 4
\end{array}
$$ ●

EXAMPLE 6   Find $(x + 5)^3$.

Since $(x + 5)^3 = (x + 5)(x + 5)(x + 5)$, the first step is to find the product $(x + 5)(x + 5)$.

$$
\begin{array}{r}
x + \ 5 \\
x + \ 5 \\
\hline
5x + 25 \\
x^2 + \ 5x \\
\hline
x^2 + 10x + 25
\end{array}
$$

Now multiply this result by $x + 5$.

$$
\begin{array}{r}
x^2 + 10x + \ 25 \\
x + 5 \\
\hline
5x^2 + 50x + 125 \\
x^3 + 10x^2 + 25x \\
\hline
x^3 + 15x^2 + 75x + 125
\end{array}
$$ ●

3.5   EXERCISES

Find each product. See Example 1.

1. $(-4x^5)(8x^2)$ **2.** $(-3x^7)(2x^5)$ **3.** $(5y^4)(3y^7)$

4. $(10p^2)(5p^3)$ **5.** $(15a^4)(2a^5)$ **6.** $(-3m^6)(-5m^4)$

7. $(5p)(3q^2)$ **8.** $(4a^3)(3b^2)$ **9.** $(-6m^3)(3n^2)$

10. $(9r^3)(-2s^2)$ **11.** $2m(3m + 2)$ **12.** $-5p(6 - 3p)$

13. $3p(-2p^3 + 4p^2)$ **14.** $4x(3 + 2x + 5x^3)$ **15.** $-8z(2z + 3z^2 + 3z^3)$

16. $7y(3 + 5y^2 - 2y^3)$ **17.** $2y^3(3 + 2y + 5y^4)$ **18.** $-2m^4(3m^2 + 5m + 6)$

19. $-4r^3(-7r^2 + 8r - 9)$ **20.** $-9a^5(-3a^6 - 2a^4 + 8a^2)$ **21.** $3a^2(2a^2 - 4ab + 5b^2)$

22. $4z^3(8z^2 + 5zy - 3y^2)$ **23.** $7m^3n^2(3m^2 + 2mn - n^3)$ **24.** $2p^2q(3p^2q^2 - 5p + 2q^2)$

Find each product. See Examples 2 and 3.

25. $(m + 7)(m + 5)$ **26.** $(n - 1)(n + 4)$ **27.** $(x + 5)(x - 5)$

28. $(y + 8)(y - 8)$ **29.** $(3r - 1)(r - 4)$ **30.** $(2k + 5)(k + 2)$

31. $(6p + 5)(p - 1)$ **32.** $(2x + 3)(6x - 4)$ **33.** $(4m + 3)(4m + 3)$

34. $(3x - 2)(3x - 2)$

35. $(b + 8)(6b - 2)$

36. $(5a + 1)(2a + 7)$

37. $(8 - 3a)(2 + a)$

38. $(6 - 5m)(2 + 3m)$

39. $(-4 + k)(2 - k)$

40. $(5 - 3x)(4 + x)$

41. $(2m - 3n)(m + 5n)$

42. $(4a + 3b)(2a - b)$

43. $(5r + 3s)(2r - 7s)$

44. $(3x + 2y)(5x - 3y)$

45. $3(2x - 5)(x + 3)$

46. $7(4m - 3)(2m + 1)$

47. $-4r(3r + 2)(2r - 5)$

48. $-3a(3a + 1)(a - 4)$

Find each product. See Example 4.

49. $(6x + 1)(2x^2 + 4x + 1)$

50. $(9y - 2)(8y^2 - 6y + 1)$

51. $(9a + 2)(9a^2 + a + 1)$

52. $(2r - 1)(3r^2 + 4r - 4)$

53. $(4m + 3)(5m^3 - 4m^2 + m - 5)$

54. $(y + 4)(3y^4 - 2y^2 + 1)$

55. $(2x - 1)(3x^5 - 2x^3 + x^2 - 2x + 3)$

56. $(2a + 3)(a^4 - a^3 + a^2 - a + 1)$

57. $(5x^2 + 2x + 1)(x^2 - 3x + 5)$

58. $(2m^2 + m - 3)(m^2 - 4m + 5)$

Find each product. See Examples 5 and 6.

59. $(x + 7)^2$

60. $(m + 6)^2$

61. $(a - 4)^2$

62. $(b - 10)^2$

63. $(2p - 5)^2$

64. $(3m + 1)^2$

65. $(5k + 3q)^2$

66. $(8m - 3n)^2$

67. $(m - 5)^3$

68. $(p + 3)^3$

69. $(2a + 1)^3$

70. $(3m - 1)^3$

71. $(k + 1)^4$

72. $(r - 1)^4$

73. $(3r - 2s)^3$

74. $(2z + 5y)^3$

Review Exercises   *Find two numbers having the given sum and product. See Sections 1.6 and 1.8.*

	Product	Sum			Product	Sum
75.	6	5		**76.**	8	6
77.	−21	−4		**78.**	−35	−2
79.	−54	3		**80.**	−96	4

3.6   Products of Binomials

1 Multiply binomials by the FOIL method.

2 Square binomials.

3 Find the difference of two squares.

1   The methods of the last section can be used to find the product of any two polynomials. These methods are the only practical methods for multiplying polynomials with three or more terms. Since many of the polynomials to be multiplied are

binomials, in this section we discuss a shortcut that eliminates writing out all the steps. To find this shortcut, let us multiply $x + 3$ and $x + 5$ using the distributive property.

$$(x + 3)(x + 5) = (x + 3)x + (x + 3)5$$
$$= (x)(x) + (3)(x) + (x)(5) + (3)(5)$$
$$= x^2 + 3x + 5x + 15$$
$$= x^2 + 8x + 15$$

The first term in the second line, $(x)(x)$, is the product of the first term in each binomial.

$$(x + 3)(x + 5) \qquad \text{Multiply the first terms:} \quad (x)(x)$$

The term $(x)(5)$ is the product of the first term of the first binomial and the last term of the second binomial. This is the **outer product.**

$$(x + 3)(x + 5) \qquad \text{Multiply the outer terms:} \quad (x)(5)$$

The term $(3)(x)$ is the product of the last term of the first binomial and the first term of the second binomial. The product of these middle terms is the **inner product.**

$$(x + 3)(x + 5) \qquad \text{Multiply the inner terms:} \quad (3)(x)$$

Finally, $(3)(5)$ is the product of the last term of each binomial.

$$(x + 3)(x + 5) \qquad \text{Multiply the last terms:} \quad (3)(5)$$

In the third step of the multiplication above, the inner product and the outer product are added. This step should be performed mentally, so that the three terms of the answer can be written without extra steps.

A summary of these steps is given below.

Multiplying Binomials

1. Multiply the two first terms of the binomials to get the first term of the answer.
2. Find the outer product and the inner product and mentally add them to get the middle term of the answer.
3. Multiply the two last terms of the binomials to get the last term of the answer.

This procedure is sometimes called the **FOIL method,** which comes from the abbreviation for *first, outer, inner, last.*

EXAMPLE 1   Find the product $(x + 8)(x - 6)$ by the FOIL method.

F   Multiply the first terms.

$$x(x) = x^2$$

O   Find the product of the outer terms.

$$x(-6) = -6x$$

I   Find the product of the inner terms.

$$8(x) = 8x$$

Add the outer and inner products mentally.

$$-6x + 8x = 2x$$

L   Multiply the last terms.

$$8(-6) = -48$$

The product of $x + 8$ and $x - 6$ is found by adding the terms found above, so

$$(x + 8)(x - 6) = x^2 - 6x + 8x - 48 = x^2 + 2x - 48.$$

As a shortcut, this product can be found in the following manner.

EXAMPLE 2   Multiply $9x - 2$ and $3x + 1$.

F: $9x(3x) = 27x^2$ O: $9x(1) = 9x$
I: $-2(3x) = -6x$ L: $-2(1) = -2$

The product is the sum of these four results, or

$$27x^2 + 9x + (-6x) + (-2) = 27x^2 + 3x - 2. \quad \bullet$$

EXAMPLE 3   Find the following products.

(a) $(2k + 5y)(k + 3y) = (2k)(k) + (2k)(3y) + (5y)(k) + (5y)(3y)$
$$= 2k^2 + 6ky + 5ky + 15y^2$$
$$= 2k^2 + 11ky + 15y^2$$

(b) $(7p + 2q)(3p - q) = 21p^2 - pq - 2q^2 \quad \bullet$

2   Certain special types of binomial products occur so often that the form of the answers should be memorized. For example, to quickly find the **square of a binomial,** $(x + y)^2$, use the method of Example 4.

EXAMPLE 4   Find $(2m + 3)^2$.

Squaring $2m + 3$ by the FOIL method gives

$$(2m + 3)(2m + 3) = 4m^2 + 12m + 9. \quad \bullet$$

The result has the square of both the first and the last terms of the binomial:

$$(2m)^2 = 4m^2 \quad \text{and} \quad 3^2 = 9.$$

We also have twice the product of the two terms of the binomial, or

$$2(2m)(3) = 12m.$$

Using the FOIL method,

Square of a Binomial

> the square of a binomial is a trinomial made up of the square of the first term, plus twice the product of the two terms, plus the square of the last term, or
>
> $$(x + y)^2 = x^2 + 2xy + y^2.$$
>
> Also, $\qquad (x - y)^2 = x^2 - 2xy + y^2.$

EXAMPLE 5   Use the formula to square each binomial.

(a) $(5z - 1)^2 = (5z)^2 - 2(5z)(1) + (1)^2 = 25z^2 - 10z + 1$

Recall that $(5z)^2 = 5^2z^2 = 25z^2$.

(b) $(3b + 5r)^2 = (3b)^2 + 2(3b)(5r) + (5r)^2 = 9b^2 + 30br + 25r^2$

(c) $(2a - 9x)^2 = 4a^2 - 36ax + 81x^2$

(d) $\left(4m + \dfrac{1}{2}\right)^2 = (4m)^2 + 2(4m)\left(\dfrac{1}{2}\right) + \left(\dfrac{1}{2}\right)^2 = 16m^2 + 4m + \dfrac{1}{4} \quad \bullet$

3   Binomial products of the form $(x + y)(x - y)$ also occur frequently. In these products, one binomial is the sum of two terms, and the other is the difference of the same two terms. For example, let us find the product of $a + 2$ and $a - 2$.

$$(a + 2)(a - 2) = a^2 - 2a + 2a - 4 = a^2 - 4$$

Using the FOIL method, the product of $x + y$ and $x - y$ is

Difference of Two Squares

> $$(x + y)(x - y) = x^2 - y^2,$$

with the result, $x^2 - y^2$, called the **difference of two squares.**

EXAMPLE 6   Find each product.

(a) $(5m + 3)(5m - 3)$

Use the formula for the difference of two squares.

$$(5m + 3)(5m - 3) = (5m)^2 - 3^2 = 25m^2 - 9$$

(b) $(4x + y)(4x - y) = (4x)^2 - y^2 = 16x^2 - y^2$

(c) $\left(z - \dfrac{1}{4}\right)\left(z + \dfrac{1}{4}\right) = z^2 - \dfrac{1}{16}$ ●

3.6 EXERCISES

Find each product. See Examples 1–3.

1. $(r - 1)(r + 3)$

2. $(x + 2)(x - 5)$

3. $(x - 7)(x - 3)$

4. $(r + 3)(r + 6)$

5. $(2x - 1)(3x + 2)$

6. $(4y - 5)(2y + 1)$

7. $(6z + 5)(z - 3)$

8. $(8a + 3)(6a + 1)$

9. $(a + 4)(2a + 1)$

10. $(3x - 1)(2x + 3)$

11. $(2r - 1)(4r + 3)$

12. $(5m + 2)(3m - 4)$

13. $(2a + 5)(3a - 2)$

14. $(11m - 10)(10m + 11)$

15. $(4 + 5x)(5 - 4x)$

16. $(8 + 3x)(2 - x)$

17. $(-3 + 2r)(4 + r)$

18. $(-5 + 6z)(2 - z)$

19. $(-3 + a)(-5 - 2a)$

20. $(-6 - 3y)(1 - 4y)$

21. $(p + 3q)(p + q)$

22. $(2r - 3s)(3r + s)$

23. $(5y + z)(2y - z)$

24. $(9m + 4k)(2m - 3k)$

25. $(8y - 9z)(y + 5z)$

26. $(4r + 9s)(-2r + 5s)$

27. $(7m + 11n)(3m - 8n)$

28. $(2.13y + 4.06)(1.92y - 3.9)$

29. $(8.17m - 2.4)(3.5m + 1.8)$

Find each square. See Examples 4 and 5.

30. $(m + 2)^2$

31. $(x + 8)^2$

32. $(r - 3)^2$

33. $(z - 5)^2$

34. $(x + 2y)^2$

35. $(3m - p)^2$

36. $(5p + 2q)^2$

37. $(8a - 3b)^2$

38. $(4a + 5b)^2$

39. $(9y + z)^2$

40. $\left(2z - \dfrac{5}{2}x\right)^2$

41. $\left(6a - \dfrac{3}{2}b\right)^2$

42. $(.2x - 3y)^2$

43. $(m - .5q)^2$

44. $(.85r + .23s)^2$

45. $(.67m - .17k)^2$

Find the following products. See Example 6.

46. $(a + 8)(a - 8)$

47. $(2b + 5)(2b - 5)$

48. $(3x + 4)(3x - 4)$

49. $(6a - p)(6a + p)$

50. $(5y + 3x)(5y - 3x)$

51. $\left(2m - \dfrac{5}{3}\right)\left(2m + \dfrac{5}{3}\right)$

52. $\left(3a - \dfrac{4}{5}\right)\left(3a + \dfrac{4}{5}\right)$

53. $(7y^2 + 10z)(7y^2 - 10z)$

54. $(6x + 5y^2)(6x - 5y^2)$

55. $(.48q + .37r)(.48q - .37r)$

56. $(.26a + .15b)(.26a - .15b)$

57. Let $a = 2$ and $b = 5$. Evaluate $(a + b)^2$ and $a^2 + b^2$. Does $(a + b)^2 = a^2 + b^2$?

58. Let $p = 7$ and $q = 3$. Evaluate $(p - q)^2$ and $p^2 - q^2$. Does $(p - q)^2 = p^2 - q^2$?

Write each statement as an equation or an inequality, using x to represent the unknown number. Do not solve.

59. The square of 3 more than a number is 5.

60. The square of the sum of a number and 6 is less than 3.

61. When 3 plus a number is multiplied by the number less 4, the result is greater than 7.

62. Twice a number plus 4, multiplied by 6 times the number, less 5, gives 8.

Review Exercises   *Simplify. See Section 3.1.*

63. $\dfrac{9y^4}{3y}$

64. $\dfrac{8p^2}{2p}$

65. $\dfrac{5m^7}{m^3}$

66. $\dfrac{-10p^4}{2p^3}$

67. $\dfrac{-8z^5}{10z^7}$

68. $\dfrac{20k^3}{50k^5}$

69. $\dfrac{36r^5s^7}{24r^9s}$

70. $\dfrac{-18p^7q^{10}}{32p^2q^{12}}$

3.7   Dividing a Polynomial by a Monomial

1   Divide a polynomial by a monomial.

1   To divide a monomial by another monomial, use the quotient rule for exponents. For example,

$$\frac{12x^2}{6x} = 2x, \qquad \frac{25m^5}{5m^2} = 5m^3, \qquad \text{and} \qquad \frac{30a^2b^8}{15a^3b^3} = \frac{2b^5}{a}.$$

Division of a Polynomial by a Monomial

> To divide a polynomial by a monomial, use the fact that
>
> $$\frac{a}{b} = a \cdot \frac{1}{b} \qquad (b \neq 0).$$

EXAMPLE 1   Divide $5m^5 - 10m^3$ by $5m^2$.

Multiply by $\dfrac{1}{5m^2}$.

$$\frac{5m^5 - 10m^3}{5m^2} = (5m^5 - 10m^3)\frac{1}{5m^2}$$

Now use the distributive property and the quotient rule for exponents.

$$(5m^5 - 10m^3)\frac{1}{5m^2} = (5m^5)\frac{1}{5m^2} - (10m^3)\frac{1}{5m^2}$$

$$= \frac{5m^5}{5m^2} - \frac{10m^3}{5m^2}$$

$$= m^3 - 2m$$

Therefore, $\dfrac{5m^5 - 10m^3}{5m^2} = m^3 - 2m.$

To check, multiply.

$$5m^2(m^3 - 2m) = 5m^5 - 10m^3$$

Since division by 0 is meaningless, the quotient

$$\frac{5m^5 - 10m^3}{5m^2}$$

has no value if $m = 0$. In the rest of the chapter, we assume that no denominators are 0.   ●

EXAMPLE 2   Divide: $\dfrac{16a^5 - 12a^4 + 8a^2}{4a^3}$.

$$\frac{16a^5 - 12a^4 + 8a^2}{4a^3} = (16a^5 - 12a^4 + 8a^2)\frac{1}{4a^3}$$

$$= (16a^5)\frac{1}{4a^3} - (12a^4)\frac{1}{4a^3} + (8a^2)\frac{1}{4a^3}$$

$$= \frac{16a^5}{4a^3} - \frac{12a^4}{4a^3} + \frac{8a^2}{4a^3}$$

$$= 4a^2 - 3a + \frac{2}{a}$$

The result is not a polynomial because of the expression $2/a$, which has a variable in the denominator. While the sum and the product of two polynomials are always polynomials, the quotient of two polynomials need not be.

To check that $4a^2 - 3a + 2/a$ is the correct result, multiply:

$$4a^3\left(4a^2 - 3a + \frac{2}{a}\right) = 4a^3(4a^2) - 4a^3(3a) + 4a^3\left(\frac{2}{a}\right)$$

$$= 16a^5 - 12a^4 + 8a^2.   ●$$

Some of the steps shown in Examples 1 and 2 may be done mentally, as shown in Example 3.

EXAMPLE 3 Divide $12x^4 - 7x^3 + x - 4$ by $4x$.

$$\frac{12x^4 - 7x^3 + x - 4}{4x} = \frac{12x^4}{4x} - \frac{7x^3}{4x} + \frac{x}{4x} - \frac{4}{4x}$$

$$= 3x^3 - \frac{7x^2}{4} + \frac{1}{4} - \frac{1}{x}$$

$$= 3x^3 - \frac{7}{4}x^2 + \frac{1}{4} - \frac{1}{x} \quad \bullet$$

EXAMPLE 4 Divide $180y^{10} - 150y^8 + 120y^6 - 90y^4 + 100y$ by $-30y^2$.
Using the methods of this section,

$$\frac{180y^{10} - 150y^8 + 120y^6 - 90y^4 + 100y}{-30y^2}$$

$$= \frac{180y^{10}}{-30y^2} - \frac{150y^8}{-30y^2} + \frac{120y^6}{-30y^2} - \frac{90y^4}{-30y^2} + \frac{100y}{-30y^2}$$

$$= -6y^8 + 5y^6 - 4y^4 + 3y^2 - \frac{10}{3y}.$$

To check, multiply this result by $-30y^2$. $\bullet$

3.7 EXERCISES

Divide.

1. $\dfrac{4x^2}{2x}$

2. $\dfrac{8m^7}{2m}$

3. $\dfrac{10a^3}{5a}$

4. $\dfrac{36p^8}{4p^3}$

5. $\dfrac{27k^4m^5}{3km^6}$

6. $\dfrac{18x^5y^6}{3x^2y^2}$

7. $\dfrac{-15m^3p^2}{5mp^4}$

8. $\dfrac{-32a^4b^5}{4a^5b}$

Divide each polynomial by $2m$. See Examples 1–4.

9. $60m^4 - 20m^2$

10. $120m^6 - 60m^3 + 80m^2$

11. $10m^5 - 16m^2 + 8m^3$

12. $6m^5 - 4m^3 + 2m^2$

13. $8m^5 - 4m^3 + 4m^2$

14. $8m^3 - 4m^2 + 6m$

15. $2m^5 - 4m^2 + 8m$

16. $m^2 + m + 1$

17. $2m^2 - 2m + 5$

Divide each polynomial by $-5q$. See Examples 1–4.

18. $-30q^4 + 15q^3 - 10q$

19. $25q^3 - 10q^2 + 5q$

20. $15q^6 - 30q^4 + 5q^2 - q$

21. $-40q^5 + 35q^3 - 20$

22. $q^5 - 10q^3 + 8q^2$

23. $3q^4 + 5q^2 - 6q$

24. $q^3 + q^2 - 9q + 1$

25. $5q^3 - 3q^2 + 2q - 7$

26. $3q^5 - 2q^4 + 10q^2$

Divide each polynomial by $3x^2$. See Examples 1–4.

27. $3x^4 + 9x^3$

28. $15x^2 - 9x^3$

29. $12x^4 - 3x^3 + 3x^2$

30. $45x^3 + 15x^2 - 9x^5$

31. $27x^3 - 9x^4 + 18x^5$

32. $-18x^6 + 6x^5 + 3x^4 - 9x^3 + 3x^2$

33. $36x + 24x^2 + 3x^3$

34. $4x^4 - 3x^3 + 2x$

35. $x^3 + 6x^2 - x$

36. $6x^5 - 3x^4 + 9x^2 + 2$

Perform each division. See Examples 1–4.

37. $\dfrac{8k^4 - 12k^3 - 2k^2 + 7k - 3}{2k}$

38. $\dfrac{27r^4 - 36r^3 - 6r^2 + 26r - 2}{3r}$

39. $\dfrac{100p^5 - 50p^4 + 30p^3 - 30p}{-10p^2}$

40. $\dfrac{2m^5 - 6m^4 + 8m^2}{-2m^3}$

41. $\dfrac{8x + 16x^2 + 10x^3}{4x^4}$

42. $\dfrac{36m^5 - 24m^4 + 16m^3 - 8m^2}{4m^3}$

43. $(16y^5 - 8y^2 + 12y) \div (4y^2)$

44. $(20a^4 - 15a^5 + 25a^3) \div (15a^4)$

45. $(120x^{11} - 60x^{10} + 140x^9 - 100x^8) \div (10x^{12})$

46. $(5 + x + 6x^2 + 8x^3) \div (3x^4)$

47. Evaluate $\dfrac{5y + 6}{2}$ when $y = 2$. Evaluate $5y + 3$ when $y = 2$. Does

$\dfrac{5y + 6}{2} = 5y + 3?$

48. Evaluate $\dfrac{10r + 7}{5}$ when $r = 1$. Evaluate $2r + 7$ when $r = 1$. Does

$\dfrac{10r + 7}{5} = 2r + 7?$

Solve each problem.

49. What polynomial, when divided by $3x^2$, yields $4x^3 + 3x^2 - 4x + 2$ as a quotient?

50. What polynomial, when divided by $4m^3$, yields $-6m^2 + 4m$ as a quotient?

51. The quotient of a certain polynomial and $-7y^2$ is $9y^2 + 3y + 5 - 2/y$. Find the polynomial.

52. The quotient of a certain polynomial and a is $2a^2 + 3a + 5$. Find the polynomial.

Review Exercises   *Find each product. See Section 3.5.*

53. $x(2x^2 - 5x + 1)$

54. $m(3m^3 - 2m^2 + 5)$

55. $-4k(5k^3 - 3k^2 + 2k)$

56. $-7z(z^2 - 5z + 6)$

57. $3m^5(2m^5 - 4m^3 + m^2)$

58. $2p^3(8p^2 - 4p + 9)$

Subtract. See Section 3.4.

59. $8x - 5$
  $\underline{3x - 7}$

60. $5a - 4$
  $\underline{7a - 2}$

61. $6x^2 - 4$
  $\underline{8x^2 + 7}$

62. $3k^2 - 4k + 1$
$\underline{4k^2 + 7k - 5}$

63. $9x^2 - 4x - 7$
$\underline{2x^2 + 6x - 8}$

64. $4m^2 - 5m - 1$
$\underline{3m^2 + 2m - 5}$

3.8   The Quotient of Two Polynomials

■ Divide a polynomial by a polynomial.

■   To divide a polynomial by a polynomial (other than a monomial), we use a method of "long division." This is similar to the method of long division used for two whole numbers. We show the division of whole numbers alongside the division of polynomials so that you may compare.

Step 1

Divide 27 into 6696.

$$27\overline{)6696}$$

Divide $2x + 3$ into $8x^3 - 4x^2 - 14x + 15$.

$$2x + 3\overline{)8x^3 - 4x^2 - 14x + 15}$$

Step 2

27 divides into 66 **2** times;
$2 \cdot 27 = 54$.

$$\begin{array}{r} 2 \\ 27\overline{)6696} \\ 54 \end{array}$$

$2x$ divides into $8x^3$ **$4x^2$** times;
$4x^2(2x + 3) = 8x^3 + 12x^2$.

$$\begin{array}{r} 4x^2 \\ 2x + 3\overline{)8x^3 - 4x^2 - 14x + 15} \\ 8x^3 + 12x^2 \end{array}$$

Step 3

Subtract; then bring down the next term.

$$\begin{array}{r} 2 \\ 27\overline{)6696} \\ 54\downarrow \\ 129 \end{array}$$

Subtract; then bring down the next term.

$$\begin{array}{r} 4x^2 \\ 2x + 3\overline{)8x^3 - 4x^2 - 14x + 15} \\ 8x^3 + 12x^2 \quad \downarrow \\ -16x^2 - 14x \end{array}$$

(To subtract two polynomials, change the sign of the second and then add.)

Step 4

27 divides into 129 **4** times;
$4 \cdot 27 = 108$.

$$\begin{array}{r} 24 \\ 27\overline{)6696} \\ 54 \\ 129 \\ 108 \end{array}$$

$2x$ divides into $-16x^2$ **$-8x$** times;
$-8x(2x + 3) = -16x^2 - 24x$.

$$\begin{array}{r} 4x^2 - 8x \\ 2x + 3\overline{)8x^3 - 4x^2 - 14x + 15} \\ 8x^3 + 12x^2 \\ -16x^2 - 14x \\ -16x^2 - 24x \end{array}$$

Step 5

Subtract; then bring down the next term.

$$
\begin{array}{r}
24 \\
27\overline{)6696} \\
54 \\
\hline
129 \\
108 \\
\hline
216
\end{array}
$$

Subtract; then bring down the next term.

$$
\begin{array}{r}
4x^2 - 8x \\
2x + 3\overline{)8x^3 - 4x^2 - 14x + 15} \\
8x^3 + 12x^2 \\
\hline
-16x^2 - 14x \\
-16x^2 - 24x \\
\hline
10x + 15
\end{array}
$$

Step 6

27 divides into 216 **8** times;
$8 \cdot 27 = 216$.

$$
\begin{array}{r}
248 \\
27\overline{)6696} \\
54 \\
\hline
129 \\
108 \\
\hline
216 \\
216
\end{array}
$$

6696 divided by 27 is 248. There is no remainder.

$2x$ divides into $10x$ **5** times;
$5(2x + 3) = 10x + 15$.

$$
\begin{array}{r}
4x^2 - 8x + 5 \\
2x + 3\overline{)8x^3 - 4x^2 - 14x + 15} \\
8x^3 + 12x^2 \\
\hline
-16x^2 - 14x \\
-16x^2 - 24x \\
\hline
10x + 15 \\
10x + 15
\end{array}
$$

$8x^3 - 4x^2 - 14x + 15$ divided by $2x + 3$ is $4x^2 - 8x + 5$. There is no remainder.

Step 7

Check by multiplication.

$27 \cdot 248 = 6696$

Check by multiplication.

$(2x + 3)(4x^2 - 8x + 5)$
$\qquad = 8x^3 - 4x^2 - 14x + 15$

EXAMPLE 1   Divide $4x^3 - 4x^2 + 5x - 8$ by $2x - 1$.

$$
\begin{array}{r}
2x^2 - x + 2 \\
2x - 1\overline{)4x^3 - 4x^2 + 5x - 8} \\
4x^3 - 2x^2 \\
\hline
-2x^2 + 5x \\
-2x^2 + x \\
\hline
4x - 8 \\
4x - 2 \\
\hline
-6
\end{array}
$$

Step 1 $2x$ divides into $4x^3$ **($2x^2$)** times; $2x^2(2x - 1) = 4x^3 - 2x^2$.

Step 2   Subtract; bring down the next term.

Step 3 $2x$ divides into $-2x^2$ **($-x$)** times; $-x(2x - 1) = -2x^2 + x$.

Step 4   Subtract; bring down the next term.

Step 5 $2x$ divides into $4x$ **2** times; $2(2x - 1) = 4x - 2$.

Step 6   Subtract. The remainder is -6.

Finally, $2x - 1$ divides into $4x^3 - 4x^2 + 5x - 8$ with a quotient of $2x^2 - x + 2$ and a remainder of -6. The result is not a polynomial because of the remainder.

$$\frac{4x^3 - 4x^2 + 5x - 8}{2x - 1} = 2x^2 - x + 2 + \frac{-6}{2x - 1}$$

Step 7   Check by multiplication.

$$(2x - 1)\left(2x^2 - x + 2 + \frac{-6}{2x - 1}\right) = 4x^3 - 4x^2 + 5x - 8 \quad \bullet$$

EXAMPLE 2   Divide $x^3 - 1$ by $x - 1$.

Here the polynomial $x^3 - 1$ is missing the x^2 term and the x term. When this is the case, use 0 as the coefficient for the missing terms.

$$x^3 - 1 = x^3 + 0x^2 + 0x - 1$$

Now divide.

$$
\begin{array}{r}
x^2 +\ x + 1 \\
x - 1\overline{)x^3 + 0x^2 + 0x - 1} \\
\underline{x^3 -\ x^2} \\
x^2 + 0x \\
\underline{x^2 -\ x} \\
x - 1 \\
\underline{x - 1}
\end{array}
$$

There is no remainder. The quotient is $x^2 + x + 1$. Check by multiplication.

$$(x^2 + x + 1)(x - 1) = x^3 - 1 \quad \bullet$$

EXAMPLE 3   Divide $x^4 + 2x^3 + 2x^2 - x - 1$ by $x^2 + 1$.

The denominator $x^2 + 1$ has a missing x term, which we fill in with $0x$. Then proceed through the division process.

$$
\begin{array}{r}
x^2 + 2x + 1 \\
x^2 + 0x + 1\overline{)x^4 + 2x^3 + 2x^2 -\ x - 1} \\
\underline{x^4 + 0x^3 +\ x^2} \\
2x^3 +\ x^2 -\ x \\
\underline{2x^3 + 0x^2 + 2x} \\
x^2 - 3x - 1 \\
\underline{x^2 + 0x + 1} \\
-3x - 2
\end{array}
$$

When the result of subtracting $(-3x - 2$, in this case) is a polynomial of smaller degree than the divisor $(x^2 + 0x + 1)$, that polynomial is the remainder. Write the result as

$$x^2 + 2x + 1 + \frac{-3x - 2}{x^2 + 1}. \quad \bullet$$

3.8 EXERCISES

Perform each division. See Example 1.

1. $\dfrac{x^2 - x - 6}{x - 3}$

2. $\dfrac{m^2 - 2m - 24}{m + 4}$

3. $\dfrac{2y^2 + 9y - 35}{y + 7}$

4. $\dfrac{y^2 + 2y + 1}{y + 1}$

5. $\dfrac{p^2 + 2p - 20}{p + 6}$

6. $\dfrac{x^2 + 11x + 16}{x + 8}$

7. $\dfrac{r^2 - 8r + 15}{r - 3}$

8. $\dfrac{t^2 - 3t - 10}{t - 5}$

9. $\dfrac{12m^2 - 20m + 3}{2m - 3}$

10. $\dfrac{2y^2 - 5y - 3}{2y + 1}$

11. $\dfrac{2a^2 - 11a + 16}{2a + 3}$

12. $\dfrac{9w^2 + 6w + 10}{3w - 2}$

13. $\dfrac{2x^2 + 5x + 3}{2x + 1}$

14. $\dfrac{4m^2 - 4m + 5}{2m - 1}$

15. $\dfrac{12r^2 - 17r + 5}{3r - 5}$

16. $\dfrac{15y^2 + 11y - 60}{3y + 7}$

17. $\dfrac{14k^2 + 19k - 30}{7k - 8}$

18. $\dfrac{15m^2 + 34m + 28}{5m + 3}$

19. $\dfrac{2x^3 - x^2 + 3x + 2}{2x + 1}$

20. $\dfrac{12t^3 - 11t^2 + 9t + 18}{4t + 3}$

21. $\dfrac{8k^4 - 12k^3 - 2k^2 + 7k - 6}{2k - 3}$

22. $\dfrac{27r^4 - 36r^3 - 6r^2 + 26r - 24}{3r - 4}$

Perform each division. See Examples 2 and 3.

23. $\dfrac{3y^3 + y^2 + 3y + 1}{y^2 + 1}$

24. $\dfrac{2r^3 - 5r^2 - 6r + 15}{r^2 - 3}$

25. $\dfrac{3k^3 - 4k^2 - 6k + 10}{k^2 - 2}$

26. $\dfrac{5z^3 - z^2 + 10z + 2}{z^2 + 2}$

27. $\dfrac{x^4 - x^2 - 6x}{x^2 - 2}$

28. $\dfrac{r^4 - 2r^2 + 5}{r^2 - 1}$

29. $\dfrac{6p^4 - 15p^3 + 14p^2 - 5p + 10}{3p^2 + 1}$

30. $\dfrac{6r^4 - 10r^3 - r^2 + 15r - 8}{2r^2 - 3}$

31. $\dfrac{4m^5 - 8m^4 - 3m^3 + 22m^2 - 15}{4m^2 - 3}$

32. $\dfrac{2x^5 + 6x^4 - x^3 + 3x^2 - x + 5}{2x^2 + 1}$

33. $\dfrac{y^3 + 1}{y + 1}$

34. $\dfrac{x^4 - 1}{x^2 - 1}$

35. $\dfrac{a^4 - 1}{a^2 + 1}$

36. $\dfrac{p^5 - 2}{p^2 - 1}$

Review Exercises *List all positive integer factors of each number. See Section 1.3.*

37. 12 **38.** 18 **39.** 20 **40.** 36

41. 50 **42.** 70 **43.** 29 **44.** 37

Multiply. See Section 3.5.

45. $2m(m^2 - m + 1)$ **46.** $4k(2k^2 - 5k + 6)$

47. $-y^2(3y^4 + 2y^3 - 1)$ **48.** $-p^3(3p^5 - 8p^4 - 6p^3)$

Chapter 3 Review Exercises

[3.1] *Evaluate each expression.*

1. $4^2 + 4^3$ **2.** $5^0 + 7^0$ **3.** 2^{-4} **4.** 7^{-2}

5. $\left(\dfrac{3}{4}\right)^{-4}$ **6.** $\left(\dfrac{1}{2}\right)^{-5}$ **7.** $2^{-1} + 4^{-1}$ **8.** $3^{-1} - 2^{-1}$

Simplify. Write each answer in exponential form, using only positive exponents. Assume that all variables represent nonzero real numbers.

9. $(-4)^5 \cdot (-4)^3$ **10.** $(-3)^7 \cdot (-3)^3$ **11.** $\dfrac{6^{-3}}{6^{-5}}$ **12.** $\dfrac{x^{-7}}{x^{-9}}$

[3.2] *Simplify.*

13. $(5^{-2})^{-4}$ **14.** $(8^{-3})^4$ **15.** $\dfrac{y^4 \cdot y^{-2}}{y^{-5}}$ **16.** $\dfrac{r^9 \cdot r^{-5}}{r^{-2} \cdot r^{-7}}$

17. $(6r^{-2})^{-1}$ **18.** $(3p)^4(3p^{-7})$ **19.** $\dfrac{(6r^{-1})^2 \cdot (2r^{-4})}{r^{-5}(r^2)^{-3}}$ **20.** $\dfrac{(2m^{-5}n^2)^3}{m^{-2}n^{-4}}$

[3.3] *Write each number in scientific notation.*

21. 15,800,000 **22.** .0004251 **23.** .0000976 **24.** .784

Write each number without exponents.

25. 1.2×10^4 **26.** 4.253×10^{-4} **27.** $(6 \times 10^4) \times (1.5 \times 10^3)$

28. $(2 \times 10^{-3}) \times (4 \times 10^5)$ **29.** $\dfrac{9 \times 10^{-2}}{3 \times 10^2}$ **30.** $\dfrac{8 \times 10^4}{2 \times 10^{-2}}$

[3.4] *Combine terms where possible in the following polynomials. Write the answers in descending powers of the variable. Give the degree of the answer.*

31. $9m^2 + 11m^2 + 2m^2$ **32.** $-4p + p^3 - p^2 + 8p + 2$

33. $12a^5 - 9a^4 + 8a^3 + 2a^2 - a + 3$ **34.** $-7y^5 - 8y^4 - y^5 + y^4 + 9y$

Add or subtract as indicated.

35. Add.

$$-2a^3 + 5a^2$$
$$\underline{3a^3 - a^2}$$

36. Subtract.

$$6y^2 - 8y + 2$$
$$\underline{5y^2 + 2y - 7}$$

37. Subtract.

$$-12k^4 - 8k^2 + 7k$$
$$\underline{k^4 + 7k^2 - 11k}$$

38. $(2m^3 - 8m^2 + 4) + (3m^3 + 2m^2 - 7)$

39. $(-5y^2 + 3y - 11) + (4y^2 - 7y + 15)$

40. $(6p^2 - p - 8) - (-4p^2 + 2p - 3)$

41. $(12r^4 - 7r^3 + 2r^2) - (5r^4 - 3r^3 + 2r^2)$

[3.5] *Find each product.*

42. $2y^2(-11y^2 + 2y + 9)$

43. $-m^5(8m^2 - 10m + 6)$

44. $(3k - 6)(2k + 1)$

45. $(12a + 1)(12a - 1)$

46. $(-7 + 2k)^2$

47. $(a + 2)(a^2 - 4a + 1)$

48. $(3r - 2)(2r^2 + 4r - 3)$

49. $(5p + 3)(p^3 - p^2 + 5)$

50. $(r + 2)^3$

[3.6] *Find each product.*

51. $(3k + 1)(2k - 3)$

52. $(2r + 5)(5r - 2)$

53. $(a + 3b)(2a - b)$

54. $(6k + 5q)(2k - 7q)$

55. $(a + 4)^2$

56. $(2r + 5s)^2$

57. $(8z - 3y)^2$

58. $(6m - 5)(6m + 5)$

59. $(5a + 6b)(5a - 6b)$

[3.7] *Perform each division.*

60. $\dfrac{-15y^4}{9y^2}$

61. $\dfrac{6y^4 - 12y^2 + 18y}{6y}$

62. $\dfrac{2p^3 - 6p^2 + 5p}{2p^2}$

63. $(-10m^4 + 5m^3 + 6m^2) \div (5m^2)$

64. $(25y^3 - 8y^2 + 15y) \div (10y^3)$

[3.8] *Perform each division.*

65. $\dfrac{2r^2 + 3r - 14}{r - 2}$

66. $\dfrac{12m^2 - 11m - 10}{3m - 5}$

67. $\dfrac{2y^3 + 17y^2 + 37y + 7}{2y + 7}$

68. $\dfrac{10a^3 + 9a^2 - 14a + 9}{5a - 3}$

69. $\dfrac{2k^4 + 3k^3 + 9k^2 - 12k - 8}{2k + 1}$

70. $\dfrac{m^4 + 4m^3 - 5m^2 - 12m + 6}{m^2 - 3}$

Chapter 3 Test

Evaluate each expression.

1. $\left(\dfrac{4}{3}\right)^{-3}$

2. $(-5)^{-2}$

Simplify. Write each answer using only positive exponents.

3. $5^{-3} \cdot 5^2 \cdot 5^{-6} \cdot 5$

4. $\dfrac{(8^{-3})^2 \cdot 8^{-4}}{8^{-3} \cdot 8^{-9}}$

5. $\left(\dfrac{6q^{-2}}{q^{-3}}\right)^{-1}$ $(q \neq 0)$

6. $\dfrac{(2p^{-2})^{-3}(4p^4)^2}{(2p^{-5})^2}$ $\quad(p \neq 0)$

7. Write .000379 in scientific notation.

Write each number without exponents.

8. $(6 \times 10^{-4}) \times (1.5 \times 10^6)$ **9.** $\dfrac{5.6 \times 10^{-7}}{1.4 \times 10^{-3}}$

For each polynomial, combine terms; then give the degree of the polynomial. Finally, select the most specific description from this list: (a) trinomial, (b) binomial, (c) monomial, (d) none of these.

10. $3x^2 + 6x - 4x^2$ **11.** $11m^3 - m^2 + m^4 + m^4 - 7m^2$

12. Subtract.

$$-5m^3 + 2m^2 - 7m + 3$$
$$\underline{8m^3 - 5m^2 + 9m - 5}$$

Perform the indicated operation.

13. $(2x^5 - 4x + 7) - (x^5 + x^2 - 2x - 5)$ **14.** $(y^2 - 5y - 3) + (3y^2 + 2y) - (y^2 - y - 1)$

15. $6m^2(m^3 + 2m^2 - 3m + 7)$ **16.** $(5m + 6)(3m - 11)$

17. $(2t + 5s)(7t - 4s)$ **18.** $(3k + 2)(2k^2 - 7k + 8)$

19. $(2k + 5m)^2$ **20.** $\left(2r + \dfrac{1}{2}t\right)^2$

21. $(6p^2 - 5r)(6p^2 + 5r)$ **22.** $\dfrac{-15y^5 - 8y^4 + 6y^3}{3y^2}$

23. $(10r^3 + 25r^2 - 15r + 8) \div (5r^3)$ **24.** $\dfrac{3x^3 - 2x^2 - 6x - 4}{x - 2}$

25. $\dfrac{10r^4 + 4r^3 - 25r^2 - 6r + 20}{2r^2 - 3}$

4

Factoring and Applications

Many quadratic equations are used in designing solar-powered houses.

4.1 Factors; The Greatest Common Factor

1. List the factors of a number.
2. Identify prime numbers.
3. Find the greatest common factor of a list of numbers.
4. Factor out the greatest common factor.
5. Factor by grouping.

1 Since the product of 6 and 2 is 12, the numbers 6 and 2 are **factors** of 12. Also, $6 \cdot 2$ is a **factored form** of 12. To **factor** means to find the factored form of a quantity. That is, factoring is the opposite of multiplication. For example,

Multiplication	*Factoring*
$6 \cdot 2 = 12,$	$12 = 6 \cdot 2.$
↑ ↑ ↑	↑ ↑ ↑
Factors Product	Product Factors

Other factored forms of 12 are $(-6)(-2)$, $3 \cdot 4$, $(-3)(-4)$, $12 \cdot 1$, and $(-12)(-1)$. More than two factors may be used, so another factored form of 12 is $2 \cdot 2 \cdot 3$. The positive integer factors of 12 are

$$1, 2, 3, 4, 6, 12.$$

By definition,

Factor

> for integers a and b, the integer a is a **factor** of b if b can be divided by a with a remainder of zero.

EXAMPLE 1

(a) The positive integer factors of 36 are 1, 2, 3, 4, 6, 9, 12, 18, and 36.

(b) The positive integer factors of 11 are 1 and 11.   ●

2   As shown in Example 1(b), the only positive integer factors of 11 are 11 and 1. A positive integer greater than 1 having only itself and 1 as factors is called a **prime number.** The first few prime numbers are

$$2, 3, 5, 7, 11, 13, 17, 19, 23, 29, 31, 37, 41, 43,$$

and so on. A positive integer (other than 1) that is not prime is called **composite.** The number 1 is neither prime nor composite.

EXAMPLE 2

Tell whether each number is prime or composite.

(a) 33

This number has factors of 3 and 11, as well as 1 and 33, so it is composite.

(b) 53

Try dividing 53 by various integers; it is divisible only by itself and 1, and so is prime.

(c) 14,976,083,922

This number ends in 2, so it is even and therefore divisible by 2. It is composite.   ●

Each composite number may be expressed as a product of prime numbers. For example,

$$30 = 2 \cdot 3 \cdot 5, \qquad 55 = 5 \cdot 11, \qquad 72 = 2^3 \cdot 3^2,$$

and so on. When a number is written as a product of primes, it is written in **prime factored form.**

EXAMPLE 3

Write each number in prime factored form.

(a) 50

Divide 50 by the first prime, 2.

$$50 = 2 \cdot 25$$

We cannot divide 25 by 2, or by the next prime, 3, but we can divide it by 5.

$$50 = 2 \cdot 5 \cdot 5$$
$$50 = 2 \cdot 5^2 \qquad \text{Prime factored form}$$

(b) $300 = 2 \cdot 150$

$\qquad = 2 \cdot 2 \cdot 75$

$\qquad = 2 \cdot 2 \cdot 3 \cdot 25$

$\qquad = 2 \cdot 2 \cdot 3 \cdot 5 \cdot 5$

$\qquad = 2^2 \cdot 3 \cdot 5^2$ $\qquad$ Prime factored form

(c) 71

Since 71 is prime, its prime factored form is 71. ●

A table giving the prime factored form of all positive integers from 2 through 100 is given inside the front cover of this book.

3 An integer that is a factor of two or more integers is called a **common factor** of those integers. For example, 6 is a common factor of 18 and 24 since 6 is a factor of both 18 and 24. Other common factors of 18 and 24 are 1, 2, and 3. The **greatest common factor** of a list of integers is the greatest of the common factors of the numbers on the list. Thus, 6 is the greatest common factor of 18 and 24, since it is the greatest of the common factors of these numbers.

EXAMPLE 4 Find the greatest common factor for each list of numbers.

(a) 30, 45

First write each number in prime factored form.

$$30 = 2 \cdot 3 \cdot 5 \qquad 45 = 3^2 \cdot 5$$

Now, take each prime the *least* number of times it appears in all the factored forms. There is no 2 in the prime factored form of 45, so there will be no 2 in the greatest common factor. The least number of times 3 appears in all the factored forms is 1, and the least number of times 5 appears is also 1. Finally,

$$\text{greatest common factor} = 3^1 \cdot 5^1 = 3 \cdot 5 = 15.$$

(b) 72, 120, 432

Find the prime factored form of each number.

$$72 = 2^3 \cdot 3^2 \qquad 120 = 2^3 \cdot 3 \cdot 5 \qquad 432 = 2^4 \cdot 3^3$$

The least number of times 2 appears in all the factored forms is 3, and the least number of times 3 appears is 1. There is no 5 in the prime factored form of either 72 or 120, so

$$\text{greatest common factor} = 2^3 \cdot 3 = 24.$$

(c) 10, 11, 14

Write the prime factored form of each number.

$$10 = 2 \cdot 5 \qquad 11 = 11 \qquad 14 = 2 \cdot 7$$

There are no primes common to all three numbers, so the greatest common factor is 1. ●

In summary, the greatest common factor of a list of numbers is found as follows.

Finding the Greatest Common Factor

Step 1 Write each number in prime factored form.

Step 2 List each different prime factor that is in every prime factorization.

Step 3 Use as exponents on the prime factors the smallest exponent from the prime factored forms. (If a prime does not appear in one of the prime factored forms, it cannot appear in the greatest common factor.)

Step 4 Multiply together the primes of Step 3. If there are no primes left after Step 3, the greatest common factor is 1.

The greatest common factor also can be found for a list of variables. For example, the terms x^4, x^5, x^6, and x^7 have x^4 as the greatest common factor, because 4 is the smallest exponent on x.

The exponent on the greatest common factor is the *smallest* exponent that appears on the factors.

EXAMPLE 5 Find the greatest common factor for each list of terms.

(a) $21m^7$, $-18m^6$, $45m^8$, $-24m^5$

First, 3 is the greatest common factor of the coefficients 21, -18, 45, and -24. The smallest exponent on m is 5, so the greatest common factor of the terms is $3m^5$.

(b) x^4y^2, x^7y^5, x^3y^7, y^{15}

There is no x in the last term, y^{15}, so x will not appear in the greatest common factor. There is a y in each term, however, and 2 is the smallest exponent on y. The greatest common factor is y^2. ●

4 The idea of a greatest common factor can be used to write a polynomial in factored form. For example, the polynomial

$$3m + 12$$

is made up of the two terms $3m$ and 12. The greatest common factor for these two terms is 3. Write $3m + 12$ so that each term is a product with 3 as one factor.

$$3m + 12 = 3 \cdot m + 3 \cdot 4$$

Now use the distributive property.

$$3m + 12 = 3 \cdot m + 3 \cdot 4 = 3(m + 4)$$

The factored form of $3m + 12$ is $3(m + 4)$. This process is called **factoring out the greatest common factor.**

EXAMPLE 6   Factor out the greatest common factor.

(a) $20m^5 + 10m^4 + 15m^3$

The greatest common factor for the terms of this polynomial is $5m^3$.

$$20m^5 + 10m^4 + 15m^3 = (5m^3)(4m^2) + (5m^3)(2m) + (5m^3)3$$
$$= 5m^3(4m^2 + 2m + 3)$$

To check your work, multiply $5m^3$ and $4m^2 + 2m + 3$. You should get the original polynomial as your answer.

(b) $x^5 + x^3 = (x^3)x^2 + (x^3)1 = x^3(x^2 + 1)$

Do not forget the 1 here; always be sure that the factored form can be multiplied out to yield the original polynomial.

(c) $20m^7p^2 - 36m^3p^4 = 4m^3p^2(5m^4 - 9p^2)$ ●

> Always look for a greatest common factor as the first step in factoring a polynomial.

5   Common factors are used in **factoring by grouping,** which is explained in the next example.

EXAMPLE 7   Factor by grouping.

(a) $2x + 6 + ax + 3a$

The first two terms have a common factor of 2, and the last two terms have a common factor of a.

$$2x + 6 + ax + 3a = 2(x + 3) + a(x + 3)$$

Now $x + 3$ is a common factor.

$$2x + 6 + ax + 3a = 2(x + 3) + a(x + 3)$$
$$= (x + 3)(2 + a)$$

(b) $m^2 + 6m + 2m + 12 = m(m + 6) + 2(m + 6)$
$$= (m + 6)(m + 2)$$

(c) $6y^2 - 21y + 8y - 28 = 3y(2y - 7) + 4(2y - 7)$
$$= (2y - 7)(3y + 4)$$ ●

Use these steps to factor four terms by grouping.

Factoring by Grouping

Step 1	Write the four terms so that the first two have a common factor and the last two have a common factor.
Step 2	Use the distributive property to factor each group of two terms.
Step 3	If possible, factor a greatest common factor from the results of Step 2.

4.1 EXERCISES

Find all the positive integer factors of each number. See Example 1.

1. 14   **2.** 18   **3.** 27   **4.** 35

5. 45   **6.** 50   **7.** 60   **8.** 72

9. 100   **10.** 130   **11.** 29   **12.** 37

Tell whether each number is prime or composite. See Example 2.

13. 32   **14.** 50   **15.** 37   **16.** 53

17. 77   **18.** 105   **19.** 145   **20.** 156

21. 197   **22.** 203   **23.** 54,682   **24.** 98,176

Find the prime factored form for the following numbers. See Example 3.

25. 120   **26.** 150   **27.** 180   **28.** 225

29. 275   **30.** 350   **31.** 475   **32.** 650

Find the greatest common factor for each list of terms. See Examples 4 and 5.

33. $12y$, 24 **34.** $72m$, 12 **35.** $30p^2$, $20p^3$, $40p^5$

36. $14r^5$, $28r^2$, $56r^8$ **37.** $18r$, $32y$, $11z$ **38.** $45m^2$, $12n$, $7p^2$

39. $18m^2n^2$, $36m^4n^5$, $12m^3n$ **40.** $50p^5r^2$, $25p^4r^7$, $30p^7r^8$ **41.** $32y^4x^5$, $24y^7x$, $36y^3x^5$

Complete the factoring.

42. $18 = 9(\quad)$ **43.** $3x^2 = 3x(\quad)$ **44.** $8x^3 = 8x(\quad)$

45. $9m^4 = 3m^2(\quad)$ **46.** $12p^5 = 6p^3(\quad)$ **47.** $-8z^9 = 4z^5(\quad)$

48. $-15k^{11} = -5k^8(\quad)$ **49.** $x^2y^3 = xy(\quad)$ **50.** $a^3b^2 = a^2b(\quad)$

51. $27a^3b^2 = 9a^2b(\quad)$ **52.** $14x^4y^3 = 2xy(\quad)$ **53.** $-16m^3n^3 = 4mn^2(\quad)$

Factor out the greatest common factor. See Example 6.

54. $21m^5 - 14m^4$ **55.** $65y^9 - 35y^5$ **56.** $100a^4 - 16a^2$ **57.** $121p^5 - 33p^4$

58. $8p^2 - 4p^4$ **59.** $11z^2 - 100$ **60.** $12z^2 - 11y^4$ **61.** $19y^3p^2 + 38y^2p^3$

62. $100m^5 - 50m^3 + 100m^2$ **63.** $13y^6 + 26y^5 - 39y^3$

64. $5x^4 + 25x^3 - 20x^2$ **65.** $45q^4p^5 - 36qp^6 + 81q^2p^3$

66. $a^5 + 2a^5b + 3a^5b^2 - 4a^5b^3$ **67.** $a^3b^5 - a^2b^7 + ab^3$

68. $m^6n^5 - 2m^5 + 5m^3n^5$ **69.** $125z^5a^3 - 60z^4a^5 + 85z^3a^4$

70. $30a^2m^2 + 60a^3m + 180a^3m^2$ **71.** $33y^8 - 44y^{12} + 77y^3 + 11y^4$

72. $26g^6h^4 + 13g^3h^4 - 39g^4h^3$ **73.** $36a^4b^3 + 32a^5b^2 - 48a^6b^3$

Factor by grouping. See Example 7.

74. $m^2 + 2m + 5m + 10$ **75.** $a^2 - 2a + 5a - 10$

76. $y^2 - 6y + 4y - 24$ **77.** $7z^2 + 3zm + 14zm + 6m^2$

78. $8k^2 + 6kq + 12kq + 9q^2$ **79.** $5m^2 + 15mp - 2mp - 6p^2$

80. $18r^2 + 12ry - 3ry - 2y^2$

81. $3a^3 + 3ab^2 + 2a^2b + 2b^3$

82. $16m^3 - 4m^2p^2 - 4mp + p^3$

83. $1 - a + ab - b$

84. $2pq^2 - 8q^2 + p - 4$

85. $6 - 2ab + 3a - a^2b$

Review Exercises *Find each product. See Section 3.6.*

86. $(x + 2)(x + 5)$

87. $(m + 3)(m + 4)$

88. $(y + 7)(y - 3)$

89. $(r + 5)(r - 9)$

90. $(q - 5)(q - 7)$

91. $(y - 4)(y - 8)$

92. $(p - 10)(p + 10)$

93. $(a + 7)(a - 7)$

94. $(m - 12)(m + 12)$

4.2 Factoring Trinomials

1 Factor trinomials with a coefficient of 1 for the squared term.

2 Factor such polynomials after factoring out the greatest common factor.

1 · The product of the polynomials $k - 3$ and $k + 1$ is

$$(k - 3)(k + 1) = k^2 - 2k - 3.$$

In this section, we see how to begin with $k^2 - 2k - 3$ and write it as the product $(k - 3)(k + 1)$. This product is called the **factored form** of $k^2 - 2k - 3$, and the process of finding the factored form is called **factoring.** In this section we limit ourselves to trinomials like $x^2 - 2x - 24$ or $y^2 + 2y - 15$, where the coefficient of the squared term is 1.

For example, to factor $x^2 + 5x + 6$, we need to find integers a and b such that

$$x^2 + 5x + 6 = (x + a)(x + b).$$

To find these integers a and b, first find the product of the two terms on the right-hand side of the equation.

$$(x + a)(x + b) = x^2 + ax + bx + ab$$

By the distributive property,

$$x^2 + ax + bx + ab = x^2 + (a + b)x + ab.$$

Based on this result, we want integers a and b such that

$$x^2 + 5x + 6 = x^2 + (a + b)x + ab.$$

Sum of a and b is 5 ↑   └─Product of a and b is 6

Can we find two integers whose sum is 5 and whose product is 6? Since many pairs of integers have a sum of 5, it is best to first list those pairs of integers whose product is 6. Both 5 and 6 are positive, so we need consider only pairs having both integers positive.

$$
\begin{array}{cc}
\textit{Product} & \textit{Sum} \\
1 \cdot 6 = 6 & 1 + 6 = 7 \\
2 \cdot 3 = \mathbf{6} & 2 + 3 = \mathbf{5}
\end{array}
$$

Both pairs have a product of 6, but only the pair 2 and 3 has a sum of 5. So 2 and 3 are the needed integers, and

$$x^2 + 5x + 6 = (x + 2)(x + 3).$$

To check, multiply the binomials. Make sure that the sum of the outer and inner products produces the correct middle term.

$$
\begin{array}{c}
3x \\
2x \quad 3x + 2x = 5x \\
(x + 2)(x + 3) = x^2 + 5x + 6
\end{array}
$$

This method can only be used to factor trinomials having the coefficient of the squared term equal to 1. Methods for factoring other trinomials will be given in the next section.

EXAMPLE 1   Factor $m^2 + 9m + 14$.

Look for two integers whose product is 14 and whose sum is 9. List the pairs of integers whose product is 14. Then examine the sums. Again, we need only positive integers, because all signs are positive.

$$
\begin{array}{ll}
14, 1 & 14 + 1 = 15 \\
7, 2 & 7 + 2 = \mathbf{9} \qquad \text{Sum is 9}
\end{array}
$$

From the list, 7 and 2 are the integers we need, since $7 \cdot 2 = 14$ and $7 + 2 = 9$. Thus $m^2 + 9m + 14 = (m + 2)(m + 7)$. This answer also could have been written $(m + 7)(m + 2)$. Because of the commutative property of multiplication, the order of the factors does not matter.   ●

EXAMPLE 2   Factor $p^2 - 2p - 15$.

Find two integers whose product is -15 and whose sum is -2. If these numbers do not come to mind right away, find them (if they exist) by listing all the pairs of integers whose product is -15. Here we need to consider negative integers as well as positive ones.

$$
\begin{array}{ll}
15, -1 & 15 + (-1) = 14 \\
5, -3 & 5 + (-3) = 2 \\
-15, 1 & -15 + 1 = -14 \\
-5, 3 & -5 + 3 = -2 \qquad \text{Sum is } -2
\end{array}
$$

The necessary integers are -5 and 3.

$$p^2 - 2p - 15 = (p - 5)(p + 3) \quad ●$$

EXAMPLE 3

Factor $x^2 - 5x + 12$.

First, list all pairs of integers whose product is 12. Then examine the sums.

$$12, 1 \qquad 12 + 1 = 13$$
$$6, 2 \qquad 6 + 2 = 8$$
$$3, 4 \qquad 3 + 4 = 7$$
$$-12, -1 \qquad -12 + (-1) = -13$$
$$-6, -2 \qquad -6 + (-2) = -8$$
$$-3, -4 \qquad -3 + (-4) = -7$$

None of the pairs of integers has a sum of -5. Because of this, the trinomial $x^2 - 5x + 12$ *cannot be factored with integer factors.* ●

The polynomial of Example 3, $x^2 - 5x + 12$, cannot be factored with integer factors. Such a polynomial is called **prime.** Another example of a prime polynomial is $k^2 - 8k + 11$.

EXAMPLE 4

Factor $z^2 - 2bz - 3b^2$.

To factor $z^2 - 2bz - 3b^2$, look for two expressions whose product is $-3b^2$ and whose sum is $-2b$. The expressions are $-3b$ and b, with

$$z^2 - 2bz - 3b^2 = (z - 3b)(z + b). ●$$

2 The polynomial in Example 5 does not have a coefficient of 1 for the squared term. (In fact, there is no squared term.) However, we get such a polynomial after factoring out the greatest common factor.

EXAMPLE 5

Factor $4x^5 - 28x^4 + 40x^3$.

First, factor out the greatest common factor, $4x^3$.

$$4x^5 - 28x^4 + 40x^3 = 4x^3(x^2 - 7x + 10)$$

Now factor $x^2 - 7x + 10$. The integers -5 and -2 have a product of 10 and a sum of -7. The complete factored form is

$$4x^5 - 28x^4 + 40x^3 = 4x^3(x - 5)(x - 2). ●$$

When you factor, always remember to look first for a greatest common factor.

4.2 EXERCISES

Complete the factoring.

1. $x^2 + 10x + 21 = (x + 7)(\qquad)$

2. $p^2 + 11p + 30 = (p + 5)(\qquad)$

3. $r^2 + 15r + 56 = (r + 7)(\qquad)$

4. $x^2 + 15x + 44 = (x + 4)(\qquad)$

5. $t^2 - 14t + 24 = (t - 2)(\qquad)$

6. $x^2 - 9x + 8 = (x - 1)(\qquad)$

7. $x^2 - 12x + 32 = (x - 4)(\qquad)$

8. $y^2 - 2y - 15 = (y + 3)(\qquad)$

9. $m^2 + 2m - 24 = (m - 4)(\qquad)$

10. $x^2 + 9x - 22 = (x - 2)(\qquad)$

11. $p^2 + 7p - 8 = (p + 8)(\qquad)$

12. $y^2 - 7y - 18 = (y + 2)(\qquad)$

13. $x^2 - 7xy + 10y^2 = (x - 2y)(\qquad)$

14. $k^2 - 3kh - 28h^2 = (k - 7h)(\qquad)$

Factor as completely as possible. If a polynomial cannot be factored, write prime. See Examples 1–3.

15. $x^2 + 6x + 5$

16. $y^2 + 9y + 8$

17. $a^2 + 9a + 20$

18. $b^2 + 8b + 15$

19. $x^2 - 8x + 7$

20. $m^2 + m - 20$

21. $p^2 + 4p + 5$

22. $n^2 + 4n + 12$

23. $y^2 - 6y + 8$

24. $r^2 - 11r + 30$

25. $s^2 + 2s - 35$

26. $h^2 + 11h + 12$

27. $n^2 - 12n - 35$

28. $a^2 - 2a - 99$

29. $b^2 - 11b + 24$

30. $x^2 - 9x + 20$

31. $k^2 - 10k + 25$

32. $z^2 - 14z + 49$

33. $y^2 - 12y - 45$

34. $p^2 + 5p - 66$

Factor completely. See Examples 4 and 5.

35. $x^2 + 4ax + 3a^2$

36. $x^2 - mx - 6m^2$

37. $y^2 - by - 30b^2$

38. $z^2 + 2zx - 15x^2$

39. $x^2 + xy - 30y^2$

40. $a^2 - ay - 56y^2$

41. $r^2 - 2rs + s^2$

42. $m^2 - 2mn - 3n^2$

43. $p^2 - 3pq - 10q^2$

44. $c^2 - 5cd + 4d^2$

45. $3m^3 + 12m^2 + 9m$

46. $3y^5 - 18y^4 + 15y^3$

47. $6a^2 - 48a - 120$

48. $h^7 - 5h^6 - 14h^5$

49. $3r^3 - 30r^2 + 72r$

50. $2x^6 - 8x^5 - 42x^4$

51. $3x^4 - 3x^3 - 90x^2$

52. $2y^3 - 8y^2 - 10y$

53. $a^5 + 3a^4b - 4a^3b^2$

54. $m^3n - 2m^2n^2 - 3mn^3$

55. $y^3z + y^2z^2 - 6yz^3$

56. $k^7 - 2k^6m - 15k^5m^2$

57. $z^{10} - 4z^9y - 21z^8y^2$

58. $x^9 + 5x^8w - 24x^7w^2$

59. Use the FOIL method from Section 3.6 to show that $(2x + 4)(x - 3) = 2x^2 - 2x - 12$. Why, then, is it incorrect to completely factor $2x^2 - 2x - 12$ as $(2x + 4)(x - 3)$?

60. Why is it incorrect to completely factor $3x^2 + 9x - 12$ as the product $(x - 1)(3x + 12)$?

61. What polynomial can be factored to give $(y - 7)(y + 6)$?

62. What polynomial can be factored to give $(a + 9)(a + 6)$?

Review Exercises *Find each product. See Section 3.6.*

63. $(2y - 7)(y + 4)$

64. $(3a + 2)(2a + 1)$

65. $(5z + 2)(3z - 2)$

66. $(4m - 3)(2m + 5)$

67. $(4p + 1)(2p - 3)$

68. $(6r - 2)(3r + 1)$

4.3 More on Factoring Trinomials

Factor trinomials not having 1 as the coefficient of the squared term, using

1 factoring by grouping;

2 the alternative method.

1 In this section we factor trinomials in which the coefficient of the squared term is *not* 1, such as $2x^2 + 7x + 6$. There are two different methods that can be used to factor such trinomials. The first of these methods is an extension of the method presented in the last section.

Recall that a trinomial such as $m^2 + 3m + 2$ is factored by finding two numbers whose product is 2 and whose sum is 3. We can factor $2x^2 + 7x + 6$ in a similar way: by finding two integers whose product is 12 and whose sum is 7.

$$\overset{\text{Sum is 7}}{2x^2 + 7x + 6}$$
$$\text{Product is } 2 \cdot 6 = 12$$

By considering the pairs of integers whose product is 12, the necessary integers are found to be 3 and 4. Use these integers to write the middle term, $7x$, as $7x = 3x + 4x$. With this, the trinomial $2x^2 + 7x + 6$ becomes

$$2x^2 + 7x + 6 = 2x^2 + \underbrace{3x + 4x}_{} + 6.$$
$$7x \text{ written as } 3x + 4x$$

Factor the right-hand side of the equation by grouping (as explained in the first section of this chapter).

$$2x^2 + 3x + 4x + 6 = x(2x + 3) + 2(2x + 3)$$
$$= (2x + 3)(x + 2)$$

Finally, the factored form of $2x^2 + 7x + 6$ is

$$2x^2 + 7x + 6 = (2x + 3)(x + 2).$$

To check, find the product of $2x + 3$ and $x + 2$.

EXAMPLE 1 Factor each trinomial.

(a) $6r^2 + r - 1$

We need to find two integers with a product of $6(-1) = -6$ and a sum of 1.

$$\overset{\text{Sum is 1}}{6r^2 + r - 1 = 6r^2 + 1r - 1}$$
$$\text{Product is } 6(-1) = -6$$

The integers are -2 and 3. Write the middle term, $+r$, as $-2r + 3r$, so that

$$6r^2 + r - 1 = 6r^2 - 2r + 3r - 1.$$

Factor by grouping on the right-hand side.

$$\begin{aligned}
6r^2 + r - 1 &= 6r^2 - 2r + 3r - 1 \\
&= 2r(3r - 1) + 1(3r - 1) \\
&= (3r - 1)(2r + 1)
\end{aligned}$$

(b) $12z^2 - 5z - 2$

We need two integers whose product is $12(-2) = -24$ and whose sum is -5. The desired integers are 3 and -8, with

$$\begin{aligned}
12z^2 - 5z - 2 &= 12z^2 + 3z - 8z - 2 \\
&= 3z(4z + 1) - 2(4z + 1) \\
&= (4z + 1)(3z - 2). \quad \bullet
\end{aligned}$$

2   In the rest of this section we show an alternative method of factoring trinomials in which the coefficient of the squared term is not 1. This alternative method is especially useful when the product of the first and last terms is large. In the next example, we use the alternative method to factor $2x^2 + 7x + 6$, the same trinomial factored above.

EXAMPLE 2   Factor $2x^2 + 7x + 6$.

The possible factors of $2x^2$ are $2x$ and x, or $-2x$ and $-x$. We normally use only positive coefficients for the first factors. If we use $2x$ and x, then the factoring of $2x^2 + 7x + 6$ is started as follows.

$$2x^2 + 7x + 6 = (2x \qquad)(x \qquad)$$

The last term of $2x^2 + 7x + 6$ is 6. There are several possible factors of 6, including 6 and 1. We don't know whether these are the correct factors or not; we have to see whether they give the correct middle term of $+7x$.

$$\overset{\displaystyle\overset{12x}{\frown}}{\underset{\displaystyle\underset{x}{\smile}}{(2x + 1)(x + 6)}} = 2x^2 + 13x + 6 \qquad \text{Incorrect}$$

Exchange the 6 and 1, and see whether the middle term is now correct.

$$\overset{\displaystyle\overset{2x}{\frown}}{\underset{\displaystyle\underset{6x}{\smile}}{(2x + 6)(x + 1)}} = 2x^2 + 8x + 6 \qquad \text{Incorrect}$$

We could have noticed from the beginning that $(2x + 6)(x + 1)$ could not be correct. This is because $2x + 6$ has a common factor of 2, while $2x^2 + 7x + 6$ does not.

> If the original polynomial has no common factor, then none of its factors will either.

Let us now try 2 and 3 as factors of 6. We cannot use $(2x + 2)(x + 3)$ because of the common factor in $2x + 2$. Let's try $(2x + 3)(x + 2)$.

$$(2x + 3)(x + 2) = 2x^2 + 7x + 6 \qquad \text{Correct}$$

We have now factored $2x^2 + 7x + 6$.

$$2x^2 + 7x + 6 = (2x + 3)(x + 2) \quad \bullet$$

As you gain experience in factoring, you will be able to do many of these steps in your head.

EXAMPLE 3

Factor $8p^2 + 14p + 5$.

The number 8 has several possible pairs of factors, but 5 has only 1 and 5 or -1 and -5. For this reason, it is easier to begin by considering the factors of 5. Ignore the negative factors since all terms of the trinomial have positive coefficients. If $8p^2 + 14p + 5$ can be factored, it will be factored as

$$(\qquad + 5)(\qquad + 1).$$

The possible factors of $8p^2$ are $8p$ and p, or $4p$ and $2p$. Try various possibilities.

$$(8p + 5)(p + 1) = 8p^2 + 13p + 5 \qquad \text{Incorrect}$$

$$(p + 5)(8p + 1) = 8p^2 + 41p + 5 \qquad \text{Incorrect}$$

$$(4p + 5)(2p + 1) = 8p^2 + 14p + 5 \qquad \text{Correct}$$

Finally, the factored form of $8p^2 + 14p + 5$ is $(4p + 5)(2p + 1)$. $\quad \bullet$

EXAMPLE 4

Factor $6x^2 - 11x + 3$.

There are several possible factors for 6, but 3 has only 1 and 3 or -1 and -3. Thus, we begin by factoring 3. Since the middle term of $6x^2 - 11x + 3$ has a negative coefficient, we have to consider negative factors. Let us try -3 and -1 as factors of 3, or

$$(\qquad - 3)(\qquad - 1).$$

The factors of $6x^2$ are $6x$ and x, or $2x$ and $3x$. Let us try $2x$ and $3x$.

$$\overset{\displaystyle \overset{-2x}{\overset{-9x}{\frown}}}{(2x - 3)(3x - 1)} = 6x^2 - 11x + 3 \qquad \text{Correct} \quad \bullet$$

EXAMPLE 5   Factor $8x^2 + 6x - 9$.

The integer 8 has several possible factors, as does -9. Since the coefficient of the middle term is small, it probably would be wise to avoid large factors such as 8 or 9. Let us begin by trying 4 and 2 as factors of 8, and 3 and -3 as factors of -9.

$$\overset{\displaystyle \overset{-12x}{\overset{6x}{\frown}}}{(4x + 3)(2x - 3)} = 8x^2 - 6x - 9 \qquad \text{Incorrect}$$

$$\overset{\displaystyle \overset{12x}{\overset{-6x}{\frown}}}{(4x - 3)(2x + 3)} = 8x^2 + 6x - 9 \qquad \text{Correct} \quad \bullet$$

EXAMPLE 6   Factor $12a^2 - ab - 20b^2$.

There are several possible factors of $12a^2$, including $12a$ and a, $6a$ and $2a$, and $3a$ and $4a$, just as there are many possible factors of $-20b^2$, including $-20b$ and b, $10b$ and $-2b$, $-10b$ and $2b$, $4b$ and $-5b$, and $-4b$ and $5b$. Once again, since our desired middle term is small we avoid the larger factors. Let us try as factors $6a$ and $2a$ and $4b$ and $-5b$.

$$(6a + 4b)(2a - 5b)$$

This cannot be correct, as we mentioned before, since $6a + 4b$ has a common factor while the given trinomial has none. Let us try $3a$ and $4a$ with $4b$ and $-5b$.

$$(3a + 4b)(4a - 5b) = 12a^2 + ab - 20b^2 \qquad \text{Incorrect}$$

Here the middle term has the wrong sign, so change the signs on the factors.

$$(3a - 4b)(4a + 5b) = 12a^2 - ab - 20b^2 \qquad \text{Correct} \quad \bullet$$

EXAMPLE 7   Factor $28x^5 - 58x^4 - 30x^3$.

First factor out the greatest common factor, $2x^3$.

$$28x^5 - 58x^4 - 30x^3 = 2x^3(14x^2 - 29x - 15)$$

Now try to factor $14x^2 - 29x - 15$. Let us try $7x$ and $2x$ as factors of $14x^2$ and -3 and 5 as factors of -15.

$$(7x - 3)(2x + 5) = 14x^2 + 29x - 15 \qquad \text{Incorrect}$$

The middle term differs only in sign, and so we change the signs on the two factors.

$$(7x + 3)(2x - 5) = 14x^2 - 29x - 15 \qquad \text{Correct}$$

Finally, the factored form of $28x^5 - 58x^4 - 30x^3$ is

$$28x^5 - 58x^4 - 30x^3 = 2x^3(7x + 3)(2x - 5). \quad \bullet$$

Do not forget to include the common factor in such a factored form.

4.3   EXERCISES

Complete the factoring.

1. $2x^2 - x - 1 = (2x + 1)($)   **2.** $3a^2 + 5a + 2 = (3a + 2)($)

3. $5b^2 - 16b + 3 = (5b - 1)($)   **4.** $2x^2 + 11x + 12 = (2x + 3)($)

5. $4y^2 + 17y - 15 = (y + 5)($)   **6.** $7z^2 + 10z - 8 = (z + 2)($)

7. $15x^2 + 7x - 4 = (3x - 1)($)   **8.** $12c^2 - 7c - 12 = (4c + 3)($)

9. $2m^2 + 19m - 10 = (2m - 1)($)   **10.** $6x^2 + x - 12 = (2x + 3)($)

11. $6a^2 + 7ab - 20b^2 = (2a + 5b)($)

12. $9m^2 - 3mn - 2n^2 = (3m - 2n)($)

13. $4k^2 + 13km + 3m^2 = (4k + m)($)

14. $6x^2 - 13xy - 5y^2 = (3x + y)($)

15. $4x^3 - 10x^2 - 6x = 2x($ $) = 2x(2x + 1)($)

16. $15r^3 - 39r^2 - 18r = 3r($ $) = 3r(5r + 2)($)

17. $6m^6 + 7m^5 - 20m^4 = m^4($ $) = m^4(3m - 4)($)

18. $16y^5 - 4y^4 - 6y^3 = 2y^3($ $) = 2y^3(4y - 3)($)

Factor as completely as possible. Remember to look for a greatest common factor first. Use either method.

19. $2x^2 + 7x + 3$ **20.** $3y^2 + 13y + 4$ **21.** $3a^2 + 10a + 7$

22. $7r^2 + 8r + 1$ **23.** $4r^2 + r - 3$ **24.** $3p^2 + 2p - 8$

25. $15m^2 + m - 2$ **26.** $6x^2 + x - 1$ **27.** $8m^2 - 10m - 3$

28. $2a^2 - 17a + 30$ **29.** $5a^2 - 7a - 6$ **30.** $12s^2 + 11s - 5$

31. $3r^2 + r - 10$ **32.** $20x^2 - 28x - 3$ **33.** $4y^2 + 69y + 17$

34. $21m^2 + 13m + 2$ **35.** $38x^2 + 23x + 2$ **36.** $20y^2 + 39y - 11$

37. $10x^2 + 11x - 6$ **38.** $6b^2 + 7b + 2$ **39.** $6w^2 + 19w + 10$

40. $20q^2 - 41q + 20$ **41.** $6q^2 + 23q + 21$ **42.** $8x^2 + 47x - 6$

43. $10m^2 - 23m + 12$ **44.** $4t^2 - 5t - 6$ **45.** $8k^2 + 2k - 15$

46. $15p^2 - p - 6$ **47.** $10m^2 - m - 24$ **48.** $16a^2 + 30a + 9$

49. $8x^2 - 14x + 3$ **50.** $24b^2 - 37b - 5$ **51.** $40m^2 + m - 6$

52. $15a^2 + 22a + 8$ **53.** $2m^3 + 2m^2 - 40m$ **54.** $15n^4 - 39n^3 + 18n^2$

55. $24a^4 + 10a^3 - 4a^2$ **56.** $18x^5 + 15x^4 - 75x^3$ **57.** $32z^2w^4 - 20zw^4 - 12w^4$

58. $15x^2y^2 - 7xy^2 - 4y^2$ **59.** $12p^2 + 7pq - 12q^2$ **60.** $6m^2 - 5mn - 6n^2$

61. $25a^2 + 25ab + 6b^2$ **62.** $6x^2 - 5xy - y^2$ **63.** $6a^2 - 7ab - 5b^2$

64. $25g^2 - 5gh - 2h^2$ **65.** $4k^4 - 2k^3w - 6k^2w^2$ **66.** $4a^4 - a^3b - 3a^2b^2$

67. $6m^6n + 7m^5n^2 + 2m^4n^3$ **68.** $12k^3q^4 - 4k^2q^5 - kq^6$ **69.** $18z^3y - 3z^2y^2 - 105zy^3$

Review Exercises   *Find each product. See Sections 3.5 and 3.6.*

70. $(3r - 1)(3r + 1)$ **71.** $(5p - 3q)(5p + 3q)$ **72.** $(2m - 3)^2$

73. $(x - 1)(x^2 + x + 1)$ **74.** $(2z - 3)(4z^2 + 6z + 9)$ **75.** $(3k - 1)(9k^2 + 3k + 1)$

4.4   Special Factorizations

Factor:

1️⃣ the difference of two squares;

2️⃣ a perfect square trinomial;

3️⃣ the difference of two cubes;

4️⃣ the sum of two cubes.

1️⃣   Recall from the last chapter that

$$(x + y)(x - y) = x^2 - y^2.$$

Based on this product, a **difference of two squares** can be factored as

$$x^2 - y^2 = (x + y)(x - y).$$

EXAMPLE 1   Factor each difference of two squares.

(a) $x^2 - 49 = x^2 - 7^2 = (x + 7)(x - 7)$

(b) $z^2 - \dfrac{9}{16} = \left(z + \dfrac{3}{4}\right)\left(z - \dfrac{3}{4}\right)$

(c) $y^2 - m^2 = (y + m)(y - m)$

(d) $p^2 + 16$ cannot be factored, so it is prime.   ●

In Example 1(d), we saw that $p^2 + 16$ cannot be factored. (Try various factors; no combination with real numbers will give a product of $p^2 + 16$.) In summary,

> while the *difference of two squares*, $x^2 - y^2$, can be factored as $(x + y)(x - y)$, the *sum of two squares*, $x^2 + y^2$, is prime.

(We assume above that $x^2 + y^2$ has no common factor other than 1.)

EXAMPLE 2   Factor $25m^2 - 16$.

This is the difference of two squares, since

$$25m^2 - 16 = (5m)^2 - 4^2.$$

Factor this as

$$(5m + 4)(5m - 4).   ●$$

EXAMPLE 3   Factor as completely as possible.

(a) $49z^2 - 64 = (7z)^2 - 8^2 = (7z + 8)(7z - 8)$

(b) $9a^2 - 4b^2 = (3a)^2 - (2b)^2 = (3a + 2b)(3a - 2b)$

(c) $p^4 - 36 = (p^2)^2 - 6^2 = (p^2 + 6)(p^2 - 6)$

Neither $p^2 + 6$ nor $p^2 - 6$ can be factored further.

(d) $m^4 - 16 = (m^2)^2 - 4^2 = (m^2 + 4)(m^2 - 4)$

While $m^2 + 4$ cannot be factored further, $m^2 - 4$ can be factored, giving

$$m^4 - 16 = (m^2 + 4)(m + 2)(m - 2). \quad \bullet$$

2   A quantity is a perfect square if it can be expressed as the square of another quantity. For example, 144, $4x^2$, and $81m^6$ are all perfect squares, since

$$144 = 12^2, \qquad 4x^2 = (2x)^2, \qquad \text{and} \qquad 81m^6 = (9m^3)^2.$$

A **perfect square trinomial** is a trinomial that is the square of a binomial. For example,

$$x^2 + 8x + 16 = (x + 4)^2.$$

Multiply to see that the square of a binomial gives the following perfect square trinomials.

$$x^2 + 2xy + y^2 = (x + y)^2$$

$$x^2 - 2xy + y^2 = (x - y)^2$$

The middle term of a perfect square trinomial is always twice the product of the two terms in the squared binomial. (We first saw this in Section 3.6.) Use this to check any attempt to factor a trinomial that appears to be a perfect square.

EXAMPLE 4   Factor $x^2 + 10x + 25$.

The term x^2 is a perfect square, and so is 25. Try to factor the trinomial as

$$x^2 + 10x + 25 = (x + 5)^2.$$

To check, take twice the product of the two terms in the squared binomial.

$$2 \cdot x \cdot 5 = 10x$$

Since $10x$ is the middle term of the trinomial, the trinomial is a perfect square and can be factored as $(x + 5)^2$. $\bullet$

EXAMPLE 5   Factor each perfect square trinomial.

(a) $x^2 - 22x + 121$

The first and last terms are perfect squares ($121 = 11^2$). We need to check to see whether the middle term of $x^2 - 22x + 121$ is twice the product of the first and last terms of the binomial $x - 11$.

$$2 \cdot x \cdot 11 = 22x$$

First term of binomial ⎯⎯ Last term of binomial

Since twice the product of the first and last terms of the binomial is the middle term, $x^2 - 22x + 121$ is a perfect square trinomial and

$$x^2 - 22x + 121 = (x - 11)^2.$$

The middle sign in the binomial, a minus sign in this case, is always the same as the middle sign in the trinomial.

(b) $9m^2 - 24m + 16 = (3m - 4)^2$

(c) $25y^2 + 20y + 16$

   The first and last terms are perfect squares.

$$25y^2 = (5y)^2 \qquad \text{and} \qquad 16 = 4^2$$

Twice the product of the first and last terms of the binomial would be

$$2 \cdot 5y \cdot 4 = 40y,$$

which is not the middle term of $25y^2 + 20y + 16$. This polynomial is not a perfect square.   ●

3   Above, we factored the difference of two squares; now we can factor the **difference of two cubes.** Use the pattern

$$x^3 - y^3 = (x - y)(x^2 + xy + y^2).$$

To check this, multiply $x - y$ and $x^2 + xy + y^2$. This pattern should be memorized.

EXAMPLE 6

(a) $m^3 - 125 = m^3 - 5^3$
$$= (m - 5)(m^2 + 5m + 5^2)$$
$$= (m - 5)(m^2 + 5m + 25)$$

(b) $8p^3 - 27 = (2p)^3 - 3^3$
$$= (2p - 3)[(2p)^2 + (2p)3 + 3^2]$$
$$= (2p - 3)(4p^2 + 6p + 9)$$

(c) $4m^3 - 32 = 4(m^3 - 8)$
$$= 4(m - 2)(m^2 + 2m + 4)$$

(d) $125t^3 - 216s^6 = (5t)^3 - (6s^2)^3$
$$= (5t - 6s^2)[(5t)^2 + (5t)(6s^2) + (6s^2)^2]$$
$$= (5t - 6s^2)(25t^2 + 30ts^2 + 36s^4)$$ ●

A common error made in factoring the difference of two cubes is to try to factor $x^2 + xy + y^2$. It is easy to confuse this factor with a perfect square trinomial, $x^2 + 2xy + y^2$. Because of the lack of a 2 in $x^2 + xy + y^2$, it is very unusual to be able to further factor an expression of the form $x^2 + xy + y^2$.

4 A sum of two squares, such as $m^2 + 25$, cannot be factored, but the **sum of two cubes** can be factored by the following pattern, which should be memorized.

$$x^3 + y^3 = (x + y)(x^2 - xy + y^2)$$

EXAMPLE 7

(a) $k^3 + 27 = k^3 + 3^3$

$\qquad = (k + 3)(k^2 - 3k + 3^2)$

$\qquad = (k + 3)(k^2 - 3k + 9)$

(b) $8m^3 + 125 = (2m)^3 + 5^3$

$\qquad = (2m + 5)[(2m)^2 - (2m)(5) + 5^2]$

$\qquad = (2m + 5)(4m^2 - 10m + 25)$

(c) $1000a^6 + 27b^3 = (10a^2)^3 + (3b)^3$

$\qquad = (10a^2 + 3b)[(10a^2)^2 - (10a^2)(3b) + (3b)^2]$

$\qquad = (10a^2 + 3b)(100a^4 - 30a^2b + 9b^2)$ ●

Let us summarize the methods of factoring discussed in this section.

Special Factorizations

Difference of two squares	$x^2 - y^2 = (x + y)(x - y)$
Perfect square trinomials	$x^2 + 2xy + y^2 = (x + y)^2$
	$x^2 - 2xy + y^2 = (x - y)^2$
Difference of two cubes	$x^3 - y^3 = (x - y)(x^2 + xy + y^2)$
Sum of two cubes	$x^3 + y^3 = (x + y)(x^2 - xy + y^2)$

4.4 EXERCISES

Factor each binomial completely. See Examples 1–3.

1. $x^2 - 16$ 2. $m^2 - 25$ 3. $p^2 - 4$ 4. $r^2 - 9$

5. $m^2 - n^2$ 6. $p^2 - q^2$ 7. $a^2 - b^2$ 8. $r^2 - t^2$

9. $9m^2 - 1$ 10. $16y^2 - 9$ 11. $25m^2 - 16$ 12. $144y^2 - 25$

13. $36t^2 - 16$ 14. $9 - 36a^2$ 15. $25a^2 - 16r^2$ 16. $100k^2 - 49m^2$

17. $x^2 + 16$ 18. $m^2 + 100$ 19. $p^4 - 36$ 20. $r^4 - 9$

21. $a^4 - 1$ 22. $x^4 - 16$ 23. $m^4 - 81$ 24. $p^4 - 256$

Factor any perfect square trinomials. See Examples 4 and 5.

25. $a^2 + 4a + 4$

26. $p^2 + 2p + 1$

27. $x^2 - 10x + 25$

28. $y^2 - 8y + 16$

29. $a^2 + 14a + 49$

30. $m^2 - 20m + 100$

31. $k^2 + 22k + 121$

32. $r^2 + 24r + 144$

33. $y^2 - 10y + 100$

34. $z^2 + 7z + 49$

35. $9y^2 + 14y + 25$

36. $16m^2 + 42m + 49$

37. $16a^2 - 40ab + 25b^2$

38. $36y^2 - 60yp + 25p^2$

39. $100m^2 + 100m + 25$

40. $100a^2 - 140ab + 49b^2$

41. $49x^2 + 28xy + 4y^2$

42. $64y^2 - 48ya + 9a^2$

43. $4c^2 + 12cd + 9d^2$

44. $16t^2 - 40tr + 25r^2$

45. $25h^2 - 20hy + 4y^2$

46. $9x^2 + 24xy + 16y^2$

47. $x^3y + 6x^2y^2 + 9xy^3$

48. $4k^3w + 20k^2w^2 + 25kw^3$

Factor each sum or difference of cubes. See Examples 6 and 7.

49. $8a^3 + 1$

50. $8a^3 - 1$

51. $27x^3 - 125$

52. $64p^3 + 27$

53. $8p^3 + q^3$

54. $y^3 - 8x^3$

55. $27a^3 - 64b^3$

56. $125t^3 + 8s^3$

57. $64x^3 + 125y^3$

58. $216z^3 - w^3$

59. $125m^3 - 8p^3$

60. $343r^3 + 1000s^3$

61. $1000z^3 + 27x^3$

62. $64y^3 - 1331w^3$

63. $64y^6 + 1$

64. $m^6 - 8$

65. $8k^6 - 27q^3$

66. $125z^3 + 64r^6$

67. $1000a^3 - 343b^9$

68. $27r^9 + 125s^3$

69. Find a value of b so that $x^2 + bx + 25 = (x + 5)^2$.

70. For what value of c is $4m^2 - 12m + c = (2m - 3)^2$?

71. Find a so that $ay^2 - 12y + 4 = (3y - 2)^2$.

72. Find b so that $100a^2 + ba + 9 = (10a + 3)^2$.

Review Exercises *Solve each equation. See Section 2.4.*

73. $m - 2 = 0$

74. $r + 1 = 0$

75. $3k - 2 = 0$

76. $4z + 5 = 0$

77. $7a + 9 = 0$

78. $3x + 7 = 0$

79. $8y + 5 = 0$

80. $12k - 11 = 0$

MISCELLANEOUS FACTORING EXERCISES

Factoring a Polynomial

Step 1	Factor out any greatest common factor.
Step 2	How many terms are in the polynomial?

Two terms Check to see whether it is either the difference of two squares or the sum or difference of two cubes.

Three terms Is it a perfect square trinomial? If the trinomial is not a perfect square, check to see whether the coefficient of the squared term is 1. If so, use the method of Section 4.2. If the coefficient of the squared term of the trinomial is not 1, use the general factoring methods of Section 4.3.

Four terms Can the polynomial be factored by grouping?

Step 3 Can any factors be factored further?

Factor as completely as possible.

1. $a^2 - 4a - 12$

2. $a^2 + 17a + 72$

3. $6y^2 - 6y - 12$

4. $7y^6 + 14y^5 - 168y^4$

5. $6a + 12b + 18c$

6. $m^2 - 3mn - 4n^2$

7. $p^2 - 17p + 66$

8. $a^2 - 3ab - 28b^2$

9. $10z^2 - 7z - 6$

10. $2m^2 - 10m - 48$

11. $5z^2 + 24z - 5$

12. $15y + 5$

13. $8a^5 - 8a^4 - 48a^3$

14. $8k^2 - 10k - 3$

15. $z^2 - 3za - 10a^2$

16. $50z^2 - 100$

17. $6n^2 - 19n + 10$

18. $100n^2r^2 + 30nr^3 - 50n^2r$

19. $2m^2 + 5m - 3$

20. $9y^2 + 12y - 5$

21. $16x + 20$

22. $m^2 + 2m - 15$

23. $6y^2 - 5y - 4$

24. $k^2 + 8k - 48$

25. $6z^2 + 31z + 5$

26. $8p^2 + 23p - 3$

27. $4k^2 - 12k + 9$

28. $8m^2 - 2m - 3$

29. $54m^2 - 24z^2$

30. $45a^3b^5 - 60a^4b^2 + 75a^6b^4$

31. $3k^2 + 4k - 4$

32. $5 + r - 5s - rs$

33. $14k^3 + 7k^2 - 70k$

34. $72y^3z^2 + 12y^2 - 24y^4z^2$

35. $y^4 - 16$

36. $20y^5 - 30y^4$

37. $8m - 16m^2$

38. $24k^4p + 60k^3p^2 + 150k^2p^3$

39. $z^3 - 8$

40. $y^2 - y - 56$

41. $32m^9 + 16m^5 + 24m^3$

42. $27p^{10} - 45p^9 - 252p^8$

43. $16r^2 + 24rm + 9m^2$

44. $8m^3 + 125$

45. $15h^2 + 11hg - 14g^2$

46. $z^2 - 12z + 36$

47. $k^2 - 11k + 30$

48. $5z^3 - 45z^2 + 70z$

49. $3k^3 - 12k^2 - 15k$

50. $y^2 - 4yk - 12k^2$

51. $1000p^3 + 27$

52. $64r^3 - 343$

53. $6 + 3m + 2p + mp$

54. $2m^2 + 7mn - 15n^2$

55. $16z^2 - 8z + 1$

56. $125m^4 - 400m^3n + 195m^2n^2$

57. $108m^2 - 36m + 3$

58. $100a^2 - 81y^2$

59. $64m^2 - 40mn + 25n^2$

60. $4y^2 - 25$

61. $32z^3 + 56z^2 - 16z$

62. $10m^2 + 25m - 60$

63. $x^2 - 4x - 5x + 20$

64. $z^2 - 6z + 7z - 42$

65. $20 + 5m + 12n + 3mn$

66. $4 - 2q - 6p + 3pq$

67. $6a^2 + 10a - 4$

68. $36y^6 - 42y^5 - 120y^4$

69. $4k^2 - 20kz + 25z^2$

70. $16k^2 - 48k + 36$

71. $64m^2 - 80mn + 25n^2$

72. $2a^2 - 7a - 30$

73. $8k^2 - 2kh - 3h^2$

74. $12p^2 + pq - 6q^2$

75. $10y^2 - 7yz - 6z^2$

76. $m^2 - 4m + 4$

77. $k^2 + 9$

78. $a^4 - 625$

79. $8a^2 + 23ab - 3b^2$

80. $m^2 - 81$

81. $9m^2 - 64$

82. $k^2 - 16$

83. $9z^2 + 64$

84. $64p^2 - 100m^2$

85. $a^2 + 8a + 16$

86. $49z^2 - 16y^2$

4.5   Solving Quadratic Equations

1⃣ Solve quadratic equations by factoring.

2⃣ Solve other equations by factoring.

1⃣   In this section we introduce **quadratic equations,** which are equations that contain a squared term and no terms of higher degree.

Quadratic Equations

> Quadratic equations have the form
> $$ax^2 + bx + c = 0,$$
> where a, b, and c are real numbers, with $a \neq 0$.

For example,

$$x^2 + 5x + 6 = 0, \qquad 2a^2 - 5a = 3, \qquad \text{and} \qquad y^2 = 4$$

are all quadratic equations.

   Some quadratic equations can be solved by factoring. A method for solving those equations that cannot be solved by factoring is given in Chapter 9. To solve a quadratic equation by factoring, use the **zero-factor property.**

Zero-Factor Property

> If a and b are real numbers and if $ab = 0$, then $a = 0$ or $b = 0$.

In other words, if the product of two numbers is zero, then at least one of the numbers must be zero.

EXAMPLE 1   Solve the equation $(x + 3)(2x - 1) = 0$.

   The product $(x + 3)(2x - 1)$ is equal to zero. By the zero-factor property, the only way that the product of these two factors can be zero is if at least one of the factors is zero. Therefore, either $x + 3 = 0$ or $2x - 1 = 0$. Solve each of these two equations.

$$x + 3 = 0 \quad \text{or} \quad 2x - 1 = 0$$
$$x = -3 \qquad\qquad 2x = 1$$
$$x = \frac{1}{2}.$$

The given equation $(x + 3)(2x - 1) = 0$ has two solutions, -3 and $1/2$. To check these answers, substitute -3 for x in the original equation. Then start over and substitute $1/2$ for x.   ●

   In Example 1 the equation to be solved was presented in factored form. If the equation is not already factored, first make sure that all terms are on one side of the equals sign, with 0 alone on the other side. Then factor the polynomial.

EXAMPLE 2   Solve the equation $x^2 - 5x = -6$.

   First, rewrite the equation with all terms on one side. To do this, add 6 on both sides.

$$x^2 - 5x + 6 = -6 + 6 \qquad \text{Add 6}$$
$$x^2 - 5x + 6 = 0$$

Now factor $x^2 - 5x + 6$. We need two numbers whose product is 6 and whose sum is -5. These two numbers are -2 and -3, so the equation becomes

$$(x - 2)(x - 3) = 0.$$

Proceed as in Example 1. Place each factor equal to 0.

$$x - 2 = 0 \quad \text{or} \quad x - 3 = 0$$

To solve the equation on the left, add 2 on both sides. In the equation on the right, add 3 on both sides. Doing this gives

$$x = 2 \quad \text{or} \quad x = 3.$$

Check both solutions by substituting first 2 and then 3 for x in the original equation.   ●

EXAMPLE 3   Solve the equation $2p^2 + 20 = 13p$.

   Subtract $13p$ from each side to get

$$2p^2 - 13p + 20 = 0.$$

Factor $2p^2 - 13p + 20$ as $(2p - 5)(p - 4)$, giving

$$(2p - 5)(p - 4) = 0.$$

Place each of these two factors equal to 0.

$$2p - 5 = 0 \quad \text{or} \quad p - 4 = 0$$

To solve the equation on the left, first add 5 on both sides of the equation. Then divide both sides by 2. To solve the equation on the right, add 4 on both sides.

$$2p - 5 = 0 \quad \text{or} \quad p - 4 = 0$$
$$2p = 5$$
$$p = \frac{5}{2} \quad \text{or} \quad p = 4$$

The solutions of $2p^2 + 20 = 13p$ are 5/2 and 4; check them by substitution in the original equation.   ●

EXAMPLE 4

Solve each equation.

(a) $16m^2 - 25 = 0$

Factor the left-hand side of the equation as the difference of two squares.

$$(4m + 5)(4m - 5) = 0$$

Place each factor equal to 0.

$$4m + 5 = 0 \quad \text{or} \quad 4m - 5 = 0$$

Solve each equation.

$$4m = -5 \quad \text{or} \quad 4m = 5$$
$$m = -\frac{5}{4} \quad \text{or} \quad m = \frac{5}{4}$$

The two solutions, $-5/4$ and $5/4$, can be checked in the original equation.

(b) $k(2k + 5) = 3$

Multiply on the left-hand side and then get all terms on one side.

$$k(2k + 5) = 3$$
$$2k^2 + 5k = 3$$
$$2k^2 + 5k - 3 = 0$$

Now factor.

$$(2k - 1)(k + 3) = 0$$

Place each factor equal to 0 and solve the equations.

$$2k - 1 = 0 \quad \text{or} \quad k + 3 = 0$$
$$2k = 1$$
$$k = \frac{1}{2} \quad \text{or} \quad k = -3$$

The two solutions are 1/2 and -3.   ●

The equation of Example 4(b) on the previous page shows that the factors must have a product of **0** before the zero-factor property may be used.

In summary, go through the following steps to solve quadratic equations by factoring.

Solving Quadratic Equations by Factoring

> *Step 1* Get all terms on one side of the equals sign, with 0 on the other side.
>
> *Step 2* Factor completely.
>
> *Step 3* Set each factor equal to 0, and solve the resulting equations.
>
> *Step 4* Check each solution in the original equation.
>
> Remember: Not all quadratic equations can be solved by factoring.

2 We also can use the zero-factor property to solve equations that have more than two factors, as shown in Example 5. (These equations are *not* quadratic equations. Why not?)

EXAMPLE 5 Solve the equation $6z^3 - 6z = 0$.

First, factor out the greatest common factor in $6z^3 - 6z$.

$$6z^3 - 6z = 0$$
$$6z(z^2 - 1) = 0$$

Now factor $z^2 - 1$ as $(z + 1)(z - 1)$ to get

$$6z(z + 1)(z - 1) = 0.$$

This product can equal zero only if at least one of the factors is zero. This means that we can now write three equations, one for each factor.

$$6z = 0 \qquad \text{or} \qquad z + 1 = 0 \qquad \text{or} \qquad z - 1 = 0$$

Solving these three equations gives three solutions,

$$z = 0 \qquad \text{or} \qquad z = -1 \qquad \text{or} \qquad z = 1.$$

Check by substituting, in turn, 0, -1, and 1 in the original equation. ●

EXAMPLE 6 Solve the equation $(2x - 1)(x^2 - 9x + 20) = 0$.

Factor $x^2 - 9x + 20$ as $(x - 5)(x - 4)$. Then rewrite the original equation as

$$(2x - 1)(x - 5)(x - 4) = 0.$$

Place each of these three factors equal to 0.

$$2x - 1 = 0 \qquad \text{or} \qquad x - 5 = 0 \qquad \text{or} \qquad x - 4 = 0$$

Solving all three of these equations gives

$$x = \frac{1}{2} \quad \text{or} \quad x = 5 \quad \text{or} \quad x = 4$$

as the solutions of the original equation. Check each solution. ●

4.5 EXERCISES

Solve each equation. See Example 1.

1. $(x - 2)(x + 4) = 0$

2. $(y - 3)(y + 5) = 0$

3. $(3x + 5)(2x - 1) = 0$

4. $(2a + 3)(a - 2) = 0$

5. $(5p + 1)(2p - 1) = 0$

6. $(3k - 8)(k + 7) = 0$

7. $(2m + 9)(3m - 1) = 0$

8. $(9a - 2)(3a + 1) = 0$

9. $(x - 1)(3x + 5) = 0$

10. $(k - 3)(k + 5) = 0$

11. $(3r - 7)(2r + 8) = 0$

12. $(5a + 2)(3a - 1) = 0$

Solve each equation. See Examples 2–4.

13. $x^2 + 5x + 6 = 0$

14. $y^2 - 3y + 2 = 0$

15. $r^2 - 5r - 6 = 0$

16. $y^2 - y - 12 = 0$

17. $m^2 + 3m - 28 = 0$

18. $p^2 - p - 6 = 0$

19. $a^2 = 24 - 5a$

20. $r^2 = 2r + 15$

21. $x^2 = 3 + 2x$

22. $m^2 = 3m + 4$

23. $z^2 = -2 - 3z$

24. $p^2 = 2p + 3$

25. $m^2 + 8m + 16 = 0$

26. $b^2 - 6b + 9 = 0$

27. $3a^2 + 5a - 2 = 0$

28. $6r^2 - r - 2 = 0$

29. $2k^2 - k - 10 = 0$

30. $6x^2 - 7x - 5 = 0$

31. $6p^2 = 4 - 5p$

32. $6x^2 - 5x = 4$

33. $6a^2 = 5 - 13a$

34. $9s^2 + 12s = -4$

35. $2z^2 + 3z = 20$

36. $25p^2 + 20p + 4 = 0$

37. $3a^2 + 7a = 20$

38. $6z^2 + 11z + 3 = 0$

39. $15r^2 = r + 2$

40. $3m^2 = 5m + 28$

41. $2b^2 + 3b - 9 = 0$

42. $5b^2 = 8b + 4$

43. $16r^2 - 25 = 0$

44. $4k^2 - 9 = 0$

45. $9m^2 - 36 = 0$

46. $16x^2 - 64 = 0$

47. $m(m - 7) = -10$

48. $z(2z + 7) = 4$

49. $2(x^2 - 66) = -13x$

50. $3(m^2 + 4) = 20m$

51. $3r(r + 1) = (2r + 3)(r + 1)$

52. $(3k + 1)(k + 1) = 2k(k + 3)$

53. $12k(k - 4) = 3(k - 4)$

54. $y^2 = 4(y - 1)$

Solve each equation. See Examples 5 and 6.

55. $(2r - 5)(3r^2 - 16r + 5) = 0$

56. $(3m - 4)(6m^2 + m - 2) = 0$

57. $(2x + 7)(x^2 - 2x - 3) = 0$

58. $(x - 1)(6x^2 + x - 12) = 0$

59. $x^3 - 25x = 0$

60. $m^3 - 4m = 0$

61. $9y^3 - 49y = 0$

62. $16r^3 - 9r = 0$

63. $r^3 - 2r^2 - 8r = 0$

64. $x^3 - x^2 - 6x = 0$

65. $a^3 + a^2 - 20a = 0$

66. $y^3 - 6y^2 + 8y = 0$

67. When three times a number is added to the square of a number, the result is 10. Find the number.

68. When a number is subtracted from its square, the result is 6. Find the number.

Review Exercises   *Solve each word problem. See Section 2.5.*

69. The length of a rectangle is 3 meters more than the width. The perimeter of the rectangle is 34 meters. Find the width of the rectangle.

70. A rectangle has a length 4 meters less than twice the width. The perimeter of the rectangle is 4 meters more than five times the width. Find the width of the rectangle.

71. When two consecutive integers are added, the result is 17 less than three times the smaller integer. Find the smaller integer.

72. If three consecutive even integers are added, the result is 44 less than four times the smallest integer. Find the smallest integer.

4.6   Applications of Quadratic Equations

Solve word problems about

1   area;

2   perimeter;

3   the Pythagorean formula;

4   consecutive integers.

1   In this section we look at problems whose solutions require quadratic equations, starting with a problem about area.

EXAMPLE 1   The width of a rectangle is 4 centimeters less than the length. The area is 96 square centimeters. Find the length and width of the rectangle.

Let x represent the length of the rectangle. Then, according to the statement of the problem, the width is $x - 4$ (the width is less than the length). See Figure 4.1. The area of a rectangle is given by the formula

$$\text{area} = LW = \text{length} \times \text{width}.$$

Figure 4.1

Substitute 96 for the area, x for the length, and $x - 4$ for the width into the formula

$$A = LW,$$

getting

$$96 = x(x - 4).$$

Multiply on the right.

$$96 = x^2 - 4x$$

Subtracting 96 from both sides gives the quadratic equation

$$0 = x^2 - 4x - 96.$$

Factor.

$$0 = (x - 12)(x + 8)$$

Place each factor equal to 0.

$$x - 12 = 0 \quad \text{or} \quad x + 8 = 0$$

Solve each equation.

$$x = 12 \quad \text{or} \quad x = -8$$

The solutions of the equations are 12 or -8. Always be careful, however, to check solutions against physical facts. Since a rectangle cannot have a negative length, discard the solution -8. Then 12 centimeters is the length of the rectangle, and $12 - 4 = 8$ centimeters is the width. ●

2 The next word problem involves **perimeter,** the distance around a figure.

EXAMPLE 2 The length of a rectangle is 4 more than the width. The area of the rectangle is numerically 1 more than the perimeter. (See Figure 4.2.) Find the length and width of the rectangle.

Let x be the width of the rectangle. Then the length is $x + 4$. The area is the product of the length and width, or

$$A = LW.$$

area $= (x + 4)x$

perimeter $= 2(x + 4) + 2x$

Figure 4.2

Substitution of $x + 4$ for the length and x for the width gives

$$A = (x + 4)x.$$

Now substitute into the formula for perimeter,

$$P = 2L + 2W.$$

$$P = 2(x + 4) + 2x$$

According to the problem, the area is numerically 1 more than the perimeter.

$$
\begin{array}{ccccc}
\text{area} & \text{is} & 1 & \text{more than} & \text{perimeter} \\
\downarrow & \downarrow\ \downarrow & & \downarrow & \downarrow \\
x(x + 4) & = & 1 & + & 2(x + 4) + 2x
\end{array}
$$

Simplify and solve this equation.

$$
\begin{aligned}
x^2 + 4x &= 1 + 2x + 8 + 2x \\
x^2 + 4x &= 9 + 4x \\
x^2 &= 9 && \text{Subtract } 4x \text{ from both sides} \\
x^2 - 9 &= 0 && \text{Subtract 9 from both sides} \\
(x + 3)(x - 3) &= 0 && \text{Factor}
\end{aligned}
$$

$$
\begin{array}{ccc}
x + 3 = 0 & \text{or} & x - 3 = 0 \\
x = -3 & \text{or} & x = 3
\end{array}
$$

A rectangle cannot have a negative width, so we ignore -3. The only valid solution is 3, so the width is 3 and the length is $3 + 4 = 7$. (Check to see that the area is numerically 1 more than the perimeter.) The rectangle is 3 by 7. ●

3 The next example requires the **Pythagorean formula** from geometry.

Pythagorean Formula

If a right triangle (a triangle with a 90° angle) has longest side of length c and two other sides of length a and b, then

$$a^2 + b^2 = c^2.$$

(See Figure 4.3.)

Figure 4.3

EXAMPLE 3

The longest side of a right triangle is 2 more than the shortest side. The middle side is 1 more than the shortest side. Find the lengths of the sides of the triangle.
Let x be the length of the shortest side. Then

$$
\begin{aligned}
x &= \text{shortest side} \\
x + 1 &= \text{middle side} \\
x + 2 &= \text{longest side.}
\end{aligned}
$$

Place these on a right triangle, as in Figure 4.4.

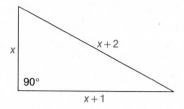

Figure 4.4

Substitute into the Pythagorean formula.

$$a^2 + b^2 = c^2$$
$$x^2 + (x + 1)^2 = (x + 2)^2$$

Since $(x + 1)^2 = x^2 + 2x + 1$, and since $(x + 2)^2 = x^2 + 4x + 4$, the equation becomes

$$x^2 + x^2 + 2x + 1 = x^2 + 4x + 4.$$

Get 0 on one side of the equation.

$$x^2 - 2x - 3 = 0$$

Factor.

$$(x - 3)(x + 1) = 0$$

Place each factor equal to 0.

$$x - 3 = 0 \qquad x + 1 = 0$$
$$x = 3 \qquad x = -1$$

We cannot have -1 as the length of a side of a triangle, so 3 is the only possible answer. The triangle has a shortest side of length 3, a medium side of length $3 + 1 = 4$, and a longest side of length $3 + 2 = 5$. Check that $3^2 + 4^2 = 5^2$. ●

4 **Consecutive integers** are integers that are next to each other, such as 5 and 6, or -11 and -10. **Consecutive odd integers** are odd integers that are next to each other, such as 21 and 23, or -17 and -15. The next example shows how quadratic equations can come up in work with consecutive integers. When working with consecutive integers, the list on page 73 may be helpful.

EXAMPLE 4

The product of two consecutive odd integers is 1 less than five times their sum. Find the integers.

Let s represent the smaller of the two integers. Since the problem mentions consecutive *odd* integers, use $s + 2$ for the larger of the two integers. According to the problem, the product is 1 less than five times the sum.

$$
\begin{array}{cccc}
 & & \text{five} & \\
\text{product} & \text{is} & \text{times sum} & \text{less 1} \\
\downarrow & \downarrow & \downarrow & \downarrow \\
s(s+2) & = & 5(s + s + 2) & -1
\end{array}
$$

Simplify this equation and solve it.

$$s^2 + 2s = 5s + 5s + 10 - 1$$

$$s^2 + 2s = 10s + 9$$

$$s^2 - 8s - 9 = 0 \qquad\qquad \text{Subtract } 10s \text{ and } 9$$

$$(s - 9)(s + 1) = 0 \qquad\qquad \text{Factor}$$

$$s - 9 = 0 \quad \text{or} \quad s + 1 = 0$$

$$s = 9 \quad \text{or} \quad s = -1$$

We need to find two consecutive odd integers.

If $s = 9$ is the first, then $s + 2 = 11$ is the second.

If $s = -1$ is the first, then $s + 2 = 1$ is the second.

Two pairs of integers satisfy the problem: 9 and 11 or −1 and 1.   ●

4.6 EXERCISES

Solve each problem. See Examples 1 and 2.

1. The length of a rectangle is 5 centimeters more than the width. The area is 66 square centimeters. Find the width of the rectangle.

2. The length of a rectangle is 1 foot more than the width. The area is 56 square feet. Find the width of the rectangle.

3. The width of a rectangle is 3 meters less than its length. The area of the rectangle is 70 square meters. Find the length of the rectangle.

4. The width of a rectangle is 7 meters less than its length. The area is 8 square meters. Find the length of the rectangle.

5. The length of a rectangle is twice its width. If the width were increased by 2 inches while the length remained the same, the resulting rectangle would have an area of 48 square inches. Find the width of the original rectangle.

6. The length of a rectangle is three times its width. If the length were decreased by 1 while the width stayed the same, the area of the new figure would be 44 square centimeters. Find the width of the original rectangle.

7. The length of a rectangle is 3 more than the width. The area is numerically 4 less than the perimeter. Find the width of the rectangle.

8. The width of a rectangle is 5 less than the length. The area is numerically 10 more than the perimeter. Find the length of the rectangle.

Exercises 9 and 10 require the formula for the area of a triangle.

$$\text{area} = \frac{1}{2}bh$$

9. The area of a triangle is 25 square centimeters. The base is twice the height. Find the height of the triangle.

10. The height of a triangle is 3 inches more than the base. The area of the triangle is 27 square inches. Find the base of the triangle.

Exercises 11 and 12 require the formula for the volume of a pyramid.

$$V = \frac{1}{3}Bh,\text{ where } B \text{ is the area of the base}$$

11. The volume of a pyramid is 32 cubic meters. Suppose the numerical value of the height is 10 less than the numerical value of the area of the base. Find the area of the base.

12. Suppose a pyramid has a rectangular base whose width is 3 centimeters less than the length. If the height is 8 centimeters and the volume is 144 cubic centimeters, find the length of the base.

Work the following problems.

13. One square has sides 1 foot less than the length of the sides of a second square. If the difference of the areas of the two squares is 37 square feet, find the length of the side of the second square.

14. The sides of one square have a length 2 meters more than the sides of a second square. If the area of the larger square is subtracted from three times the area of the smaller square, the answer is 12 square meters. Find the length of the side of the second square.

15. John wishes to build a box to hold his tools. The box is to be 4 feet high, and the width of the box is to be 1 foot less than the length. The volume of the box will be 120 cubic feet. Find the length of the box. (Hint: The formula for the volume of a box is $V = LWH$.)

L = length
W = width
H = height
$H = 4$
L
$W = L - 1$

16. The volume of a box must be 315 cubic meters. The length of the box is to be 7 meters, and the height is to be 4 meters more than the width. Find the width of the box.

The following exercises require the Pythagorean formula. See Example 3.

17. The longest side of a right triangle is 1 more than the medium side. The shortest side is 7 less than the medium side. Find the length of the medium side of the triangle.

18. The medium side of a right triangle is 1 more than the shortest side. The longest side is 1 less than twice the shortest side. Find the length of the shortest side of the triangle.

19. The longest side of a right triangle is 1 more than twice the shortest side. The medium side is 1 less than twice the shortest side. Find the length of the shortest side of the triangle.

20. If the shortest side of a right triangle is tripled, with 4 added to the result, the result is the longest side. The medium side is 10 more than twice the shortest side. Find the length of the shortest side of the triangle.

Work the following problems. See Example 4.

21. The product of two consecutive integers is 2 more than twice their sum. Find the first integer.

22. The product of two consecutive even integers is 60 more than twice the larger. Find the first integer.

23. Find three consecutive even integers such that four times the sum of all three equals the product of the smaller two.

24. If the square of the sum of two consecutive integers is reduced by three times their product, the result is 31. Find the integers.

25. One number is 4 more than another. The square of the smaller increased by three times the larger is 66. Find the numbers.

26. If the square of the larger of two numbers is reduced by six times the smaller, the result is five times the larger. The larger is twice the smaller. Find the numbers.

27. The sum of three times the square of an integer and twice the integer is 8. Find the integer.

28. When four times an integer is subtracted from twice the square of the integer, the result is 16. Find the integer.

Work the following problems involving formulas.

If an object is dropped, the distance d it falls in t seconds (disregarding air resistance) is given by

$$d = \frac{1}{2}gt^2,$$

where g is approximately 32 feet per second per second. Find the distance an object would fall in

29. 4 seconds;   **30.** 8 seconds.

How long would it take an object to fall

31. 1600 feet?   **32.** 2304 feet?

If an object is projected straight up with an initial velocity of v_0 feet per second, its height h after t seconds is given by

$$h = v_0 t - 16t^2.$$

Suppose an object is thrown upward with an initial velocity of 64 feet per second. Find its height after

33. 1 second;   **34.** 2 seconds;   **35.** 3 seconds.

36. When will the object hit the ground? (Hint: It will hit the ground when $h = 0$.)

Review Exercises   *Decide whether the following inequalities are true or false when x is replaced with -2. See Sections 1.5–1.8.*

37. $x^2 - x + 4 \leq 0$ **38.** $x^2 + 2x - 3 < 0$ **39.** $2x^2 + 3x + 2 > 0$

40. $3x^2 - 5x + 1 < 0$ **41.** $(x - 1)(x^2 + 3x + 7) \leq 0$ **42.** $(x + 3)(x^2 - 5x + 1) \geq 0$

4.7   Solving Quadratic Inequalities   (Optional)

1   Solve quadratic inequalities and graph their solutions.

1   A **quadratic inequality** is an inequality that involves a second-degree polynomial. Examples of quadratic inequalities include

$$2x^2 + 3x - 5 < 0, \qquad x^2 \leq 4, \qquad \text{and} \qquad x^2 + 5x + 6 > 0.$$

Examples 1 and 2 show how to solve such inequalities.

EXAMPLE 1   Solve $x^2 + 5x + 6 > 0$.

To begin, find the solution of the corresponding quadratic equation,

$$x^2 + 5x + 6 = 0.$$

Factor to get

$$(x + 2)(x + 3) = 0,$$

from which

$$x + 2 = 0 \qquad \text{or} \qquad x + 3 = 0$$
$$x = -2 \qquad \text{or} \qquad x = -3.$$

Since -2 and -3 are the only values that satisfy $x^2 + 5x + 6 = 0$, all other values of x will make $x^2 + 5x + 6$ either less than 0 or greater than 0. The values -2 and -3 determine three regions on the number line, as shown in Figure 4.5. Region A includes all numbers less than -3. Region B includes the numbers between -3 and -2, and Region C includes all numbers greater than -2.

Figure 4.5

All the values of x in a given region will make $x^2 + 5x + 6$ positive, or else all the values of x in the given region will make $x^2 + 5x + 6$ negative. We need to test only one value of x from each region to see which regions satisfy $x^2 + 5x + 6 > 0$.

First, are the points in Region A part of the solution? As a trial value, choose any number less than -3, say -4.

$$x^2 + 5x + 6 > 0$$
$$(-4)^2 + 5(-4) + 6 > 0 \qquad \text{Let } x = -4$$
$$16 - 20 + 6 > 0 \qquad \text{Simplify}$$
$$2 > 0 \qquad \text{True}$$

Since $2 > 0$ is true, all the points in Region A belong to the solution of the given inequality.

For Region B, choose a value between -3 and -2, say $-2\ 1/2$, or $-5/2$.

$$\left(-\frac{5}{2}\right)^2 + 5\left(-\frac{5}{2}\right) + 6 > 0 \qquad \text{Let } x = -\frac{5}{2}$$
$$\frac{25}{4} + \left(-\frac{25}{2}\right) + 6 > 0 \qquad \text{Simplify}$$
$$-\frac{1}{4} > 0 \qquad \text{False}$$

Since $-1/4 > 0$ is false, no point in Region B belongs to the solution.

For Region C, try the number 0.

$$0^2 + 5(0) + 6 > 0 \qquad \text{Let } x = 0$$
$$6 > 0 \qquad \text{True}$$

Since $6 > 0$ is true, the points in Region C belong to the solution.

The solution is shown in Figure 4.6. The graph of the quadratic inequality $x^2 + 5x + 6 > 0$ includes all values of x less than -3, and all values of x greater than -2. Write the solution as

$$x < -3 \qquad \text{or} \qquad x > -2. \quad \bullet$$

Figure 4.6

A word of warning: There is no shortcut way to write the solution $x < -3$ or $x > -2$.

EXAMPLE 2 Solve $x^2 - 3x - 10 \leq 0$.

To begin, factor the corresponding equation $x^2 - 3x - 10 = 0$, to get $(x - 5)(x + 2) = 0$. The solutions of the equation are -2 and 5. These points determine three regions on the number line. See Figure 4.7. This time, these points also will belong to the solution, because we want all values of x that make $x^2 - 3x - 10 < 0$ or that make $x^2 - 3x - 10 = 0$.

Figure 4.7

Do the points in Region A belong to the solution? To find out, select any point in Region A, such as -6. Does -6 satisfy the original inequality?

$$x^2 - 3x - 10 \leq 0$$
$$(-6)^2 - 3(-6) - 10 \leq 0 \qquad \text{Let } x = -6$$
$$36 + 18 - 10 \leq 0 \qquad \text{Simplify}$$
$$44 \leq 0 \qquad \text{False}$$

Since $44 \leq 0$ is false, the points in Region A do not belong to the solution. What about Region B? Let us try the value $x = 0$.

$$0^2 - 3(0) - 10 \leq 0 \qquad \text{Let } x = 0$$
$$-10 \leq 0 \qquad \text{True}$$

Since $-10 \leq 0$ is true, the points in Region B do belong to the solution. Try $x = 6$ to check Region C.

$$6^2 - 3(6) - 10 \leq 0 \qquad \text{Let } x = 6$$
$$36 - 18 - 10 \leq 0 \qquad \text{Simplify}$$
$$8 \leq 0 \qquad \text{False}$$

Since $8 \leq 0$ is false, the points in Region C do not belong to the solution.

The points in Region B are the only ones that satisfy $x^2 - 3x - 10 \leq 0$. As shown in Figure 4.8, the solution includes the points in Region B together with the endpoints -2 and 5. The solution is written

$$-2 \leq x \leq 5. \quad \bullet$$

Figure 4.8

4.7 EXERCISES

Solve each inequality and graph the solution. See Examples 1 and 2.

1. $(m + 2)(m - 5) < 0$ **2.** $(k - 1)(k + 3) > 0$ **3.** $(t + 6)(t + 5) \geq 0$

4. $(g - 2)(g - 4) \leq 0$ **5.** $(a + 3)(a - 3) < 0$ **6.** $(b - 2)(b + 2) > 0$

7. $(a + 6)(a - 7) \geq 0$ **8.** $(z - 5)(z - 4) \leq 0$ **9.** $m^2 + 5m + 6 > 0$

10. $y^2 - 3y + 2 < 0$ **11.** $z^2 - 4z - 5 \leq 0$ **12.** $3p^2 - 5p - 2 \leq 0$

13. $5m^2 + 3m - 2 < 0$ **14.** $2k^2 + 7k - 4 > 0$ **15.** $6r^2 - 5r - 4 < 0$

16. $6r^2 + 7r - 3 > 0$ **17.** $a^2 - 16 < 0$ **18.** $9m^2 - 36 > 0$

19. $r^2 - 100 \geq 0$ **20.** $q^2 - 7q + 6 < 0$ **21.** $2k^2 - 7k - 15 \leq 0$

22. $6m^2 + m - 1 > 0$ **23.** $30r^2 + 3r - 6 \leq 0$ **24.** $12p^2 + 11p + 2 < 0$

25. $r^2 > 16$ **26.** $m^2 \geq 25$

The following inequalities are not quadratic inequalities, but they may be solved in a similar manner.

27. $(a + 2)(3a - 1)(a - 4) \geq 0$ **28.** $(2p - 7)(p - 1)(p + 3) \leq 0$

29. $(r - 2)(r^2 - 3r - 4) < 0$ **30.** $(m + 5)(m^2 - m - 6) > 0$

Review Exercises   *Write in lowest terms. See Section 1.1.*

31. $\dfrac{8}{12}$ **32.** $\dfrac{5}{10}$ **33.** $\dfrac{14}{42}$ **34.** $\dfrac{18}{32}$

35. $\dfrac{50}{72}$ **36.** $\dfrac{25}{60}$ **37.** $\dfrac{26}{156}$ **38.** $\dfrac{34}{136}$

Chapter 4   Review Exercises

[4.1] *Find the prime factored form for each number.*

1. 48   **2.** 180   **3.** 600   **4.** 29

Factor out the greatest common factor.

5. $6 - 18r^5 + 12r^3$ **6.** $100y^6 - 50y^3 + 300y^4$

7. $15m^3n^4 - 20m^2n^5 + 50m^3n^6$ **8.** $32y^4r^3 - 48y^5r^2 + 24y^7r^5$

Factor by grouping.

9. $6p^2 + 9p + 4p + 6$ **10.** $4y^2 + 3y + 8y + 6$

11. $15m^2 + 20mp - 12mp - 16p^2$ **12.** $12r^2 + 18rq - 10rq - 15q^2$

[4.2] *Factor completely.*

13. $r^2 - 6r - 27$

14. $p^2 + p - 30$

15. $z^2 - 7z - 44$

16. $z^2 - 11zx + 10x^2$

17. $r^2 - 4rs - 96s^2$

18. $p^2 + 2pq - 120q^2$

19. $y^2 - 8yz + 15z^2$

20. $p^7 - p^6q - 2p^5q^2$

21. $5p^6 - 45p^5 + 70p^4$

[4.3] *Factor completely.*

22. $2k^2 - 5k + 2$

23. $3z^2 + 11z - 4$

24. $6r^2 - 5r - 6$

25. $6m^3 - 21m^2 - 45m$

26. $24k^5 - 20k^4 + 4k^3$

27. $2z^2 + 9zy - 5y^2$

28. $3p^2 - 2pq - 8q^2$

29. $7m^2 + 19mn - 6n^2$

30. $10r^3s + 17r^2s^2 + 6rs^3$

[4.4] *Factor completely.*

31. $100a^2 - 9$

32. $49y^2 - 25z^2$

33. $144p^2 - 36q^2$

34. $y^4 - 625$

35. $m^2 + 9$

36. $9r^2 - 42r + 49$

37. $16m^2 + 40mn + 25n^2$

38. $25a^2 + 15ab + 9b^2$

39. $54x^3 - 72x^2 + 24x$

40. $125r^3 - 216s^3$

41. $343x^3 + 64$

42. $1000t^3 - 27$

[4.5] *Solve each equation.*

43. $r^2 + 3r = 10$

44. $m^2 - 5m + 4 = 0$

45. $k^2 = 8k - 15$

46. $3k^2 - 11k - 20 = 0$

47. $100b^2 - 49 = 0$

48. $p^2 = 12(p - 3)$

49. $(3z - 1)(z^2 + 3z + 2) = 0$

50. $(2p + 3)(p^2 - 4p + 3) = 0$

51. $x^3 - 9x = 0$

[4.6] *Solve each word problem.*

52. The length of a rectangle is 6 meters more than the width. The area is 40 square meters. Find the width of the rectangle.

53. The area of a triangle is 12 square meters. The base is 2 meters longer than the height. Find the height of the triangle.

54. A pyramid has a rectangular base with a length that is 2 meters more than the width. The height of the pyramid is 6 meters, and the volume is 48 cubic meters. Find the width of the base.

55. The product of two consecutive even integers is 4 more than twice their sum. Find the integers.

56. The longest side of a right triangle is 4 more than three times the length of the shortest side. The length of the medium side is 1 less than that of the longest side. Find the length of the shortest side of the triangle.

[4.7] *Solve each inequality.*

57. $(q + 5)(q - 3) > 0$

58. $(2r - 1)(r + 4) \geq 0$

59. $m^2 - 5m + 6 \leq 0$

60. $z^2 - 8z + 15 < 0$

61. $2p^2 + 5p - 12 \geq 0$

62. $(m + 3)(m - 1)(2m + 5) \geq 0$

Chapter 4 Test

Find the prime factored form for each number.

1. 80

2. 675

Factor.

3. $16m^2 - 24m^3 + 32m^4$

4. $28pq + 14p + 56p^2q^3$

5. $m^2 - 9m - 3m + 27$

6. $12 - 6a + 2b - ab$

7. $x^2 - 4x - 45$

8. $3p^4q + 18p^3q - 21p^2q$

9. $3a^2 + 13a - 10$

10. $30z^5 - 69z^4 - 15z^3$

11. $12r^2p^2 + 19rp^2 + 5p^2$

12. $6t^2 - tx - 2x^2$

13. $50m^2 - 98$

14. $144a^2 - 169b^2$

15. $a^4 - 625$

16. $4p^2 + 12p + 9$

17. $25z^2 - 10z + 1$

18. $4y^3 + 16y^2 + 16y$

19. $8p^3 - 125$

20. $27r^3 + 64t^6$

Solve each equation.

21. $3x^2 + 5x = 2$

22. $p(2p + 3) = 20$

23. $(m - 3)(6m^2 - 11m - 10) = 0$

24. $z^3 = 16z$

Solve each word problem.

25. The length of a rectangle is 1 inch less than twice its width. The area is 15 square inches. Find the width of the rectangle.

26. One number is 9 more than another. Their product is 11 more than five times their sum. Find the numbers.

27. The longest side of a right triangle is 7 less than three times the smallest. The middle side is 1 less than twice the smallest. Find the length of the smallest side.

Graph the solution of each inequality.

28. $m^2 + 2m - 24 > 0$

29. $2p^2 + 5p - 3 \leq 0$

30. $6r^2 + r - 2 \geq 0$

5

Rational Expressions

*Equations with rational
expressions are solved to find
the best angles for a hang glider.*

5.1 The Fundamental Property of Rational Expressions

1 Find the values for which a rational expression is meaningless.

2 Find the numerical value of a rational expression.

3 Write rational expressions in lowest terms.

1 The quotient of two integers (with denominator not 0) is called a rational number. In the same way, the quotient of two polynomials is called a **rational expression.** Examples of rational expressions include

$$\frac{-6x}{x^3 + 8}, \qquad \frac{9x}{y + 3}, \qquad \text{and} \qquad \frac{2m^3}{9}.$$

However, $8x/0$ is not a rational expression since division by zero is not possible. For that reason, be careful when substituting a number for a variable in the denominator of a rational expression. For example, in

$$\frac{8x^2}{x - 3}$$

x can take on any value except 3. When $x = 3$, the denominator becomes $3 - 3 = 0$, making the expression meaningless.

EXAMPLE 1   Find any values for which the following rational expressions are meaningless.

(a) $\dfrac{p+5}{p+2}$

Since $p = -2$ will make the denominator equal 0, the expression is meaningless for -2.

(b) $\dfrac{9m^2}{m^2 - 5m + 6}$

To find the numbers that make the denominator 0, solve the equation

$$m^2 - 5m + 6 = 0.$$

Factor the polynomial and set each factor equal to 0.

$$(m - 2)(m - 3) = 0$$

$$m - 2 = 0 \quad \text{or} \quad m - 3 = 0$$

$$m = 2 \quad \text{or} \quad m = 3$$

The original expression is meaningless for 2 and for 3.

(c) $\dfrac{2r}{r^2 + 1}$

This denominator is never equal to 0, so there are no values for which the rational expression is meaningless.   ●

2   The following example shows how to find the numerical value of a rational expression.

EXAMPLE 2   Find the numerical value of $\dfrac{3x + 6}{2x - 4}$ for the given values of x.

(a) $x = 1$

Replace x with 1.

$$\frac{3x + 6}{2x - 4} = \frac{3(1) + 6}{2(1) - 4} \qquad \text{Let } x = 1$$

$$= \frac{9}{-2}$$

$$= -\frac{9}{2}$$

(b) $x = 2$

If we substitute 2 for x, the denominator is 0 and the rational expression is meaningless.   ●

3 A rational expression represents a number for each value of the variable that does not make the denominator 0. For this reason, the properties of rational numbers also apply to rational expressions. The **fundamental property of rational expressions** permits us to write a rational expression in lowest terms.

Fundamental Property of Rational Expressions

> If P/Q is a rational expression and if K represents any rational expression, with $K \neq 0$, then
>
> $$\frac{PK}{QK} = \frac{P}{Q}.$$

This property is based on the identity property of multiplication, since

$$\frac{PK}{QK} = \frac{P}{Q} \cdot \frac{K}{K} = \frac{P}{Q} \cdot 1 = \frac{P}{Q}.$$

In the next example, we show how to write both a rational number and a rational expression in lowest terms. Notice the similarity in the procedures.

EXAMPLE 3

Write in lowest terms.

(a) $\dfrac{30}{72}$ (b) $\dfrac{14k^2}{2k^3}$

Begin by factoring.

$$\frac{30}{72} = \frac{2 \cdot 3 \cdot 5}{2 \cdot 2 \cdot 2 \cdot 3 \cdot 3} \qquad\qquad \frac{14k^2}{2k^3} = \frac{2 \cdot 7 \cdot k \cdot k}{2 \cdot k \cdot k \cdot k}$$

Group any factors common to the numerator and denominator.

$$\frac{30}{72} = \frac{5 \cdot (2 \cdot 3)}{2 \cdot 2 \cdot 3 \cdot (2 \cdot 3)} \qquad\qquad \frac{14k^2}{2k^3} = \frac{7(2 \cdot k \cdot k)}{k(2 \cdot k \cdot k)}$$

Use the fundamental property.

$$\frac{30}{72} = \frac{5}{2 \cdot 2 \cdot 3} = \frac{5}{12} \qquad\qquad \frac{14k^2}{2k^3} = \frac{7}{k} \quad \bullet$$

EXAMPLE 4

Write each rational expression in lowest terms.

(a) $\dfrac{3x - 12}{5x - 20}$

Begin by factoring both numerator and denominator. Then use the fundamental property.

$$\frac{3x - 12}{5x - 20} = \frac{3(x - 4)}{5(x - 4)} = \frac{3}{5}$$

(b) $\dfrac{m^2 + 2m - 8}{2m^2 - m - 6}$

Begin by factoring both numerator and denominator, if possible. Then use the fundamental property.

$$\frac{m^2 + 2m - 8}{2m^2 - m - 6} = \frac{(m + 4)(m - 2)}{(2m + 3)(m - 2)} = \frac{m + 4}{2m + 3} \quad \bullet$$

EXAMPLE 5   Write $\dfrac{x - y}{y - x}$ in lowest terms.

At first glance, there does not seem to be any way in which we can factor $x - y$ and $y - x$ to get a common factor. However,

$$y - x = -1(-y + x) = -1(x - y).$$

With these factors, use the fundamental property to simplify the rational expression.

$$\frac{x - y}{y - x} = \frac{1(x - y)}{-1(x - y)} = \frac{1}{-1} = -1 \quad \bullet$$

As suggested by Example 5,

the quotient of two expressions that are exactly opposite in sign is -1.

EXAMPLE 6   Write each rational expression in lowest terms.

(a) $\dfrac{2 - m}{m - 2}$

Since $2 - m$ and $m - 2$ (or $-2 + m$) are exactly opposite in sign,

$$\frac{2 - m}{m - 2} = -1.$$

(b) $\dfrac{3 + r}{3 - r}$

The quantities $3 + r$ and $3 - r$ are *not* exactly opposite in sign, so this rational expression cannot be written in simpler form. $\bullet$

5.1 EXERCISES

Find any values for which the following expressions are meaningless. See Example 1.

1. $\dfrac{3}{4x}$

2. $\dfrac{5}{2x}$

3. $\dfrac{8}{x - 4}$

4. $\dfrac{6}{x + 3}$

5. $\dfrac{x^2}{x + 5}$

6. $\dfrac{3x^2}{2x - 1}$

7. $\dfrac{a + 4}{a^2 - 8a + 15}$

8. $\dfrac{p + 6}{p^2 - p - 12}$

9. $\dfrac{8r + 2}{2r^2 - r - 3}$

10. $\dfrac{7k + 2}{3k^2 - k - 10}$

11. $\dfrac{9y}{y^2 + 16}$

12. $\dfrac{12z}{z^2 + 100}$

*Find the numerical value of each expression when (a) $x = 2$ and (b) $x = -3$.
See Example 2.*

13. $\dfrac{4x - 2}{3x}$

14. $\dfrac{-5x + 1}{2x}$

15. $\dfrac{4x^2 - 2x}{3x}$

16. $\dfrac{x^2 - 1}{x}$

17. $\dfrac{(-8x)^2}{3x + 9}$

18. $\dfrac{2x^2 + 5}{3 + x}$

19. $\dfrac{x + 8}{x^2 - 4x + 2}$

20. $\dfrac{2x - 1}{x^2 - 7x + 3}$

21. $\dfrac{5x^2}{6 - 3x - x^2}$

22. $\dfrac{-2x^2}{8 + x - x^2}$

23. $\dfrac{2x + 5}{x^2 + 3x - 10}$

24. $\dfrac{3x - 7}{2x^2 - 3x - 2}$

Write each expression in lowest terms. See Examples 3 and 4.

25. $\dfrac{12k^2}{6k}$

26. $\dfrac{9m^3}{3m}$

27. $\dfrac{-8y^6}{6y^3}$

28. $\dfrac{16x^4}{-8x^2}$

29. $\dfrac{12m^2p}{9mp^2}$

30. $\dfrac{6a^2b^3}{24a^3b^2}$

31. $\dfrac{6(y + 2)}{8(y + 2)}$

32. $\dfrac{9(m + 2)}{5(m + 2)}$

33. $\dfrac{(x + 1)(x - 1)}{(x + 1)^2}$

34. $\dfrac{3(t + 5)}{(t + 5)(t - 1)}$

35. $\dfrac{8r - 16}{4}$

36. $\dfrac{9r + 6}{3}$

37. $\dfrac{12m^2 - 9}{3}$

38. $\dfrac{15p^2 - 10}{5}$

39. $\dfrac{32y + 20}{24}$

40. $\dfrac{40q - 25}{20}$

41. $\dfrac{2q - 6}{5q - 10}$

42. $\dfrac{9p + 12}{21p + 28}$

43. $\dfrac{m^2 - n^2}{m + n}$

44. $\dfrac{a^2 - b^2}{a - b}$

45. $\dfrac{5m^2 - 5m}{10m - 10}$

46. $\dfrac{3y^2 - 3y}{2(y - 1)}$

47. $\dfrac{16r^2 - 4s^2}{4r - 2s}$

48. $\dfrac{11s^2 - 22s^3}{6 - 12s}$

49. $\dfrac{m^2 - 4m + 4}{m^2 + m - 6}$

50. $\dfrac{a^2 - a - 6}{a^2 + a - 12}$

51. $\dfrac{x^2 + 3x - 4}{x^2 - 1}$

52. $\dfrac{8m^2 + 6m - 9}{16m^2 - 9}$

Write each expression in lowest terms. See Examples 5 and 6.

53. $\dfrac{m - 5}{5 - m}$

54. $\dfrac{3 - p}{p - 3}$

55. $\dfrac{-a + b}{b - a}$

56. $\dfrac{b - a}{a - b}$

57. $\dfrac{x^2 - 1}{1 - x}$

58. $\dfrac{p^2 - q^2}{q - p}$

59. $\dfrac{m^2 - 4m}{4m - m^2}$

60. $\dfrac{s^2 - r^2}{r^2 - s^2}$

Review Exercises   *Multiply or divide as indicated. See Section 1.1.*

61. $\dfrac{3}{4} \cdot \dfrac{5}{8}$

62. $\dfrac{7}{10} \cdot \dfrac{3}{5}$

63. $\dfrac{8}{15} \cdot \dfrac{20}{3}$

64. $\dfrac{15}{4} \cdot \dfrac{12}{5}$

65. $\dfrac{6}{5} \div \dfrac{3}{10}$

66. $\dfrac{21}{8} \div \dfrac{7}{4}$

67. $\dfrac{27}{8} \div \dfrac{5}{12}$

68. $\dfrac{2}{3} \div \dfrac{4}{9}$

5.2 Multiplication and Division of Rational Expressions

1 Multiply rational expressions.

2 Divide rational expressions.

1 To multiply two fractions, multiply the numerators and multiply the denominators. Rational expressions are multiplied by the same rule.

Multiplying Rational Expressions

> The product of the rational expressions P/Q and R/S is
> $$\frac{P}{Q} \cdot \frac{R}{S} = \frac{PR}{QS}.$$

The next example shows the multiplication of both two rational numbers and two rational expressions. This parallel discussion lets you compare the steps.

EXAMPLE 1 Multiply. Write answers in lowest terms.

(a) $\dfrac{3}{10} \cdot \dfrac{5}{9}$

(b) $\dfrac{6}{x} \cdot \dfrac{x^2}{12}$

Find the product of the numerators and the product of the denominators.

$$\frac{3}{10} \cdot \frac{5}{9} = \frac{3 \cdot 5}{10 \cdot 9} \qquad \qquad \frac{6}{x} \cdot \frac{x^2}{12} = \frac{6 \cdot x^2}{x \cdot 12}$$

Use the fundamental property to write each product in lowest terms.

$$\frac{3}{10} \cdot \frac{5}{9} = \frac{3 \cdot 5}{2 \cdot 5 \cdot 3 \cdot 3} = \frac{1}{6} \qquad \frac{6}{x} \cdot \frac{x^2}{12} = \frac{6 \cdot x \cdot x}{2 \cdot 6 \cdot x} = \frac{x}{2}$$

Notice in the second step above that we do not multiply the factors together, since we want to look for common factors to write the product in lowest terms. ●

EXAMPLE 2 Find the product of $\dfrac{x + y}{2x}$ and $\dfrac{x^2}{(x + y)^2}$.

Use the definition of multiplication.

$$\frac{x + y}{2x} \cdot \frac{x^2}{(x + y)^2} = \frac{(x + y)x^2}{2x(x + y)^2}$$

$$= \frac{(x + y)x \cdot x}{2x(x + y)(x + y)}$$

$$= \frac{x}{2(x + y)}$$

In the last two steps, factor and use the fundamental property of rational expressions to write the product in lowest terms. ●

EXAMPLE 3   Find the product of $\dfrac{x^2 + 3x}{x^2 - 3x - 4}$ and $\dfrac{x^2 - 5x + 4}{x^2 + 2x - 3}$.

First factor the numerators and denominators whenever possible. Then use the fundamental property to write the product in lowest terms.

$$\frac{x^2 + 3x}{x^2 - 3x - 4} \cdot \frac{x^2 - 5x + 4}{x^2 + 2x - 3} = \frac{x(x + 3)}{(x - 4)(x + 1)} \cdot \frac{(x - 4)(x - 1)}{(x + 3)(x - 1)}$$

$$= \frac{x(x + 3)(x - 4)(x - 1)}{(x - 4)(x + 1)(x + 3)(x - 1)}$$

$$= \frac{x}{x + 1} \quad \bullet$$

2   To *divide* the fraction a/b by the nonzero fraction c/d, multiply a/b by the reciprocal of c/d, which is d/c. Division of rational expressions is defined in the same way.

Dividing Rational Expressions

If P/Q and R/S are any two rational expressions, with $R/S \neq 0$, then their quotient is

$$\frac{P}{Q} \div \frac{R}{S} = \frac{P}{Q} \cdot \frac{S}{R} = \frac{PS}{QR}.$$

EXAMPLE 4   Divide: $\dfrac{y}{y + 3} \div \dfrac{y}{y + 5}$.

Multiply the first rational expression and the reciprocal of the second.

$$\frac{y}{y + 3} \div \frac{y}{y + 5} = \frac{y}{y + 3} \cdot \frac{y + 5}{y}$$

$$= \frac{y(y + 5)}{(y + 3)y} = \frac{y + 5}{y + 3}$$

This result cannot be simplified further. $\bullet$

EXAMPLE 5   Divide: $\dfrac{(3m)^2}{(2p)^3} \div \dfrac{6m^3}{16p^2}$.

Use the properties of exponents as necessary.

$$\frac{(3m)^2}{(2p)^3} \div \frac{6m^3}{16p^2} = \frac{9m^2}{8p^3} \div \frac{6m^3}{16p^2}$$

$$= \frac{9m^2}{8p^3} \cdot \frac{16p^2}{6m^3} = \frac{9 \cdot 16m^2p^2}{8 \cdot 6p^3m^3} = \frac{3}{mp} \quad \bullet$$

EXAMPLE 6 Divide: $\dfrac{x^2 - 4}{(x + 3)(x - 2)} \div \dfrac{(x + 2)(x + 3)}{2x}$.

First, use the definition of division.

$$\frac{x^2 - 4}{(x + 3)(x - 2)} \div \frac{(x + 2)(x + 3)}{2x} = \frac{x^2 - 4}{(x + 3)(x - 2)} \cdot \frac{2x}{(x + 2)(x + 3)}$$

Next, be sure all numerators and all denominators are factored.

$$= \frac{(x + 2)(x - 2)}{(x + 3)(x - 2)} \cdot \frac{2x}{(x + 2)(x + 3)}$$

Now multiply numerators and denominators and simplify.

$$= \frac{(x + 2)(x - 2)(2x)}{(x + 3)(x - 2)(x + 2)(x + 3)}$$

$$= \frac{2x}{(x + 3)^2} \quad \bullet$$

EXAMPLE 7 Divide: $\dfrac{m^2 - 4}{m^2 - 1} \div \dfrac{2m^2 + 4m}{1 - m}$.

Use the definition of division.

$$\frac{m^2 - 4}{m^2 - 1} \div \frac{2m^2 + 4m}{1 - m} = \frac{m^2 - 4}{m^2 - 1} \cdot \frac{1 - m}{2m^2 + 4m}$$

$$= \frac{(m + 2)(m - 2)}{(m + 1)(m - 1)} \cdot \frac{1 - m}{2m(m + 2)}$$

Since $\dfrac{1 - m}{m - 1} = -1$,

$$\frac{(m + 2)(m - 2)}{(m + 1)(m - 1)} \cdot \frac{1 - m}{2m(m + 2)} = \frac{-1(m - 2)}{2m(m + 1)} = \frac{2 - m}{2m(m + 1)}. \quad \bullet$$

5.2 EXERCISES

Multiply or divide. Write each answer in lowest terms. See Examples 1 and 5.

1. $\dfrac{9m^2}{16} \cdot \dfrac{4}{3m}$

2. $\dfrac{21z^4}{8} \cdot \dfrac{12}{7z^3}$

3. $\dfrac{4p^2}{8p} \cdot \dfrac{3p^3}{16p^4}$

4. $\dfrac{6x^3}{9x} \cdot \dfrac{12x}{x^2}$

5. $\dfrac{8a^4}{12a^3} \cdot \dfrac{9a^5}{3a^2}$

6. $\dfrac{14p^5}{2p^2} \cdot \dfrac{8p^6}{28p^3}$

7. $\dfrac{3r^2}{9r^3} \div \dfrac{8r^4}{6r^5}$

8. $\dfrac{25m^{10}}{9m^5} \div \dfrac{15m^6}{10m^4}$

9. $\dfrac{3m^2}{(4m)^3} \div \dfrac{9m^3}{32m^4}$

10. $\dfrac{5x^3}{(4x)^2} \div \dfrac{15x^2}{8x^4}$

11. $\dfrac{-6r^4}{3r^5} \div \dfrac{(2r^2)^2}{-4}$

12. $\dfrac{-10a^6}{3a^2} \div \dfrac{(3a)^3}{81a}$

Multiply or divide. Write each answer in lowest terms. See Examples 2–4, 6, and 7.

13. $\dfrac{a + b}{2} \cdot \dfrac{12}{(a + b)^2}$

14. $\dfrac{3(x - 1)}{y} \cdot \dfrac{2y}{5(x - 1)^2}$

15. $\dfrac{2k + 8}{6} \div \dfrac{3k + 12}{2}$

16. $\dfrac{5m + 25}{10} \cdot \dfrac{12}{6m + 30}$

17. $\dfrac{9y - 18}{6y + 12} \cdot \dfrac{3y + 6}{15y - 30}$

18. $\dfrac{12p + 24}{36p - 36} \div \dfrac{6p + 12}{8p - 8}$

19. $\dfrac{3r + 12}{8} \cdot \dfrac{16r}{9r + 36}$

20. $\dfrac{2r + 2p}{8z} \div \dfrac{r^2 + rp}{72}$

21. $\dfrac{y^2 - 16}{y + 3} \div \dfrac{y - 4}{y^2 - 9}$

22. $\dfrac{9(y - 4)^2}{8(z + 3)^2} \cdot \dfrac{16(z + 3)}{3(y - 4)}$

23. $\dfrac{6(m + 2)}{3(m - 1)^2} \div \dfrac{(m + 2)^2}{9(m - 1)}$

24. $\dfrac{4y + 12}{2y - 10} \div \dfrac{y^2 - 9}{y^2 - y - 20}$

25. $\dfrac{2 - y}{8} \cdot \dfrac{7}{y - 2}$

26. $\dfrac{9 - 2z}{3} \cdot \dfrac{9}{2z - 9}$

27. $\dfrac{8 - r}{8 + r} \div \dfrac{r - 8}{r + 8}$

28. $\dfrac{6 - y}{6 + 2y} \div \dfrac{6 + y}{3 + y}$

29. $\dfrac{m^2 - 16}{4 - m} \cdot \dfrac{-4 + m}{-4 - m}$

30. $\dfrac{6r - 18}{3r^2 + 2r - 8} \cdot \dfrac{12r - 16}{4r - 12}$

31. $\dfrac{k^2 - k - 6}{k^2 + k - 12} \div \dfrac{k^2 + 2k - 3}{k^2 + 3k - 4}$

32. $\dfrac{m^2 + 3m + 2}{m^2 + 5m + 4} \cdot \dfrac{m^2 + 10m + 24}{m^2 + 5m + 6}$

33. $\dfrac{z^2 - z - 6}{z^2 - 2z - 8} \cdot \dfrac{z^2 + 7z + 12}{z^2 - 9}$

34. $\dfrac{y^2 + y - 2}{y^2 + 3y - 4} \div \dfrac{y + 2}{y + 3}$

35. $\dfrac{2k^2 + 3k - 2}{6k^2 - 7k + 2} \cdot \dfrac{4k^2 - 5k + 1}{k^2 + k - 2}$

36. $\dfrac{6n^2 - 5n - 6}{6n^2 + 5n - 6} \cdot \dfrac{12n^2 - 17n + 6}{12n^2 - n - 6}$

37. $\dfrac{2m^2 - 5m - 12}{m^2 - 10m + 24} \div \dfrac{4m^2 - 9}{m^2 - 9m + 18}$

38. $\dfrac{2m^2 + 7m + 3}{m^2 - 9} \cdot \dfrac{m^2 - 3m}{2m^2 + 11m + 5}$

39. $\dfrac{m^2 + 2mp - 3p^2}{m^2 - 3mp + 2p^2} \div \dfrac{m^2 + 4mp + 3p^2}{m^2 + 2mp - 8p^2}$

40. $\dfrac{r^2 + rs - 12s^2}{r^2 - rs - 20s^2} \div \dfrac{r^2 - 2rs - 3s^2}{r^2 + rs - 30s^2}$

41. $\dfrac{(x + 1)^3(x + 4)}{x^2 + 5x + 4} \div \dfrac{x^2 + 2x + 1}{x^2 + 3x + 2}$

42. $\dfrac{(q - 3)^4(q + 2)}{q^2 + 3q + 2} \div \dfrac{q^2 - 6q + 9}{q^2 + 4q + 4}$

43. $\left(\dfrac{x^2 + 10x + 25}{x^2 + 10x} \cdot \dfrac{10x}{x^2 + 15x + 50} \right) \div \dfrac{x + 5}{x + 10}$

44. $\left(\dfrac{m^2 - 12m + 32}{8m} \cdot \dfrac{m^2 - 8m}{m^2 - 8m + 16} \right) \div \dfrac{m - 8}{m - 4}$

Review Exercises   *Write the prime factored form of each number. See Section 4.1.*

45. 12

46. 50

47. 72

48. 105

Factor. See Sections 4.2 and 4.3.

49. $x^2 - 4x$

50. $p^2 + 6p$

51. $2y^2 + 5y - 3$

52. $8z^2 + 2z - 15$

5.3 The Least Common Denominator

■ Find least common denominators.

② Write rational expressions with given denominators.

■ Just as with rational numbers, to add and subtract rational expressions (in the next section), we often need to find least common denominators. A **least common denominator** is the least expression that all denominators divide into without a remainder. For example, the least common denominator for 2/9 and 5/12 is 36, since 36 is the smallest number that both 9 and 12 divide into. Least common denominators are found by a procedure similar to that used in Chapter 4 for finding the greatest common factor, except that

least common denominators are found by multiplying together each different factor the *greatest* number of times it appears in any denominator.

In Example 1, we find the least common denominator both for numerical denominators and algebraic denominators.

EXAMPLE 1   Find the least common denominator.

(a) $\dfrac{1}{24}, \dfrac{7}{15}$

(b) $\dfrac{1}{8x}, \dfrac{3}{10x}$

Write each denominator in factored form, with numerical coefficients in prime factored form.

$$24 = 2 \cdot 2 \cdot 2 \cdot 3$$
$$15 = 3 \cdot 5$$

$$8x = 2 \cdot 2 \cdot 2 \cdot x$$
$$10x = 2 \cdot 5 \cdot x$$

The least common denominator is found by taking each different factor the greatest number of times it appears as a factor in any of the denominators.

The factor 2 appears three times in one product and not at all in the other, so the greatest number of times 2 appears is three. The greatest number of times both 3 and 5 appear is one, so

least common denominator
$$= 2 \cdot 2 \cdot 2 \cdot 3 \cdot 5 = 120.$$

Here 2 appears three times in one product and once in the other, so the greatest number of times the 2 appears is three. The greatest number of times the 5 appears is one, and the greatest number of times x appears in either product is one. Thus,

least common denominator
$$= 2 \cdot 2 \cdot 2 \cdot 5 \cdot x = 40x. \quad \bullet$$

EXAMPLE 2   Find the least common denominator for $\dfrac{5}{6r^2}$ and $\dfrac{3}{4r^3}$.

Factor each denominator.

$$6r^2 = 2 \cdot 3 \cdot r^2 \qquad 4r^3 = 2 \cdot 2 \cdot r^3$$

The greatest number of times 2 appears is two, the greatest number of times 3 appears is one, and the greatest number of times r appears is three; therefore,

$$\text{least common denominator} = 2 \cdot 2 \cdot 3 \cdot r^3 = 12r^3. \quad \bullet$$

EXAMPLE 3   Find the least common denominator.

(a) $\dfrac{6}{5m}, \dfrac{4}{m^2 - 3m}$

Factor each denominator.

$$5m = 5 \cdot m \qquad m^2 - 3m = m(m - 3)$$

Take each different factor the greatest number of times it appears as a factor.

$$\text{least common denominator} = 5 \cdot m \cdot (m - 3) = 5m(m - 3)$$

Since m is *not* a factor of $m - 3$, both factors, m and $m - 3$, must appear in the least common denominator.

(b) $\dfrac{1}{r^2 - 4r - 5}, \dfrac{3}{r^2 - r - 20}$

Factor each denominator.

$$r^2 - 4r - 5 \; = (r - 5)(r + 1)$$
$$r^2 - \; r - 20 = (r - 5)(r + 4)$$

The least common denominator is

$$(r - 5)(r + 1)(r + 4).$$

(c) $\dfrac{1}{q - 5}, \dfrac{3}{5 - q}$

The expression $5 - q$ can be written as $-1(q - 5)$, since

$$-1(q - 5) = -q + 5 = 5 - q.$$

Because of this, either $q - 5$ or $5 - q$ can be used as the least common denominator. $\bullet$

Let us now summarize the steps in finding a least common denominator.

Finding the Least Common Denominator

Step 1   Completely factor all denominators.

Step 2   Take each different factor the *greatest* number of times that it appears as a factor in any of the denominators.

Step 3   The least common denominator is the product of all factors to the greatest power found in Step 2.

2   Once the least common denominator has been found, we can use the fundamental property to rewrite rational expressions with the least common denominator. The next example shows how to do this.

EXAMPLE 4   Rewrite each rational expression with the indicated denominator.

(a) $\dfrac{9k}{25} = \dfrac{}{50k}$

The given rational expression has a denominator of 25. To get a denominator of $50k$, multiply both numerator and denominator by $2k$.

$$\frac{9k}{25} = \frac{9k(2k)}{25(2k)} = \frac{18k^2}{50k}$$

(b) $\dfrac{12p}{p^2 + 8p} = \dfrac{}{p(p + 8)(p - 4)}$

Factor $p^2 + 8p$ as $p(p + 8)$. This shows that we must multiply by $p - 4$.

$$\frac{12p}{p^2 + 8p} = \frac{12p}{p(p + 8)} \cdot \frac{p - 4}{p - 4} = \frac{12p(p - 4)}{p(p + 8)(p - 4)}$$ ●

5.3 EXERCISES

Find the least common denominator for the following fractions. See Examples 1–3.

1. $\dfrac{5}{12}, \dfrac{7}{10}$

2. $\dfrac{1}{4}, \dfrac{5}{6}$

3. $\dfrac{7}{15}, \dfrac{11}{20}, \dfrac{5}{24}$

4. $\dfrac{9}{10}, \dfrac{12}{25}, \dfrac{11}{35}$

5. $\dfrac{17}{100}, \dfrac{13}{120}, \dfrac{29}{180}$

6. $\dfrac{17}{250}, \dfrac{1}{300}, \dfrac{127}{360}$

7. $\dfrac{9}{x^2}, \dfrac{8}{x^5}$

8. $\dfrac{2}{m^7}, \dfrac{3}{m^8}$

9. $\dfrac{2}{5p}, \dfrac{5}{6p}$

10. $\dfrac{4}{15k}, \dfrac{3}{4k}$

11. $\dfrac{2}{25m}, \dfrac{17}{30m}$

12. $\dfrac{9}{40a}, \dfrac{11}{60a}$

13. $\dfrac{7}{15y^2}, \dfrac{5}{36y^4}$

14. $\dfrac{4}{25m^3}, \dfrac{7}{10m^4}$

15. $\dfrac{3}{50r^5}, \dfrac{7}{60r^3}$

16. $\dfrac{9}{25a^5}, \dfrac{17}{80a^6}$

17. $\dfrac{1}{5a^2b^3}, \dfrac{2}{15a^5b}$

18. $\dfrac{7}{3r^4s^5}, \dfrac{2}{9r^6s^8}$

19. $\dfrac{7}{6p}, \dfrac{3}{4p - 8}$

20. $\dfrac{7}{8k}, \dfrac{13}{12k - 24}$

21. $\dfrac{5}{32r^2}, \dfrac{9}{16r - 32}$

22. $\dfrac{13}{18m^3}, \dfrac{8}{9m - 36}$

23. $\dfrac{7}{6r - 12}, \dfrac{4}{9r - 18}$

24. $\dfrac{4}{5p - 30}, \dfrac{5}{6p - 36}$

25. $\dfrac{5}{12p + 60}, \dfrac{1}{p^2 + 5p}$

26. $\dfrac{1}{r^2 + 7r}, \dfrac{3}{5r + 35}$

27. $\dfrac{3}{8y + 16}, \dfrac{2}{y^2 + 3y + 2}$

28. $\dfrac{2}{9m - 18}, \dfrac{9}{m^2 - 7m + 10}$

29. $\dfrac{2}{m - 3}, \dfrac{4}{3 - m}$

30. $\dfrac{7}{8 - a}, \dfrac{2}{a - 8}$

31. $\dfrac{9}{p - q}, \dfrac{3}{q - p}$

32. $\dfrac{4}{z - x}, \dfrac{8}{x - z}$

33. $\dfrac{6}{a^2 + 6a}, \dfrac{4}{a^2 + 3a - 18}$

34. $\dfrac{3}{y^2 - 5y}, \dfrac{2}{y^2 - 2y - 15}$

35. $\dfrac{5}{k^2 + 2k - 35}, \dfrac{3}{k^2 + 3k - 40}$

36. $\dfrac{9}{z^2 + 4z - 12}, \dfrac{1}{z^2 + z - 30}$

37. $\dfrac{3}{2y^2 + 7y - 4}, \dfrac{7}{2y^2 - 7y + 3}$

38. $\dfrac{2}{5a^2 + 13a - 6}, \dfrac{6}{5a^2 - 22a + 8}$

39. $\dfrac{1}{6r^2 - r - 15}, \dfrac{4}{3r^2 - 8r + 5}$

40. $\dfrac{8}{2m^2 - 11m + 14}, \dfrac{2}{2m^2 - m - 21}$

Rewrite each rational expression with the given denominator. See Example 4.

41. $\dfrac{7}{11} = \dfrac{}{66}$

42. $\dfrac{5}{8} = \dfrac{}{56}$

43. $\dfrac{9}{r} = \dfrac{}{6r}$

44. $\dfrac{7}{k} = \dfrac{}{9k}$

45. $\dfrac{-11}{m} = \dfrac{}{8m}$

46. $\dfrac{-5}{z} = \dfrac{}{6z}$

47. $\dfrac{12}{35y} = \dfrac{}{70y^3}$

48. $\dfrac{17}{9r} = \dfrac{}{36r^2}$

49. $\dfrac{15m^2}{8k} = \dfrac{}{32k^4}$

50. $\dfrac{5t^2}{3y} = \dfrac{}{9y^2}$

51. $\dfrac{19z}{2z - 6} = \dfrac{}{6z - 18}$

52. $\dfrac{2r}{5r - 5} = \dfrac{}{15r - 15}$

53. $\dfrac{-2a}{9a - 18} = \dfrac{}{18a - 36}$

54. $\dfrac{-5y}{6y + 18} = \dfrac{}{24y + 72}$

55. $\dfrac{6}{k^2 - 4k} = \dfrac{}{k(k - 4)(k + 1)}$

56. $\dfrac{15}{m^2 - 9m} = \dfrac{}{m(m - 9)(m + 8)}$

57. $\dfrac{36r}{r^2 - r - 6} = \dfrac{}{(r - 3)(r + 2)(r + 1)}$

58. $\dfrac{4m}{m^2 - 8m + 15} = \dfrac{}{(m - 5)(m - 3)(m + 2)}$

Review Exercises   *Add or subtract as indicated. See Section 1.1.*

59. $\dfrac{2}{3} + \dfrac{5}{3}$

60. $\dfrac{9}{5} + \dfrac{2}{5}$

61. $\dfrac{1}{2} + \dfrac{2}{5}$

62. $\dfrac{5}{4} + \dfrac{1}{3}$

63. $\dfrac{8}{10} - \dfrac{2}{15}$

64. $\dfrac{7}{12} - \dfrac{6}{15}$

65. $\dfrac{5}{24} + \dfrac{1}{18}$

66. $\dfrac{11}{36} + \dfrac{7}{45}$

5.4 Addition and Subtraction of Rational Expressions

1. Add rational expressions having the same denominator.
2. Add rational expressions having different denominators.
3. Subtract rational expressions.

1. To find the sum of two rational expressions, use a procedure similar to that for adding two fractions.

Adding Rational Expressions

If P/Q and R/Q are rational expressions, then

$$\frac{P}{Q} + \frac{R}{Q} = \frac{P+R}{Q}.$$

Again, the first example shows how the addition of rational expressions compares with that of rational numbers.

EXAMPLE 1 Add.

(a) $\dfrac{4}{7} + \dfrac{2}{7}$ (b) $\dfrac{3x}{x+1} + \dfrac{2x}{x+1}$

Since the denominators are the same, the sum is found by adding the two numerators and keeping the same (common) denominator.

$$\frac{4}{7} + \frac{2}{7} = \frac{4+2}{7}$$

$$= \frac{6}{7}$$

$$\frac{3x}{x+1} + \frac{2x}{x+1} = \frac{3x+2x}{x+1}$$

$$= \frac{5x}{x+1} \qquad \bullet$$

2. To add two rational expressions with different denominators, use the steps given below. These are the same steps that are used to add fractions with different denominators.

Adding with Different Denominators

Step 1 Find the least common denominator.

Step 2 Rewrite each rational expression as a fraction with the least common denominator as the denominator.

Step 3 Add the numerators to get the numerator of the sum. The least common denominator is the denominator of the sum.

EXAMPLE 2   Add.

(a) $\dfrac{1}{12} + \dfrac{7}{15}$ (b) $\dfrac{2}{3y} + \dfrac{1}{4y}$

First find the least common denominator, using the methods of the last section.

least common denominator   least common denominator
$= 2^2 \cdot 3 \cdot 5 = 60$ $= 2^2 \cdot 3 \cdot y = 12y$

Now rewrite each rational expression as a fraction with the least common denominator, either 60 or 12y, as the denominator.

$\dfrac{1}{12} + \dfrac{7}{15} = \dfrac{1(5)}{12(5)} + \dfrac{7(4)}{15(4)}$ $\dfrac{2}{3y} + \dfrac{1}{4y} = \dfrac{2(4)}{3y(4)} + \dfrac{1(3)}{4y(3)}$

$= \dfrac{5}{60} + \dfrac{28}{60}$ $= \dfrac{8}{12y} + \dfrac{3}{12y}$

Since the fractions now have common denominators, add the numerators. (Write in lowest terms if necessary.)

$\dfrac{5}{60} + \dfrac{28}{60} = \dfrac{5 + 28}{60}$ $\dfrac{8}{12y} + \dfrac{3}{12y} = \dfrac{8 + 3}{12y}$

$= \dfrac{33}{60} = \dfrac{11}{20}$ $= \dfrac{11}{12y}$ ●

EXAMPLE 3   Add $\dfrac{x}{x^2 - 1}$ and $\dfrac{x}{x + 1}$.

To find the least common denominator, factor both denominators.

$$x^2 - 1 = (x + 1)(x - 1) \qquad x + 1 \text{ cannot be factored}$$

Our sum now is written

$$\frac{x}{(x + 1)(x - 1)} + \frac{x}{x + 1}.$$

The least common denominator is $(x + 1)(x - 1)$. Here only the second fraction must be changed. Multiply the numerator and denominator of the second fraction by $x - 1$.

$$\frac{x}{(x + 1)(x - 1)} + \frac{x(x - 1)}{(x + 1)(x - 1)}$$

With both denominators now the same, add the numerators.

$$\frac{x + x(x - 1)}{(x + 1)(x - 1)} = \frac{x + x^2 - x}{(x + 1)(x - 1)} = \frac{x^2}{(x + 1)(x - 1)} \quad ●$$

EXAMPLE 4   Add $\dfrac{2x}{x^2 + 5x + 6}$ and $\dfrac{x + 1}{x^2 + 2x - 3}$.

To begin, factor the denominators completely.

$$\frac{2x}{(x + 2)(x + 3)} + \frac{x + 1}{(x + 3)(x - 1)}$$

The least common denominator is $(x + 2)(x + 3)(x - 1)$. By the fundamental property of rational expressions,

$$\frac{2x}{(x + 2)(x + 3)} + \frac{x + 1}{(x + 3)(x - 1)}$$

$$= \frac{2x(x - 1)}{(x + 2)(x + 3)(x - 1)} + \frac{(x + 1)(x + 2)}{(x + 3)(x - 1)(x + 2)}.$$

Since the two rational expressions above have the same denominator, add their numerators.

$$\frac{2x(x - 1)}{(x + 2)(x + 3)(x - 1)} + \frac{(x + 1)(x + 2)}{(x + 3)(x - 1)(x + 2)}$$

$$= \frac{2x(x - 1) + (x + 1)(x + 2)}{(x + 2)(x + 3)(x - 1)}$$

$$= \frac{2x^2 - 2x + x^2 + 3x + 2}{(x + 2)(x + 3)(x - 1)}$$

$$= \frac{3x^2 + x + 2}{(x + 2)(x + 3)(x - 1)}$$

Here it is convenient to leave the denominator in factored form.   ●

3   To *subtract* rational expressions, use the following rule.

Subtracting Rational Expressions

If P/Q and R/Q are rational expressions, then

$$\frac{P}{Q} - \frac{R}{Q} = \frac{P - R}{Q}.$$

EXAMPLE 5   Find $\dfrac{12}{m^2} - \dfrac{8}{m^2}$.

By the definition of subtraction,

$$\frac{12}{m^2} - \frac{8}{m^2} = \frac{12 - 8}{m^2} = \frac{4}{m^2}.$$ ●

EXAMPLE 6   Find $\dfrac{9}{x-2} - \dfrac{3}{x}$.

The least common denominator is $x(x-2)$.

$$\frac{9}{x-2} - \frac{3}{x} = \frac{9x}{x(x-2)} - \frac{3(x-2)}{x(x-2)}$$

$$= \frac{9x - 3(x-2)}{x(x-2)} = \frac{9x - 3x + 6}{x(x-2)} = \frac{6x + 6}{x(x-2)} \quad \bullet$$

EXAMPLE 7   Find $\dfrac{q}{q^2 - 4q - 5} - \dfrac{3}{2q^2 - 13q + 15}$.

Start by factoring each denominator.

$$\frac{q}{q^2 - 4q - 5} - \frac{3}{2q^2 - 13q + 15} = \frac{q}{(q+1)(q-5)} - \frac{3}{(q-5)(2q-3)}$$

Now rewrite each of the two rational expressions with the least common denominator, which is $(q+1)(q-5)(2q-3)$. Then subtract numerators.

$$\frac{q}{(q+1)(q-5)} - \frac{3}{(q-5)(2q-3)}$$

$$= \frac{q(2q-3)}{(q+1)(q-5)(2q-3)} - \frac{3(q+1)}{(q+1)(q-5)(2q-3)}$$

$$= \frac{q(2q-3) - 3(q+1)}{(q+1)(q-5)(2q-3)}$$

$$= \frac{2q^2 - 3q - 3q - 3}{(q+1)(q-5)(2q-3)}$$

$$= \frac{2q^2 - 6q - 3}{(q+1)(q-5)(2q-3)} \quad \bullet$$

5.4 EXERCISES

Find the sums or differences. Write the answers in lowest terms. See Examples 1 and 5.

1. $\dfrac{2}{p} + \dfrac{5}{p}$

2. $\dfrac{3}{r} + \dfrac{6}{r}$

3. $\dfrac{9}{k} - \dfrac{12}{k}$

4. $\dfrac{15}{z} - \dfrac{25}{z}$

5. $\dfrac{y}{y+1} + \dfrac{1}{y+1}$

6. $\dfrac{3m}{m-4} + \dfrac{-12}{m-4}$

7. $\dfrac{p-q}{3} - \dfrac{p+q}{3}$

8. $\dfrac{a+b}{2} - \dfrac{a-b}{2}$

9. $\dfrac{m^2}{m+6} + \dfrac{6m}{m+6}$

10. $\dfrac{y^2}{y-1} + \dfrac{-y}{y-1}$

11. $\dfrac{q^2 - 4q}{q-2} + \dfrac{4}{q-2}$

12. $\dfrac{z^2 - 10z}{z-5} + \dfrac{25}{z-5}$

Find the sums or differences. See Examples 2–4, 6, and 7.

13. $\dfrac{m}{3} + \dfrac{1}{2}$

14. $\dfrac{p}{6} - \dfrac{2}{3}$

15. $\dfrac{7}{5} - \dfrac{z}{4}$

16. $\dfrac{9}{10} - \dfrac{r}{2}$

17. $\dfrac{4}{3} - \dfrac{1}{y}$

18. $\dfrac{8}{5} - \dfrac{2}{a}$

19. $\dfrac{5m}{6} - \dfrac{2m}{3}$

20. $\dfrac{3}{x} + \dfrac{5}{2x}$

21. $\dfrac{4 + 2k}{5} + \dfrac{2 + k}{10}$

22. $\dfrac{5 - 4r}{8} - \dfrac{2 - 3r}{6}$

23. $\dfrac{3m + 5}{3} - \dfrac{m + 2}{6}$

24. $\dfrac{5r + 4}{3} - \dfrac{2r - 3}{9}$

25. $\dfrac{m + 2}{m} + \dfrac{m + 3}{4m}$

26. $\dfrac{2x - 5}{x} + \dfrac{x - 1}{2x}$

27. $\dfrac{6}{y^2} - \dfrac{2}{y}$

28. $\dfrac{3}{p} + \dfrac{5}{p^2}$

29. $\dfrac{9}{2p} - \dfrac{4}{p^2}$

30. $\dfrac{15}{4k^2} - \dfrac{3}{k}$

31. $\dfrac{-1}{x^2} + \dfrac{3}{xy}$

32. $\dfrac{9}{p^2} + \dfrac{4}{px}$

33. $\dfrac{8}{x - 2} - \dfrac{4}{x + 2}$

34. $\dfrac{6}{m - 5} - \dfrac{2}{m + 5}$

35. $\dfrac{2x}{x + y} - \dfrac{3x}{2x + 2y}$

36. $\dfrac{1}{a - b} - \dfrac{a}{4a - 4b}$

37. $\dfrac{1}{m^2 - 9} + \dfrac{1}{3m + 9}$

38. $\dfrac{-6}{y^2 - 4} - \dfrac{3}{2y + 4}$

39. $\dfrac{1}{m^2 - 1} - \dfrac{1}{m^2 + 3m + 2}$

40. $\dfrac{1}{y^2 - 4} + \dfrac{3}{y^2 + 5y + 6}$

41. $\dfrac{4}{2 - q} + \dfrac{7}{q - 2}$

42. $\dfrac{9}{8 - y} + \dfrac{6}{y - 8}$

43. $\dfrac{3}{4p - 5} + \dfrac{9}{5 - 4p}$

44. $\dfrac{8}{3 - 7y} - \dfrac{2}{7y - 3}$

45. $\dfrac{8}{m - 2} + \dfrac{3}{5m} + \dfrac{7}{5m(m - 2)}$

46. $\dfrac{-1}{7z} + \dfrac{3}{z + 2} + \dfrac{4}{7z(z + 2)}$

47. $\dfrac{4}{r^2 - r} + \dfrac{6}{r^2 + 2r} - \dfrac{1}{r^2 + r - 2}$

48. $\dfrac{6}{k^2 + 3k} - \dfrac{1}{k^2 - k} + \dfrac{2}{k^2 + 2k - 3}$

49. $\dfrac{k - 1}{k^2 + 2k - 8} + \dfrac{3k - 2}{k^2 + 3k - 4}$

50. $\dfrac{r + 1}{r^2 - 3r - 10} + \dfrac{r - 1}{r^2 + r - 30}$

51. $\dfrac{4y - 1}{2y^2 + 5y - 3} - \dfrac{y + 3}{6y^2 + y - 2}$

52. $\dfrac{2q + 1}{3q^2 + 10q - 8} - \dfrac{3q + 5}{2q^2 + 5q - 12}$

53. $\dfrac{x + 3y}{x^2 + 2xy + y^2} + \dfrac{x - y}{x^2 + 4xy + 3y^2}$

54. $\dfrac{m}{m^2 - 1} + \dfrac{m - 1}{m^2 + 2m + 1}$

Review Exercises *Simplify each expression, using the order of operations as necessary. See Sections 1.1 and 1.3.*

55. $\dfrac{\dfrac{2}{3} + \dfrac{5}{3}}{\dfrac{3}{4} - \dfrac{1}{4}}$

56. $\dfrac{\dfrac{5}{8} - \dfrac{3}{8}}{\dfrac{2}{5} + \dfrac{1}{5}}$

57. $\dfrac{\dfrac{5}{6} - \dfrac{2}{3}}{\dfrac{3}{4} + \dfrac{1}{12}}$

58. $\dfrac{\dfrac{9}{7} - \dfrac{3}{14}}{\dfrac{1}{3} + \dfrac{5}{12}}$

5.5   Complex Fractions

Simplify complex fractions by:

1 simplifying numerator and denominator;

2 multiplying by the least common denominator.

A rational expression with fractions in the numerator, denominator, or both, is called a **complex fraction.** Examples of complex fractions include

$$\frac{3 + \dfrac{4}{x}}{5}, \qquad \frac{\dfrac{3x^2 - 5x}{6x^2}}{2x - \dfrac{1}{x}}, \qquad \text{and} \qquad \frac{3 + x}{5 - \dfrac{2}{x}}.$$

The parts of a complex fraction are named as follows.

$$\frac{\dfrac{2}{p} - \dfrac{1}{q}}{\dfrac{3}{p} + \dfrac{5}{q}} \quad \begin{array}{l} \leftarrow \text{Numerator of complex fraction} \\ \leftarrow \text{Main fraction bar} \\ \leftarrow \text{Denominator of complex fraction} \end{array}$$

1   Since a fraction represents a quotient, one method of simplifying complex fractions is to rewrite both the numerator and denominator as single fractions, and then to perform the indicated division.

EXAMPLE 1   Simplify each complex fraction.

(a) $\dfrac{\dfrac{2}{3} + \dfrac{5}{9}}{\dfrac{1}{4} + \dfrac{1}{12}}$

(b) $\dfrac{6 + \dfrac{3}{x}}{\dfrac{x}{4} + \dfrac{1}{8}}$

First, write each numerator as a single fraction.

$$\frac{2}{3} + \frac{5}{9} = \frac{2(3)}{3(3)} + \frac{5}{9}$$

$$= \frac{6}{9} + \frac{5}{9} = \frac{11}{9}$$

$$6 + \frac{3}{x} = \frac{6}{1} + \frac{3}{x}$$

$$= \frac{6x}{x} + \frac{3}{x} = \frac{6x + 3}{x}$$

Do the same thing with each denominator.

$$\frac{1}{4} + \frac{1}{12} = \frac{1(3)}{4(3)} + \frac{1}{12}$$

$$= \frac{3}{12} + \frac{1}{12} = \frac{4}{12}$$

$$\frac{x}{4} + \frac{1}{8} = \frac{x(2)}{4(2)} + \frac{1}{8}$$

$$= \frac{2x}{8} + \frac{1}{8} = \frac{2x + 1}{8}$$

The original complex fraction can now be written as

$$\frac{\dfrac{11}{9}}{\dfrac{4}{12}},$$

$$\frac{\dfrac{6x + 3}{x}}{\dfrac{2x + 1}{8}}.$$

Now use the rule for division and the fundamental property.

$$\frac{11}{9} \div \frac{4}{12} = \frac{11}{9} \cdot \frac{12}{4}$$

$$= \frac{132}{36}$$

$$= \frac{11}{3}$$

$$\frac{6x + 3}{x} \div \frac{2x + 1}{8} = \frac{6x + 3}{x} \cdot \frac{8}{2x + 1}$$

$$= \frac{3(2x + 1)}{x} \cdot \frac{8}{2x + 1}$$

$$= \frac{24}{x} \quad \bullet$$

EXAMPLE 2 Simplify the complex fraction $\dfrac{\dfrac{xp}{q^3}}{\dfrac{p^2}{qx^2}}$.

Here, the numerator and denominator are already single fractions, so use the division rule and then the fundamental property.

$$\frac{xp}{q^3} \div \frac{p^2}{qx^2} = \frac{xp}{q^3} \cdot \frac{qx^2}{p^2} = \frac{x^3}{q^2 p} \quad \bullet$$

EXAMPLE 3 Simplify the complex fraction $\dfrac{\dfrac{x}{x + y}}{\dfrac{1}{x} + \dfrac{1}{y}}$.

Since the numerator is already a single fraction, it is only necessary to simplify the denominator. Do this by adding $1/x$ and $1/y$.

$$\frac{1}{x} + \frac{1}{y} = \frac{y}{xy} + \frac{x}{xy} = \frac{x + y}{xy}$$

Now divide.

$$\frac{x}{x + y} \div \frac{x + y}{xy} = \frac{x}{x + y} \cdot \frac{xy}{x + y} = \frac{x^2 y}{(x + y)^2} \quad \bullet$$

2 Alternatively, complex fractions may be simplified by multiplying both numerator and denominator by the least common denominator of all the denominators appearing in the complex fraction.

In the next example, we use this second method to simplify the same complex fractions as in Example 1 above.

EXAMPLE 4   Simplify each complex fraction.

(a) $\dfrac{\dfrac{2}{3} + \dfrac{5}{9}}{\dfrac{1}{4} + \dfrac{1}{12}}$

(b) $\dfrac{6 + \dfrac{3}{x}}{\dfrac{x}{4} + \dfrac{1}{8}}$

Find the least common denominator for all the denominators in the complex fraction.

The least common denominator for 3, 9, 4, and 12 is 36.

The least common denominator for x, 4, and 8 is $8x$.

Multiply numerator and denominator of the complex fraction by the least common denominator.

$$\frac{\dfrac{2}{3} + \dfrac{5}{9}}{\dfrac{1}{4} + \dfrac{1}{12}} = \frac{36\left(\dfrac{2}{3} + \dfrac{5}{9}\right)}{36\left(\dfrac{1}{4} + \dfrac{1}{12}\right)}$$

$$= \frac{36\left(\dfrac{2}{3}\right) + 36\left(\dfrac{5}{9}\right)}{36\left(\dfrac{1}{4}\right) + 36\left(\dfrac{1}{12}\right)}$$

$$= \frac{24 + 20}{9 + 3}$$

$$= \frac{44}{12} = \frac{11}{3}$$

$$\frac{6 + \dfrac{3}{x}}{\dfrac{x}{4} + \dfrac{1}{8}} = \frac{8x\left(6 + \dfrac{3}{x}\right)}{8x\left(\dfrac{x}{4} + \dfrac{1}{8}\right)}$$

$$= \frac{8x(6) + 8x\left(\dfrac{3}{x}\right)}{8x\left(\dfrac{x}{4}\right) + 8x\left(\dfrac{1}{8}\right)}$$

$$= \frac{48x + 24}{2x^2 + x}$$

$$= \frac{24(2x + 1)}{x(2x + 1)} = \frac{24}{x} \quad \bullet$$

EXAMPLE 5 Simplify the complex fraction $\dfrac{\dfrac{3}{5m} - \dfrac{2}{m^2}}{\dfrac{9}{2m} + \dfrac{3}{4m^2}}$.

The least common denominator for $5m$, m^2, $2m$, and $4m^2$ is $20m^2$. Multiply numerator and denominator by $20m^2$.

$$\frac{\dfrac{3}{5m} - \dfrac{2}{m^2}}{\dfrac{9}{2m} + \dfrac{3}{4m^2}} = \frac{20m^2\left(\dfrac{3}{5m} - \dfrac{2}{m^2}\right)}{20m^2\left(\dfrac{9}{2m} + \dfrac{3}{4m^2}\right)}$$

$$= \frac{20m^2\left(\dfrac{3}{5m}\right) - 20m^2\left(\dfrac{2}{m^2}\right)}{20m^2\left(\dfrac{9}{2m}\right) + 20m^2\left(\dfrac{3}{4m^2}\right)} = \frac{12m - 40}{90m + 15} \quad \bullet$$

We now can summarize the two methods for simplifying a complex fraction.

Simplifying Complex Fractions

Method 1	Simplify the numerator and denominator of the complex fraction separately. Then divide the simplified numerator by the simplified denominator.
Method 2	Multiply numerator and denominator of the complex fraction by the least common denominator of all the denominators appearing in the complex fraction.

5.5 EXERCISES

Simplify each complex fraction. Use either method. See Examples 1–5.

1. $\dfrac{\dfrac{5}{8} + \dfrac{2}{3}}{\dfrac{7}{3} - \dfrac{1}{4}}$

2. $\dfrac{\dfrac{6}{5} - \dfrac{1}{9}}{\dfrac{2}{5} + \dfrac{5}{3}}$

3. $\dfrac{1 - \dfrac{3}{8}}{2 + \dfrac{1}{4}}$

4. $\dfrac{3 + \dfrac{5}{4}}{1 - \dfrac{7}{8}}$

5. $\dfrac{\dfrac{p}{q^2}}{\dfrac{p^2}{q}}$

6. $\dfrac{\dfrac{a}{x}}{\dfrac{a^2}{2x}}$

7. $\dfrac{\dfrac{x}{y}}{\dfrac{x^2}{y}}$

8. $\dfrac{\dfrac{p^4}{r}}{\dfrac{p^2}{r^2}}$

9. $\dfrac{\dfrac{m^3p^4}{5m}}{\dfrac{8mp^5}{p^2}}$

10. $\dfrac{\dfrac{9z^5x^3}{2x}}{\dfrac{8z^2x^5}{3z}}$

11. $\dfrac{\dfrac{x+1}{4}}{\dfrac{x-3}{x}}$

12. $\dfrac{\dfrac{m+6}{m}}{\dfrac{m-6}{2}}$

13. $\dfrac{\dfrac{3}{q}}{\dfrac{1-q}{6q^2}}$

14. $\dfrac{\dfrac{6}{x}}{\dfrac{1+x}{8x^5}}$

15. $\dfrac{\dfrac{2x+3}{12}}{\dfrac{x-1}{15}}$

16. $\dfrac{\dfrac{15}{k+1}}{\dfrac{10}{3(k+1)}}$

17. $\dfrac{\dfrac{3}{y}+1}{\dfrac{3+y}{2}}$

18. $\dfrac{6+\dfrac{2}{r}}{\dfrac{r+2}{3}}$

19. $\dfrac{\dfrac{1}{x}+x}{\dfrac{x^2+1}{8}}$

20. $\dfrac{\dfrac{3}{m}-m}{\dfrac{3-m^2}{4}}$

21. $\dfrac{x+\dfrac{1}{x}}{\dfrac{4}{x}+y}$

22. $\dfrac{y-\dfrac{6}{y}}{y+\dfrac{2}{y}}$

23. $\dfrac{\dfrac{p+3}{p}}{\dfrac{1}{p}+\dfrac{1}{5}}$

24. $\dfrac{r+\dfrac{1}{r}}{\dfrac{1}{r}-r}$

25. $\dfrac{\dfrac{2}{p^2}-\dfrac{3}{5p}}{\dfrac{4}{p}+\dfrac{1}{4p}}$

26. $\dfrac{\dfrac{2}{m^2}-\dfrac{3}{m}}{\dfrac{2}{5m^2}+\dfrac{1}{3m}}$

27. $\dfrac{\dfrac{5}{x^2y}-\dfrac{2}{xy^2}}{\dfrac{3}{x^2y^2}+\dfrac{4}{xy}}$

28. $\dfrac{\dfrac{1}{m^3p}+\dfrac{2}{mp^2}}{\dfrac{4}{mp}+\dfrac{1}{m^2p}}$

29. $\dfrac{\dfrac{1}{4}-\dfrac{1}{a^2}}{\dfrac{1}{2}+\dfrac{1}{a}}$

30. $\dfrac{\dfrac{1}{9}-\dfrac{1}{m^2}}{\dfrac{1}{3}+\dfrac{1}{m}}$

31. $\dfrac{\dfrac{1}{z+5}}{\dfrac{4}{z^2-25}}$

32. $\dfrac{\dfrac{a}{a+1}}{\dfrac{2}{a^2-1}}$

33. $\dfrac{\dfrac{1}{m+1}-1}{\dfrac{1}{m+1}+1}$

34. $\dfrac{\dfrac{2}{x-1}+2}{\dfrac{2}{x-1}-2}$

35. $\dfrac{\dfrac{1}{m-1}+\dfrac{2}{m+2}}{\dfrac{2}{m+2}-\dfrac{1}{m-3}}$

36. $\dfrac{\dfrac{5}{r+3}-\dfrac{1}{r-1}}{\dfrac{2}{r+2}+\dfrac{3}{r+3}}$

The following exercises are real "head-scratchers." (Hint: Work from the lower right up.)

37. $1-\dfrac{1}{1+\dfrac{1}{1+1}}$

38. $3-\dfrac{2}{4+\dfrac{2}{4-2}}$

39. $r+\dfrac{r}{4-\dfrac{2}{6+2}}$

40. $\dfrac{2q}{7}-\dfrac{q}{6+\dfrac{8}{4+4}}$

Review Exercises *Use the distributive property to simplify. See Section 1.10.*

41. $9\left(\dfrac{4x}{3} + \dfrac{2}{9}\right)$ **42.** $8\left(\dfrac{3r}{4} - \dfrac{9}{8}\right)$ **43.** $12\left(\dfrac{11p^2}{3} - \dfrac{9p}{4}\right)$ **44.** $6\left(\dfrac{5z^2}{2} + \dfrac{8z}{3}\right)$

Solve each equation. See Section 2.4.

45. $3x - 5 = 7x + 3$ **46.** $9z + 2 = 7z - 6$ **47.** $8(2q + 5) - 1 = 7q$

48. $6(z - 3) + 5 = 8z$ **49.** $9 - (5 - 3y) = 6$ **50.** $-(8 - a) + 5a = -7$

5.6   Equations Involving Rational Expressions

1 Solve equations involving rational expressions.

2 Solve for a specified variable.

1   To solve equations with fractions, first obtain a new equation that does not have fractions. To do this, multiply both sides by the least common denominator of all denominators in the fractions of the equation.

EXAMPLE 1   Solve the equation $\dfrac{x}{3} + \dfrac{x}{4} = 10 + x$.

Since the least common denominator of the two fractions is 12, begin by multiplying both sides of the equation by 12.

$$12\left(\frac{x}{3} + \frac{x}{4}\right) = 12(10 + x)$$

Now use the distributive property on both the left and the right sides.

$$12\left(\frac{x}{3}\right) + 12\left(\frac{x}{4}\right) = 12(10) + 12x$$

$$\frac{12x}{3} + \frac{12x}{4} = 120 + 12x$$

$$4x + 3x = 120 + 12x$$

This equation has no fractions. Solve it by the methods we used to solve equations earlier.

$$7x = 120 + 12x$$

$$-5x = 120$$

$$x = -24$$

Check this solution by substituting -24 for x in the original equation.

$$\frac{x}{3} + \frac{x}{4} = 10 + x$$

$$\frac{-24}{3} + \frac{-24}{4} = 10 + (-24)$$

$$-8 + (-6) = -14 \qquad \text{True}$$

This true statement shows that -24 is the solution.   ●

EXAMPLE 2   Solve $\dfrac{p}{2} - \dfrac{p-1}{3} = 1$.

Multiply both sides by the least common denominator, 6.

$$6\left(\frac{p}{2} - \frac{p-1}{3}\right) = 6 \cdot 1$$

$$6\left(\frac{p}{2}\right) - 6\left(\frac{p-1}{3}\right) = 6$$

$$3p - 2(p-1) = 6$$

Be very careful to put parentheses around $p - 1$; otherwise an incorrect solution may be found. Continue simplifying.

$$3p - 2p + 2 = 6 \qquad \text{Distributive property}$$

$$p + 2 = 6$$

$$p = 4$$

Check to see whether 4 is correct by replacing p with 4 in the original equation.   ●

When solving equations that have a variable in the denominator, remember that the number 0 cannot be used as a denominator. Therefore, the solution cannot be a number that will make the denominator equal 0.

EXAMPLE 3   Solve $\dfrac{x}{x-2} = \dfrac{2}{x-2} + 2$.

Multiply both sides by $x - 2$, the least common denominator.

$$(x-2)\left(\frac{x}{x-2}\right) = (x-2)\left(\frac{2}{x-2}\right) + (x-2)(2)$$

$$x = 2 + 2x - 4$$

$$x = -2 + 2x$$

$$-x = -2$$

$$x = 2$$

The proposed solution is 2. However, 2 cannot be a solution because 2 makes both denominators equal 0. The equation is meaningless and has no solution.   ●

EXAMPLE 4   Solve $\dfrac{2m}{m^2 - 4} + \dfrac{1}{m - 2} = \dfrac{2}{m + 2}$.

Since $m^2 - 4 = (m + 2)(m - 2)$, use $(m + 2)(m - 2)$ as the least common denominator. Multiply both sides by $(m + 2)(m - 2)$.

$$(m + 2)(m - 2)\left(\dfrac{2m}{m^2 - 4} + \dfrac{1}{m - 2}\right) = (m + 2)(m - 2)\dfrac{2}{m + 2}$$

$$(m + 2)(m - 2)\dfrac{2m}{(m + 2)(m - 2)} + (m + 2)(m - 2)\dfrac{1}{m - 2}$$

$$= (m + 2)(m - 2)\dfrac{2}{m + 2}$$

$$2m + m + 2 = 2(m - 2)$$

$$3m + 2 = 2m - 4$$

$$m = -6$$

Check that -6 is a solution for the given equation.   ●

EXAMPLE 5   Solve $\dfrac{2}{x^2 - x} = \dfrac{1}{x^2 - 1}$.

To solve the equation, begin by finding a least common denominator. Since $x^2 - x$ can be factored as $x(x - 1)$, and $x^2 - 1$ can be factored as $(x + 1)(x - 1)$, the least common denominator is $x(x + 1)(x - 1)$. Multiply both sides of the equation by $x(x + 1)(x - 1)$.

$$x(x + 1)(x - 1)\dfrac{2}{x(x - 1)} = x(x + 1)(x - 1)\dfrac{1}{(x + 1)(x - 1)}$$

$$2(x + 1) = x$$

$$2x + 2 = x$$

$$2 = -x$$

$$x = -2$$

To be sure that -2 is a solution, substitute -2 for x in the original equation.   ●

EXAMPLE 6   Solve $\dfrac{1}{x - 1} + \dfrac{1}{2} = \dfrac{2}{x^2 - 1}$.

The least common denominator is $2(x + 1)(x - 1)$. Multiply both sides of the equation by this common denominator.

$$2(x + 1)(x - 1)\left(\dfrac{1}{x - 1} + \dfrac{1}{2}\right) = 2(x + 1)(x - 1)\dfrac{2}{(x + 1)(x - 1)}$$

Continue simplifying the equation.

$$2(x + 1)(x - 1)\frac{1}{x - 1} + 2(x + 1)(x - 1)\frac{1}{2}$$

$$= 2(x + 1)(x - 1)\frac{2}{(x + 1)(x - 1)}$$

$$2(x + 1) + (x + 1)(x - 1) = 4$$
$$2x + 2 + x^2 - 1 = 4$$
$$x^2 + 2x + 1 = 4$$
$$x^2 + 2x - 3 = 0$$

Factoring gives

$$(x + 3)(x - 1) = 0.$$

Therefore, it seems that -3 or 1 are solutions. But 1 makes a denominator of the original equation equal 0, so 1 is not a solution. However, -3 is a solution, as can be shown by substituting -3 for x in the original equation.   ●

2   In Chapter 2 we saw how to **solve a formula for a specified variable.** In the next example we see how this process applies to formulas with fractions.

EXAMPLE 7   Solve the formula $\dfrac{1}{R} = \dfrac{1}{r_1} + \dfrac{1}{r_2}$ for r_2.

Here r_1 (read "r-sub-one") and r_2 are different variables. The least common denominator for R, r_1, and r_2 is Rr_1r_2, so multiply both sides of the formula by Rr_1r_2.

$$Rr_1r_2\left(\frac{1}{R}\right) = Rr_1r_2\left(\frac{1}{r_1} + \frac{1}{r_2}\right)$$

$$Rr_1r_2\left(\frac{1}{R}\right) = Rr_1r_2\left(\frac{1}{r_1}\right) + Rr_1r_2\left(\frac{1}{r_2}\right)$$

$$r_1r_2 = Rr_2 + Rr_1$$

Get the terms containing r_2 (the desired variable) on one side of the equals sign. Do this here by subtracting Rr_2 from both sides.

$$r_1r_2 - Rr_2 = Rr_1$$

Factor out the common factor of r_2 on the left.

$$r_2(r_1 - R) = Rr_1$$

Finally, divide both sides of the equation by $r_1 - R$.

$$r_2 = \frac{Rr_1}{r_1 - R}   ●$$

5.6 EXERCISES

Solve each equation and check your answers. See Examples 1–3.

1. $\dfrac{1}{4} = \dfrac{x}{2}$

2. $\dfrac{2}{m} = \dfrac{5}{12}$

3. $\dfrac{9}{k} = \dfrac{3}{4}$

4. $\dfrac{15}{f} = \dfrac{30}{8}$

5. $\dfrac{7}{y} = \dfrac{8}{3}$

6. $\dfrac{2}{z} = \dfrac{11}{5}$

7. $\dfrac{6}{x} - \dfrac{4}{x} = 5$

8. $\dfrac{3}{x} + \dfrac{2}{x} = 5$

9. $\dfrac{x}{2} - \dfrac{x}{4} = 6$

10. $\dfrac{4}{y} + \dfrac{2}{3} = 1$

11. $\dfrac{9}{m} = 5 - \dfrac{1}{m}$

12. $\dfrac{3x}{5} + 2 = \dfrac{1}{4}$

13. $\dfrac{2t}{7} - 5 = t$

14. $\dfrac{1}{2} + \dfrac{2}{m} = 1$

15. $\dfrac{x+1}{2} = \dfrac{x+2}{3}$

16. $\dfrac{t-4}{3} = t + 2$

17. $\dfrac{3m}{2} + m = 5$

18. $\dfrac{9}{x+1} = 3$

19. $\dfrac{9}{x-2} = 3$

20. $\dfrac{2k+3}{k} = \dfrac{3}{2}$

21. $\dfrac{5-y}{y} + \dfrac{3}{4} = \dfrac{7}{y}$

22. $\dfrac{x}{x-4} = \dfrac{2}{x-4} + 5$

23. $\dfrac{a-4}{4} = \dfrac{a+8}{16}$

24. $\dfrac{m-2}{5} = \dfrac{m+8}{10}$

25. $\dfrac{2p+8}{9} = \dfrac{10p+4}{27}$

26. $\dfrac{5r-3}{7} = \dfrac{15r-2}{28}$

27. $\dfrac{2y-1}{y} + 2 = \dfrac{1}{2}$

28. $\dfrac{a}{2} - \dfrac{17+a}{5} = 2a$

29. $\dfrac{m-2}{4} + \dfrac{m+1}{3} = \dfrac{10}{3}$

30. $\dfrac{y+2}{5} + \dfrac{y-5}{3} = \dfrac{7}{5}$

31. $\dfrac{a+7}{8} - \dfrac{a-2}{3} = \dfrac{4}{3}$

32. $\dfrac{m+2}{5} - \dfrac{m-6}{7} = 2$

33. $\dfrac{p}{2} - \dfrac{p-1}{4} = \dfrac{5}{4}$

34. $\dfrac{r}{6} - \dfrac{r-2}{3} = \dfrac{-4}{3}$

35. $\dfrac{5y}{3} - \dfrac{2y-1}{4} = \dfrac{1}{4}$

36. $\dfrac{8k}{5} - \dfrac{3k-4}{2} = \dfrac{5}{2}$

37. $\dfrac{y-1}{2} - \dfrac{y-3}{4} = 1$

38. $\dfrac{r+5}{3} - \dfrac{r-1}{4} = \dfrac{7}{4}$

39. $\dfrac{3y-1}{9} - \dfrac{2y-5}{8} = \dfrac{1}{4}$

Solve each equation and check your answers. See Examples 4–6.

40. $\dfrac{8}{2k-4} + \dfrac{3}{5k-10} = \dfrac{23}{5}$

41. $\dfrac{1}{3p+15} + \dfrac{5}{4p+20} = \dfrac{19}{24}$

42. $\dfrac{m}{2m+2} = \dfrac{-2m}{4m+4} + \dfrac{2m-3}{m+1}$

43. $\dfrac{5p+1}{3p+3} = \dfrac{5p-5}{5p+5} + \dfrac{3p-1}{p+1}$

44. $\dfrac{x+1}{x-3} = \dfrac{4}{x-3} + 6$

45. $\dfrac{p}{p-2} + 4 = \dfrac{2}{p-2}$

46. $\dfrac{2}{y} = \dfrac{y}{5y - 12}$

47. $\dfrac{8x + 3}{x} = 3x$

48. $\dfrac{2}{k - 3} - \dfrac{3}{k + 3} = \dfrac{12}{k^2 - 9}$

49. $\dfrac{1}{r + 5} - \dfrac{3}{r - 5} = \dfrac{-10}{r^2 - 25}$

50. $\dfrac{x + 4}{x^2 - 3x + 2} - \dfrac{5}{x^2 - 4x + 3} = \dfrac{x - 4}{x^2 - 5x + 6}$

51. $\dfrac{3y}{y^2 + 5y + 6} = \dfrac{5y}{y^2 + 2y - 3} - \dfrac{2}{y^2 + y - 2}$

52. $\dfrac{3}{r^2 + r - 2} - \dfrac{1}{r^2 - 1} = \dfrac{7}{2(r^2 + 3r + 2)}$

53. $\dfrac{4}{p} - \dfrac{2}{p + 1} = 3$

54. $\dfrac{6}{r} + \dfrac{1}{r - 2} = 3$

55. $\dfrac{2}{m - 1} + \dfrac{1}{m + 1} = \dfrac{5}{4}$

56. $\dfrac{5}{z - 2} + \dfrac{10}{z + 2} = 7$

Solve for the specified variable. See Example 7.

57. $\dfrac{1}{x} = \dfrac{1}{y} - \dfrac{1}{z}$;   for y

58. $\dfrac{3}{k} = \dfrac{1}{p} + \dfrac{1}{q}$;   for q

59. $9x + \dfrac{3}{z} = \dfrac{5}{y}$;   for z

60. $2a - \dfrac{5}{b} + \dfrac{1}{c} = 0$;   for b

61. $I = \dfrac{E}{R + r}$;   for R

62. $I = \dfrac{E}{R + r}$;   for r

63. $S = \dfrac{a}{1 - r}$;   for r

64. $h = \dfrac{2A}{B + b}$;   for b

65. $\dfrac{1}{R} = \dfrac{1}{r_1} + \dfrac{1}{r_2}$;   for r_1

Review Exercises   *Write a mathematical expression for each phrase. See Section 2.5.*

66. Sharon goes 800 kilometers in p hours; find her rate.

67. Joann drives for 10 hours, going d kilometers. Find her rate.

68. Sam goes 780 kilometers at z kilometers per hour. Find his time.

69. Walt can do a job in x hours. What portion of the job is done in 1 hour?

70. Kathy needs a hours to tune up her car. How much of the job does she do in 1 hour?

MISCELLANEOUS EXERCISES

A common error when working with rational expressions is to confuse *operations* on rational expressions with the *solution of equations* with rational expressions. For example, the four possible operations on the rational expressions

$$\frac{1}{x} \quad \text{and} \quad \frac{1}{x-2}$$

can be performed as follows.

Add: $\quad \dfrac{1}{x} + \dfrac{1}{x-2} = \dfrac{x-2}{x(x-2)} + \dfrac{x}{x(x-2)} = \dfrac{x-2+x}{x(x-2)} = \dfrac{2x-2}{x(x-2)}$

Subtract: $\quad \dfrac{1}{x} - \dfrac{1}{x-2} = \dfrac{x-2}{x(x-2)} - \dfrac{x}{x(x-2)} = \dfrac{x-2-x}{x(x-2)} = \dfrac{-2}{x(x-2)}$

Multiply: $\quad \dfrac{1}{x} \cdot \dfrac{1}{x-2} = \dfrac{1}{x(x-2)}$

Divide: $\quad \dfrac{1}{x} \div \dfrac{1}{x-2} = \dfrac{1}{x} \cdot \dfrac{x-2}{1} = \dfrac{x-2}{x}$

On the other hand, the *equation*

$$\frac{1}{x} + \frac{1}{x-2} = \frac{3}{4}$$

is solved by multiplying both sides by the least common denominator, $4x(x-2)$, giving an equation with no denominators.

$$4x(x-2)\frac{1}{x} + 4x(x-2)\frac{1}{x-2} = 4x(x-2)\frac{3}{4}$$
$$4x - 8 + 4x = 3x^2 - 6x$$
$$0 = 3x^2 - 14x + 8$$
$$0 = (3x-2)(x-4)$$
$$x = \frac{2}{3} \quad \text{or} \quad x = 4$$

In each of the following exercises, decide whether the given rational expressions should be added, subtracted, multiplied, or divided and perform the operation, or else solve the given equation.

1. $\dfrac{6}{m} + \dfrac{2}{m}$

2. $\dfrac{b^2 c^3}{b^5 c^4} \cdot \dfrac{c^5}{b^7}$

3. $\dfrac{2}{x^2 + 2x - 3} \div \dfrac{8x^2}{3x - 3}$

4. $\dfrac{4}{m-2} = 1$

5. $\dfrac{2r^2 - 3r - 9}{2r^2 - r - 6} \cdot \dfrac{r^2 + 2r - 8}{r^2 - 2r - 3}$

6. $\dfrac{1}{m^2 - 3m} + \dfrac{4}{m^2 - 9}$

7. $\dfrac{p + 3}{8} = \dfrac{p - 2}{9}$

8. $\dfrac{4t^2 - t}{6t^2 + 10t} \div \dfrac{8t^2 + 2t - 1}{3t^2 + 11t + 10}$

9. $\dfrac{5}{y - 1} + \dfrac{2}{3y - 3}$

10. $\dfrac{1}{z} + \dfrac{1}{z + 2} = \dfrac{8}{15}$

11. $\dfrac{2}{r - 1} + \dfrac{1}{r} = \dfrac{5}{2}$

12. $\dfrac{2}{y} - \dfrac{7}{5y}$

13. $\dfrac{4}{9z} - \dfrac{3}{2z}$

14. $\dfrac{r - 3}{2} = \dfrac{2r - 5}{5}$

15. $\dfrac{1}{m^2 + 5m + 6} + \dfrac{2}{m^2 + 4m + 3}$

16. $\dfrac{2k^2 - 3k}{20k^2 - 5k} \div \dfrac{2k^2 - 5k + 3}{4k^2 + 11k - 3}$

5.7   Applications of Rational Expressions

Solve word problems with rational expressions involving

1 numbers;

2 distance;

3 work.

4 Solve problems about variation.

1   We are now ready to discuss applications that involve rational expressions. Our first application, involving numbers, is used to show how problems with fractions are set up and solved.

EXAMPLE 1   If the same number is added to both the numerator and denominator of the fraction 3/4, the result is 5/6. Find the number.

If x represents the number added to numerator and denominator, then

$$\frac{3 + x}{4 + x}$$

represents the result of adding the same number to both the numerator and denominator. Since this result is 5/6,

$$\frac{3 + x}{4 + x} = \frac{5}{6}.$$

To solve this equation, multiply both sides by the least common denominator, $6(4 + x)$.

$$6(4 + x)\frac{3 + x}{4 + x} = 6(4 + x)\frac{5}{6}$$

$$6(3 + x) = 5(4 + x)$$

$$18 + 6x = 20 + 5x$$

$$x = 2$$

Check the solution in the words of the problem to see that 2 is the correct number. •

2 The next example shows how to solve word problems involving distance.

EXAMPLE 2   The Big Muddy River has a current of 3 miles per hour. A motorboat takes as long to go 12 miles downstream as to go 8 miles upstream. Find the speed of the boat in still water.

This problem requires the distance formula,

$$d = rt \quad (\text{distance} = \text{rate} \cdot \text{time}).$$

Let x represent the speed of the boat in still water. Since the current pushes the boat when the boat is going downstream, the speed of the boat downstream will be the sum of the speed of the boat and the speed of the current, or $x + 3$ miles per hour. Also, the boat's speed going upstream is given by $x - 3$ miles per hour.

We can summarize the information of the problem in a chart.

	d	r	t
Downstream	12	$x + 3$	
Upstream	8	$x - 3$	

To fill in the last column, representing time, solve the formula $d = rt$ for t.

$$d = rt$$

$$\frac{d}{r} = t \qquad \text{Divide by } r$$

Then the time upstream is the distance divided by the rate, or

$$\frac{8}{x - 3},$$

and the time downstream is also the distance divided by the rate, or

$$\frac{12}{x + 3}.$$

Now complete the chart.

	d	r	t	
Downstream	12	$x + 3$	$\dfrac{12}{x + 3}$	Times are equal
Upstream	8	$x - 3$	$\dfrac{8}{x - 3}$	

According to the original problem, the time upstream equals the time downstream. The two times from the chart must therefore be equal, giving the equation

$$\frac{12}{x + 3} = \frac{8}{x - 3}.$$

To solve this equation, multiply both sides by $(x + 3)(x - 3)$.

$$(x + 3)(x - 3)\frac{12}{x + 3} = (x + 3)(x - 3)\frac{8}{x - 3}$$
$$12(x - 3) = 8(x + 3)$$
$$12x - 36 = 8x + 24$$
$$4x = 60$$
$$x = 15$$

The speed of the boat in still water is 15 miles per hour. To check, first find the speed of the boat downstream, which is $15 + 3 = 18$ miles per hour. Traveling 12 miles would take

$$d = rt,$$
$$12 = 18t,$$
$$t = \frac{2}{3} \text{ hour.}$$

On the other hand, the speed of the boat upstream is $15 - 3 = 12$ miles per hour, and traveling 8 miles would take

$$d = rt,$$
$$8 = 12t,$$
$$t = \frac{2}{3} \text{ hour.}$$

The time upstream equals the time downstream, as required. ●

3 The third example shows a word problem about the length of time needed to do a job. This type of problem is often called a work problem.

EXAMPLE 3   With a riding lawn mower, John, the grounds keeper in a large park, can cut the lawn in 8 hours. With a small mower, his assistant Walt needs 14 hours to cut the same lawn. If both John and Walt work on the lawn, how long will it take to cut it?

Let x be the number of hours that it takes John and Walt to cut the lawn, working together. Certainly x will be less than 8, since John alone can cut the lawn in 8 hours. In one hour, John can do 1/8 of the lawn, and in one hour Walt can do 1/14 of the lawn. Since it takes them x hours to cut the lawn when working together, in one hour together they can do $1/x$ of the lawn. The amount of the lawn cut by John in one hour plus the amount cut by Walt in one hour must equal the amount they can do together in one hour, or

$$\underset{\substack{\text{Amount} \\ \text{by John}}}{\longrightarrow}\ \overset{\overset{\text{Amount by Walt}}{\downarrow}}{\frac{1}{8} + \frac{1}{14}} = \frac{1}{x}.\ \longleftarrow \text{Amount together}$$

Since $56x$ is the least common denominator for 8, 14, and x, multiply both sides of the equation by $56x$.

$$56x\left(\frac{1}{8} + \frac{1}{14}\right) = 56x \cdot \frac{1}{x}$$

$$56x \cdot \frac{1}{8} + 56x \cdot \frac{1}{14} = 56x \cdot \frac{1}{x}$$

$$7x + 4x = 56$$

$$11x = 56$$

$$x = \frac{56}{11}$$

Working together, John and Walt can cut the lawn in 56/11 hours, or 5 1/11 hours, about 5 hours and 5 minutes.   ●

4   Equations with fractions often result when discussing **variation.** Two variables **vary directly** if one is a constant multiple of the other. That is,

Direct Variation

> y **varies directly** as x if there exists a constant k such that
>
> $$y = kx.$$

EXAMPLE 4   Suppose y varies directly as x, and $y = 20$ when $x = 4$. Find y when $x = 9$.

Since y varies directly as x, there is a constant k such that $y = kx$. We know that $y = 20$ when $x = 4$. Substituting these values into $y = kx$ gives

$$y = kx$$

$$20 = k \cdot 4$$

from which $k = 5.$

Since $y = kx$ and $k = 5$, we have

$$y = 5x.$$

When $x = 9$,

$$y = 5x = 5 \cdot 9 = 45.$$

Thus, $y = 45$ when $x = 9$. •

Other common types of variation are defined below, where k represents a constant.

Variation

y varies directly as the square of x	$y = kx^2$
m varies inversely as p	$m = \dfrac{k}{p}$
r varies inversely as the square of s	$r = \dfrac{k}{s^2}$

EXAMPLE 5

Suppose z varies inversely as the square of y, and $z = 8$ when $y = 1/2$. Find z when $y = 3/4$.

Since z varies inversely as the square of y, there is a constant k such that

$$z = \frac{k}{y^2}.$$

To find k, replace z with 8 and y with 1/2.

$$8 = \frac{k}{\left(\dfrac{1}{2}\right)^2}$$

$$8 = \frac{k}{\dfrac{1}{4}}$$

Multiply both sides by 1/4 to get

$$k = 2,$$

or

$$z = \frac{2}{y^2}.$$

When $y = 3/4$,

$$z = \frac{2}{\left(\dfrac{3}{4}\right)^2} = \frac{2}{\dfrac{9}{16}} = \frac{2 \cdot 16}{9} = \frac{32}{9}. \quad •$$

5.7 EXERCISES

Solve each problem. See Example 1.

1. One half of a number is 3 more than one sixth of the same number. What is the number?

2. The numerator of the fraction 4/7 is increased by an amount so that the value of the resulting fraction is 27/21. By what amount was the numerator increased?

3. In a certain fraction, the denominator is 5 larger than the numerator. If 3 is added to both the numerator and the denominator, the result is 3/4. Find the original fraction.

4. The denominator of a certain fraction is three times the numerator. If 1 is added to the numerator and subtracted from the denominator, the result equals 1/2. Find the original fraction.

5. One number is 3 more than another. If the smaller is added to two thirds the larger, the result is four fifths the sum of the original numbers. Find the numbers.

6. The sum of a number and its reciprocal is 5/2. Find the number.

7. If twice the reciprocal of a number is subtracted from the number, the result is −7/3. Find the number.

8. The sum of the reciprocals of two consecutive integers is 5/6. Find the integers.

9. If three times a number is added to twice its reciprocal, the answer is 5. Find the number.

10. If twice a number is subtracted from three times its reciprocal, the result is 1. Find the number.

11. A man and his son worked four days at a job. The son's daily wage was 2/5 that of the father. If together they earned $672, what were their daily wages?

12. The profits from a student show are to be given to two scholarships so that one scholarship receives 3/2 as much money as the other. If the total amount given to the two scholarships is $390, find the amount that goes to the scholarship that receives the lesser amount.

13. A new instructor is paid 3/4 the salary of an experienced professor. In a certain college, the total salary paid an instructor and a professor was $56,000. Find the salary paid the professor.

14. A child takes 5/8 the number of pills that an adult takes for the same illness. Together the child and the adult use 26 pills. Find the number used by the adult.

Solve each problem. See Example 2.

15. Sam can row 4 miles per hour in still water. It takes as long to row 8 miles upstream as 24 miles downstream. How fast is the current?

	d	r	t
Upstream	8	$4 - x$	
Downstream	24	$4 + x$	

16. Mary flew from Philadelphia to Des Moines at 180 miles per hour and from Des Moines to Philadelphia at 150 miles per hour. The trip at the slower speed took 1 hour longer than the trip at the faster speed. Find the distance between the two cities. (Assume there was no wind in either direction.)

	d	r	t
P to D	x	180	
D to P	x	150	

17. On a business trip, Arlene traveled to her destination at an average speed of 60 miles per hour. Coming home, her average speed was 50 miles per hour and the trip took 1/2 hour longer. How far did she travel each way?

18. Rae flew her airplane 500 miles against the wind in the same time it took her to fly it 600 miles with the wind. If the speed of the wind was 10 miles per hour, what is the speed of her plane in still air?

19. The distance from Seattle, Washington, to Victoria, British Columbia, is about 148 miles by ferry. It takes about 4 hours less to travel by ferry from Victoria to Vancouver, British Columbia, a distance of about 74 miles. What is the average speed of the ferry?

20. A boat goes 210 miles downriver in the same time it can go 140 miles upriver. The speed of the current is 5 miles per hour. Find the speed of the boat in still water.

Solve each problem. See Example 3.

21. Paul can tune up his Toyota in 2 hours. His friend Marco can do the job in 3 hours. How long would it take them if they worked together?

22. George can paint a room, working alone, in 8 hours. Jenny can paint the same room, working alone, in 6 hours. How long will it take them if they work together?

23. Machine A can make all the bolts for an order in 7 hours, but machine B takes 12 hours. How long will it take the two machines working together?

24. One pipe can fill a swimming pool in 6 hours, and another pipe can do it in 9 hours. How long will it take the two pipes working together to fill the pool 3/4 full?

25. Dennis can do a job in 4 days. When Dennis and Sue work together, the job takes 2 1/3 days. How long would the job take Sue working alone?

26. An inlet pipe can fill a swimming pool in 9 hours, and an outlet pipe can empty the pool in 12 hours. Through an error, both pipes are left open. How long will it take to fill the pool?

27. A cold water faucet can fill a sink in 12 minutes, and a hot water faucet can fill it in 15. The drain can empty the sink in 25 minutes. If both faucets are on and the drain is open, how long will it take to fill the sink?

28. Refer to Exercise 26. Assume the error was discovered after both pipes had been running for 3 hours, and the outlet pipe was then closed. How much more time would then be required to fill the pool? (*Hint:* How much of the job had been done when the error was discovered?)

29. An experienced employee can enter tax data into a computer twice as fast as a new employee. Working together, it takes the employees 2 hours. How long would it take the experienced employee working alone?

30. One painter can paint a house three times faster than another. Working together, they can paint a house in 4 days. How long would it take the faster painter working alone?

Solve the following problems about variation. See Examples 4 and 5.

31. If x varies directly as y, and $x = 9$ when $y = 2$, find x when y is 7.

32. If z varies directly as x, and $z = 15$ when $x = 4$, find z when x is 11.

33. If m varies directly as p^2, and $m = 20$ when $p = 2$, find m when p is 5.

34. If a varies directly as b^2, and $a = 48$ when $b = 4$, find a when $b = 7$.

35. If y varies inversely as x, and $y = 10$ when $x = 3$, find y when $x = 12$.

36. If r varies inversely as s, and $r = 7$ when $s = 8$, find r when $s = 12$.

37. If p varies inversely as q^2, and $p = 4$ when $q = 1/2$, find p when $q = 3/2$.

38. If z varies inversely as x^2, and $z = 9$ when $x = 2/3$, find z when $x = 5/4$.

39. The circumference of a circle varies directly as the radius. A circle with a radius of 7 centimeters has a circumference of 43.96 centimeters. Find the circumference if the radius changes to 11 centimeters.

40. The pressure exerted by a certain liquid at a given point varies directly as the depth of the point beneath the surface of the liquid. The pressure at 10 feet is 50 pounds per square inch. What is the pressure at 20 feet?

41. For a body falling freely from rest (disregarding air resistance), the distance the body falls varies directly as the square of the time. If an object is dropped from the top of a tower 400 feet high and hits the ground in 5 seconds, how far did it fall in the first 3 seconds?

42. The current in a simple electrical circuit varies inversely as the resistance. If the current is 50 amps (an *amp* is a unit for measuring current) when the resistance is 10 ohms (an *ohm* is a unit for measuring resistance), find the current if the resistance is 5 ohms.

43. The force required to compress a spring varies directly as the change in the length of the spring. If a force of 12 pounds is required to compress a certain spring 3 inches, how much force is required to compress the spring 5 inches?

44. The illumination produced by a light source varies inversely as the square of the distance from the source. If the illumination produced 4 feet from a light source is 75 footcandles, find the illumination produced 9 feet from the same source.

Review Exercises *Find the value of y when (a) x = 2 and (b) x = −4. See Sections 1.4 and 2.4.*

45. $y = 4x - 7$ **46.** $y = 3 - 2x$ **47.** $4x - y = 1$ **48.** $y + 3x = 2$

49. $3x + 7y = 10$ **50.** $2x - 3y = 5$ **51.** $x = -3y$ **52.** $y = 2x$

Chapter 5   Review Exercises

[5.1] *Find any values for which the following expressions are meaningless.*

1. $\dfrac{2}{7x}$ **2.** $\dfrac{3}{m - 5}$ **3.** $\dfrac{r - 3}{r^2 - 2r - 8}$ **4.** $\dfrac{3z + 5}{2z^2 + 5z - 3}$

Find the numerical value of each expression when (a) x = 3 and (b) x = −1.

5. $\dfrac{x^2}{x + 2}$ **6.** $\dfrac{5x + 3}{2x - 1}$ **7.** $\dfrac{8x}{x^2 - 2}$ **8.** $\dfrac{x - 5}{x - 3}$

Write each expression in lowest terms.

9. $\dfrac{15p^2}{5p}$ **10.** $\dfrac{6y^2z^3}{9y^4z^2}$ **11.** $\dfrac{9x^2 - 16}{6x + 8}$ **12.** $\dfrac{m - 5}{5 - m}$

[5.2] *Find each product or quotient. Write each answer in lowest terms.*

13. $\dfrac{10p^5}{5} \div \dfrac{3p^7}{20}$ **14.** $\dfrac{8z^2}{(4z)^3} \div \dfrac{4z^5}{32z}$ **15.** $\dfrac{7y + 14}{8y - 5} \div \dfrac{4y + 8}{16y - 10}$

16. $\dfrac{3k + 5}{k + 2} \cdot \dfrac{k^2 - 4}{18k^2 - 50}$ **17.** $\dfrac{6 - y}{6 + y} \div \dfrac{y - 6}{y + 6}$ **18.** $\dfrac{z^2 + z - 2}{z^2 + 7z + 10} \div \dfrac{z - 3}{z + 5}$

19. $\dfrac{2p^2 + 3p - 2}{p^2 + 5p + 6} \cdot \dfrac{p^2 - 2p - 15}{2p^2 - 7p - 15}$ **20.** $\dfrac{8r^2 + 23r - 3}{64r^2 - 1} \div \dfrac{r^2 - 4r - 21}{64r^2 + 16r + 1}$

[5.3] *Find the least common denominator for the following fractions.*

21. $\dfrac{1}{15}, \dfrac{7}{30}, \dfrac{4}{45}$

22. $\dfrac{3}{8y}, \dfrac{7}{12y^2}, \dfrac{1}{16y^3}$

23. $\dfrac{1}{y^2 + 2y}, \dfrac{4}{y^2 + 6y + 8}$

24. $\dfrac{3}{z^2 + z - 6}, \dfrac{2}{z^2 + 4z + 3}$

Rewrite each rational expression with the given denominator.

25. $\dfrac{4}{9}, \dfrac{}{45}$

26. $\dfrac{12}{m}, \dfrac{}{5m}$

27. $\dfrac{3}{8m^2}, \dfrac{}{24m^3}$

28. $\dfrac{12}{y - 4}, \dfrac{}{8y - 32}$

29. $\dfrac{-2k}{3k + 15}, \dfrac{}{15k + 75}$

30. $\dfrac{12y}{y^2 - y - 2}, \dfrac{}{(y - 2)(y + 1)(y - 4)}$

[5.4] *Add or subtract as indicated. Write all answers in lowest terms.*

31. $\dfrac{11}{3r} - \dfrac{8}{3r}$

32. $\dfrac{b}{b + 5} + \dfrac{5}{b + 5}$

33. $\dfrac{7}{k} - \dfrac{2}{5}$

34. $\dfrac{3 + 5m}{2} - \dfrac{m}{4}$

35. $\dfrac{8}{r^2} - \dfrac{3}{2r}$

36. $\dfrac{3p + q}{5} - \dfrac{p - q}{3}$

37. $\dfrac{2}{y + 1} - \dfrac{3}{y - 1}$

38. $\dfrac{2}{r - 5} + \dfrac{3}{5 - r}$

39. $\dfrac{10}{p^2 - 2p} - \dfrac{2}{p^2 - 5p + 6}$

[5.5] *Simplify each complex fraction.*

40. $\dfrac{\dfrac{5k - 1}{k}}{\dfrac{4k + 3}{8k}}$

41. $\dfrac{\dfrac{6}{r} - 1}{\dfrac{6 - r}{4r}}$

42. $\dfrac{z + \dfrac{1}{x}}{z - \dfrac{1}{x}}$

43. $\dfrac{\dfrac{1}{a + b} - 1}{\dfrac{1}{a + b} + 1}$

[5.6] *Solve each equation. Check your answer.*

44. $\dfrac{2}{p} = \dfrac{5}{8}$

45. $\dfrac{3}{k} - \dfrac{2}{k} = 7$

46. $\dfrac{y}{2} - \dfrac{y}{5} = 6$

47. $\dfrac{3}{4}r - 1 = -4$

48. $\dfrac{z + 3}{8} = \dfrac{z - 2}{3}$

49. $\dfrac{4}{p - 2} = 3$

50. $\dfrac{5 + m}{m} + \dfrac{3}{4} = \dfrac{-2}{m}$

51. $\dfrac{y}{3} - \dfrac{y - 2}{8} = -1$

52. $\dfrac{2}{z} = \dfrac{z + 1}{z + 3}$

53. $\dfrac{3y - 1}{y - 2} = \dfrac{5}{y - 2} + 1$

54. $\dfrac{3}{m - 2} + \dfrac{1}{m - 1} = \dfrac{7}{m^2 - 3m + 2}$

Solve for the specified variable.

55. $\dfrac{1}{k} + \dfrac{3}{r} = \dfrac{5}{z};$ for r

56. $\dfrac{2}{a} + \dfrac{4}{b} = \dfrac{1}{c};$ for b

57. $x = \dfrac{3y}{2y + z};$ for y

[5.7] *Solve each word problem.*

58. When half a number is subtracted from two thirds of the number, the result is 2. Find the number.

59. A certain fraction has a numerator that is 4 more than the denominator. If 6 is subtracted from the denominator, the result is 3. Find the original fraction.

60. Five times a number is added to three times the reciprocal of the number, giving 17/2. Find the number.

61. The commission received by a salesperson for selling a small car is 2/3 that received for selling a large car. On a recent day, Linda sold one of each, earning a commission of $300. Find the commission for each type of car.

62. A boat goes 7 miles per hour in still water. It takes as long to go 20 miles upstream as 50 miles downstream. Find the speed of the current.

63. Kerrie flew her plane 400 kilometers with the wind in the same time it took her to go 200 kilometers against the wind. The speed of the wind is 50 kilometers per hour. Find the speed of the plane in still air.

64. A man can plant his garden in 5 hours, working alone. His daughter can do the same job in 8 hours. How long would it take them if they worked together?

65. When Mary and Sue work together on a job, they can do it in 3 3/7 days. Mary can do the job working alone in 8 days. How long would it take Sue working alone?

66. One painter can paint a house twice as fast as another. Working together, they can paint the house in 1 1/3 days. How long would it take the faster painter working alone?

67. If x varies directly as y, and $x = 12$ when $y = 5$, find x when $y = 3$.

68. If m varies directly as q^2, and $m = 8$ when $q = 4$, find m when $q = 6$.

69. If r varies inversely as s, and $r = 9$ when $s = 1/2$, find r when $s = 2$.

70. If z varies inversely as y^2, and $z = 5$ when $y = 2$, find z when $y = 3/4$.

Chapter 5   Test

1. Find any values for which $\dfrac{8k + 1}{k^2 - 4k + 3}$ is meaningless.

2. Find the numerical value of $\dfrac{6r + 1}{2r^2 - 3r - 20}$ when (a) $r = -1$ and (b) $r = 4$.

Write each rational expression in lowest terms.

3. $\dfrac{8m^2p^2}{6m^3p^5}$

4. $\dfrac{5y^3 - 5y}{2y + 2}$

Multiply or divide, as indicated. Write all answers in lowest terms.

5. $\dfrac{a^6b}{a^3} \cdot \dfrac{b^2}{a^2b^3}$

6. $\dfrac{8y - 16}{9} \div \dfrac{6 - 3y}{5}$

7. $\dfrac{6m^2 - m - 2}{8m^2 + 10m + 3} \cdot \dfrac{4m^2 + 7m + 3}{3m^2 + 5m + 2}$

8. $\dfrac{5a^2 + 7a - 6}{2a^2 + 3a - 2} \div \dfrac{5a^2 + 17a - 12}{2a^2 + 5a - 3}$

Find the least common denominator for the following fractions.

9. $\dfrac{3}{10p^2}, \dfrac{1}{25p^3}, \dfrac{-7}{30p^5}$

10. $\dfrac{r - 1}{2r^2 + 7r + 6}, \dfrac{2r + 1}{2r^2 - 7r - 15}$

Rewrite each rational expression with the given denominator.

11. $\dfrac{11}{7r}, \dfrac{}{49r^2}$

12. $\dfrac{5}{8m - 16}, \dfrac{}{24m^2 - 48m}$

Add or subtract as indicated. Write all answers in lowest terms.

13. $\dfrac{5}{x} - \dfrac{6}{x}$

14. $\dfrac{-3}{a + 1} + \dfrac{5}{6a + 6}$

15. $\dfrac{m^2}{m - 3} + \dfrac{m + 1}{3 - m}$

16. $\dfrac{3}{2k^2 + 3k - 2} + \dfrac{k}{k^2 + 3k + 2}$

Simplify each complex fraction.

17. $\dfrac{\dfrac{1}{k} - 2}{\dfrac{1}{3} + k}$

18. $\dfrac{\dfrac{1}{p + 4} - 2}{\dfrac{1}{p + 4} + 2}$

Solve each equation.

19. $\dfrac{3}{2p} + \dfrac{12}{5p} = \dfrac{13}{20}$

20. $\dfrac{p}{p - 2} = \dfrac{2}{p - 2} + 3$

21. $\dfrac{2}{z^2 - 2z - 3} = \dfrac{3}{z - 3} + \dfrac{2}{z + 1}$

For each problem, write an equation and solve it.

22. If four times a number is added to the reciprocal of twice the number, the result is 3. Find the number.

23. The current in a river is 5 miles per hour. A boat can go 125 miles downstream in the same time as 75 miles upstream. Find the speed of the boat in still water.

24. A man can paint a room in his house, working alone, in 5 hours. His wife can do the job in 4 hours. How long will it take them to paint the room if they work together?

25. If x varies directly as y, and $x = 8$ when $y = 12$, find x when $y = 28$.

6

Graphing Linear Equations

The slope of a line, or of a hill, is a measure of steepness.

6.1 Linear Equations in Two Variables

- **1** Write a solution as an ordered pair.
- **2** Decide whether a given ordered pair is a solution of a given equation.
- **3** Complete ordered pairs for a given equation.
- **4** Understand coordinate systems.
- **5** Graph ordered pairs.

The equations discussed so far, such as

$$3x + 5 = 12 \quad \text{or} \quad 2x^2 + x + 5 = 0,$$

have contained only one variable. In this chapter, we study equations in *two* variables, such as

$$y = 4x + 5 \quad \text{or} \quad 2x + 3y = 6.$$

Both of these equations are examples of *linear equations*.

Linear Equation

A **linear equation** in two variables is an equation that can be put in the form

$$ax + by = c,$$

where a, b, and c are real numbers and a and b are not both 0.

1 A solution of a linear equation requires two numbers, one for each variable. For example, the equation $y = 4x + 5$ is satisfied if we replace x with 2 and y with 13, since

$$13 = 4(2) + 5.$$

Thus, $x = 2$ and $y = 13$ is a solution of the equation $y = 4x + 5$. The phrase "$x = 2$ and $y = 13$" is abbreviated

$$(2, 13).$$

This abbreviation gives the x-value, 2, and the y-value, 13, as a pair of numbers, written inside parentheses. The x-value is always given first. A pair of numbers written in this order is called an **ordered pair.**

Of course, letters other than x and y may be used in the equation, with the numbers in the ordered pair placed in alphabetical order. For example, one solution to the equation $3p - q = -11$ is $p = -2$ and $q = 5$. This solution is written as the ordered pair $(-2, 5)$.

2 The next example shows how to decide whether an ordered pair is a solution of an equation.

EXAMPLE 1   Decide whether the given ordered pair is a solution of the given equation.

(a) $(3, 2)$; $2x + 3y = 12$

To see whether $(3, 2)$ is a solution of the equation $2x + 3y = 12$, substitute 3 for x and 2 for y in the given equation.

$$2x + 3y = 12$$
$$2(3) + 3(2) = 12 \qquad \text{Let } x = 3; \text{ let } y = 2$$
$$6 + 6 = 12$$
$$12 = 12 \qquad \text{True}$$

This result is true, so $(3, 2)$ is a solution of $2x + 3y = 12$.

(b) $(-2, -7)$; $2m + 3n = 12$

$$2(-2) + 3(-7) = 12 \qquad \text{Let } m = -2; \text{ let } n = -7$$
$$-4 + (-21) = 12$$
$$-25 = 12 \qquad \text{False}$$

This result is false, so $(-2, -7)$ is *not* a solution of $2m + 3n = 12$.   ●

3 By choosing a number for one variable in a linear equation, we can find the value of the other variable, as shown in the next example.

EXAMPLE 2   Complete the given ordered pairs for the equation $y = 4x + 5$.

(a) $(7, \quad)$

In this ordered pair, $x = 7$. (Remember that x always comes first.) To find the corresponding value of y, replace x with 7 in the equation $y = 4x + 5$.

$$y = 4(7) + 5 = 28 + 5 = 33$$

This gives the ordered pair (7, 33).

(b) (, 13)

In this ordered pair, $y = 13$. To find the value of x, replace y with 13 in the equation and then solve for x.

$$y = 4x + 5$$
$$13 = 4x + 5 \qquad \text{Let } y = 13$$
$$8 = 4x \qquad \text{Subtract 5 from both sides}$$
$$2 = x \qquad \text{Divide both sides by 4}$$

The ordered pair is (2, 13).   ●

EXAMPLE 3   Complete the given ordered pairs for the equation $5x - y = 24$.

Equation	*Ordered pairs*
$5x - y = 24$	(5,) (−3,) (0,)

To find the y-value for the ordered pair (5,   ), replace x with 5 in the given equation and solve for y.

$$5x - y = 24$$
$$5(5) - y = 24 \qquad \text{Let } x = 5$$
$$25 - y = 24$$
$$-y = -1 \qquad \text{Subtract 25 from both sides}$$
$$y = 1$$

This gives the ordered pair (5, 1).

Complete the ordered pair (−3,   ) by letting $x = -3$ in the given equation. Also, complete (0,   ) by letting $x = 0$.

If	$x = -3,$	If	$x = 0,$
then	$5x - y = 24$	then	$5x - y = 24$
becomes	$5(-3) - y = 24$	becomes	$5(0) - y = 24$
	$-15 - y = 24$		$0 - y = 24$
	$-y = 39$		$-y = 24$
	$y = -39.$		$y = -24.$

The completed ordered pairs are as follows.

Equation	*Ordered pairs*
$5x - y = 24$	(5, 1) (−3, −39) (0, −24) ●

EXAMPLE 4   Complete the given ordered pairs for the equation $x = 5$.

Equation	*Ordered pairs*
$x = 5$	(, −2) (, 6) (, 3)

The given equation is $x = 5$. No matter which value of y we might choose, the value of x is always the same, 5. Each ordered pair can be completed by placing 5 in the first position.

Equation	*Ordered pairs*
$x = 5$	(5, −2) (5, 6) (5, 3) ●

When an equation such as $x = 5$ is discussed along with equations of two variables, it is customary to think of $x = 5$ as an equation in two variables by rewriting $x = 5$ as $x + 0y = 5$. This form of the equation shows that for any value of y, the value of x is 5.

4   Each of the equations we have seen in this section has many ordered pairs as solutions. Each choice of a real number for one variable will lead to a particular real number for the other variable. This is true of linear equations in general: linear equations in two variables have an infinite number of solutions.

In Chapter 2 we used a number line to graph solutions of equations in one variable. Now we want to graph solutions of an equation in *two* variables. Since the solutions of such an equation are ordered pairs of numbers in the form (x, y), we need two number lines to do this, one for x and one for y. These two number lines are drawn as shown in Figure 6.1. The horizontal number line is called the **x-axis.** The vertical line is called the **y-axis.** Together, the x-axis and y-axis form a **coordinate system.**

The coordinate system is divided into four regions, called **quadrants.** These quadrants are numbered counterclockwise, as shown in Figure 6.1. Points on the axes themselves are not in any quadrant. The point at which the x-axis and y-axis meet is called the **origin.** The origin is labeled 0 in Figure 6.1.

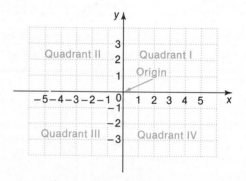

Figure 6.1

5   By referring to the two axes, every point on the plane can be associated with an ordered pair. The numbers in the ordered pair are called the **coordinates** of the point. For example, to locate the point associated with the ordered pair (2, 3), start at the origin. Since the *x*-coordinate is 2, go 2 units to the right along the *x*-axis. Then since the *y*-coordinate is 3, turn and go up 3 units on a line parallel to the *y*-axis. This is called **plotting** the point (2, 3). (See Figure 6.2.) From now on we will refer to the point (2, 3) when we mean the point with *x*-coordinate 2 and *y*-coordinate 3.

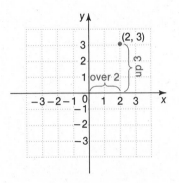

Figure 6.2

EXAMPLE 5   Plot the given points on a coordinate system.

(a) (1, 5)   (b) (−2, 3)   (c) (−1, −4)

(d) (7, −2)   (e) $\left(\dfrac{3}{2}, 2\right)$ (f) (5, 0)

To locate the point (−1, −4), for example, go 1 unit to the left along the *x*-axis. Then turn and go 4 units down, parallel to the *y*-axis. To plot the point (3/2, 2), go 3/2 (or 1 1/2) units to the right along the *x*-axis. Then turn and go 2 units up, parallel to the *y*-axis. Figure 6.3 shows the graphs of the points in this example.   ●

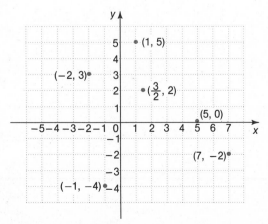

Figure 6.3

EXAMPLE 6   In a certain city, the cost of a taxi ride of x miles is

$$y = 25x + 250,$$

where y represents the cost in cents. Complete the given ordered pairs for this equation.

$$(1, \quad) \quad (2, \quad) \quad (3, \quad)$$

To complete the ordered pair $(1, \quad)$, let $x = 1$.

$$y = 25x + 250$$
$$y = 25(1) + 250 \qquad \text{Let } x = 1$$
$$y = 25 + 250$$
$$y = 275$$

This gives the ordered pair $(1, 275)$, which says that a taxi ride of 1 mile costs 275 cents, or \$2.75.

Complete the ordered pairs $(2, \quad)$ and $(3, \quad)$ as follows.

$$y = 25x + 250 \qquad\qquad\qquad y = 25x + 250$$
$$y = 25(2) + 250 \quad \text{Let } x = 2 \qquad y = 25(3) + 250 \quad \text{Let } x = 3$$
$$y = 50 + 250 \qquad\qquad\qquad y = 75 + 250$$
$$y = 300 \qquad\qquad\qquad\qquad y = 325$$

This gives the ordered pairs $(2, 300)$ and $(3, 325)$.

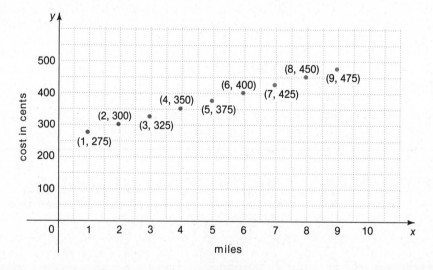

Figure 6.4

Check that other ordered pairs that satisfy the equation $y = 25x + 250$ are (4, 350), (5, 375), (6, 400), (7, 425), (8, 450), and (9, 475). All of the ordered pairs from this example are plotted in Figure 6.4. We have used a different scale on the y-axis, since the y-values in the ordered pairs are much larger than the x-values. Here, each square represents 100 in the vertical direction.   ●

6.1   EXERCISES

Decide whether the given ordered pair is a solution of the given equation. See Example 1.

1. $x + y = 9$;   (2, 7)

2. $3x + y = 8$;   (0, 8)

3. $2x - y = 6$;   (2, -2)

4. $2x + y = 5$;   (2, 1)

5. $4x - 3y = 6$;   (1, 2)

6. $5x - 3y = 1$;   (0, 1)

7. $y = 3x$;   (1, 3)

8. $x = -4y$;   (8, -2)

9. $x = -6$;   (-6, 8)

10. $y = 2$;   (9, 2)

11. $x + 4 = 0$;   (-5, 1)

12. $x - 6 = 0$;   (5, -1)

Complete the given ordered pairs for the equation $y = 3x + 5$. See Example 2.

13. (2,   )

14. (5,   )

15. (8,   )

16. (0,   )

17. (-3,   )

18. (-4,   )

19. (, 14)

20. (, -10)

Complete the ordered pairs using the given equations. See Example 3.

Equation	Ordered pairs
21. $y = 2x + 1$	(3,) (0,) (-1,)
22. $y = 3x - 5$	(2,) (0,) (-3,)
23. $y = 8 - 3x$	(2,) (0,) (-3,)
24. $y = -2 - 5x$	(4,) (0,) (-4,)
25. $2a + b = 9$	(0,) (3,) (12,)
26. $-3m + n = 4$	(1,) (0,) (-2,)

Complete the ordered pairs using the given equations. See Example 4.

Equation	Ordered pairs
27. $x = -4$	(, 6) (, 2) (, -3)
28. $y = -8$	(4,) (0,) (-4,)
29. $x + 9 = 0$	(, 8) (, 3) (, 0)
30. $y - 4 = 0$	(9,) (-5,) (0,)
31. $y = -3x$	(-2,) (0,) (, -6)
32. $x = 4y$	(0,) (, 3) (-8,)

Write the x- and y-coordinates of the points labeled in the figure.

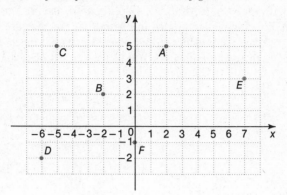

33. *A*   **34.** *B*   **35.** *C*   **36.** *D*   **37.** *E*   **38.** *F*

Plot the following ordered pairs on a coordinate system. See Example 5.

39. (6, 1)   **40.** (4, −2)   **41.** (−4, −5)   **42.** (−2, 4)

43. (−5, −1)   **44.** (−3, 5)   **45.** (3, −5)   **46.** (4, 0)

47. (−2, 0)   **48.** (0, 6)   **49.** (0, −5)   **50.** (0, 0)

Without plotting the given point, state the quadrant in which each point lies.

51. (2, 3)   **52.** (2, −3)   **53.** (−2, 3)   **54.** (−2, −3)

55. (−1, −1)   **56.** (4, 7)   **57.** (−3, 6)   **58.** (1, −5)

59. (5, −4)   **60.** (9, −1)   **61.** (0, 0)   **62.** (−2, 0)

Complete the ordered pairs using the given equation. Then plot the ordered pairs. See Examples 2–5.

Equation	Ordered pairs
63. $y = 2x + 6$	(0,) (2,) (, 0) (, 2)
64. $y = 8 − 4x$	(0,) (3,) (, 0) (, 16)
65. $3x + 5y = 15$	(0,) (10,) (, 0) (, 6)
66. $2x − 5y = 10$	(0,) (10,) (, 0) (, −6)
67. $y = 3x$	(0,) (−2,) (4,) (, −3)
68. $x + 2y = 0$	(0,) (, 3) (4,) (, −1)
69. $y + 2 = 0$	(5,) (0,) (−3,) (−2,)
70. $x − 4 = 0$	(, 7) (, 0) (, −4) (, 4)

71. In statistics we often want to know whether two quantities (such as the height and weight of an individual) are related in such a way that we can predict one when given the other. To find out, ordered pairs that give these quantities for a number of individuals are plotted on a graph (called a *scatter diagram*). If the points lie approximately on a line, the variables have a linear relationship. Make a scatter diagram by plotting the following ordered pairs of heights and weights for six women on the given axes: (62, 105),   (65, 130),   (67, 142),   (63, 115),   (66, 120), (60, 98).

72. In Exercise 71, is there a linear relationship between height and weight? (Do the points lie approximately on a straight line?)

Review Exercises   *Solve each equation. See Section 2.4.*

73. $3m + 5 = 13$

74. $2k - 7 = 9$

75. $3 - y = 12$

76. $-4 - x = 6$

77. $7 + 5p = 12$

78. $9 - 3r = 15$

79. $8 - q = -7$

80. $-3 + 8z = -19$

6.2   Graphing Linear Equations

■ Graph linear equations by completing and plotting ordered pairs.
② Find intercepts.
③ Graph linear equations with just one intercept.
④ Graph linear equations of the form $y = $ a number or $x = $ a number.

■   There are an infinite number of ordered pairs that satisfy an equation in two variables. For example, to find ordered pairs that are solutions of the equation $x + 2y = 7$, we could choose as many values of x (or y) as desired, and then complete each ordered pair.

For instance, if we choose $x = 1$, then

$$x + 2y = 7$$
$$\mathbf{1} + 2y = 7 \qquad \text{Let } x = 1$$
$$2y = 6$$
$$y = 3,$$

so the ordered pair $(1, 3)$ is a solution of the equation. In the same way, $(-3, 5)$, $(3, 2)$, $(0, 7/2)$, $(-2, 9/2)$, $(-1, 4)$, $(6, 1/2)$, and $(7, 0)$ are all solutions of the equation $x + 2y = 7$. These ordered pairs have been plotted in Figure 6.5.

Figure 6.5

Notice that the points plotted in this figure all lie on a straight line. The line that goes through these points is shown in Figure 6.6. In fact, all ordered pairs satisfying the equation $x + 2y = 7$ produce points that lie on this same straight line. This graph gives a "picture" of all the solutions of the equation $x + 2y = 7$. (We only show a portion of the line here, but it goes on forever in both directions.)

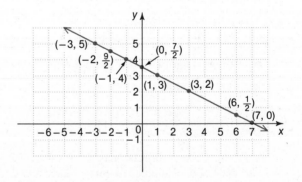

Figure 6.6

It can be shown that

the graph of any linear equation in two variables is a straight line.

(Remember that the word *line* appears in the name "*linear* equation.")
    We can graph a straight line if we know any two different points on the line. However, it is a good idea to plot a third point as a check.

EXAMPLE 1   Graph the linear equation $3x + 2y = 6$.
    We need at least two different points to draw the graph. For many linear equations, two points can be found by first letting $x = 0$, and then letting $y = 0$.

If $x = 0$:

$$3x + 2y = 6$$
$$3(0) + 2y = 6 \qquad \text{Let } x = 0$$
$$0 + 2y = 6$$
$$2y = 6$$
$$y = 3.$$

If $y = 0$:

$$3x + 2y = 6$$
$$3x + 2(0) = 6 \qquad \text{Let } y = 0$$
$$3x + 0 = 6$$
$$3x = 6$$
$$x = 2.$$

This gives the ordered pairs $(0, 3)$ and $(2, 0)$. To get a third point (as a check), let x or y equal some other number. For example, let $x = -2$. (We could have used any other number here as well.) Replace x with -2.

$$3x + 2y = 6$$
$$3(-2) + 2y = 6 \qquad \text{Let } x = -2$$
$$-6 + 2y = 6$$
$$2y = 12$$
$$y = 6$$

Now plot these three ordered pairs, $(0, 3)$, $(2, 0)$, and $(-2, 6)$, and draw a line through them. This line, shown in Figure 6.7, is the graph of $3x + 2y = 6$.   ●

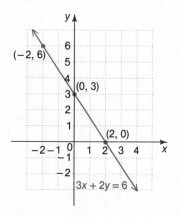

Figure 6.7

EXAMPLE 2   Graph the linear equation $4x - 5y = 20$.

Again, we need at least two different points to draw the graph. By first letting $x = 0$ and then letting $y = 0$, we can complete two ordered pairs.

$$4x - 5y = 20 \qquad\qquad\qquad 4x - 5y = 20$$
$$4(0) - 5y = 20 \quad \text{Let } x = 0 \qquad 4x - 5(0) = 20 \quad \text{Let } y = 0$$
$$-5y = 20 \qquad\qquad\qquad 4x = 20$$
$$y = -4 \qquad\qquad\qquad\quad x = 5$$

The ordered pairs are $(0, -4)$ and $(5, 0)$. To get a third ordered pair (as a check), choose some number other than 0 for x or y. This time, let us choose $y = 2$. Replacing y with 2 in the equation $4x - 5y = 20$ leads to the ordered pair $(15/2, 2)$.

Plot these three ordered pairs, $(0, -4)$, $(5, 0)$, and $(15/2, 2)$, and draw a line through them. This line, shown in Figure 6.8, is the graph of $4x - 5y = 20$.   ●

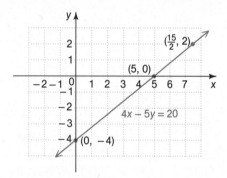

Figure 6.8

2   The graph in Figure 6.8 crosses the y-axis at $(0, -4)$ and the x-axis at $(5, 0)$. For this reason, -4 is called the **y-intercept** and 5 is called the **x-intercept** of the graph. The intercepts are particularly useful for graphing linear equations, as we saw in Examples 1 and 2. The intercepts are found by replacing a variable with 0 in the equation; that is,

Finding Intercepts

> **to find the x-intercept,** let $y = 0$ in the given equation and solve for x;
>
> **to find the y-intercept,** let $x = 0$ in the given equation and solve for y.

EXAMPLE 3   Find the intercepts for the graph of $2x + y = 4$. Draw the graph.

To find the y-intercept, let $x = 0$, and to find the x-intercept, let $y = 0$.

$$2x + y = 4 \qquad\qquad\qquad 2x + y = 4$$
$$2(0) + y = 4 \quad \text{Let } x = 0 \qquad 2x + 0 = 4 \quad \text{Let } y = 0$$
$$0 + y = 4 \qquad\qquad\qquad 2x = 4$$
$$y = 4 \qquad\qquad\qquad\quad x = 2$$

The *y*-intercept is 4. The *x*-intercept is 2. The two intercepts are shown in Figure 6.9. •

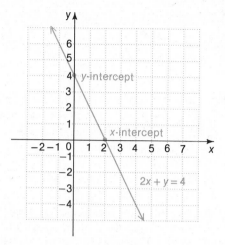

Figure 6.9

3   In the examples above we found the *x*- and *y*-intercepts to help draw the graph. This is not always possible, as the following examples show. Example 4 shows what to do when the *x*- and *y*-intercepts are the same point.

EXAMPLE 4   Graph the linear equation $x = 3y$.

   If we let $x = 0$, we get $y = 0$, giving the ordered pair $(0, 0)$. If $y = 0$, we also get $(0, 0)$. This is the same pair, so we want to find two more ordered pairs satisfying the equation $x = 3y$. If we choose 2 for *y*, we get 6 for *x*, giving the ordered pair $(6, 2)$. For a check point, we choose -6 for *x* and get -2 for *y*. This gives the ordered pair $(-6, -2)$. These three ordered pairs were used to get the graph shown in Figure 6.10. •

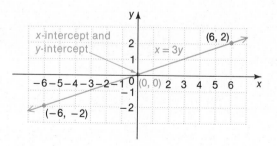

Figure 6.10

Generalizing from Example 4,

Line through the Origin

> the graph of a linear equation of the form
>
> $$x = ay \qquad \text{or} \qquad y = ax$$
>
> goes through the origin, $(0, 0)$.

4   The equation $y = -4$ is a linear equation in which the coefficient of x is 0. (To see this, write $y = -4$ as $y = 0x - 4$.) Also, $x = 3$ is a linear equation in which the coefficient of y is 0. These equations lead to horizontal or vertical straight lines, as the next examples show.

EXAMPLE 5   Graph the linear equation $y = -4$.

As the equation states, for any value of x that we might choose, y is always equal to -4. To get ordered pairs that are solutions of this equation, choose any numbers for x but always let y equal -4. Three ordered pairs that can be used are $(-2, -4)$, $(0, -4)$, and $(3, -4)$. Drawing a line through these points gives the horizontal line shown in Figure 6.11.   ●

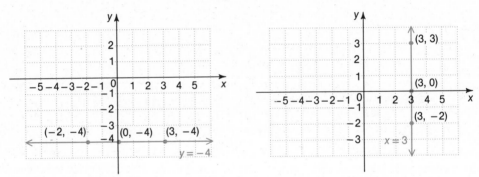

Figure 6.11   **Figure 6.12**

Horizontal Line

> The graph of the linear equation $y = k$, where k is a real number, is the horizontal line going through the point $(0, k)$.

EXAMPLE 6   Graph the linear equation $x = 3$.

All the ordered pairs that are solutions of this equation have an x-value of 3. We can use any number for y. Three ordered pairs that work are $(3, 3)$, $(3, 0)$, and $(3, -2)$. Drawing a line through these points gives the vertical line shown in Figure 6.12.   ●

Vertical Line

> The graph of the linear equation $x = k$, where k is a real number, is the vertical line going through the point $(k, 0)$.

The different forms of straight-line equations and the methods of graphing them are summarized below.

Graphing Straight Lines

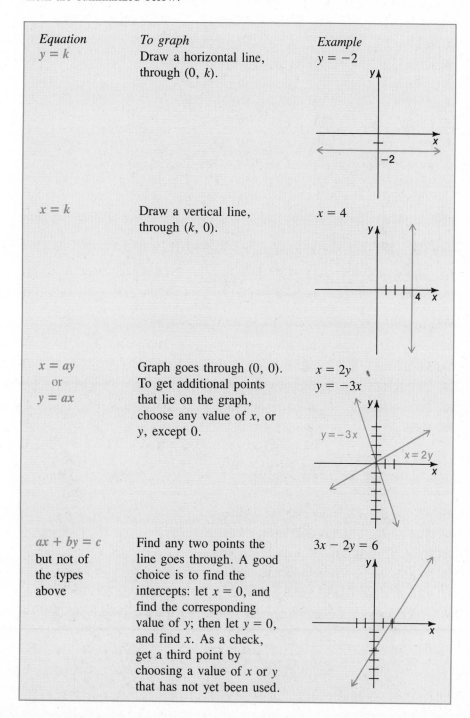

Equation	To graph	Example
$y = k$	Draw a horizontal line, through $(0, k)$.	$y = -2$
$x = k$	Draw a vertical line, through $(k, 0)$.	$x = 4$
$x = ay$ or $y = ax$	Graph goes through $(0, 0)$. To get additional points that lie on the graph, choose any value of x, or y, except 0.	$x = 2y$ $y = -3x$
$ax + by = c$ but not of the types above	Find any two points the line goes through. A good choice is to find the intercepts: let $x = 0$, and find the corresponding value of y; then let $y = 0$, and find x. As a check, get a third point by choosing a value of x or y that has not yet been used.	$3x - 2y = 6$

6.2 EXERCISES

Complete the ordered pairs for each equation. Then graph the equation by plotting the points and drawing a line through them. See Examples 1 and 2.

1. $x + y = 5$ (0,) (, 0) (2,)

2. $y = x - 3$ (0,) (, 0) (5,)

3. $y = x + 4$ (0,) (, 0) (−2,)

4. $y + 5 = x$ (0,) (, 0) (6,)

5. $y = 3x - 6$ (0,) (, 0) (3,)

6. $x = 2y + 1$ (0,) (, 0) (3,)

7. $2x + 5y = 20$ (0,) (, 0) (5,)

8. $3x - 4y = 12$ (0,) (, 0) (8,)

9. $x + 5 = 0$ (, 2) (, 0) (, −3)

10. $y - 4 = 0$ (3,) (0,) (−2,)

Find the intercepts for each equation. See Example 3.

11. $2x + 3y = 6$ **12.** $7x + 2y = 14$ **13.** $3x - 5y = 9$ **14.** $6x - 5y = 12$

15. $2y = 5x$ **16.** $x = -3y$ **17.** $-2x = 8$ **18.** $6y = 12$

Graph each linear equation. See Examples 1, 2, and 4–6.

19. $x - y = 2$ **20.** $x + y = 6$ **21.** $y = x + 4$ **22.** $y = x - 5$

23. $x + 2y = 6$ **24.** $3x - y = 6$ **25.** $4x = 3y - 12$ **26.** $5x = 2y - 10$

27. $3x = 6 - 2y$ **28.** $2x + 3y = 12$ **29.** $2x - 7y = 14$ **30.** $3x + 5y = 15$

31. $3x + 7y = 14$ **32.** $6x - 5y = 30$ **33.** $y = 2x$ **34.** $y = -3x$

35. $y + 6x = 0$ **36.** $x - 4y = 0$ **37.** $x + 2 = 0$ **38.** $y - 3 = 0$

39. $y = -1$ **40.** $x = 2$ **41.** $x = 0$ **42.** $y = 0$

Translate each of the statements of Exercises 43–48 into an equation. Then graph the equation.

43. The *x*-value is 2 more than the *y*-value.

44. The *y*-value is 3 less than the *x*-value.

45. The *y*-value is 3 less than twice the *x*-value.

46. The *x*-value is 4 more than three times the *y*-value.

47. If 3 is added to the *y*-value, the result is 4 less than twice the *x*-value.

48. If 6 is subtracted from 4 times the *y*-value, the result is three times the *x*-value.

49. As a rough estimate, the weight of a man taller than about 60 inches is approximated by $y = 5.5x - 220$, where x is the height of the person in inches, and y is the weight in pounds. Estimate the weights of men whose heights are
(a) 62 inches;   (b) 64 inches;   (c) 68 inches;   (d) 72 inches.
(e) Graph $y = 5.5x - 220$.

50. The graph shows the median cost of a new single-family house in thousands of dollars from 1975 to 1981. (The middle entry in a list of numbers arranged in numerical order is called the *median*.) Use the graph to find the following information.
(a) What was the median cost of a new house in 1976? in 1979?
(b) During what year did the cost of a new house increase from about $49,000 to about $56,000?

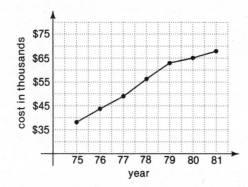

51. The demand for an item is closely related to its price. As price goes up, demand goes down. On the other hand, when price goes down, demand goes up. Suppose the demand for a certain small calculator is 500 when its price is $30 and 4000 when its price is $15.
(a) Let x be the price and y be the demand (in thousands) for the calculator. Graph the two given pairs of prices and demand.
(b) Assume the relationship is linear. Draw a line through the two points from part (a). From your graph estimate the demand if the price drops to $10.

Review Exercises   *Find each quotient. See Section 1.9.*

52. $\dfrac{4 - 2}{8 - 5}$

53. $\dfrac{-3 - 5}{2 - 7}$

54. $\dfrac{-2 - (-4)}{3 - (-1)}$

55. $\dfrac{5 - (-7)}{-4 - (-1)}$

56. $\dfrac{-2 - (-5)}{-9 - 12}$

57. $\dfrac{-6 - 3}{4 - (-5)}$

58. $\dfrac{-9 - 4}{-2 - 3}$

59. $\dfrac{12 - (-4)}{-3 - 5}$

60. $\dfrac{-2 - (-7)}{3 - 3}$

6.3 The Slope of a Line

▌1▐ Find the slope of a line given two points.

▌2▐ Find the slope from the equation of a line.

▌3▐ Use the slope to determine whether two lines are parallel, perpendicular, or neither.

To graph a straight line, we need at least two different points that are on the line. We also can graph a line if we know one point that the line goes through, along with the "steepness" of the line.

▌1▐ One way to get a measure of the "steepness" of a line is to compare the vertical change in the line (the rise) to the horizontal change (the run) as we move along the line from one fixed point to another. This measure of steepness is called the **slope** of the line. Slope is defined as

Slope

$$\text{slope} = \frac{\text{difference in } y\text{-values}}{\text{difference in } x\text{-values}}.$$

The slope is sometimes called the ratio of rise to run. As shown in Figure 6.13, if (x_1, y_1) (read "x-sub-one, y-sub-one") and (x_2, y_2) are any two *different* points on a line, then the slope, m, of the line is

Slope Formula

$$m = \frac{y_2 - y_1}{x_2 - x_1}.$$

Figure 6.13

EXAMPLE 1   Find the slope of each of the following lines.

(a) The line through $(-4, 7)$ and $(1, -2)$

Use the definition given above. Let $(-4, 7) = (x_2, y_2)$ and $(1, -2) = (x_1, y_1)$. Then

$$\text{slope} = \frac{\text{difference in } y\text{-values}}{\text{difference in } x\text{-values}}$$

$$= \frac{y_2 - y_1}{x_2 - x_1}$$

$$= \frac{7 - (-2)}{-4 - 1} = \frac{9}{-5} = -\frac{9}{5}.$$

See Figure 6.14.

Figure 6.14

(b) The line through $(12, -5)$ and $(-9, -2)$

$$\text{slope} = \frac{-5 - (-2)}{12 - (-9)} = \frac{-3}{21} = -\frac{1}{7}$$

We get the same slope if we subtract in reverse order.

$$\frac{-2 - (-5)}{-9 - 12} = \frac{3}{-21} = -\frac{1}{7} \quad \bullet$$

It makes no difference which point is (x_1, y_1) or (x_2, y_2); however,

it is important to always start with the x- and y-values of *one* point (either one) and subtract the corresponding values of the *other* point.

The next examples show how to look for slopes of horizontal and vertical lines.

EXAMPLE 2   Find the slope of the line through (−8, 4) and (2, 4).
Use the definition of slope.

$$\text{slope} = \frac{4 - 4}{-8 - 2} = \frac{0}{-10} = 0$$

The graph in Figure 6.15 shows that the line through these two points is horizontal. Since all points on a horizontal line have the same y-value, *the slope of any horizontal line is 0.* •

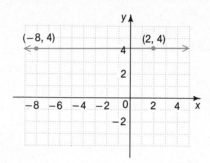

Figure 6.15

EXAMPLE 3   Find the slope of the line through (6, 2) and (6, −9).

$$\text{slope} = \frac{2 - (-9)}{6 - 6} = \frac{11}{0} \qquad \text{Undefined}$$

Division by 0 is not possible, so the slope is undefined. The graph in Figure 6.16 shows that the line through these two points is vertical. Since all points on a vertical line have the same x-value, *the slope of any vertical line is undefined.* •

Figure 6.16

**Slope of
Horizontal and
Vertical Lines**

> **Horizontal lines,** which have equations of the form $y = k$, have a slope of 0.
>
> **Vertical lines,** which have equations of the form $x = k$, have undefined slope.

▣   The slope of a line can be found directly from its equation. To see how this is done, first let us find the slope of the line

$$y = -3x + 5.$$

To find the slope, we need two points on the line. Get these two points by choosing two different values of x, say -2 and 4.

If $x = -2$:		If $x = 4$:	
$y = -3(-2) + 5$	Let $x = -2$	$y = -3(4) + 5$	Let $x = 4$
$y = 6 + 5$		$y = -12 + 5$	
$y = 11.$		$y = -7.$	

The ordered pairs are $(-2, 11)$ and $(4, -7)$. Now find the slope, m.

$$m = \frac{11 - (-7)}{-2 - 4} = \frac{18}{-6} = -3$$

The slope, -3, is the same number as the coefficient of x in the equation $y = -3x + 5$. It can be shown that this always happens, as long as the equation is solved for y. This fact is used to find the slope of a line when we know its equation.

**Slope of a Line
from Its
Equation**

> 1. Solve the equation for y.
> 2. The slope is given by the coefficient of x.

EXAMPLE 4   Find the slope of each of the following lines.

(a) $2x - 5y = 4$

Solve the equation for y.

$$2x - 5y = 4$$
$$-5y = -2x + 4$$
$$y = \frac{2}{5}x - \frac{4}{5}$$

The slope is given by the coefficient of x, so the slope is

$$m = \frac{2}{5}.$$

(b) $8x + 4y = 1$

Solve for y; you should get

$$y = -2x + \frac{1}{4}.$$

The slope of this line is the coefficient of x, or $m = -2$. ●

3 As we said, the slope of a line measures the steepness of a line. Since parallel lines are equally steep, they should have equal slopes. Also, lines having slopes with a product of -1 can be shown to be perpendicular. In summary,

Parallel and Perpendicular Lines

> two lines with the same slope are parallel; two lines that have slopes with a product of -1 are perpendicular.

EXAMPLE 5 Decide whether each pair of lines is parallel, perpendicular, or neither.

(a) $\quad x + 2y = 7$

$\quad -2x + \ y = 3$

Find the slope of each line by first solving each equation for y.

$$\begin{array}{ll}
x + 2y = 7 & \qquad -2x + y = 3 \\
2y = -x + 7 & \qquad y = 2x + 3 \\
y = -\dfrac{1}{2}x + \dfrac{7}{2} & \\
\text{Slope is } -\dfrac{1}{2} & \qquad \text{Slope is } 2
\end{array}$$

Since the slopes are not equal, the lines are not parallel. Check the product of the slopes: $(-1/2)(2) = -1$. The two lines are perpendicular because the product of their slopes is -1.

(b) $3x - \ y = 4$

$\quad 6x - 2y = 9$

Find the slopes. You should find that both lines have a slope of 3, so the lines are parallel.

(c) $4x + 3y = 6$

$\quad 2x - \ y = 5$

Here the slopes are $-4/3$ and 2. These lines are neither parallel nor perpendicular. ●

6.3   EXERCISES

Find the slope of each of the following lines. See Example 1.

1.

2.

3.

4.

5.

6.

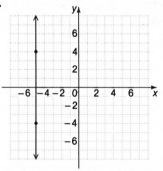

Find the slope of the line going through each pair of points. Round to the nearest thousandth in Exercises 16 and 17. See Examples 1–3.

7. $(-4, 1)$, $(2, 8)$

8. $(3, 7)$, $(5, 2)$

9. $(-1, 2)$, $(-3, -7)$

10. $(5, -4)$, $(-5, -9)$

11. $(8, 0)$, $(0, 5)$

12. $(0, -3)$, $(2, 0)$

13. $(-1, 6)$, $(4, 6)$

14. $(5, 3)$, $(5, -2)$

15. $(-9, 1)$, $(-9, 0)$

16. $(1.23, 4.80)$, $(2.56, -3.75)$

17. $(0.03, 1.57)$, $(3.54, -2.01)$

Find the slope of each of the following lines. See Example 4.

18. $y = 5x + 2$

19. $y = -x + 4$

20. $y = x + 1$

21. $y = 6 - 5x$

22. $y = 3 + 9x$

23. $2x + y = 5$

24. $4x - y = 8$

25. $-6x + 4y = 1$

26. $3x - 2y = 5$

27. $2x + 5y = 4$

28. $9x + 7y = 5$

29. $y + 4 = 0$

Decide whether each pair of lines is parallel, perpendicular, or neither. See Example 5.

30. $y - x = 3$
$y - x = 5$

31. $x + y = 5$
$x - y = 1$

32. $y - x = 4$
$y + x = 3$

33. $2x - 5y = 4$
$4x - 10y = 1$

34. $3x - 2y = 4$
$2x + 3y = 1$

35. $3x - 5y = 2$
$5x + 3y = -1$

36. $4x - 3y = 4$
$8x - 6y = 0$

37. $x - 4y = 2$
$2x + 4y = 1$

38. $8x - 9y = 2$
$3x + 6y = 1$

39. $5x - 3y = 8$
$3x - 5y = 10$

40. $6x + y = 12$
$x - 6y = 12$

41. $2x - 5y = 11$
$4x + 5y = 2$

Review Exercises   *Solve for y. See Section 2.2.*

42. $y - 2 = 3(x - 4)$

43. $y + 1 = 2(x - 5)$

44. $y - (-3) = -2(x - 1)$

45. $y - (-4) = -(x + 1)$

46. $y - (-5) = 4[x - (-1)]$

47. $y - 2 = -3[x - (-1)]$

48. $y - \dfrac{2}{3} = -\dfrac{3}{4}(x + 2)$

49. $y - \left(-\dfrac{3}{5}\right) = -\dfrac{1}{2}[x - (-3)]$

50. $y - \left(-\dfrac{5}{8}\right) = \dfrac{3}{8}(x - 5)$

6.4   The Equation of a Line

1   Write the equation of a line given its slope and *y*-intercept.

2   Graph a line given its slope and a point on the line.

3   Write the equation of a line given its slope and a point on the line.

4   Write the equation of a line given two points on the line.

In the last section we saw how to find the slope of a line from its equation. For example, the slope of the line having the equation $y = 2x + 3$ is 2, the coefficient of *x*. What does the number 3 represent? If we let $x = 0$, the equation becomes

$$y = 2(0) + 3 = 0 + 3 = 3.$$

Since we found $y = 3$ by letting $x = 0$, the number 3 is the *y*-intercept of the graph of $y = 2x + 3$.

1   An equation solved for *y* is said to be in **slope-intercept form** because both the slope and the *y*-intercept of the line can be found from the equation.

Slope-Intercept Form

> When the equation of a line is in the form
>
> $$y = mx + b,$$
>
> the slope of the line is m and the y-intercept is b.

Given the slope and y-intercept of a line, the slope-intercept form can be used to find the equation of the line.

EXAMPLE 1   Find the equation of each of the following lines.

(a) With slope 5 and y-intercept 3

   Use the slope-intercept form. Let $m = 5$ and $b = 3$.

$$y = mx + b$$
$$y = 5x + 3$$

(b) With slope 2/3 and y-intercept -1

   Here $m = 2/3$ and $b = -1$.

$$y = mx + b$$
$$y = \frac{2}{3}x - 1 \quad \bullet$$

2   We can use the slope and y-intercept to graph a line. For example, to graph $y = \frac{2}{3}x - 1$, first locate the y-intercept, -1, on the y-axis. From the definition of slope and the fact that the slope of this line is 2/3, we know that

$$\frac{\text{difference in } y\text{-values}}{\text{difference in } x\text{-values}} = \frac{2}{3}.$$

Because of this, we can get another point on the graph of the line by counting from the y-intercept 2 units up and then going 3 units to the right. The line is then drawn through this point and the y-intercept, as shown in Figure 6.17. This method can be extended to graph a line with a given slope through any given point.

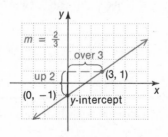

Figure 6.17

EXAMPLE 2

Graph the line through $(-2, 3)$ with slope $-5/4$.

First, locate the point $(-2, 3)$. Write the slope as

$$\frac{\text{difference in } y\text{-values}}{\text{difference in } x\text{-values}} = \frac{-5}{4}.$$

(We could have used $5/-4$ instead.) Another point on the line is located by counting 5 units *down* (because of the negative sign) and then 4 units to the right. Finally, draw the line through this new point and the given point. See Figure 6.18. ●

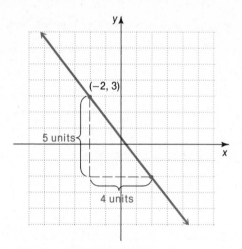

Figure 6.18

3 Given a point on a line and the slope of the line, we can find the equation of the line. To do this, let m represent the slope of the line and let (x_1, y_1) represent the given point on the line. Let (x, y) represent any other point on the line. Then by the definition of slope,

$$\frac{y - y_1}{x - x_1} = m$$

or $y - y_1 = m(x - x_1)$.

This result is the **point-slope form** of the equation of a line.

Point-Slope Form

> An equation of the line with slope m going through (x_1, y_1) is
>
> $$y - y_1 = m(x - x_1).$$

EXAMPLE 3

Find the equation of each of the following lines. Write the equation in the form $ax + by = c$.

(a) Through $(-2, 4)$, with slope -3

The given point is $(-2, 4)$ so $x_1 = -2$ and $y_1 = 4$. Also, $m = -3$. Substitute these values into the point-slope form.

$$y - y_1 = m(x - x_1)$$
$$y - 4 = -3[x - (-2)]$$
$$y - 4 = -3(x + 2)$$
$$y - 4 = -3x - 6$$
$$y = -3x - 2$$
$$3x + y = -2$$

(b) Through $(4, 2)$, with slope 3/5

Here $x_1 = 4$, $y_1 = 2$, and $m = 3/5$.

$$y - y_1 = m(x - x_1)$$
$$y - 2 = \frac{3}{5}(x - 4)$$

Multiply both sides by 5 to clear of fractions.

$$5(y - 2) = 5 \cdot \frac{3}{5}(x - 4)$$

$$5(y - 2) = 3(x - 4)$$
$$5y - 10 = 3x - 12$$
$$5y = 3x - 2$$
$$-3x + 5y = -2 \quad \bullet$$

4   The point-slope form also can be used to find an equation of a line when two points on the line are known.

EXAMPLE 4   Find the equation of the line through the points $(-2, 5)$ and $(3, 4)$. Write the equation in the form $ax + by = c$.

First find the slope of the line, using the definition of slope.

$$\text{slope} = \frac{5 - 4}{-2 - 3} = \frac{1}{-5} = -\frac{1}{5}$$

Now use either $(-2, 5)$ or $(3, 4)$ and the point-slope form. Using $(3, 4)$ gives

$$y - y_1 = m(x - x_1)$$
$$y - 4 = -\frac{1}{5}(x - 3)$$
$$5(y - 4) = -1(x - 3)$$
$$5y - 20 = -x + 3$$
$$5y = -x + 23$$
$$x + 5y = 23.$$

We would get the same result using $(-2, 5)$ for (x_1, y_1). $\bullet$

A summary of the types of *linear equations* is given here.

Linear Equations

$ax + by = c$	**General form** (neither a nor b is 0) Slope is $-a/b$ x-intercept is c/a y-intercept is c/b
$x = k$	**Vertical line** Slope is undefined x-intercept is k
$y = k$	**Horizontal line** Slope is 0 y-intercept is k
$y = mx + b$	**Slope-intercept form** Slope is m y-intercept is b
$y - y_1 = m(x - x_1)$	**Point-slope form** Slope is m Line goes through (x_1, y_1)

6.4 EXERCISES

Write an equation for each line given its slope and y-intercept. See Example 1.

1. $m = 3$, y-intercept 5

2. $m = -2$, y-intercept 4

3. $m = -1$, y-intercept -6

4. $m = \dfrac{5}{3}$, y-intercept $\dfrac{1}{2}$

5. $m = \dfrac{2}{5}$, y-intercept $-\dfrac{1}{4}$

6. $m = 8$, y-intercept 0

7. $m = 0$, y-intercept -5

8. $m = -2.15$, y-intercept .832

9. $m = 4.61$, y-intercept -2.38

Graph the line going through the given point and having the given slope. (In Exercises 21–24, recall the type of lines having 0 slope and undefined slope.) See Example 2.

10. $(2, 5)$, $m = \dfrac{1}{2}$

11. $(-4, -3)$, $m = -\dfrac{2}{5}$

12. $(-1, -1)$, $m = -\dfrac{3}{8}$

13. $(0, 2)$, $m = \dfrac{7}{4}$ **14.** $(-3, 0)$, $m = \dfrac{5}{9}$ **15.** $(6, 4)$, $m = 2$

16. $(1, 8)$, $m = 1$ **17.** $(-4, 7)$, $m = -3$ **18.** $(2, 9)$, $m = -4$

19. $(4, -1)$, $m = 2$ **20.** $(3, -5)$, $m = 1$ **21.** $(1, 2)$, $m = 0$

22. $(-4, -8)$, $m = 0$ **23.** $(3, 5)$,   undefined slope   **24.** $(2, 3)$,   undefined slope

Write an equation for the line passing through the given point and having the given slope. See Example 3.

25. $(5, 3)$, $m = 2$ **26.** $(1, 4)$, $m = 3$ **27.** $(2, -8)$, $m = -2$

28. $(-1, 7)$, $m = -4$ **29.** $(3, 5)$, $m = \dfrac{2}{3}$ **30.** $(2, -4)$, $m = \dfrac{4}{5}$

31. $(-3, -2)$, $m = -\dfrac{3}{4}$ **32.** $(-8, -2)$, $m = -\dfrac{5}{9}$ **33.** $(6, 0)$, $m = -\dfrac{8}{11}$

Write equations of the lines passing through each pair of points. Write the equations in the form ax + by = c. See Example 4.

34. $(7, 4)$, $(8, 5)$ **35.** $(-2, 1)$, $(3, 4)$

36. $(-8, -2)$, $(-1, -7)$ **37.** $(3, -4)$, $(-2, -1)$

38. $(-7, -5)$, $(-9, -2)$ **39.** $(0, 2)$, $(3, 0)$

40. $(4, 0)$, $(0, -2)$ **41.** $(2, -5)$, $(-4, 7)$

42. $(3, -7)$, $(-5, 0)$ **43.** $\left(\dfrac{1}{2}, \dfrac{3}{2}\right)$, $\left(-\dfrac{1}{4}, \dfrac{5}{4}\right)$

44. $\left(-\dfrac{2}{3}, \dfrac{8}{3}\right)$, $\left(\dfrac{1}{3}, \dfrac{7}{3}\right)$ **45.** $\left(-1, \dfrac{5}{8}\right)$, $\left(\dfrac{1}{8}, 2\right)$

The cost y of an item is often expressed as y = mx + b, where x is the number of items produced. The number b gives the fixed cost (the cost that is the same no matter how many items are produced), and the number m is the variable cost (the cost to produce an additional item). Write the cost equation for each of the following.

46. Fixed cost 50, variable cost 9

47. Fixed cost 100, variable cost 12

48. Fixed cost 70.5, variable cost 3.5

49. Refer to Exercise 47 and find the total cost to make (a) 50 items and (b) 125 items.

50. Refer to Exercise 48 and find the total cost to make (a) 25 items and (b) 110 items.

The sales of a company for a given year can be written as an ordered pair in which the first number gives the year (perhaps since the company started business) and the second number gives the sales for that year. If the sales increase at a steady rate, a linear equation for sales can be found. Sales for two years are given for each of two companies below.

Company A		Company B	
Year	Sales	Year	Sales
x	*y*	*x*	*y*
1	24	1	18
5	48	4	27

51. (a) Write two ordered pairs of the form (year, sales) for Company A.
  (b) Write an equation of the line through the two pairs in part (a). This is a sales equation for Company A.

52. (a) Write two ordered pairs of the form (year, sales) for Company B.
  (b) Write an equation of the line through the two pairs in part (a). This is a sales equation for Company B.

Review Exercises   *Solve each inequality. See Sections 2.8 and 2.9.*

53. $m + 3 < 10$ **54.** $k - 5 \geq 10$ **55.** $2p + 7 \leq 8$ **56.** $3p - 9 \geq 4$
57. $6 - 2p < 12$ **58.** $5 - 3p < -8$ **59.** $-4 - p > 7$ **60.** $-8 - 3p < 4$

6.5 Graphing Linear Inequalities

1 Graph $\leq$ or $\geq$ linear inequalities.
2 Graph $<$ or $>$ linear inequalities.
3 Graph inequalities with a boundary through the origin.

1   In Section 6.2 we discussed methods for graphing linear equations, such as $2x + 3y = 6$. In this section we extend this discussion to linear inequalities, such as

$$2x + 3y \leq 6.$$

(Recall that $\leq$ is read "is less than or equal to.")
  The inequality $2x + 3y \leq 6$ means that

$$2x + 3y < 6 \quad \text{or} \quad 2x + 3y = 6.$$

We know that the graph of $2x + 3y = 6$ is a line. This line will be the boundary of a region that includes the ordered pairs that are solutions to the inequality $2x + 3y < 6$. The line and the region make up the complete solution. To find the required region, solve the given inequality for y.

$$2x + 3y \leq 6$$
$$3y \leq -2x + 6$$
$$y \leq -\frac{2}{3}x + 2$$

The last statement tells us that ordered pairs in which y is *less than or equal to* $(-2/3)x + 2$ will be solutions to the inequality. The ordered pairs in which y is equal to $(-2/3)x + 2$ are on a line, so the pairs in which y is less than $(-2/3)x + 2$ will be *below* that line. To indicate the solution, shade the region below the line, as in Figure 6.19. The shaded region, along with the original line, is the graph we want.

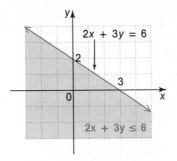

Figure 6.19

A quick way to find the correct region to shade is to use a test point. Choose any point *not on the line*. Because $(0, 0)$ is easy to substitute into the inequality it is often a good choice, and we will use it here. Substitute 0 for x and 0 for y in the given inequality to see whether the resulting statement is true or false. In the example above,

$$2x + 3y \leq 6$$
$$2(0) + 3(0) \leq 6 \qquad \text{Let } x = 0 \text{ and } y = 0$$
$$0 + 0 \leq 6$$
$$0 \leq 6. \qquad \text{True}$$

Since the last statement is true, shade the region that includes the test point $(0, 0)$. This agrees with the result shown in Figure 6.19.

2 Inequalities that do not include the equals sign are graphed in a similar way.

EXAMPLE 1 Graph the inequality $x - y > 5$.

This inequality does not include the equals sign. Therefore, the points on the line $x - y = 5$ do not belong to the graph, but the line still serves as a boundary for two regions, one of which satisfies the inequality. To graph the inequality, first graph the equation $x - y = 5$. Use a dashed line to show that the points on the line are not solutions of the inequality $x - y > 5$. Choose a test point to see which region satisfies the inequality. Let us choose (0, 0) again.

$$x - y > 5 \qquad \text{Original inequality}$$
$$0 - 0 > 5 \qquad \text{Let } x = 0 \text{ and } y = 0$$
$$0 > 5 \qquad \text{False}$$

Since $0 > 5$ is false, the graph of the inequality includes the region that does *not* contain (0, 0). Shade this region, as shown in Figure 6.20. As a check, we could test a point on the other side of the line. Verify that the ordered pair $(5, -1)$, for example, leads to a true result. ●

Figure 6.20

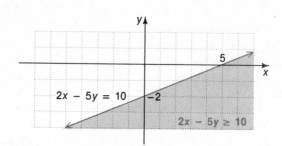

Figure 6.21

EXAMPLE 2 Graph the inequality $2x - 5y \geq 10$.

Graph the equation $2x - 5y = 10$. Use a solid line to show that the points on the line are solutions of the inequality $2x - 5y \geq 10$. Choose any test point not on the line. Again, we choose (0, 0).

$$2x - 5y \geq 10 \qquad \text{Original inequality}$$
$$2(0) - 5(0) \geq 10 \qquad \text{Let } x = 0 \text{ and } y = 0$$
$$0 - 0 \geq 10$$
$$0 \geq 10 \qquad \text{False}$$

Since $0 \geq 10$ is false, shade the region *not* containing the test point $(0, 0)$. (See Figure 6.21.) ●

EXAMPLE 3   Graph the inequality $x \leq 3$.

First, graph $x = 3$, a vertical line going through the point $(3, 0)$. Use a solid line. (Why?) Then, let us choose $(0, 0)$ as a test point.

$$x \leq 3 \qquad \text{Original inequality}$$
$$0 \leq 3 \qquad \text{Let } x = 0$$
$$0 \leq 3 \qquad \text{True}$$

Since $0 \leq 3$ is true, shade the region containing $(0, 0)$, as in Figure 6.22. ●

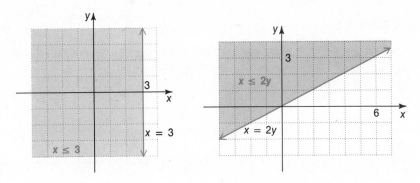

Figure 6.22   **Figure 6.23**

3   The next example shows how to graph an inequality having a boundary line going through the origin, an inequality in which $(0, 0)$ cannot be used as a test point.

EXAMPLE 4   Graph the inequality $x \leq 2y$.

Begin by graphing $x = 2y$. Some ordered pairs that can be used to graph this line are $(0, 0)$, $(6, 3)$, and $(4, 2)$. Use a solid line. We cannot use $(0, 0)$ as a test point since $(0, 0)$ is on the line $x = 2y$. We must choose a test point off the line $x = 2y$. Let us choose $(1, 3)$, which is not on the line.

$$x \leq 2y \qquad \text{Original inequality}$$
$$1 \leq 2(3) \qquad \text{Let } x = 1 \text{ and } y = 3$$
$$1 \leq 6 \qquad \text{True}$$

Since $1 \leq 6$ is true, shade the side of the graph containing the test point $(1, 3)$. (See Figure 6.23.) ●

A summary of the steps used to graph a linear inequality in two variables is given below.

**Graphing a
Linear
Inequality**

1. Graph the line that is the boundary of the region. Use the method of Section 6.2. Draw a solid line if the inequality has $\leq$ or $\geq$; draw a dashed line if the inequality has $<$ or $>$.

2. Use any point off the line as a test point. Substitute for x and y in the inequality. If a true statement results, shade the region containing the test point. If a false statement results, shade the region not containing the test point.

6.5 EXERCISES

In Exercises 1–12, the straight line for each inequality has been drawn.
Complete each graph by shading the correct region. See Example 1.

1. $x + y \leq 4$

2. $x + y \geq 2$

3. $x + 2y \leq 7$

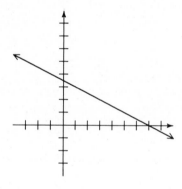

4. $2x + y \leq 5$

5. $-3x + 4y < 12$

6. $4x - 5y > 20$

7. $5x + 3y > 15$

8. $6x - 5y < 30$

9. $x < 4$

10. $y > -1$

11. $x \le 4y$

12. $-2x > y$

Graph each linear inequality. See Examples 1–4.

13. $x + y \le 8$ **14.** $x + y \ge 4$ **15.** $x - y \le -2$ **16.** $x - y \le 3$

17. $x + 2y \ge 4$ **18.** $x + 3y \le 6$ **19.** $2x + 3y > 6$ **20.** $3x + 4y > 12$

21. $3x - 4y < 12$ **22.** $2x - 3y < -6$ **23.** $3x + 7y \ge 21$ **24.** $2x + 5y \ge 10$

25. $4x - 5y \ge 20$ **26.** $3x + 5y \le 15$ **27.** $4x + 7y \le 14$ **28.** $x - y \le 2$

29. $x < 4$ **30.** $x < -2$ **31.** $y \le 2$ **32.** $y \le -3$

33. $x \ge -2$ **34.** $x \le 3y$ **35.** $x \le 5y$ **36.** $x \ge -2y$

37. $-4x \le y$ **38.** $2x + 3y \ge 0$ **39.** $3x + 4y \le 0$ **40.** $x + y < 0$

41. A company will ship x units of merchandise to outlet I and y units of merchandise to outlet II. The company must ship a total of at least 500 units to these two outlets. Express this by writing

$$x + y \ge 500.$$

(a) Graph this inequality. (Here $x \ge 0$ and $y \ge 0$.)

(b) Give some sample values of x and y that satisfy the inequality.

42. Ms. Branson takes x vitamin C tablets each day at a cost of 10¢ each and y multivitamins each day at a cost of 15¢ each. She wants the total cost to be no more than 50¢ a day. To express this we write

$$10x + 15y \leq 50.$$

(a) Graph this inequality. (Here $x \geq 0$ and $y \geq 0$.)

(b) Give some values of x and y that satisfy the inequality.

Review Exercises *Find the value of $3x^2 - 2x + 5$ for each value of x.*
See Section 3.4.

43. 2   **44.** -4 **45.** 3   **46.** 0

Find the value of $2x^4 - x^2$ for each value of x.

47. 3   **48.** -2 **49.** -1 **50.** -3

6.6 Functions

1️⃣ Learn the definition of a function.

2️⃣ Use the vertical line test for a function.

3️⃣ Find domains and ranges.

4️⃣ Learn to use *f(x)* notation.

1️⃣ We have now studied equations in two variables, such as $4x + 5y = 8$. A special type of equation in two variables, called a function, comes up often enough that it deserves special study.

Function

> A **function** is a rule or correspondence in which each value of x leads to exactly one value of y.

2️⃣ Given a graph, we can use the definition of a function to decide whether the graph represents a function or not. By the definition of a function, each value of x must lead to exactly one value of y. In Figure 6.24, the indicated value of x leads to *two* values of y, so this graph is not the graph of a function. We can draw a vertical line that cuts the graph in more than one point.

On the other hand, in Figure 6.25 any vertical line will cut the graph in no more than one point. Because of this, the graph in Figure 6.25 is the graph of a function.

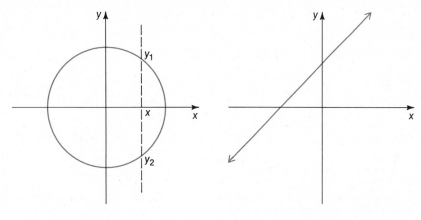

Figure 6.24   **Figure 6.25**

In summary, we have the **vertical line test** for a function.

**Vertical Line
Test**

If a vertical line cuts a graph in more than one point, the graph is not the
graph of a function.

As Figure 6.25 suggests, any nonvertical line is the graph of a function. For
this reason, any linear equation of the form $ax + by = c$, where $b \neq 0$, defines a
function.

EXAMPLE 1   Decide whether or not the following equations are functions.

(a) $y = 2x - 9$

This linear equation can be written as $1y - 2x = -9$. Since the coefficient of y
is not zero, the equation defines a function.

(b)

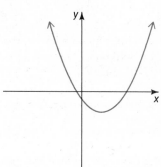

Use the vertical line test. Any vertical line will cross the graph above just once,
so this is the graph of a function.

(c)

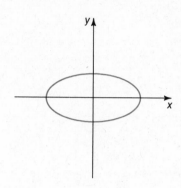

The vertical line test shows that this graph is not the graph of a function; a vertical line can cross the graph twice.

(d) $x = y^2$

Suppose that we choose the x-value 36. If $x = 36$, then

$$x = y^2 \quad \text{becomes} \quad y^2 = 36.$$

The equation $y^2 = 36$ has *two* solutions: $y = 6$ and $y = -6$. Because the *one* x-value, 36, leads to *two* y-values, the equation $x = y^2$ is *not* a function.

(e) $2x + y < 4$

Since this is an inequality, any choice of a value for x will lead to an *infinite* number of y-values. For example, if $x = 3$,

$$2x + y < 4$$
$$2(3) + y < 4 \qquad \text{Let } x = 3$$
$$6 + y < 4$$
$$y < -2.$$

If $x = 3$, y can take *any* value less than -2. Since $x = 3$ leads to more than one y-value, the inequality $2x + y < 4$ is not a function.   ●

3   The set of all numbers that can be used as replacements for x in a function is called the **domain** of the function. The set of all possible values of y is called the **range** of the function.

EXAMPLE 2   Find the domain and range for the following functions.

(a) $y = 6x - 9$

Any number at all may be used for x, so the domain is the set of all real numbers. Also, any number may be used for y, so the range is also the set of all real numbers.

(b) $y = x^2$

We may square any number, so the domain is the set of all real numbers. However, since the square of a real number cannot be negative and since $y = x^2$, the values of y cannot be negative, making the range the set of all nonnegative numbers. This range can be written as $y \geq 0$.   ●

4   It is common to use the letters f, g, and h to name functions. For example, the function $y = 3x + 5$ is often written

$$f(x) = 3x + 5,$$

where $f(x)$ is read "f of x." For the function $f(x) = 3x + 5$, if $x = 7$ then

$$f(7) = 3 \cdot 7 + 5 = 21 + 5 = 26.$$

(Read this result, $f(7) = 26$, as "f of 7 equals 26.")
To find $f(-3)$, replace x with -3.

$$f(x) = 3x + 5$$
$$f(-3) = 3(-3) + 5$$
$$f(-3) = -9 + 5 = -4$$

Note: The symbol $f(x)$ does *not* mean f times x.

EXAMPLE 3   For the function $f(x) = x^2 - 3$, find the following.

(a) $f(2)$

Replace x with 2.

$$f(x) = x^2 - 3$$
$$f(2) = 2^2 - 3$$
$$f(2) = 4 - 3 = 1$$

(b) $f(0) = 0^2 - 3 = 0 - 3 = -3$

(c) $f(-3) = (-3)^2 - 3 = 9 - 3 = 6$ ●

EXAMPLE 4   Let $P(x) = 5x^2 - 4x + 3$. Find the following. (This function is named P instead of f or g to show that it is a polynomial.)

(a) $P(0)$

Replace x with 0.

$$P(x) = 5x^2 - 4x + 3$$
$$P(0) = 5 \cdot 0^2 - 4 \cdot 0 + 3$$
$$P(0) = 3$$

(b) $P(-2) = 5 \cdot (-2)^2 - 4 \cdot (-2) + 3 = 20 + 8 + 3 = 31$

(c) $P(3) = 5 \cdot 3^2 - 4 \cdot 3 + 3 = 36$ ●

6.6 EXERCISES

Decide which of the following are functions. See Example 1.

1.

2.

3.

4.

5.

6.

Decide which of the following are functions. See Example 1.

7. $y = 5x - 1$

8. $y = 4x + 5$

9. $2x + 3y = 6$

10. $4x - 3y = 12$

11. $y = x^2 + 3$

12. $y = 5 - x^2$

13. $x = y^2 - 4$

14. $y = x^2 + 6$

15. $2x + y < 6$

16. $3x - 4y > 2$

17. $y = \dfrac{1}{x}$

18. $y = \dfrac{1}{x + 2}$

Recall that $|x|$ represents the absolute value of x. For example, $|3| = 3$, $|-5| = 5$, and so on. Decide which of the following are functions.

19. $y = |x|$

20. $x = |y|$

21. $x = |y| - 3$

22. $y = |x| + 8$

23. $y = |x - 1|$

24. $x = |y + 4|$

25. $|x + y| = 2$

26. $|x - y| = 4$

Find the domain and range of the following functions. See Example 2.

27. $y = 2x + 5$

28. $y = 5x - 6$

29. $2x - y = 6$

30. $2x + 3y = 12$

31. $y = x^2 - 3$

32. $y = x^2 + 4$

33. $y = (x + 4)^2$

34. $y = (x - 2)^2$

35. $y = -x^2 + 6$

36. $y = -x^2 - 8$

37. $y = -(x - 3)^2$

38. $y = -(x + 5)^2$

39. $y = |x| + 2$

40. $y = |x| - 3$

41. $y = |x - 4|$

42. $y = |x + 3|$

For the following, find (a) $f(2)$, (b) $f(0)$, and (c) $f(-3)$. See Example 3.

43. $f(x) = 3x + 2$ **44.** $f(x) = 4x - 1$ **45.** $f(x) = 4 - x$ **46.** $f(x) = 2 - 3x$

47. $f(x) = -4 - 4x$ **48.** $f(x) = -5 - 6x$ **49.** $f(x) = x^2 + 2$ **50.** $f(x) = x^2 - 5$

51. $f(x) = (x - 3)^2$ **52.** $f(x) = -(x - 4)^2$ **53.** $f(x) = -|x + 2|$ **54.** $f(x) = -|x - 3|$

For the following, find (a) $P(0)$, (b) $P(-3)$, and (c) $P(2)$. See Example 4.

55. $P(x) = x^2 + 2x$ **56.** $P(x) = 2x^2 + 3x - 6$

57. $P(x) = -x^2 - 8x + 9$ **58.** $P(x) = -3x^2 + 4x - 2$

59. $P(x) = x^3 - 4x^2 + 1$ **60.** $P(x) = x^3 + 5x^2 - 11x + 2$

Review Exercises   *Add the polynomials. See Section 3.3.*

61. $x - 2y$ **62.** $5x - 7y$ **63.** $9a - 5b$ **64.** $-11p + 8q$
     $\underline{3x + 2y}$ $\underline{12x + 7y}$ $\underline{-9a + 7b}$ $\underline{11p - 9q}$

Chapter 6   Review Exercises

[6.1] *Decide whether the given ordered pair is a solution of the given equation.*

1. $x + y = 7$; $(3, 4)$ **2.** $2x + y = 5$; $(1, 4)$ **3.** $x + 3y = 9$; $(1, 3)$

4. $2x + 5y = 7$; $(1, 1)$ **5.** $3x - y = 4$; $(1, -1)$ **6.** $5x - 3y = 16$; $(2, -2)$

Complete the given ordered pairs for each equation.

Equation	Ordered pairs
7. $y = 3x - 2$	$(-1, \quad)$ $(0, \quad)$ $(\quad, 5)$
8. $2y = 4x + 1$	$(0, \quad)$ $(\quad, 0)$ $(\quad, 2)$
9. $4x + 3y = 9$	$(0, \quad)$ $(\quad, 0)$ $(-2, \quad)$
10. $x = 2y$	$(0, \quad)$ $(8, \quad)$ $(\quad, -3)$
11. $x + 4 = 0$	$(\quad, -3)$ $(\quad, 0)$ $(\quad, 5)$
12. $y - 5 = 0$	$(-2, \quad)$ $(0, \quad)$ $(8, \quad)$

[6.2] *Graph each linear equation.*

13. $y = 2x + 3$ **14.** $x + y = 5$ **15.** $2x - y = 5$ **16.** $x + 2y = 0$

17. $3y = x$ **18.** $y = 4x - 1$ **19.** $y + 3 = 0$ **20.** $x - y = 0$

Find the intercepts for each equation.

21. $y = 2x - 5$ **22.** $2x + y = 7$ **23.** $3x - y = 8$ **24.** $5x - 2y = 0$

[6.3] *Find the slope of each line.*

25. Through $(2, 3)$ and $(-1, 1)$ **26.** Through $(4, -1)$ and $(-2, -3)$

27. Through $(0, 0)$ and $(-1, -2)$ **28.** Through $(2, 5)$ and $(2, -2)$

29. $y = 3x - 1$ **30.** $y = \dfrac{2}{3}x + 5$ **31.** $y = 8$ **32.** $x = 2$

Decide whether each pair of lines is parallel, perpendicular, or neither.

33. $3x + 2y = 5$ **34.** $x - 3y = 8$ **35.** $4x + 3y = 10$ **36.** $x - 2y = 3$
      $6x + 4y = 12$ $3x + y = 6$ $3x - 4y = 12$ $x + 2y = 3$

[6.4] *Write an equation for each line.*

37. $m = 3$, y-intercept -2 **38.** $m = -1$, y-intercept $\dfrac{3}{4}$

39. $m = \dfrac{2}{3}$, y-intercept 5 **40.** $m = \dfrac{-1}{4}$, y-intercept $\dfrac{-5}{4}$

41. Through $(8, 6)$, $m = -3$ **42.** Through $(5, -2)$, $m = 1$

43. Through $(-1, 4)$, $m = \dfrac{2}{3}$ **44.** Through $(1, -1)$, $m = \dfrac{-3}{4}$

45. Through $(2, 1)$ and $(-2, 2)$ **46.** Through $(3, -5)$ and $(-4, -1)$

47. Through $(5, 0)$ and $(5, -1)$ **48.** Through $(-2, 6)$ and $(3, 6)$

[6.5] *Complete the graph of each linear inequality by shading the correct region.*

49. $x - y \le 3$

50. $3x - y \ge 5$

Graph each linear inequality.

51. $x + 2y \le 6$ **52.** $3x + 5y \ge 9$ **53.** $y \le -2$ **54.** $x - 2y > 0$

[6.6] *Decide which of the following are functions.*

55.

56.

57.

58. $2x + 3y = 12$ **59.** $y = x^2$ **60.** $x - 5y < 10$ **61.** $y = |x|$

Find the domain and range of the following functions.

62. $y = 2x + 1$ **63.** $4x - 3y = 12$ **64.** $y = x^2 + 1$ **65.** $y = |x - 1|$

Find (a) $f(2)$ and (b) $f(-1)$.

66. $f(x) = 3x + 2$ **67.** $f(x) = 2x^2 - 1$ **68.** $f(x) = -(x + 1)^2$ **69.** $f(x) = |x + 3|$

70. Let $P(x) = -x^2 - 4x + 2$. Find $P(-1)$ and $P(-3)$.

Chapter 6   Test

Complete the ordered pairs using the given equations.

Equation	Ordered pairs
1. $y = 5x - 6$	(0,) (−2,) (, 14)
2. $2x + 7y = 21$	(0,) (, 0) (3,) (, 2)
3. $x = 3y$	(0,) (, 2) (8,) (−12,)
4. $y - 2 = 0$	(5,) (4,) (0,) (−3,)

Graph each linear equation. Give the x- and y-intercepts.

5. $x + y = 4$ **6.** $2x + y = 6$ **7.** $3x - 4y = 18$

8. $2x + y = 0$ **9.** $x + 5 = 0$ **10.** $y = 2$

Find the slope of each line.

11. Through $(-2, 4)$ and $(5, 1)$ **12.** $y = \dfrac{-3}{4}x + 6$

13. $4x + 7y = 10$ **14.** $x - 5 = 0$

Write an equation for each line. Write it in the form ax + by = c.

15. Through $(1, -3)$, $m = -4$

16. $m = 3$, y-intercept -1

17. $m = \dfrac{-3}{4}$, y-intercept 2

18. Through $(-2, -6)$ and $(-1, 3)$

Complete the graph of each linear inequality.

19. $2x + y \le 8$

20. $y < -3$

Decide which are functions.

21.

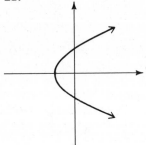

22. $y = 3x + 5$

23. $x = y^2 - 1$

24. Find the domain and range of $y = |x + 1|$.

25. For $f(x) = 6x - 2$ find $f(-3)$ and $f(5)$.

7

Linear Systems

A system of equations can show how soon a faster plane can overtake a slower one.

7.1 Solving Systems of Linear Equations by Graphing

1 Decide whether a given ordered pair is a solution of a system.

2 Solve linear systems by graphing.

3 Identify systems with no solutions or with an infinite number of solutions.

A **system of linear equations** consists of two or more linear equations with the same variables. Examples of systems of linear equations include

$$2x + 3y = 4 \qquad x + 3y = 1 \qquad\qquad x - y = 1$$
$$3x - y = -5 \qquad -y = 4 - 2x \qquad \text{and} \qquad y = 3.$$

In the system on the right, think of $y = 3$ as an equation in two variables by writing it as $0x + y = 3$.

1 The **solution of a system** of linear equations includes all the ordered pairs that make both equations true at the same time.

EXAMPLE 1   Is $(4, -3)$ a solution of the following systems?

(a) $x + 4y = -8$

$3x + 2y = 6$

To decide whether $(4, -3)$ is a solution of the system, substitute 4 for x and -3 for y in each equation.

$x + 4y = -8$	$3x + 2y = 6$
$4 + 4(-3) = -8$	$3(4) + 2(-3) = 6$
$4 + (-12) = -8$	$12 + (-6) = 6$
$-8 = -8$ True	$6 = 6$ True

Since $(4, -3)$ satisfies both equations, it is a solution.

(b) $2x + 5y = -7$

$3x + 4y = 2$

Again, substitute 4 for x and -3 for y in both equations.

$2x + 5y = -7$	$3x + 4y = 2$
$2(4) + 5(-3) = -7$	$3(4) + 4(-3) = 2$
$8 + (-15) = -7$	$12 + (-12) = 2$
$-7 = -7$ True	$0 = 2$ False

Here, $(4, -3)$ is not a solution since it does not satisfy the second equation.   ●

Finding the solution of a system of equations comes up again and again in applications. In this chapter we discuss methods of solving a system of two linear equations in two variables.

2   One way to find the solution of a system of two linear equations is to graph both equations on the same axes. The coordinates of any point where the lines cross give the solution of the system. Since two different straight lines cross in no more than one point, there never can be more than one solution for such a system.

EXAMPLE 2   Solve each system of equations by graphing both equations on the same axes.

(a) $2x + 3y = 4$

$3x - y = -5$

Figure 7.1 shows the graphs of $2x + 3y = 4$ and $3x - y = -5$ on the same axes. (It is important to draw the graphs carefully, since we will read the solution from the graph.) The figure suggests that the graphs cross at the point $(-1, 2)$, which is the solution of the system. To check this, substitute -1 for x and 2 for y

in the two equations. The ordered pair $(-1, 2)$ should satisfy *both* equations. Since it does, the solution of this system is $(-1, 2)$.

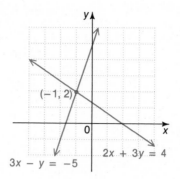

Figure 7.1

(b) $2x + y = 0$

$\quad 4x - 3y = 10$

To find the solution of the system, carefully graph the two lines on the same axes. As suggested by Figure 7.2, the solution is $(1, -2)$, the point at which the two graphs cross.   ●

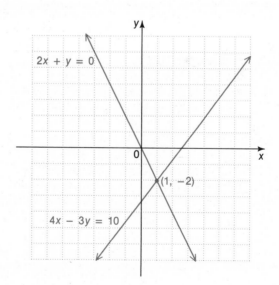

Figure 7.2

3   Sometimes the graphs of the two equations in a system do not intersect at all or they result in the same line, as shown in Example 3.

EXAMPLE 3   Solve each system by graphing.

(a) $2x + y = 2$
     $2x + y = 8$

The graphs of these lines are shown in Figure 7.3. The two lines are parallel and therefore have no points in common. There is no solution for this system. A system of equations like this, with no solution, is called an **inconsistent system.** A system of equations that has a solution is a **consistent system.**

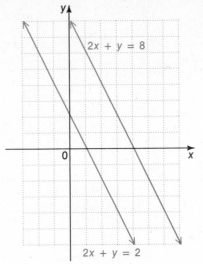

Figure 7.3

(b) $2x + 5y = 1$
     $6x + 15y = 3$

The graphs of these two equations are the same line. See Figure 7.4. Here the second equation can be obtained by multiplying both sides of the first equation by 3. In this case, every point on the line is a solution of the system, and the solution is an infinite number of ordered pairs. We will write "same line" to indicate this situation. Equations like these, which have the same graph, are called **dependent equations. Independent equations** have different graphs.   ●

Figure 7.4

Examples 2 and 3 show the three cases that may occur in a system of two equations with two unknowns.

**Possible
Types of
Solutions**

1. The graphs cross at exactly one point, which gives the solution of the system.

2. The graphs are parallel lines, so there is no solution.

3. The graphs are the same line. The solution is an infinite set of ordered pairs.

7.1 EXERCISES

Decide whether the given ordered pair is the solution of the given system. See Example 1.

1. $(2, -5)$
$3x + y = 1$
$2x + 3y = -11$

2. $(-1, 6)$
$2x + y = 4$
$3x + 2y = 9$

3. $(4, -2)$
$x + y = 2$
$2x + 5y = 2$

4. $(-6, 3)$
$x + 2y = 0$
$3x + 5y = 3$

5. $(2, 0)$
$3x + 5y = 6$
$4x + 2y = 5$

6. $(0, -4)$
$2x - 5y = 20$
$3x + 6y = -20$

7. (5, 2)
$4x + 3y = 26$
$3x + 7y = 29$

8. (9, 1)
$2x + 5y = 23$
$3x + 2y = 29$

9. (6, −8)
$x + 2y + 10 = 0$
$2x − 3y + 30 = 0$

10. (−5, 2)
$3x − 5y + 20 = 0$
$2x + 3y + \ 4 = 0$

11. (5, −2)
$x − 5 = 0$
$y + 2 = 0$

12. (−8, 3)
$x − 8 = 0$
$y − 3 = 0$

Solve each system of equations by graphing both equations on the same axes.
See Example 2.

13. $x + y = 6$
$x − y = 2$

14. $x + y = −1$
$x − y = 3$

15. $x + y = 4$
$y − x = 4$

16. $y − x = −5$
$x + y = 1$

17. $2x + \ y = 6$
$x − 3y = −4$

18. $4x + y = 2$
$2x − y = 4$

19. $3x − 2y = −3$
$3x + \ y = 6$

20. $2x + 3y = 12$
$2x − \ y = 4$

21. $5x + 4y = 7$
$2x − 3y = 12$

22. $2x + 5y = 17$
$3x − 4y = −9$

23. $4x + 5y = 3$
$2x − 5y = 9$

24. $2x + \ y = 5$
$3x − 4y = 24$

25. $3x + 2y = −10$
$x − 2y = −6$

26. $4x + \ y = 5$
$3x − 2y = 12$

27. $3x − 4y = −24$
$5x + 2y = −14$

28. $x − 2y = −5$
$4x + 3y = −9$

29. $x − 2y = 5$
$4x + 3y = 20$

30. $−4x + 3y = 16$
$2x − 3y = −8$

31. $3x − 4y = 8$
$4x + 5y = −10$

32. $3x + 2y = 10$
$4x − 3y = −15$

33. $2x + 5y = 12$
$x − 2y = −3$

34. $2x + 3y = 3$
$x + \ y = 3$

35. $x + 2y − 5 = 0$
$2x + \ y − 1 = 0$

36. $2x − y − 2 = 0$
$3x + y − 3 = 0$

37. $5x + \ y − 7 = 0$
$2x + 2y + 2 = 0$

38. $2x + 5y − 20 = 0$
$x + \ y − 10 = 0$

39. $x + y = 4$
$y = −2$

40. $2x + y = 1$
$y = 3$

41. $x = 2$
$3x − y = −1$

42. $x = 5$
$2x − y = 4$

Solve each system by graphing. If the two equations produce parallel lines,
write no solution. *If the two equations produce the same line, write* same line.
See Example 3.

43. $2x + 3y = 5$
$4x + 6y = 9$

44. $5x − 4y = 5$
$10x − 8y = 23$

45. $3x = y + 5$
$6x − 2y = 5$

46. $4y + 1 = x$
$2x − 3 = 8y$

47. $2x − y = 4$
$4x = 2y + 8$

48. $3x = 5 − y$
$6x + 2y = 10$

49. $x + 2y = 0$
$4y = −2x$

50. $y = 3x$
$y + 3 = 3x$

51. $x + y = 4$
$2x = 8 − 2y$

Review Exercises   *Add. See Section 3.4.*

52. $2m + 3n$
$5m - n$

53. $6p + 2q$
$4p + 5q$

54. $x - 2y$
$-x + 3y$

55. $3r - 2t$
$5r + 2t$

56. $-2x + y$ and $-y + 5x$

57. $4a + 3b$ and $-3b - 2a$

58. $6z + 5w$ and $-5w - 6z$

59. $-3m + 2n$ and $-2n + 3m$

7.2   Solving Systems of Linear Equations by Addition

1️⃣ Solve linear systems by addition.

2️⃣ Multiply one or both equations of a system so that the addition method can be used.

3️⃣ Put equations in the proper form to use the addition method.

4️⃣ Use the addition method to solve an inconsistent system.

5️⃣ Use the addition method to solve a system of dependent equations.

Graphing to solve a system of equations has a serious drawback: It is difficult to estimate a solution such as $(1/3, -5/6)$ accurately from a graph.

1️⃣   An algebraic method that depends on the addition property of equality can be used to solve systems. We know that addition of the same quantity to each side of an equation results in equal sums.

$$\text{If } \ A = B, \quad \text{then} \ \ A + C = B + C.$$

This can be taken a step further. Addition of *equal* quantities, rather than the *same* quantity, to both sides of an equation also results in equal sums.

$$\text{If } \ A = B \ \text{ and } \ C = D, \quad \text{then} \ \ A + C = B + D.$$

The use of the addition property to solve systems is called the **addition method** for solving systems of equations. For many systems, this method is more efficient than graphing.

EXAMPLE 1   Use the addition method to find the solution of the system

$$x + y = 5$$
$$x - y = 3.$$

Each equation of this system is a statement of equality, so, as discussed above, the sum of the right-hand sides equals the sum of the left-hand sides. Adding in this way gives

$$(x + y) + (x - y) = 5 + 3.$$

Combine terms and simplify to get

$$2x = 8$$
$$x = 4.$$

This result, $x = 4$, gives the x-value of the solution of the given system. To find the y-value of the solution, substitute 4 for x in either of the two equations of the system. We choose the first equation, $x + y = 5$.

$$x + y = 5$$
$$4 + y = 5 \quad \text{Let } x = 4$$
$$y = 1$$

Then $y = 1$ gives the y-value of the solution. The solution is given by the ordered pair (4, 1), which can be checked by substituting into both equations of the given system.

$$
\begin{array}{lcl}
x + y = 5 & \qquad & x - y = 3 \\
4 + 1 = 5 & & 4 - 1 = 3 \\
5 = 5 \quad \text{True} & & 3 = 3 \quad \text{True}
\end{array}
$$

Both results are true, so the solution of the given system is (4, 1). ●

EXAMPLE 2 Solve the system

$$-2x + y = -11$$
$$5x - y = 26.$$

As above, add left-hand sides and right-hand sides. The work is sometimes easier if we draw a line under the second equation and add vertically. (Like terms must be lined up in columns.)

$$
\begin{array}{rcl}
-2x + y & = & -11 \\
\underline{5x - y} & = & \underline{26} \\
3x & = & 15 \quad \text{Add in columns} \\
x & = & 5
\end{array}
$$

Substitute 5 for x in either of the original equations. We choose the first.

$$-2x + y = -11$$
$$-2(5) + y = -11 \quad \text{Let } x = 5$$
$$-10 + y = -11$$
$$y = -1$$

The solution is (5, −1). Check this solution by substitution into both of the original equations. ●

2 In both examples above, a variable was eliminated by the addition step. Sometimes it is necessary to multiply both sides of one or both equations in a system by some number before adding.

EXAMPLE 3 Solve the system

$$x + 3y = 7 \qquad (1)$$
$$2x + 5y = 12. \qquad (2)$$

Adding the two equations gives $3x + 8y = 19$, which does not help find the solution. However, if we first multiply both sides of equation (1) by -2, the terms with the variable x will drop out when we add. Multiplying by -2 gives

$$-2(x + 3y) = -2(7)$$
$$-2x - 6y = -14. \qquad (3)$$

Now add equations (3) and (2).

$$
\begin{array}{ll}
-2x - 6y = -14 & (3) \\
\underline{2x + 5y = 12} & (2) \\
-y = -2 &
\end{array}
$$

From this result, $y = 2$. Substituting back into equation (1) gives

$$x + 3y = 7$$
$$x + 3(2) = 7 \qquad \text{Let } y = 2$$
$$x + 6 = 7$$
$$x = 1.$$

The solution of this system is $(1, 2)$. Check to see that it satisfies both of the original equations. •

EXAMPLE 4 Solve the system

$$2x + 3y = -15 \qquad (1)$$
$$5x + 2y = 1. \qquad (2)$$

Here we use the multiplication property of equality with both equations instead of just one, as in Example 3. Multiply by numbers that will cause the coefficients of x (or of y) in the two equations to be additive inverses of each other. For example, multiply both sides of equation (1) by 5, and both sides of equation (2) by -2.

$$
\begin{array}{l}
10x + 15y = -75 \\
\underline{-10x - 4y = -2} \\
11y = -77 \qquad \text{Add}
\end{array}
$$

This gives $y = -7$. Substituting -7 for y in either equation (1) or (2) gives $x = 3$. The solution of the system is $(3, -7)$.

We could have obtained the same result by multiplying both sides of equation (1) by 2 and both sides of equation (2) by -3 and then adding. (Check this.) •

A summary of the steps used to solve a linear system of equations by the addition method is given below.

Solving Linear Systems

> *Step 1*   Write both equations of the system in the form $ax + by = c$.
>
> *Step 2*   Multiply one or both equations by appropriate numbers so that the coefficients of x (or y) are negatives of each other.
>
> *Step 3*   Add the two equations to get an equation with only one variable.
>
> *Step 4*   Solve the equation from Step 3.
>
> *Step 5*   Substitute the solution from Step 4 into either of the original equations.
>
> *Step 6*   Solve the resulting equation from Step 5 for the remaining variable.
>
> *Step 7*   Check the answer.

3   To use the addition method, the terms of the two equations must be in the same order. When this is not the case, the terms should first be rearranged, as the next example shows. This example also shows an alternate way to get the second number when finding the solution of a system.

EXAMPLE 5   Solve the system

$$4x = 9 - 3y \qquad (1)$$
$$5x - 2y = 8. \qquad (2)$$

We must rearrange the terms in equation (1) so that the like terms can be lined up in columns. Add $3y$ to both sides to get the system

$$4x + 3y = 9 \qquad (3)$$
$$5x - 2y = 8.$$

Let us eliminate y by multiplying both sides of equation (3) by 2 and both sides of equation (2) by 3, and then adding.

$$
\begin{array}{r}
8x + 6y = 18 \\
15x - 6y = 24 \\
\hline
23x \qquad\ = 42
\end{array}
$$

$$x = \frac{42}{23}$$

If we substitute $x = 42/23$ into one of the given equations, we can find y. But the arithmetic involved would be messy. Instead, we can eliminate x by starting again with the original equations. Multiply both sides of equation (3) by 5 and both sides of equation (2) by -4, and then add again.

$$20x + 15y = 45$$
$$\underline{- 20x + 8y = -32}$$
$$23y = 13$$

$$y = \frac{13}{23}$$

The solution is (42/23, 13/23).   ●

When the value of the first variable is a complicated fraction, the method used in Example 5 avoids errors that often occur when working with fractions. Of course, this method could be used in solving any system of equations.

4   In the previous section we saw that the graphs of the equations in a linear system are sometimes two parallel lines and sometimes the same line. Now we can use the addition method to solve such systems. The next example illustrates the solution of an inconsistent system, where the graphs are parallel lines.

EXAMPLE 6   Solve by the addition method.

$$2x + 4y = 5$$
$$4x + 8y = -9$$

If we multiply both sides of $2x + 4y = 5$ by -2 and then add $4x + 8y = -9$, we get

$$-4x - 8y = -10$$
$$\underline{4x + 8y = -9}$$
$$0 = -19. \quad \text{False}$$

The false statement $0 = -19$ shows that the given system is self-contradictory. *It has no solution*. This means that the graphs of the equations of this system are parallel lines, as shown in Figure 7.5.   ●

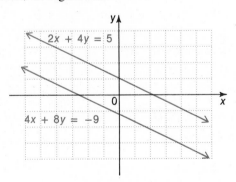

Figure 7.5

5   The next example shows the result of using the addition method when the system is dependent, that is, the graphs of the equations in a system are the same line.

EXAMPLE 7   Solve by the addition method.

$$3x - y = 4$$
$$-9x + 3y = -12$$

If we multiply both sides of the first equation by 3 and then add the two equations, we get

$$
\begin{array}{r}
9x - 3y = 12 \\
-9x + 3y = -12 \\
\hline
0 = 0.
\end{array}
$$ True

This result, $0 = 0$, is true for any ordered pair (x, y) that satisfies either equation. Every solution of one equation is also a solution of the other. Thus the system has an infinite number of solutions: all the ordered pairs that lie on the common graph. In the answers at the back of this book, a solution of such a system of dependent equations is indicated by the words *same line*.   ●

One of three possibilities may occur when the addition method is used to solve a linear system of equations.

1.   The result of the addition step is a statement such as $x = 2$ or $y = -3$. The solution will be exactly one ordered pair. The graphs of the equations of the system will cross in exactly one point.

2.   The result of the addition step is a false statement, such as $0 = 4$. In this case, the graphs are parallel lines and there is no solution for the system. The system is inconsistent.

3.   The result of the addition step is a true statement, such as $0 = 0$. The graphs of the equations of the system are the same line, and there is an infinite number of ordered pairs that are solutions. The equations are dependent.

7.2 EXERCISES

Solve each system by the addition method. Check your answers. See Examples 1 and 2.

1. $x - y = 3$
$x + y = -1$

2. $x + y = 7$
$x - y = -3$

3. $x + y = 2$
$2x - y = 4$

4. $3x - y = 8$
$x + y = 4$

5. $2x + y = 14$
$x - y = 4$

6. $2x + y = 2$
$-x - y = 1$

7. $3x + 2y = 6$
$-3x - y = 0$

8. $5x - y = 9$
$-5x + 2y = -8$

9. $6x - y = 1$
$-6x + 5y = 7$

10. $6x + y = -2$
$-6x + 3y = -14$

11. $2x - y = 5$
$4x + y = 4$

12. $x - 4y = 13$
$-x + 6y = -18$

13. $5x - y = 15$
$7x + y = 21$

14. $x - 4y = 12$
$-x + 6y = -18$

Solve each system by the addition method. Check your answers. See Example 3.

15. $2x - y = 7$
$3x + 2y = 0$

16. $x + y = 7$
$-3x + 3y = -9$

17. $x + 3y = 16$
$2x - y = 4$

18. $4x - 3y = 8$
$2x + y = 14$

19. $x + 4y = -18$
$3x + 5y = -19$

20. $2x + y = 3$
$5x - 2y = -15$

21. $3x - 2y = -6$
$-5x + 4y = 16$

22. $-4x + 3y = 0$
$5x - 6y = 9$

23. $2x - y = -8$
$5x + 2y = -20$

24. $5x + 3y = -9$
$7x + y = -3$

25. $2x + y = 5$
$5x + 3y = 11$

26. $2x + 7y = -53$
$4x + 3y = -7$

Solve each system by the addition method. Check your answers. Round to the nearest thousandth in Exercises 39 and 40. See Examples 4 and 5.

27. $5x - 4y = -1$
$-7x + 5y = 8$

28. $3x + 2y = 12$
$5x - 3y = 1$

29. $3x + 5y = 33$
$4x - 3y = 15$

30. $2x + 5y = 3$
$5x - 3y = 23$

31. $3x + 5y = -7$
$5x + 4y = 10$

32. $2x + 3y = -11$
$5x + 2y = 22$

33. $2x + 3y = -12$
$5x - 7y = -30$

34. $2x + 9y = 16$
$5x - 6y = 40$

35. $4x - 3y = -7$
$6x + 5y = 18$

36. $8x + 3y = -4$
$12x + 7y = 4$

37. $5x + 2y = -11$
$3x - 3y = -15$

38. $6x - 3y = 15$
$4x - 5y = 19$

39. $6.5x + 2.3y = 15$
$5.4x - 4.6y = 12$

40. $-2.2x + 7.1y = -4.8$
$3.8x + 14.2y = 6.8$

41. $.13x - .52y = -.39$
$.39x + .08y = -2.81$

Use the addition method to solve each system. Check your answers. See Examples 6 and 7.

42. $2x - y = 1$
$2x - y = 4$

43. $5x - 2y = 6$
$10x - 4y = 10$

44. $3x - 5y = 2$
$6x - 10y = 8$

45. $x + 3y = 5$
$2x + 6y = 10$

46. $6x - 2y = 12$
$-3x + y = -6$

47. $2x + 3y = 8$
$4x + 6y = 12$

48. $4x + y = 6$
$-8x - 2y = 21$

49. $3x + 5y = -19$
$6x + 7y = -23$

50. $3x - 2y = -13$
$9x + 5y = 16$

51. $6x + y = 33$
$-2x + 3y = 19$

52. $5x - 3y = -3$
$7x + 5y = -41$

53. $2x - 3y = 0$
$4x + 4y = 0$

54. $3x - 5y = 0$
$6x + 10y = 0$

55. $4x - 2y = 1$
$8x - 4y = 1$

56. $4x + y = 4$
$-8x - 2y = -8$

57. $24x + 12y = 19$
$16x - 18y = -9$

58. $9x + 4y = -4$
$6x + 6y = -11$

59. $9x - 5y = 7$
$21x + 20y = 10$

Review Exercises *Solve each equation. Check the solutions. See Sections 2.4 and 5.6.*

60. $-2(y - 2) + 5y = 10$

61. $2m - 3(4 - m) = 8$

62. $p + 4(6 - 2p) = 3$

63. $4\left(\dfrac{3 - 2k}{2}\right) + 3k = -3$

64. $4x - 2\left(\dfrac{1 - 3x}{2}\right) = 6$

65. $a + 3\left(\dfrac{1 - a}{2}\right) = 5$

66. $4\left(\dfrac{-2 + y}{3}\right) - 2y = 2$

67. $3p + 2\left(\dfrac{2p - 1}{3}\right) = 4$

68. $4r + 5\left(\dfrac{2r + 7}{4}\right) = 1$

7.3 Solving Systems of Linear Equations by Substitution

■ Solve linear systems by substitution.

■ Solve linear systems with fractions.

■ We have looked at the graphical method and the addition method for solving systems of linear equations. A third method is the **substitution method,** which is particularly useful for solving systems in which one equation is solved for one of the variables.

EXAMPLE 1   Solve the system

$$3x + 5y = 26$$
$$y = 2x.$$

The second of these two equations says that $y = 2x$. Substituting $2x$ for y in the first equation gives

$$3x + 5y = 26$$
$$3x + 5(2x) = 26 \qquad \text{Let } y = 2x$$
$$3x + 10x = 26$$
$$13x = 26$$
$$x = 2.$$

Since $y = 2x$, we have $y = 2(2) = 4$. Check that the solution of the given system is $(2, 4)$.   ●

EXAMPLE 2   Use substitution to solve the system

$$2x + 5y = 7$$
$$x = -1 - y.$$

The second equation gives x in terms of y. Substitute $-1 - y$ for x in the first equation.

$$2x + 5y = 7$$
$$2(-1 - y) + 5y = 7 \qquad \text{Let } x = -1 - y$$
$$-2 - 2y + 5y = 7$$
$$-2 + 3y = 7$$
$$3y = 9$$
$$y = 3$$

Since $x = -1 - y$, we have $x = -1 - 3$, or $x = -4$. Check that the solution of the given system is $(-4, 3)$.   ●

EXAMPLE 3   Use substitution to solve the system

$$x = 5 - 2y$$
$$2x + 4y = 6.$$

Substitute $5 - 2y$ for x in the second equation.

$$2x + 4y = 6$$
$$2(5 - 2y) + 4y = 6 \qquad \text{Let } x = 5 - 2y$$
$$10 - 4y + 4y = 6$$
$$10 = 6 \qquad \text{False}$$

As we saw in the last section, this false result means that the equations of the system have graphs that are parallel lines. The system is inconsistent and has no solution. .   ●

EXAMPLE 4   Use substitution to solve the system

$$2x + 3y = 8$$
$$4x + 3y = 4.$$

To use the substitution method, we need an equation giving x in terms of y (or y in terms of x). Let us choose the first equation of the system, $2x + 3y = 8$, and solve it for x. To get x alone on one side of the equation, first subtract $3y$ on both sides.

$$2x + 3y = 8$$
$$2x = 8 - 3y$$

Now divide both sides of this equation by 2.

$$x = \frac{8 - 3y}{2}$$

Finally, substitute this result for x in the second equation of the system.

$$4x + 3y = 4$$

$$4\left(\frac{8 - 3y}{2}\right) + 3y = 4 \qquad \text{Let } x = \frac{8 - 3y}{2}$$

$$2(8 - 3y) + 3y = 4$$

$$16 - 6y + 3y = 4$$

$$-3y = -12$$

$$y = 4$$

Let $y = 4$ in $x = \dfrac{8 - 3y}{2}$.

$$x = \frac{8 - 3 \cdot 4}{2} = \frac{8 - 12}{2} = \frac{-4}{2} = -2$$

The solution of the given system is $(-2, 4)$. Check this solution in both equations.   ●

EXAMPLE 5   Use substitution to solve the system

$$2x = 4 - y \qquad (1)$$

$$6 + 3y + 4x = 16 - x. \qquad (2)$$

To begin, simplify the second equation by adding x and subtracting 6 on both sides. This gives the simplified system

$$2x = 4 - y \qquad (1)$$

$$5x + 3y = 10. \qquad (3)$$

To use the substitution method, we must solve one of the equations for either x or y. Since the coefficient of y in equation (1) is -1, we can avoid fractions by solving this equation for y.

$$2x = 4 - y \qquad (1)$$

$$2x - 4 = -y$$

$$-2x + 4 = y$$

Now substitute $-2x + 4$ for y in equation (3).

$$5x + 3y = 10$$

$$5x + 3(-2x + 4) = 10$$

$$5x - 6x + 12 = 10$$

$$-x + 12 = 10$$

$$-x = -2$$

$$x = 2$$

Since $y = -2x + 4$ and $x = 2$,

$$y = -2(2) + 4 = 0,$$

and the solution is $(2, 0)$.   ●

2   When a system includes equations with fractions as coefficients, eliminate the fractions by multiplying both sides by a common denominator. Then solve the resulting system.

EXAMPLE 6   Solve the system

$$3x + \frac{1}{4}y = 2 \qquad (1)$$

$$\frac{1}{2}x + \frac{3}{4}y = \frac{-5}{2} \qquad (2)$$

by any method.

Begin by eliminating fractions. To clear equation (1) of fractions, multiply both sides by 4.

$$4\left(3x + \frac{1}{4}y\right) = 4(2)$$

$$4(3x) + 4\left(\frac{1}{4}y\right) = 4(2) \qquad \text{Distributive property}$$

$$12x + y = 8 \qquad (3)$$

Now clear equation (2) of fractions by multiplying both sides by the common denominator 4.

$$4\left(\frac{1}{2}x + \frac{3}{4}y\right) = 4\left(\frac{-5}{2}\right)$$

$$4\left(\frac{1}{2}x\right) + 4\left(\frac{3}{4}y\right) = 4\left(\frac{-5}{2}\right) \qquad \text{Distributive property}$$

$$2x + 3y = -10 \qquad (4)$$

Solve the system of equations (3) and (4).

$$12x + y = 8 \qquad (3)$$
$$2x + 3y = -10 \qquad (4)$$

To use the substitution method, we must solve one equation for either x or y. In equation (3) the coefficient of y is 1, so we will avoid fractions by solving this equation for y.

$$12x + y = 8 \qquad (3)$$
$$y = -12x + 8$$

Now substitute the result for y in equation (4).

$$2x + 3(-12x + 8) = -10$$
$$2x - 36x + 24 = -10$$
$$-34x = -34$$
$$x = 1$$

From $y = -12x + 8$ and $x = 1$, we get $y = -4$. The solution is $(1, -4)$. Check by substituting 1 for x and -4 for y in both of the original equations. Verify that we get the same solution if the addition method is used to solve the system of equations (3) and (4). ●

7.3 EXERCISES

Solve each system by the substitution method. Check each solution. See Examples 1–4.

1. $x + y = 6$
  $y = 2x$

2. $x + 3y = -11$
  $y = -4x$

3. $3x + 2y = 26$
  $x = y + 2$

4. $4x + 3y = -14$
  $x = y - 7$

5. $x + 5y = 3$
  $x = 2y + 10$

6. $5x + 2y = 14$
  $y = 2x - 11$

7. $3x - y = 6$
  $y = 3x - 5$

8. $4x - y = 4$
  $y = 4x + 3$

9. $3x - 2y = 14$
  $2x + y = 0$

10. $2x - 5 = -y$
  $x + 3y = 0$

11. $x + y = 6$
  $x - y = 4$

12. $3x - 2y = 13$
  $x + y = 6$

13. $6x - 8y = 4$
  $3x = 4y + 2$

14. $12x + 18y = 12$
  $2x = 2 - 3y$

15. $2x + 3y = 11$
  $4y - x = 0$

16. $4x + 5y = 5$
  $2x + 3y = 1$

17. $6x + 5y = 13$
  $3x + 2y = 4$

18. $5x - 2y = -3$
  $3y + 2x = 11$

19. $3x + 4y = -10$
  $x + 6 = 0$

20. $4x + y = 5$
  $x - 2 = 0$

21. $5x + 2y = -19$
  $y - 3 = 0$

Solve each system by either the addition method or the substitution method. First simplify equations where necessary. Check each solution. See Example 5.

22. $5x - 4y = 42 - 8y - 2$
  $2x + y = x + 1$

23. $4x - 2y + 8 = 3x + 4y - 1$
  $3x + y = x + 8$

24. $5x - 4y - 8x - 2 = 6x + 3y - 3$
  $4x - y = -2y - 8$

25. $2x - 8y + 3y + 2 = 5y + 16$
  $8x - 2y = 4x + 28$

26. $7x - 9 + 2y - 8 = -3y + 4x + 13$
  $4y - 8x = -8 + 9x + 32$

27. $-2x + 3y = 12 + 2y$
  $2x - 5y + 4 = -8 - 4y$

28. $2x + 5y = 7 + 4y - x$
  $5x + 3y + 8 = 22 - x + y$

29. $y + 9 = 3x - 2y + 6$
  $5 - 3x + 24 = -2x + 4y + 3$

30. $5x - 2y = 16 + 4x - 10$
  $4x + 3y = 60 + 2x + y$

31. $4 + 4x - 3y = 34 + x$
  $5y + 4x = 4y - 2 + 3x$

Solve each system by either the addition method or the substitution method. First clear all fractions. Check each solution. See Example 6.

32. $\dfrac{5}{3}x + 2y = \dfrac{1}{3} + y$

$2x - 3 + \dfrac{y}{3} = -2 + x$

33. $\dfrac{x}{6} + \dfrac{y}{6} = 1$

$-\dfrac{1}{2}x - \dfrac{1}{3}y = -5$

34. $\dfrac{x}{2} - \dfrac{y}{3} = \dfrac{5}{6}$

$\dfrac{x}{5} - \dfrac{y}{4} = \dfrac{1}{10}$

35. $\dfrac{x}{3} - \dfrac{3y}{4} = -\dfrac{1}{2}$

$\dfrac{2x}{3} + \dfrac{y}{2} = 3$

36. $\dfrac{x}{5} + 2y = \dfrac{8}{5}$

$\dfrac{3x}{5} + \dfrac{y}{2} = \dfrac{-7}{10}$

37. $\dfrac{x}{2} + \dfrac{y}{3} = \dfrac{7}{6}$

$\dfrac{x}{4} - \dfrac{3y}{2} = \dfrac{9}{4}$

38. $\dfrac{5x}{2} - \dfrac{y}{3} = \dfrac{5}{6}$

$\dfrac{4x}{3} + y = \dfrac{19}{3}$

39. $\dfrac{2x}{3} + \dfrac{y}{6} = 9$

$\dfrac{x}{4} - \dfrac{3y}{2} = -6$

40. $\dfrac{3x}{2} + \dfrac{y}{5} = 2$

$\dfrac{5x}{2} - \dfrac{3y}{10} = \dfrac{13}{2}$

Review Exercises *Solve each word problem. See Section 2.5.*

41. If three times a number is added to 6, the result is 69. Find the number.

42. The product of 5 and 1 more than a number is 35. Find the number.

43. The perimeter of a rectangle is 46 feet. The width is 7 feet less than the length. Find the width.

44. The area of a rectangle is numerically 20 more than the width, and the length is 6 centimeters. What is the width?

45. A cashier has ten-dollar bills and twenty-dollar bills. There are 6 more tens than twenties. If there are 32 bills altogether, how many of them are twenties?

46. Janet traveled for 2 hours at a constant speed. Because of road work, she reduced her speed by 7 miles per hour for the next 2 hours. If she traveled 206 miles, what was her speed on the first part of the trip?

7.4 Applications of Linear Systems

Use linear systems to solve word problems about

1 two numbers;

2 money;

3 mixtures;

4 rate or speed using the distance formula.

In Chapter 2 we solved word problems using one variable. Many practical problems have two unknowns and are more easily translated into equations if two variables are used. With two variables, we need a system of two equations to find the desired solution. The examples in this section illustrate a method of solving word problems using two equations and two variables.

The steps for solving word problems with two variables are as follows.

Solving Word Problems with Two Variables

> *Step 1* Choose a different variable for each of the two unknown values you are asked to find. Write down what each variable is to represent.
>
> *Step 2* Translate the problem into two equations using both variables.
>
> *Step 3* Solve the system of two equations.
>
> *Step 4* Answer the question or questions asked in the problem.
>
> *Step 5* Check your solution by using the original words of the problem.

1 The first example shows how to use two variables to solve a problem about two unknown numbers.

EXAMPLE 1

The sum of two numbers is 63. Their difference is 19. Find the two numbers.

Step 1 Let x represent one number and y the other.

Step 2 From the information in the problem, set up a system of equations.

$$x + y = 63 \qquad \text{The sum is 63}$$
$$x - y = 19 \qquad \text{The difference is 19}$$

Step 3 Solve the system from Step 2. We use the addition method. Adding gives

$$\begin{array}{r} x + y = 63 \\ x - y = 19 \\ \hline 2x \quad\;\; = 82. \end{array}$$

From this last equation, $x = 41$. Substitute 41 for x in either equation to find $y = 22$.

Step 4 The numbers required in the problem are 41 and 22.

Step 5 The sum of 41 and 22 is 63, and their difference is $41 - 22 = 19$. The solution satisfies the conditions of the problem. ●

2 The next example shows how to solve a common type of word problem that involves two quantities and their costs.

EXAMPLE 2   Admission prices at a football game were $6 for adults and $2 for children. The total receipts from the game were $2528. Tickets were sold to 454 people. How many adults and how many children attended the game?

Step 1   Let a represent the number of adult tickets sold and c represent the number of children's tickets sold.

Step 2   The information given in the problem is summarized in the table. The entries in the "Receipts" column were found by multiplying the number of tickets sold by the price per ticket.

Kind of ticket	Number sold	Cost of each (in dollars)	Receipts (in dollars)
Adult	a	6	$6a$
Child	c	2	$2c$

The total number of tickets sold was 454, so

$$a + c = 454.$$

Since the total receipts were $2528, the right-hand column leads to

$$6a + 2c = 2528.$$

Step 3   We have used the information in the problem to set up the system of equations

$$a + c = 454 \qquad (1)$$
$$6a + 2c = 2528. \qquad (2)$$

To solve the system of equations, multiply both sides of equation (1) by -2 to get $-2a - 2c = -908$. (We could have divided both sides of equation (2) by -2 instead.) Now add the result to equation (2).

$$
\begin{array}{r}
-2a - 2c = -908 \\
6a + 2c = 2528 \\
\hline
4a = 1620
\end{array}
$$

From this last equation, $a = 405$. We know that $a + c = 454$; therefore, $c = 49$. (Check this.)

Step 4   There were 405 adults and 49 children at the game.

Step 5   Since 405 adults paid $6 each and 49 children paid $2 each, the receipts should be

$$405(6) + 49(2) = 2528,$$

or $2528. This agrees with the given information.   ●

Try to identify each step in the solution of the problems in the rest of the examples.

3 Mixture problems occur in many fields of application of mathematics. One important type of mixture problem comes up in the study of chemistry. This kind of problem can be solved as shown in the next example.

EXAMPLE 3

A pharmacist needs 100 liters of 50% alcohol solution. She has on hand 30% alcohol solution and 80% alcohol solution, which she can mix. How many liters of each will be required to make the 100 liters of 50% alcohol solution?

Let x represent the number of liters of 30% alcohol needed, and let y represent the number of liters of 80% alcohol. The information given in the problem is summarized in the table. (Each percent has been changed to its decimal form in the third column.)

Liters of solution	Percent	Liters of pure alcohol
x	30	$.30x$
y	80	$.80y$
100	50	$.50(100)$

The pharmacist will have $.30x$ liters of alcohol from the x liters of 30% solution and $.80y$ liters of alcohol from the y liters of 80% solution, for a total of $.30x + .80y$ liters of pure alcohol. In the mixture, she wants 100 liters of 50% solution. This 100 liters would contain $.50(100) = 50$ liters of pure alcohol. Since the amounts of pure alcohol must be equal,

$$.30x + .80y = 50.$$

The total number of liters is 100, or

$$x + y = 100.$$

These two equations give the system

$$.30x + .80y = 50$$
$$x + y = 100.$$

Let us solve this system by the substitution method. Solving the second equation of the system for x gives $x = 100 - y$. Substitute $100 - y$ for x in the first equation to get

$$.30(100 - y) + .80y = 50 \qquad \text{Let } x = 100 - y$$
$$30 - .30y + .80y = 50$$
$$.50y = 20$$
$$y = 40.$$

Then $x = 100 - y = 100 - 40 = 60$. The pharmacist should use 60 liters of the 30% solution and 40 liters of the 80% solution. Since $.30(60) + (.80)40 = 50$, this mix will give 100 liters of 50% solution, as required in the original problem.   ●

4   Word problems that use the distance formula, relating distance, rate, and time, often result in a system of two linear equations.

EXAMPLE 4   Two cars start from positions 400 miles apart and travel toward each other. They meet after 4 hours. Find the speed of each car if one car travels 20 miles per hour faster than the other.

We need the formula that relates distance, rate, and time, $d = rt$. Let x be the speed of the faster car and y the speed of the slower car. Since each car travels for 4 hours, the time, t, for each car is 4. This information is shown in the chart. The distance is found by using the formula $d = rt$ and the expressions already entered in the chart.

	r	t	d
Faster car	x	4	$4x$
Slower car	y	4	$4y$

Since the total distance traveled by both cars is 400 miles,

$$4x + 4y = 400.$$

The faster car goes 20 miles per hour more than the slower, giving

$$x = 20 + y.$$

We now have a system of equations,

$$4x + 4y = 400$$
$$x = 20 + y.$$

This system can be solved by substitution. Replace x with $20 + y$ in the first equation of the system and solve for y.

$$4(20 + y) + 4y = 400$$
$$80 + 4y + 4y = 400$$
$$80 + 8y = 400$$
$$8y = 320$$
$$y = 40$$

Since $x = 20 + y$, we have $x = 20 + 40 = 60$. The speeds of the two cars were 40 miles per hour and 60 miles per hour. If each car travels for 4 hours, the total distance traveled is

$$4(40) + 4(60) = 160 + 240 = 400$$

miles, as required.   ●

The problems in this section also could be solved using only one variable, but for most of them the solution is simpler with two variables. (But do not forget that if you use two variables, you also must write two equations.)

7.4 EXERCISES

Write a system of equations for each problem. Then solve the system. Formulas are in the back of the book. See Example 1.

1. The sum of two numbers is 52, and their difference is 34. Find the numbers.

2. Find two numbers whose sum is 56 and whose difference is 18.

3. A certain number is three times as large as a second number. Their sum is 96. What are the two numbers?

4. One number is five times as large as another. The difference of the numbers is 48. Find the numbers.

5. Two angles have a sum of 90°. Their difference is 20°. Find the angles.

6. The sum of two angles is 180°. One angle is 30° less than twice the other. Find the angles.

7. A rectangle is twice as long as it is wide. Its perimeter is 60 inches. Find the dimensions of the rectangle.

8. The perimeter of a triangle is 21 inches. If two sides are of equal length, and the third side is 3 inches longer than one of the equal sides, find the length of the three sides.

Write a system of equations for each problem. Then solve the system. See Example 2.

9. The cashier at the Evergreen Ranch has some ten-dollar bills and some twenty-dollar bills. The total value of the money is $1480. If there is a total of 85 bills, how many of each type are there?

Kind of bill	Number of bills	Total value
$10	x	$10x$
$20	y	
Totals	85	$1480

10. A bank teller has 154 bills of $1 and $5 denominations. How many of each type of bill does he have if the total value of the money is $466?

11. A club secretary bought 8¢ and 10¢ pieces of candy to give to the members. She spent a total of $15.52. If she bought 170 pieces of candy, how many of each kind did she buy?

12. There were 311 tickets sold for a basketball game, some for students and some for nonstudents. Student tickets cost 25¢ each and nonstudent tickets cost 75¢ each. The total receipts were $108.75. How many of each type of ticket were sold?

13. A bank clerk has a total of 124 bills, both fives and tens. The total value of the money is $840. How many of each type of bill does he have?

14. A library buys a total of 54 books. Some cost $8 each and some cost $11 each. The total cost of the books is $492. How many of each type of book does the library buy?

15. An artist bought some large canvases at $7 each and some small ones at $4 each, paying $219 in total. Altogether, the artist bought 39 canvases. How many of each size were bought?

16. A hospital bought a total of 146 bottles of glucose solution. Small bottles cost $2 each, and large bottles are $3 each. The total cost was $336. How many of each size bottle were bought?

17. Ms. Sullivan has $10,000 to invest, part at 10% and part at 14%. She wants the income from simple interest on the two investments to total $1100 yearly. How much should she invest at each rate?

18. Mr. Emerson has twice as much money invested at 14% as he has at 16%. If his yearly income from investments is $880, how much does he have invested at each rate?

Write a system of equations for each problem. Then solve the system. See Example 3.

19. A 90% antifreeze solution is to be mixed with a 75% solution to make 20 liters of a 78% solution. How many liters of 90% and 75% solutions should be used?

Liters of solution	Percent	Liters of pure antifreeze
x	90	$.90x$
y	75	$.75y$
20	78	

20. A 40% potassium iodide solution is to be mixed with a 70% solution to get 60 liters of a 50% solution. How many liters of the 40% and 70% solutions will be needed?

21. How many liters of a 25% indicator solution should be mixed with a 55% solution to get 12 liters of a 45% solution?

22. A 60% solution of salt is to be mixed with an 80% solution to get 40 liters of a 65% solution. How many liters of the 60% and the 80% solutions will be needed?

23. A merchant wishes to mix coffee worth $6 per pound with coffee worth $3 per pound to get 90 pounds of a mixture worth $4 per pound. How many pounds of the $6 and the $3 coffee will be needed?

24. A grocer wishes to blend candy selling for $1.20 a pound with candy selling for $1.80 a pound to get a mixture that will be sold for $1.40 a pound. How many pounds of the $1.20 and the $1.80 candy should be used to get 30 pounds of the mixture?

25. How many barrels of olives worth $40 per barrel must be mixed with olives worth $60 per barrel to get 50 barrels of a mixture worth $48 per barrel?

26. A glue merchant wishes to mix some glue worth $70 per barrel with some glue worth $90 per barrel to get 80 barrels of a mixture worth $77.50 per barrel. How many barrels of each type should be used?

Write a system of equations for each problem. Then solve the system. See Example 4.

27. A boat takes 3 hours to go 24 miles upstream, and it can go 36 miles downstream in the same time. Find the speed of the current and the speed of the boat in still water. Let x = the speed of the boat in still water and y = the speed of the current.

	d	r	t
Downstream	36	$x + y$	3
Upstream	24	$x - y$	3

28. It takes a boat 1 1/2 hours to go 12 miles downstream, and 6 hours to return. Find the speed of the boat in still water and the speed of the current.

29. If a plane can travel 400 miles per hour into the wind and 540 miles per hour with the wind, find the speed of the wind and the speed of the plane in still air.

30. A small plane travels 100 miles per hour with the wind and 60 miles per hour against it. Find the speed of the wind and the speed of the plane in still air.

The next problems are "brain-busters."

31. At the beginning of a walk for charity, John and Harriet are 30 miles apart. If they leave at the same time and walk in the same direction, John overtakes Harriet in 60 hours. If they walk toward each other, they meet in 5 hours. What are their speeds?

32. Mr. Anderson left Farmersville in a plane at noon to travel to Exeter. Mr. Bentley left Exeter in his automobile at 2 P.M. to travel to Farmersville. It is 400 miles from Exeter to Farmersville. If the sum of their speeds is 120 miles per hour, and if they met at 4 P.M., find the speed of each.

33. The Smith family is coming to visit, and no one knows how many children they have. Janet, one of the girls, says she has as many brothers as sisters; her brother Steve says he has twice as many sisters as brothers. How many boys and how many girls are in the family?

34. In the Lopez family, the number of boys is one more than half the number of girls. One of the Lopez boys, Rico, says that he has one more sister than brothers. How many boys and girls are in the family?

Review Exercises   *Graph each linear inequality. See Section 6.5.*

35. $x + y \leq 5$

36. $2x - y \geq 7$

37. $3x + 2y > 6$

38. $x + 3y < 9$

39. $5x + 4y > 0$

40. $3x - 4y < 0$

7.5   Solving Systems of Linear Inequalities

1 Solve systems of linear inequalities by graphing.

In Section 6.5, we saw how to graph the solution of a linear inequality. Let us review the method. For example, to graph the solution of $x + 3y > 12$, first graph the line $x + 3y = 12$ by finding a few ordered pairs that satisfy the equation. Because the points on the line do not satisfy the inequality, use a dashed line. To decide which side of the line should be shaded, choose any test point not on the line, such as $(0, 0)$. Substitute 0 for x and 0 for y in the given inequality.

$$x + 3y > 12$$
$$0 + 0 > 12$$
$$0 > 12 \qquad \text{False}$$

Since the test point does not satisfy the inequality, shade the region on the side of the line that does not include (0, 0), as in Figure 7.6.

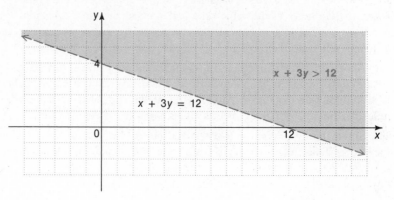

Figure 7.6

1️⃣ The same method is used to find the solution of a system of two linear inequalities, as shown in Examples 1 and 2. A **system of linear inequalities** consists of two or more linear inequalities. The solution of a system of linear inequalities includes all points that make all inequalities of the system true at the same time.

EXAMPLE 1   Graph the solution of the linear system

$$3x + 2y \leq 6$$
$$2x - 5y \geq 10.$$

First graph the inequality $3x + 2y \leq 6$, using the steps described above. Make the line solid rather than dashed, because the points on the line are also part of the solution. Then, on the same axes, graph the second inequality, $2x - 5y \geq 10$. The solution of the system is given by the overlap of the regions of the two graphs. This solution is the darkest shaded region in Figure 7.7 and includes portions of the two boundary lines. ●

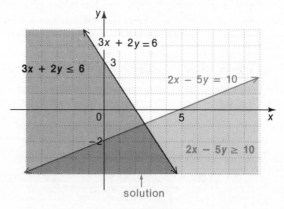

Figure 7.7

EXAMPLE 2   Graph the solution of the system

$$x - y > 5$$
$$2x + y < 2.$$

Figure 7.8 shows the graphs of both $x - y > 5$ and $2x + y < 2$. Dashed lines show that the graphs of the inequalities do not include their boundary lines. The solution of the system is the darkest shaded region in the figure. The solution does not include either boundary line.   ●

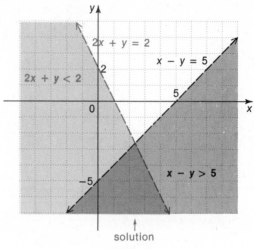

Figure 7.8

EXAMPLE 3   Graph the solution of the system

$$4x - 3y \le 8$$
$$x \ge 2.$$

Recall that $x = 2$ is a vertical line through the point $(2, 0)$. The graph of the solution is the darkest shaded region in Figure 7.9.   ●

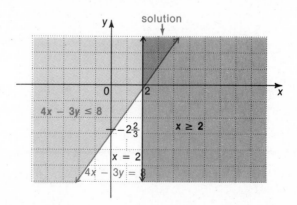

Figure 7.9

7.5 EXERCISES

Graph the solution of each system of linear inequalities. See Examples 1–3.

1. $x + y \leq 6$
$\quad x - y \leq 1$

2. $x + y \geq 2$
$\quad x - y \leq 3$

3. $2x - 3y \leq 6$
$\quad x + \ y \geq -1$

4. $4x + 5y \leq 20$
$\quad x - 2y \leq 5$

5. $\ x + 4y \leq 8$
$\quad 2x - \ y \leq 4$

6. $3x + y \leq 6$
$\quad 2x - y \leq 8$

7. $x - 4y \leq 3$
$\quad\quad x \geq 2y$

8. $2x + 3y \leq 6$
$\quad x - \ y \geq 5$

9. $x + 2y \leq 4$
$\quad x + 1 \geq y$

10. $\quad\ y \leq 2x - 5$
$\quad x - 3y \leq 2$

11. $4x + 3y \leq 6$
$\quad x - 2y \geq 4$

12. $\quad 3x - \ y \leq 4$
$\quad -6x + 2y \leq -10$

13. $\ x - 2y > 6$
$\quad 2x + \ y > 4$

14. $3x + \ y < 4$
$\quad x + 2y > 2$

15. $\quad\ x < 2y + 3$
$\quad x + y > 0$

16. $2x + 3y < 6$
$\quad 4x + 6y > 18$

17. $x - 3y \leq 6$
$\quad\quad x \geq -1$

18. $2x + 5y \geq 10$
$\quad\quad x \leq 4$

19. $3x - 2y \geq 9$
$\quad\quad y \leq 3$

20. $4x + 5y < 8$
$\quad\quad y > -2$

21. $x \geq 2$
$\quad y \leq 3$

22. $x \geq -1$
$\quad y \geq 4$

23. $x \leq 0$
$\quad y \leq 0$

24. $x \geq 0$
$\quad y \geq 0$

Review Exercises   *Find each value. See Section 1.3.*

25. 5^2

26. 7^2

27. 11^2

28. 15^2

29. 6^3

30. 3^3

31. 2^4

32. 3^5

Chapter 7   Review Exercises

[7.1] Decide whether the given ordered pair is a solution of the given system.

1. $(3, 4)$
$\quad 4x - 2y = 4$
$\quad 5x + \ y = 17$

2. $(-2, 1)$
$\quad 5x + 3y = -7$
$\quad 2x - 3y = -7$

3. $(-5, 2)$
$\quad x - 4y = -10$
$\quad 2x + 3y = -4$

4. $(6, 3)$
$\quad 3x + 8y = 42$
$\quad 4x - 3y = 15$

5. $(-1, -3)$
$\quad x + 2y = -7$
$\quad -x + 3y = -8$

6. $(2, 6)$
$\quad 3x - \ y = 0$
$\quad 4x + 2y = 20$

Solve each system by graphing.

7. $\ x + y = 3$
$\quad 2x - y = 3$

8. $\ x - 2y = -6$
$\quad 2x + \ y = -2$

9. $2x + 3y = 1$
$\quad 4x - \ y = -5$

10. $\quad x = 2y + 2$
$\quad 2x - 4y = 4$

11. $y + 2 = 0$
$\quad 3y = 6x$

12. $2x + 5y = 10$
$\quad 2x + 5y = 8$

[7.2] *Solve each system by the addition method.*

13. $x + y = 6$
$\quad 2x + y = 8$

14. $3x - y = 13$
$\quad x - 2y = 1$

15. $5x + 4y = 7$
$\quad 3x - 4y = 17$

16. $-4x + 3y = -7$
$\quad 6x - 5y = 11$

17. $3x - 4y = 7$
$\quad 6x - 8y = 14$

18. $2x + y = 5$
$\quad 2x + y = 8$

19. $3x - 2y = 14$
$\quad 5x - 4y = 24$

20. $2x + 6y = 18$
$\quad 3x + 5y = 19$

21. $3x - 4y = -1$
$\quad -6x + 8y = 2$

22. $4x + y = 5$
$\quad -12x - 3y = -15$

23. $5x + 4y = 3$
$\quad 7x + 5y = 3$

24. $3x + 5y = -1$
$\quad 5x + 4y = 7$

[7.3] *Solve each system by the substitution method.*

25. $3x + y = 14$
$\quad x = 2y$

26. $2x - 5y = 5$
$\quad y = x + 2$

27. $4x + 5y = 35$
$\quad x = 2y - 1$

28. $5x + y = -6$
$\quad x = 3y + 2$

29. $2x + 3y = 5$
$\quad 3x + 4y = 8$

30. $6x + 5y = 9$
$\quad 2x - 3y = 17$

Solve each system by any method. First simplify equations and clear of fractions where necessary.

31. $2x + y - x = 3y + 5$
$\quad y + 2 = x - 5$

32. $5x - 3 + y = 4y + 8$
$\quad 2y + 1 = x - 3$

33. $\dfrac{x}{2} + \dfrac{y}{3} = \dfrac{-8}{3}$
$\quad \dfrac{x}{4} + 2y = \dfrac{1}{2}$

34. $\dfrac{3x}{4} - \dfrac{y}{3} = \dfrac{7}{6}$
$\quad \dfrac{x}{2} + \dfrac{2y}{3} = \dfrac{5}{3}$

35. $\dfrac{2x}{5} - \dfrac{y}{2} = \dfrac{7}{10}$
$\quad \dfrac{x}{3} + y = 2$

36. $\dfrac{5x}{3} - \dfrac{y}{2} = -\dfrac{31}{3}$
$\quad 2x + \dfrac{y}{3} = \dfrac{26}{3}$

[7.4] *Solve each word problem by any method. Use two variables.*

37. The sum of two numbers is 42, and their difference is 14. Find the numbers.

38. One number is 2 more than twice as large as another. Their sum is 17. Find the numbers.

39. The perimeter of a rectangle is 40 meters. Its length is 1 1/2 times its width. Find the length and width of the rectangle.

40. A cashier has 20 bills, all of which are ten-dollar or twenty-dollar bills. The total value of the money is $250. How many of each type does he have?

41. Ms. Branson has $18,000 to invest. She wants the total annual income from the money to be $2600. She can invest part of it at 12% and the rest at 16%. How much should she invest at each rate?

42. Candy that sells for $1.30 a pound is to be mixed with candy selling for $.90 a pound to get 50 pounds of a mix that will sell for $1 per pound. How much of each type should be used?

43. A 40% antifreeze solution is to be mixed with a 70% solution to get 60 liters of a 50% solution. How many liters of the 40% and 70% solutions will be needed?

44. A certain plane flying with the wind travels 540 miles in 2 hours. Later, flying against the same wind, the plane travels 690 miles in 3 hours. Find the speed of the plane in still air and the speed of the wind.

[7.5] *Graph each system of linear inequalities.*

45. $x + y \leq 3$
 $2x \geq y$

46. $x + y \geq 4$
 $x - y \leq 2$

47. $2x + y < 6$
 $y - 2x < 6$

48. $x \geq 2$
 $y \leq 5$

49. $y \geq 3x$
 $2x + 3y \leq 4$

50. $y + 2 < 2x$
 $x > 3$

Chapter 7   Test

Solve each system by graphing.

1. $2x + y = 5$
 $3x - y = 15$

2. $3x + 2y = 8$
 $5x + 4y = 10$

3. $x + 2y = 6$
 $2x - y = 7$

Solve each system by the addition method.

4. $2x - 5y = -13$
 $3x + 5y = 43$

5. $4x + 3y = 25$
 $5x + 4y = 32$

6. $6x + 5y = -13$
 $-3x - \dfrac{5y}{2} = \dfrac{13}{2}$

7. $2x - y = 5$
 $4x + 3y = 0$

8. $4x + 5y = 8$
 $-8x - 10y = -6$

9. $\dfrac{6}{5}x - y = \dfrac{1}{5}$
 $\dfrac{-2}{3}x + \dfrac{1}{6}y = \dfrac{1}{3}$

Solve each system by substitution.

10. $2x + y = 1$
 $x = 8 + y$

11. $4x + 3y = 0$
 $2x + y = -4$

Solve each system by any method.

12. $8 + 3x - 4y = 14 - 3y$
 $3x + y + 12 = 9x - y$

13. $\dfrac{x}{2} - \dfrac{y}{4} = -4$
 $\dfrac{2x}{3} + \dfrac{5y}{4} = 1$

Solve the following word problems.

14. The sum of two numbers is 39. If one number is doubled, the result is 3 less than the other. Find the numbers.

15. The local record shop is having a sale. Some records cost $5 and some cost $7.50. Joe has exactly $40 to spend and wants to buy 6 records. How many can he buy at each price?

16. A 40% solution of acid is to be mixed with a 60% solution to get 100 liters of a 45% solution. How many liters of each solution should be used?

17. Two cars leave from the same place and travel in the same direction. One car travels one and one third times as fast as the other. After 3 hours, they are 45 miles apart. What is the speed of each car?

Graph the solution of each system of inequalities.

18. $2x + 7y \leq 14$
    $x - y \geq 1$

19. $2x - y \leq 6$
    $4y + 12 \geq -3x$

20. $3x - 5y < 15$
    $y < 2$

8

Roots and Radicals

A triangle, based on the Pythagorean theorem, is useful in designing machines.

8.1 Finding Roots

1 Find square roots.

2 Decide whether a given root is rational or irrational.

3 Find decimal approximations for irrational square roots.

4 Use the Pythagorean theorem.

5 Find higher roots.

To square a number, multiply it by itself.

$$\text{If } a = 7, \text{ then } a^2 = 7 \cdot 7 = 49.$$
$$\text{If } a = 10, \text{ then } a^2 = 10 \cdot 10 = 100.$$
$$\text{If } a = -5, \text{ then } a^2 = (-5) \cdot (-5) = 25.$$
$$\text{If } a = -\frac{1}{2}, \text{ then } a^2 = \left(-\frac{1}{2}\right) \cdot \left(-\frac{1}{2}\right) = \frac{1}{4}.$$

In this chapter, we consider the opposite problem.

$$\text{If } a^2 = 49, \text{ then } a = ?$$
$$\text{If } a^2 = 100, \text{ then } a = ?$$
$$\text{If } a^2 = 25, \text{ then } a = ?$$
$$\text{If } a^2 = \frac{1}{4}, \text{ then } a = ?$$

1   To answer these questions, find a number that can be multiplied by itself to result in the given number. The number found is the **square root** of the given number.

EXAMPLE 1   To find the square root of 49, think of a number that multiplied by itself gives 49. One square root of 49 is 7, since $7 \cdot 7 = 49$. Another square root of 49 is -7, since $(-7)(-7) = 49$. Therefore, 49 has two square roots, 7 and -7. One is positive and one is negative.   •

All numbers with rational square roots are called **perfect squares.** The first 100 integer perfect squares are listed in a table inside the front cover of this book.

The positive square root of a number is written with the symbol $\sqrt{}$. For example, the positive square root of 121 is 11, written

$$\sqrt{121} = 11.$$

The symbol $-\sqrt{}$ is used for the negative square root of a number. For example, the negative square root of 121 is -11, written

$$-\sqrt{121} = -11.$$

The symbol $\sqrt{}$ is called a **radical sign** and, used alone, always represents the nonnegative square root. The number inside the radical sign is called the **radicand** and the entire expression, radical sign and radicand, is called a **radical.**

If a is nonnegative,

$$\sqrt{a} \text{ is the nonnegative square root of } a,$$
$$-\sqrt{a} \text{ is the negative square root of } a.$$

Also, $\sqrt{0} = 0$, and for nonnegative a,

$$\sqrt{a} \cdot \sqrt{a} = (\sqrt{a})^2 = a.$$

EXAMPLE 2   Find each square root.

(a) $\sqrt{144}$

The radical $\sqrt{144}$ represents the positive square root of 144. Think of a positive number whose square is 144. The number is 12 (see the table of perfect squares), and

$$\sqrt{144} = 12.$$

(b) $-\sqrt{1024}$

This symbol represents the negative square root of 1024. From the table,

$$-\sqrt{1024} = -32.$$

(c) $\sqrt{256} = 16$ (d) $-\sqrt{900} = -30$

(e) $\sqrt{\dfrac{4}{9}} = \dfrac{2}{3}$ (f) $-\sqrt{\dfrac{16}{49}} = -\dfrac{4}{7}$ •

2 A number that is not a perfect square has a square root that is not a rational number. For example, $\sqrt{5}$ is not a rational number, because it cannot be written as the ratio of two integers. However, $\sqrt{5}$ is a real number and corresponds to a point on the number line. A real number that is not rational is called an **irrational number.** The number $\sqrt{5}$ is irrational. Many square roots of integers are irrational.

If a is a positive integer that is not a perfect square, then $\sqrt{a}$ is irrational.

Not every number has a *real number* square root. For example, there is no real number that can be squared to get -36. (The square of a real number can never be negative.) Because of this $\sqrt{-36}$ is not a real number.

If a is a negative number, then $\sqrt{a}$ is not a real number.

EXAMPLE 3   Tell whether each square root is rational or irrational.

(a) $\sqrt{17}$

Since 17 is not a perfect square (see the table or check with a calculator), $\sqrt{17}$ is irrational.

(b) $\sqrt{64}$

The number 64 is a perfect square, 8^2, so $\sqrt{64} = 8$, a rational number.

(c) $\sqrt{85}$ is irrational.

(d) $\sqrt{81}$ is rational ($\sqrt{81} = 9$).   ●

Not all irrational numbers are square roots of integers. For example, π (approximately 3.14159) is an irrational number that is not a square root of any integer.

3 If a number is irrational, we can still find a decimal that approximately equals the number. This can be done with calculators. For square roots, we can also use the square root table, as shown in Example 4.

EXAMPLE 4   Find a decimal approximation for each square root. Round answers to the nearest thousandth.

(a) $\sqrt{11}$

Using the square root key of a calculator gives $3.31662479 \approx 3.317$. To use the square root table, find 11 at the left. The approximate square root is given in the column having $\sqrt{n}$ at the top. You should find that

$$\sqrt{11} \approx 3.317,$$

where $\approx$ means approximately equal to.

(b) $\sqrt{39} \approx 6.245.$ Use the table or a calculator.

(c) $\sqrt{740}$

There is no 740 in the "n" column of the square root table. However, $740 = 74 \times 10$, so we can find $\sqrt{740}$ in the "$\sqrt{10n}$" column. Using the table as shown or a calculator,

$$\sqrt{740} \approx 27.203.$$

(d) $\sqrt{180} \approx 13.416$

Look in the "n" column for 18; then read across to the "$\sqrt{10n}$" column, or use a calculator. ●

4 One application of square roots comes from using the Pythagorean theorem. Recall from Section 4.6 that this theorem says that if c is the length of the longest side of a right triangle, and a and b are the lengths of the two shorter sides, then

$$a^2 + b^2 = c^2.$$

EXAMPLE 5 Find the third side of the given right triangle with sides a, b, and c, where c is the longest side.

(a) $a = 3$, $b = 4$

Use the theorem to find c^2 first.

$$c^2 = a^2 + b^2$$
$$c^2 = 3^2 + 4^2$$
$$= 9 + 16 = 25$$

Now find the positive square root of 25 to get c.

$$c = \sqrt{25} = 5$$

(Although -5 is also a square root of 5, the length of a side of a triangle must be a positive number.)

(b) $c = 9$, $b = 5$

Substitute the given values in the formula $c^2 = a^2 + b^2$. Then solve for a^2.

$$9^2 = a^2 + 5^2$$
$$81 = a^2 + 25$$
$$56 = a^2$$

Use the table or a calculator to find $a = \sqrt{56} \approx 7.483$. ●

5 Finding the square root of a number is the inverse of squaring a number. In a similar way, there are inverses to finding the cube of a number, or finding the fourth or higher power of a number. These inverses are called finding the **cube root,** written $\sqrt[3]{a}$, the **fourth root,** written $\sqrt[4]{a}$, and so on. We could write $\sqrt[2]{a}$ instead of $\sqrt{a}$, but the simpler symbol $\sqrt{a}$ is customary since the square root is the most commonly used root. A table of selected powers, which may help you find roots, is given inside the front cover of this book. Some calculators also can be used to find these roots.

EXAMPLE 6 Find each cube root.

(a) $\sqrt[3]{8}$

We need a number that can be cubed to give 8. Since $2^3 = 8$, we find that $\sqrt[3]{8} = 2$.

(b) $\sqrt[3]{-8}$

Since $(-2)^3 = -8$, we have $\sqrt[3]{-8} = -2$. ●

As these examples suggest, the cube root of a positive number is positive, and the cube root of a negative number is negative.

There is only one real number cube root for each real number.

When the root is even (square root, fourth root, and so on), the radicand must be nonnegative to get a real number root. Also, for even roots the symbol $\sqrt{}$, $\sqrt[4]{}$, $\sqrt[6]{}$, and so on is used for the *nonnegative* root.

EXAMPLE 7   Find each root.

(a) $\sqrt[4]{16}$

$\sqrt[4]{16} = 2$ because 2 is positive and $2^4 = 16$. Also $-\sqrt[4]{16} = -2$, but there is no real number that equals $\sqrt[4]{-16}$.

(b) $\sqrt[3]{64}$

Since $4^3 = 64$, we have $\sqrt[3]{64} = 4$.

(c) $-\sqrt[5]{32}$

First find $\sqrt[5]{32}$. Since 2 is the number whose fifth power is 32,

$$\sqrt[5]{32} = 2.$$

We want $-\sqrt[5]{32}$, so

$$-\sqrt[5]{32} = -2. \quad ●$$

8.1 EXERCISES

Find all square roots of each number. See Example 1.

1. 9   **2.** 16   **3.** 121   **4.** $\dfrac{196}{25}$

5. $\dfrac{400}{81}$ **6.** $\dfrac{900}{49}$ **7.** 625   **8.** 961

9. 1521   **10.** 2209   **11.** 3969   **12.** 4624

Find each root that exists. See Example 2.

13. $\sqrt{4}$ **14.** $\sqrt{9}$ **15.** $\sqrt{25}$ **16.** $\sqrt{36}$

17. $-\sqrt{64}$ **18.** $-\sqrt{100}$ **19.** $\sqrt{\dfrac{169}{49}}$ **20.** $\sqrt{\dfrac{196}{25}}$

21. $\sqrt{\dfrac{900}{121}}$ **22.** $\sqrt{1600}$ **23.** $-\sqrt{1681}$ **24.** $-\sqrt{2116}$

25. $\sqrt{2601}$ **26.** $\sqrt{3025}$ **27.** $-\sqrt{4900}$ **28.** $-\sqrt{5625}$

29. $\sqrt{-9}$ **30.** $\sqrt{-25}$ **31.** $-\sqrt{\dfrac{-49}{9}}$ **32.** $-\sqrt{\dfrac{-81}{16}}$

Write rational *or* irrational *for each number. If a number is rational, give its exact value. If a number is irrational, give a decimal approximation for the square root. See Examples 3 and 4.*

33. $\sqrt{16}$ **34.** $\sqrt{81}$ **35.** $\sqrt{15}$ **36.** $\sqrt{31}$
37. $\sqrt{47}$ **38.** $\sqrt{53}$ **39.** $\sqrt{68}$ **40.** $\sqrt{72}$
41. $-\sqrt{121}$ **42.** $-\sqrt{144}$ **43.** $\sqrt{110}$ **44.** $\sqrt{170}$
45. $\sqrt{400}$ **46.** $\sqrt{900}$ **47.** $-\sqrt{200}$ **48.** $-\sqrt{260}$

Use a calculator with a square root key to find the following. Round to the nearest thousandth.

 49. $\sqrt{571}$ **50.** $\sqrt{693}$ **51.** $\sqrt{798}$ **52.** $\sqrt{453}$
53. $\sqrt{3.94}$ **54.** $\sqrt{1.03}$ **55.** $\sqrt{.00895}$ **56.** $\sqrt{.000402}$

Find the missing side of each right triangle with sides a, b, and c, where c is the longest side. See Example 5.

57. $a = 6,\ b = 8$ **58.** $a = 5,\ b = 12$ **59.** $c = 17,\ a = 8$ **60.** $c = 26,\ b = 10$
61. $a = 10,\ b = 8$ **62.** $a = 9,\ b = 7$ **63.** $c = 12,\ b = 7$ **64.** $c = 8,\ a = 3$

Find each of the following roots that are real numbers. Use the table of selected powers inside the front cover if necessary. See Examples 6 and 7.

65. $\sqrt[3]{1000}$ **66.** $\sqrt[3]{8}$ **67.** $\sqrt[3]{125}$ **68.** $\sqrt[3]{216}$
69. $-\sqrt[3]{8}$ **70.** $-\sqrt[3]{64}$ **71.** $\sqrt[3]{-8}$ **72.** $\sqrt[3]{-27}$
73. $\sqrt[4]{1}$ **74.** $-\sqrt[4]{16}$ **75.** $\sqrt[4]{-16}$ **76.** $-\sqrt[4]{-625}$
77. $-\sqrt[4]{81}$ **78.** $-\sqrt[4]{256}$ **79.** $\sqrt[5]{1}$ **80.** $\sqrt[5]{-32}$

Use the square root key on your calculator twice to find approximations for the following roots. Round answers to the nearest thousandth.

 81. $-\sqrt[4]{32}$ **82.** $\sqrt[4]{125}$ **83.** $\sqrt[4]{27}$ **84.** $-\sqrt[4]{28}$
85. $\sqrt[4]{1.42}$ **86.** $\sqrt[4]{2.04}$ **87.** $\sqrt[4]{265.3}$ **88.** $-\sqrt[4]{57.68}$

Review Exercises   *Find all positive integer factors of each number. See Section 4.1.*

89. 24   **90.** 70   **91.** 300   **92.** 48
93. 72   **94.** 75   **95.** 150   **96.** 120

8.2   Products and Quotients of Radicals

1️⃣   Multiply radicals.

2️⃣   Simplify radicals using the product rule.

3️⃣   Divide radicals.

4️⃣   Simplify radical quotients using the quotient rule.

5️⃣   Use product and quotient rules to simplify higher roots.

1️⃣   In this section, we develop rules for finding products and quotients of radicals. To get a rule for products, first look at these examples:

$$\sqrt{4} \cdot \sqrt{9} = 2 \cdot 3 = 6 \quad \text{and} \quad \sqrt{4 \cdot 9} = \sqrt{36} = 6,$$

showing that

$$\sqrt{4} \cdot \sqrt{9} = \sqrt{4 \cdot 9}.$$

This result is an example of the **product rule for radicals:**

Product Rule

$$\sqrt{x} \cdot \sqrt{y} = \sqrt{x \cdot y},$$

as long as x and y are not negative. (Recall that the square root of a negative number is not a real number.) That is, the product of two radicals is the radical of the product.

EXAMPLE 1   Use the product rule for radicals to find each product.

(a) $\sqrt{2} \cdot \sqrt{3} = \sqrt{2 \cdot 3} = \sqrt{6}$

(b) $\sqrt{7} \cdot \sqrt{5} = \sqrt{35}$

(c) $\sqrt{11} \cdot \sqrt{a} = \sqrt{11a}$ Assume $a > 0$ ●

2️⃣   One important use of the product rule is in simplifying radicals. To **simplify** a radical, write it so that there is no perfect square factor under the radical sign. Example 2 shows how this is done.

EXAMPLE 2   Simplify each radical.

(a) $\sqrt{20}$

   Since 20 has a perfect square factor of 4,

$$\sqrt{20} = \sqrt{4 \cdot 5} \qquad \text{4 is a perfect square}$$
$$= \sqrt{4} \cdot \sqrt{5} \qquad \text{Product rule}$$
$$= 2\sqrt{5}. \qquad \sqrt{4} = 2$$

Thus, $\sqrt{20} = 2\sqrt{5}$. Since 5 has no perfect square factor, other than 1, $2\sqrt{5}$ is called the **simplified form** of $\sqrt{20}$. (We wrote the perfect square factor first when we factored 20. This is usually a good practice to follow.)

(b) $\sqrt{72}$

Look down the list of perfect squares in the square root table. Find the largest of these numbers that is a factor of 72. The largest is 36, so

$$\sqrt{72} = \sqrt{36 \cdot 2} \qquad \text{36 is a perfect square}$$
$$= \sqrt{36} \cdot \sqrt{2}$$
$$= 6\sqrt{2}.$$

(c) $\sqrt{300} = \sqrt{100 \cdot 3} \qquad \text{100 is a perfect square}$
$$= \sqrt{100} \cdot \sqrt{3}$$
$$= 10\sqrt{3}$$

(d) $\sqrt{15}$

The number 15 has no perfect square factors, so that $\sqrt{15}$ cannot be simplified further.   ●

Sometimes the product rule can be used to simplify an answer, as Example 3 shows.

EXAMPLE 3   Find each product and simplify.

(a) $\sqrt{9} \cdot \sqrt{75} = 3\sqrt{75}$
$$= 3\sqrt{25 \cdot 3}$$
$$= 3\sqrt{25} \cdot \sqrt{3}$$
$$= 3 \cdot 5\sqrt{3}$$
$$= 15\sqrt{3}$$

(b) $\sqrt{8} \cdot \sqrt{12} = \sqrt{8 \cdot 12}$
$$= \sqrt{4 \cdot 2 \cdot 4 \cdot 3}$$
$$= \sqrt{4} \cdot \sqrt{4} \cdot \sqrt{2 \cdot 3}$$
$$= 2 \cdot 2 \cdot \sqrt{6}$$
$$= 4\sqrt{6} \quad ●$$

③   The **quotient rule for radicals** is very similar to the product rule:

Quotient Rule

$$\frac{\sqrt{x}}{\sqrt{y}} = \sqrt{\frac{x}{y}},$$

as long as x and y are not negative and y is not 0. That is, the quotient of the radicals is the radical of a quotient.

Like the product rule, the quotient rule can be used to divide radicals, as in Example 4, as well as to simplify radicals, as in Example 5.

EXAMPLE 4   Use the quotient rule to divide $27\sqrt{15}$ by $9\sqrt{3}$.
Work as follows.

$$\frac{27\sqrt{15}}{9\sqrt{3}} = \frac{27}{9} \cdot \frac{\sqrt{15}}{\sqrt{3}} = 3\sqrt{\frac{15}{3}} = 3\sqrt{5} \quad \bullet$$

4   The next example shows the quotient rule used to simplify radicals.

EXAMPLE 5   Use the quotient rule to simplify each radical.

(a) $\sqrt{\dfrac{25}{9}} = \dfrac{\sqrt{25}}{\sqrt{9}} = \dfrac{5}{3}$

(b) $\sqrt{\dfrac{144}{49}} = \dfrac{\sqrt{144}}{\sqrt{49}} = \dfrac{12}{7}$

(c) $\sqrt{\dfrac{3}{4}} = \dfrac{\sqrt{3}}{\sqrt{4}} = \dfrac{\sqrt{3}}{2} \quad \bullet$

Some problems require both the product and the quotient rules, as Examples 6 and 7 show.

EXAMPLE 6   Simplify $\sqrt{\dfrac{3}{5}} \cdot \sqrt{\dfrac{4}{5}}$.

Use the quotient rule, and then the product rule.

$$\sqrt{\frac{3}{5}} \cdot \sqrt{\frac{4}{5}} = \frac{\sqrt{3}}{\sqrt{5}} \cdot \frac{\sqrt{4}}{\sqrt{5}} = \frac{\sqrt{3} \cdot \sqrt{4}}{\sqrt{5} \cdot \sqrt{5}}$$

$$= \frac{\sqrt{3} \cdot 2}{\sqrt{25}} = \frac{2\sqrt{3}}{5} \quad \bullet$$

The properties of this section also apply when variables appear under the radical sign, as long as all the variables represent only nonnegative numbers. For example, $\sqrt{5^2} = 5$, but $\sqrt{(-5)^2} \neq -5$. That is,

$\sqrt{a^2} = a$ only if a is nonnegative.

EXAMPLE 7   Simplify each radical. Assume all variables represent positive real numbers.

(a) $\sqrt{25m^4} = \sqrt{25} \cdot \sqrt{m^4} = 5m^2$

(b) $\sqrt{64p^{10}} = 8p^5$

(c) $\sqrt{r^9} = \sqrt{r^8 \cdot r} = \sqrt{r^8} \cdot \sqrt{r} = r^4\sqrt{r}$

(d) $\sqrt{\dfrac{5}{x^2}} = \dfrac{\sqrt{5}}{\sqrt{x^2}} = \dfrac{\sqrt{5}}{x} \quad \bullet$

5   The product rule and the quotient rule for radicals also work for other roots, as shown in the next example. To simplify cube roots, look for factors that are *perfect cubes*. A **perfect cube** is a number with a rational cube root. For example, $\sqrt[3]{64} = 4$, and since 4 is a rational number 64 is a perfect cube. Higher roots are handled in a similar manner.

EXAMPLE 8   Simplify each radical.

(a) $\sqrt[3]{32} = \sqrt[3]{8 \cdot 4} = \sqrt[3]{8} \cdot \sqrt[3]{4} = 2\sqrt[3]{4}$

(b) $\sqrt[3]{108} = \sqrt[3]{27 \cdot 4} = \sqrt[3]{27} \cdot \sqrt[3]{4} = 3\sqrt[3]{4}$

(c) $\sqrt[3]{\dfrac{8}{125}} = \dfrac{\sqrt[3]{8}}{\sqrt[3]{125}} = \dfrac{2}{5}$

(d) $\sqrt[4]{32} = \sqrt[4]{16} \cdot \sqrt[4]{2} = 2\sqrt[4]{2}$

(e) $\sqrt[4]{\dfrac{16}{625}} = \dfrac{\sqrt[4]{16}}{\sqrt[4]{625}} = \dfrac{2}{5}$ ●

8.2   EXERCISES

Use the product rule to simplify each expression. See Examples 1–3.

1. $\sqrt{8} \cdot \sqrt{2}$
2. $\sqrt{27} \cdot \sqrt{3}$
3. $\sqrt{6} \cdot \sqrt{6}$
4. $\sqrt{11} \cdot \sqrt{11}$
5. $\sqrt{21} \cdot \sqrt{21}$
6. $\sqrt{17} \cdot \sqrt{17}$
7. $\sqrt{3} \cdot \sqrt{7}$
8. $\sqrt{2} \cdot \sqrt{5}$
9. $\sqrt{27}$
10. $\sqrt{45}$
11. $\sqrt{28}$
12. $\sqrt{40}$
13. $\sqrt{18}$
14. $\sqrt{75}$
15. $\sqrt{48}$
16. $\sqrt{80}$
17. $\sqrt{125}$
18. $\sqrt{150}$
19. $\sqrt{700}$
20. $\sqrt{1100}$
21. $10\sqrt{27}$
22. $4\sqrt{8}$
23. $2\sqrt{20}$
24. $5\sqrt{80}$
25. $\sqrt{27} \cdot \sqrt{48}$
26. $\sqrt{75} \cdot \sqrt{27}$
27. $\sqrt{50} \cdot \sqrt{72}$
28. $\sqrt{98} \cdot \sqrt{8}$
29. $\sqrt{7} \cdot \sqrt{21}$
30. $\sqrt{12} \cdot \sqrt{48}$
31. $\sqrt{15} \cdot \sqrt{45}$
32. $\sqrt{20} \cdot \sqrt{45}$
33. $\sqrt{80} \cdot \sqrt{15}$
34. $\sqrt{60} \cdot \sqrt{12}$
35. $\sqrt{50} \cdot \sqrt{20}$
36. $\sqrt{72} \cdot \sqrt{12}$

Use the quotient rule and the product rule, as necessary, to simplify each expression. See Examples 4–6.

37. $\sqrt{\dfrac{100}{9}}$
38. $\sqrt{\dfrac{225}{16}}$
39. $\sqrt{\dfrac{36}{49}}$
40. $\sqrt{\dfrac{256}{9}}$
41. $\sqrt{\dfrac{5}{16}}$
42. $\sqrt{\dfrac{11}{25}}$
43. $\sqrt{\dfrac{30}{49}}$
44. $\sqrt{\dfrac{10}{121}}$
45. $\sqrt{\dfrac{1}{5}} \cdot \sqrt{\dfrac{4}{5}}$
46. $\sqrt{\dfrac{2}{3}} \cdot \sqrt{\dfrac{2}{27}}$
47. $\sqrt{\dfrac{2}{5}} \cdot \sqrt{\dfrac{8}{125}}$
48. $\sqrt{\dfrac{3}{8}} \cdot \sqrt{\dfrac{3}{2}}$
49. $\dfrac{\sqrt{75}}{\sqrt{3}}$
50. $\dfrac{\sqrt{200}}{\sqrt{2}}$
51. $\dfrac{\sqrt{48}}{\sqrt{3}}$
52. $\dfrac{\sqrt{72}}{\sqrt{8}}$
53. $\dfrac{15\sqrt{10}}{5\sqrt{2}}$
54. $\dfrac{18\sqrt{20}}{2\sqrt{10}}$
55. $\dfrac{25\sqrt{50}}{5\sqrt{5}}$
56. $\dfrac{26\sqrt{10}}{13\sqrt{5}}$

Simplify each expression. Assume that all variables represent positive real numbers. See Example 7.

57. $\sqrt{y} \cdot \sqrt{y}$ **58.** $\sqrt{m} \cdot \sqrt{m}$ **59.** $\sqrt{x} \cdot \sqrt{z}$ **60.** $\sqrt{p} \cdot \sqrt{q}$

61. $\sqrt{x^2}$ **62.** $\sqrt{y^2}$ **63.** $\sqrt{x^4}$ **64.** $\sqrt{y^4}$

65. $\sqrt{x^2 y^4}$ **66.** $\sqrt{x^4 y^8}$ **67.** $\sqrt{x^3}$ **68.** $\sqrt{y^5}$

69. $\sqrt{\dfrac{16}{x^2}}$ **70.** $\sqrt{\dfrac{100}{m^4}}$ **71.** $\sqrt{\dfrac{11}{r^4}}$ **72.** $\sqrt{\dfrac{23}{y^6}}$

Simplify each radical. See Example 8.

73. $\sqrt[3]{40}$ **74.** $\sqrt[3]{48}$ **75.** $\sqrt[3]{54}$ **76.** $\sqrt[3]{135}$

77. $\sqrt[3]{128}$ **78.** $\sqrt[3]{192}$ **79.** $\sqrt[4]{80}$ **80.** $\sqrt[4]{243}$

81. $\sqrt[3]{\dfrac{8}{27}}$ **82.** $\sqrt[4]{\dfrac{1}{256}}$ **83.** $\sqrt[4]{\dfrac{10,000}{81}}$ **84.** $\sqrt[3]{\dfrac{216}{125}}$

Review Exercises *Rewrite each fraction with the given denominator. See Section 5.3.*

85. $\dfrac{9}{13} = \dfrac{}{39}$ **86.** $\dfrac{5}{11} = \dfrac{}{66}$ **87.** $\dfrac{2}{3} = \dfrac{}{15}$ **88.** $\dfrac{3}{14} = \dfrac{}{56}$

89. $\dfrac{2}{x} = \dfrac{}{3x}$ **90.** $\dfrac{5}{2y} = \dfrac{}{2y^2}$ **91.** $\dfrac{5}{\sqrt{3}} = \dfrac{}{2\sqrt{3}}$ **92.** $\dfrac{8}{\sqrt{5}} = \dfrac{}{3\sqrt{5}}$

8.3   Rationalizing the Denominator

  1   Rationalize the denominator.

  2   Simplify expressions by rationalizing the denominator.

  3   Rationalize the denominator for cube roots.

  1   We found decimal approximations for radicals in the first section of this chapter. It is sometimes easier to find these decimals if the denominators contain no radicals. For example, to eliminate the radical in the denominator of

$$\frac{\sqrt{3}}{\sqrt{2}},$$

multiply the numerator and the denominator by $\sqrt{2}$ to get a perfect square radicand in the denominator.

$$\frac{\sqrt{3}}{\sqrt{2}} = \frac{\sqrt{3} \cdot \sqrt{2}}{\sqrt{2} \cdot \sqrt{2}} = \frac{\sqrt{6}}{2} \qquad \sqrt{2} \cdot \sqrt{2} = 2$$

This process of changing the denominator from a radical (irrational number) to a rational number is called **rationalizing the denominator.** The value of the number is not changed; only the form of the number is changed. This process of changing the form of a fraction with radicals is also important in further work in mathematics.

EXAMPLE 1

Rationalize each denominator.

(a) $\dfrac{9}{\sqrt{6}}$

Multiply both numerator and denominator by $\sqrt{6}$.

$$\frac{9}{\sqrt{6}} = \frac{9 \cdot \sqrt{6}}{\sqrt{6} \cdot \sqrt{6}} = \frac{9\sqrt{6}}{6} = \frac{3\sqrt{6}}{2} \qquad \sqrt{6} \cdot \sqrt{6} = 6$$

(b) $\dfrac{12}{\sqrt{8}}$

Begin by simplifying the radical.

$$\sqrt{8} = \sqrt{4} \cdot \sqrt{2} = 2\sqrt{2}$$

Then multiply numerator and denominator by $\sqrt{2}$.

$$\frac{12}{\sqrt{8}} = \frac{12}{2\sqrt{2}} = \frac{12 \cdot \sqrt{2}}{2\sqrt{2} \cdot \sqrt{2}} = \frac{12\sqrt{2}}{2\sqrt{4}} = \frac{12\sqrt{2}}{2 \cdot 2} = \frac{12\sqrt{2}}{4} = 3\sqrt{2} \quad \bullet$$

2   Radicals are considered simplified only if the denominator is rationalized, as shown in Examples 2–4.

EXAMPLE 2

Simplify $\sqrt{\dfrac{27}{5}}$ by rationalizing the denominator.

First, use the quotient rule for radicals.

$$\sqrt{\frac{27}{5}} = \frac{\sqrt{27}}{\sqrt{5}}$$

Now rationalize the denominator by multiplying both numerator and denominator by $\sqrt{5}$.

$$\frac{\sqrt{27}}{\sqrt{5}} = \frac{\sqrt{27} \cdot \sqrt{5}}{\sqrt{5} \cdot \sqrt{5}}$$

$$= \frac{\sqrt{9 \cdot 3} \cdot \sqrt{5}}{5} = \frac{\sqrt{9} \cdot \sqrt{3} \cdot \sqrt{5}}{5}$$

$$= \frac{3 \cdot \sqrt{3 \cdot 5}}{5} = \frac{3\sqrt{15}}{5} \quad \bullet$$

EXAMPLE 3 Simplify $\sqrt{\dfrac{5}{8}} \cdot \sqrt{\dfrac{1}{6}}$.

Use the product rule and then the quotient rule.

$$\sqrt{\frac{5}{8}} \cdot \sqrt{\frac{1}{6}} = \sqrt{\frac{5}{8} \cdot \frac{1}{6}} = \sqrt{\frac{5}{48}} = \frac{\sqrt{5}}{\sqrt{48}} = \frac{\sqrt{5}}{\sqrt{16} \cdot \sqrt{3}} = \frac{\sqrt{5}}{4\sqrt{3}}$$

Now rationalize the denominator by multiplying both numerator and denominator by $\sqrt{3}$.

$$\frac{\sqrt{5}}{4\sqrt{3}} = \frac{\sqrt{5} \cdot \sqrt{3}}{4\sqrt{3} \cdot \sqrt{3}} = \frac{\sqrt{15}}{4\sqrt{9}} = \frac{\sqrt{15}}{4 \cdot 3} = \frac{\sqrt{15}}{12} \quad \bullet$$

EXAMPLE 4 Rationalize the denominator of $\dfrac{\sqrt{4x}}{\sqrt{y}}$. Assume that x and y represent positive real numbers.

Multiply numerator and denominator by $\sqrt{y}$.

$$\frac{\sqrt{4x}}{\sqrt{y}} = \frac{\sqrt{4x} \cdot \sqrt{y}}{\sqrt{y} \cdot \sqrt{y}} = \frac{\sqrt{4xy}}{y} = \frac{2\sqrt{xy}}{y} \quad \bullet$$

3 To rationalize a denominator with a cube root, change the radicand in the denominator to a perfect cube, as shown in the next example.

EXAMPLE 5 Rationalize each denominator.

(a) $\sqrt[3]{\dfrac{3}{2}}$

Multiply the numerator and the denominator by enough factors of 2 to make the denominator a perfect cube. This will eliminate the radical in the denominator. Here we need to multiply by $\sqrt[3]{2^2}$.

$$\sqrt[3]{\frac{3}{2}} = \frac{\sqrt[3]{3}}{\sqrt[3]{2}} = \frac{\sqrt[3]{3} \cdot \sqrt[3]{2^2}}{\sqrt[3]{2} \cdot \sqrt[3]{2^2}} = \frac{\sqrt[3]{3 \cdot 2^2}}{\sqrt[3]{2^3}} = \frac{\sqrt[3]{12}}{2} \qquad \sqrt[3]{2^3} = \sqrt[3]{8} = 2$$

(b) $\dfrac{\sqrt[3]{3}}{\sqrt[3]{4}}$

Since $4 \cdot 2 = 2^2 \cdot 2 = 2^3$, multiply numerator and denominator by $\sqrt[3]{2}$.

$$\frac{\sqrt[3]{3}}{\sqrt[3]{4}} = \frac{\sqrt[3]{3} \cdot \sqrt[3]{2}}{\sqrt[3]{4} \cdot \sqrt[3]{2}} = \frac{\sqrt[3]{6}}{\sqrt[3]{8}} = \frac{\sqrt[3]{6}}{2} \quad \bullet$$

8.3 EXERCISES

Perform the indicated operations, and write all answers in simplest form. See Examples 1–3.

1. $\dfrac{6}{\sqrt{5}}$ **2.** $\dfrac{4}{\sqrt{2}}$ **3.** $\dfrac{5}{\sqrt{5}}$ **4.** $\dfrac{15}{\sqrt{15}}$

5. $\dfrac{3}{\sqrt{7}}$

6. $\dfrac{12}{\sqrt{10}}$

7. $\dfrac{8\sqrt{3}}{\sqrt{5}}$

8. $\dfrac{9\sqrt{6}}{\sqrt{5}}$

9. $\dfrac{12\sqrt{10}}{8\sqrt{3}}$

10. $\dfrac{9\sqrt{15}}{6\sqrt{2}}$

11. $\dfrac{8}{\sqrt{27}}$

12. $\dfrac{12}{\sqrt{18}}$

13. $\dfrac{3}{\sqrt{50}}$

14. $\dfrac{5}{\sqrt{75}}$

15. $\dfrac{12}{\sqrt{72}}$

16. $\dfrac{21}{\sqrt{45}}$

17. $\dfrac{9}{\sqrt{32}}$

18. $\dfrac{50}{\sqrt{125}}$

19. $\dfrac{\sqrt{8}}{\sqrt{2}}$

20. $\dfrac{\sqrt{27}}{\sqrt{3}}$

21. $\dfrac{\sqrt{10}}{\sqrt{5}}$

22. $\dfrac{\sqrt{6}}{\sqrt{3}}$

23. $\dfrac{\sqrt{40}}{\sqrt{3}}$

24. $\dfrac{\sqrt{5}}{\sqrt{8}}$

25. $\sqrt{\dfrac{1}{2}}$

26. $\sqrt{\dfrac{1}{8}}$

27. $\sqrt{\dfrac{10}{7}}$

28. $\sqrt{\dfrac{2}{3}}$

29. $\sqrt{\dfrac{9}{5}}$

30. $\sqrt{\dfrac{16}{7}}$

31. $\sqrt{\dfrac{7}{5}}\cdot\sqrt{\dfrac{5}{3}}$

32. $\sqrt{\dfrac{1}{3}}\cdot\sqrt{\dfrac{2}{5}}$

33. $\sqrt{\dfrac{3}{4}}\cdot\sqrt{\dfrac{1}{5}}$

34. $\sqrt{\dfrac{1}{10}}\cdot\sqrt{\dfrac{10}{3}}$

35. $\sqrt{\dfrac{21}{7}}\cdot\sqrt{\dfrac{21}{8}}$

36. $\sqrt{\dfrac{1}{11}}\cdot\sqrt{\dfrac{33}{16}}$

37. $\sqrt{\dfrac{2}{5}}\cdot\sqrt{\dfrac{3}{10}}$

38. $\sqrt{\dfrac{9}{8}}\cdot\sqrt{\dfrac{7}{16}}$

39. $\sqrt{\dfrac{16}{27}}\cdot\sqrt{\dfrac{1}{9}}$

40. $\sqrt{\dfrac{5}{8}}\cdot\sqrt{\dfrac{5}{6}}$

Perform the indicated operations, and write all answers in simplest form. Rationalize all denominators. Assume that all variables represent positive real numbers. See Example 4.

41. $\sqrt{\dfrac{6}{p}}$

42. $\sqrt{\dfrac{4r^3}{s}}$

43. $\sqrt{\dfrac{6p^3}{3m}}$

44. $\sqrt{\dfrac{a^3b}{6}}$

45. $\sqrt{\dfrac{x^2}{4y}}$

46. $\sqrt{\dfrac{m^2n}{2}}$

47. $\sqrt{\dfrac{9a^2r}{5}}$

48. $\sqrt{\dfrac{2x^2z^4}{3y}}$

Rationalize the denominators of the following cube roots. See Example 5.

49. $\sqrt[3]{\dfrac{1}{2}}$

50. $\sqrt[3]{\dfrac{1}{4}}$

51. $\sqrt[3]{\dfrac{1}{32}}$

52. $\sqrt[3]{\dfrac{1}{5}}$

53. $\sqrt[3]{\dfrac{1}{11}}$

54. $\sqrt[3]{\dfrac{3}{2}}$

55. $\sqrt[3]{\dfrac{2}{5}}$

56. $\sqrt[3]{\dfrac{4}{9}}$

57. $\sqrt[3]{\dfrac{3}{4}}$

58. $\sqrt[3]{\dfrac{3}{25}}$

59. $\sqrt[3]{\dfrac{7}{36}}$

60. $\sqrt[3]{\dfrac{11}{49}}$

Review Exercises   *Combine like terms. See Section 2.1.*

61. $2x + 3x - x$

62. $-5a + 2a + 7a$

63. $m + 2 - 3m - 5$

64. $-2p + 4p + 7 - 9 - 3p$

65. $4y + 3z + 5z - y$

66. $5w + 2t - w + 3t$

8.4   Addition and Subtraction of Radicals

---

1. Add and subtract radicals.
2. Simplify radical sums and differences.
3. Simplify with multiplication.

1   The distributive property can be used to add or subtract radicals. For example,

$$8\sqrt{3} + 6\sqrt{3} = (8 + 6)\sqrt{3} \quad \text{Distributive property}$$
$$= 14\sqrt{3}.$$

Also, $2\sqrt{11} - 7\sqrt{11} = -5\sqrt{11}$. Only **like radicals,** those that are multiples of the same root of the same number, can be combined this way.

EXAMPLE 1   Add or subtract, as indicated.

(a) $3\sqrt{6} + 5\sqrt{6} = (3 + 5)\sqrt{6} = 8\sqrt{6}$

(b) $5\sqrt{10} - 7\sqrt{10} = (5 - 7)\sqrt{10} = -2\sqrt{10}$

(c) $\sqrt[3]{5} + \sqrt[3]{5} = 1\sqrt[3]{5} + 1\sqrt[3]{5} = (1 + 1)\sqrt[3]{5} = 2\sqrt[3]{5}$

(d) $\sqrt[4]{7} + 2\sqrt[4]{7} = 1\sqrt[4]{7} + 2\sqrt[4]{7} = 3\sqrt[4]{7}$

(e) $\sqrt{3} + \sqrt{7}$ cannot be simplified further.   ●

2   Sometimes it is necessary first to simplify each radical in a sum or difference. Then add or subtract, if possible.

EXAMPLE 2   Simplify as much as possible.

(a) $3\sqrt{2} + \sqrt{8} = 3\sqrt{2} + \sqrt{4 \cdot 2} \quad \text{Simplify } \sqrt{8}$
$$= 3\sqrt{2} + \sqrt{4} \cdot \sqrt{2}$$
$$= 3\sqrt{2} + 2\sqrt{2}$$
$$= 5\sqrt{2}$$

(b) $\sqrt{18} - \sqrt{27} = \sqrt{9 \cdot 2} - \sqrt{9 \cdot 3}$
$$= \sqrt{9} \cdot \sqrt{2} - \sqrt{9} \cdot \sqrt{3}$$
$$= 3\sqrt{2} - 3\sqrt{3}$$

Since $\sqrt{2}$ and $\sqrt{3}$ are unlike radicals, this difference cannot be simplified further.

(c) $2\sqrt{12} + 3\sqrt{75} = 2(\sqrt{4} \cdot \sqrt{3}) + 3(\sqrt{25} \cdot \sqrt{3})$
$$= 2(2\sqrt{3}) + 3(5\sqrt{3})$$
$$= 4\sqrt{3} + 15\sqrt{3}$$
$$= 19\sqrt{3}$$

(d) $3\sqrt[3]{16} + 5\sqrt[3]{2} = 3(\sqrt[3]{8} \cdot \sqrt[3]{2}) + 5\sqrt[3]{2}$

$\qquad\qquad\quad = 3(2\sqrt[3]{2}) + 5\sqrt[3]{2}$

$\qquad\qquad\quad = 6\sqrt[3]{2} + 5\sqrt[3]{2}$

$\qquad\qquad\quad = 11\sqrt[3]{2}$ •

3   Some radical expressions require both multiplication and addition (or subtraction). The order of operations presented earlier still applies.

EXAMPLE 3   Simplify each expression. Assume that all variables represent nonnegative real numbers.

(a) $\sqrt{5} \cdot \sqrt{15} + 4\sqrt{3} = \sqrt{5 \cdot 15} + 4\sqrt{3}$

$\qquad\qquad\qquad\quad = \sqrt{75} + 4\sqrt{3}$

$\qquad\qquad\qquad\quad = \sqrt{25 \cdot 3} + 4\sqrt{3}$

$\qquad\qquad\qquad\quad = \sqrt{25} \cdot \sqrt{3} + 4\sqrt{3}$

$\qquad\qquad\qquad\quad = 5\sqrt{3} + 4\sqrt{3}$

$\qquad\qquad\qquad\quad = 9\sqrt{3}$

(b) $\sqrt{2} \cdot \sqrt{6k} + \sqrt{27k} = \sqrt{12k} + \sqrt{27k}$

$\qquad\qquad\qquad\quad = \sqrt{4 \cdot 3k} + \sqrt{9 \cdot 3k}$

$\qquad\qquad\qquad\quad = \sqrt{4} \cdot \sqrt{3k} + \sqrt{9} \cdot \sqrt{3k}$

$\qquad\qquad\qquad\quad = 2\sqrt{3k} + 3\sqrt{3k}$

$\qquad\qquad\qquad\quad = 5\sqrt{3k}$

(c) $\sqrt[3]{2} \cdot \sqrt[3]{16m^3} - \sqrt[3]{108m^3} = \sqrt[3]{32m^3} - \sqrt[3]{108m^3}$

$\qquad\qquad\qquad\qquad\quad = \sqrt[3]{(8m^3)4} - \sqrt[3]{(27m^3)4}$

$\qquad\qquad\qquad\qquad\quad = 2m\sqrt[3]{4} - 3m\sqrt[3]{4}$

$\qquad\qquad\qquad\qquad\quad = -m\sqrt[3]{4}$ •

Remember:

a sum or difference of radicals can be simplified only if the radicals are **like radicals.**

8.4 EXERCISES

Simplify and combine terms wherever possible. See Examples 1 and 2.

1. $2\sqrt{3} + 5\sqrt{3}$ **2.** $6\sqrt{5} + 8\sqrt{5}$ **3.** $4\sqrt{7} - 9\sqrt{7}$ **4.** $6\sqrt{2} - 8\sqrt{2}$

5. $\sqrt{6} + \sqrt{6}$ **6.** $\sqrt{11} + \sqrt{11}$ **7.** $\sqrt{17} + 2\sqrt{17}$ **8.** $3\sqrt{19} + \sqrt{19}$

9. $5\sqrt{7} - \sqrt{7}$ **10.** $12\sqrt{14} - \sqrt{14}$ **11.** $5\sqrt{8} + \sqrt{8}$ **12.** $3\sqrt{27} - \sqrt{27}$

13. $\sqrt{45} + 2\sqrt{20}$ **14.** $\sqrt{24} + 5\sqrt{54}$ **15.** $3\sqrt{18} + \sqrt{2}$ **16.** $2\sqrt{48} - \sqrt{3}$

17. $-\sqrt{12} + \sqrt{75}$ **18.** $2\sqrt{27} - \sqrt{300}$ **19.** $5\sqrt{72} - 2\sqrt{50}$ **20.** $6\sqrt{18} - 4\sqrt{32}$

21. $5\sqrt{7} - 2\sqrt{28} + 6\sqrt{63}$ **22.** $3\sqrt{11} + 5\sqrt{44} - 3\sqrt{99}$ **23.** $6\sqrt{5} + 3\sqrt{20} - 8\sqrt{45}$

24. $7\sqrt{3} + 2\sqrt{12} - 5\sqrt{27}$ **25.** $6\sqrt{2} + 5\sqrt{27} - 4\sqrt{12}$ **26.** $9\sqrt{24} - 2\sqrt{54} + 3\sqrt{20}$

27. $2\sqrt{8} - 5\sqrt{32} + 2\sqrt{48}$ **28.** $5\sqrt{72} - 3\sqrt{48} - 4\sqrt{128}$ **29.** $4\sqrt{50} + 3\sqrt{12} + 5\sqrt{45}$

30. $6\sqrt{18} + 2\sqrt{48} - 6\sqrt{28}$ **31.** $\dfrac{1}{4}\sqrt{288} - \dfrac{1}{6}\sqrt{72}$ **32.** $\dfrac{2}{3}\sqrt{27} - \dfrac{3}{4}\sqrt{48}$

33. $\dfrac{3}{5}\sqrt{75} - \dfrac{2}{3}\sqrt{45}$ **34.** $\dfrac{5}{8}\sqrt{128} - \dfrac{3}{4}\sqrt{160}$ **35.** $\sqrt{3} \cdot \sqrt{7} + 2\sqrt{21}$

36. $\sqrt{13} \cdot \sqrt{2} + 3\sqrt{26}$ **37.** $\sqrt{6} \cdot \sqrt{2} + 3\sqrt{3}$ **38.** $4\sqrt{15} \cdot \sqrt{3} - 2\sqrt{5}$

39. $4\sqrt[3]{16} - 3\sqrt[3]{54}$ **40.** $5\sqrt[3]{128} + 3\sqrt[3]{250}$ **41.** $3\sqrt[3]{24} + 6\sqrt[3]{81}$

42. $2\sqrt[4]{48} - \sqrt[4]{243}$ **43.** $5\sqrt[4]{32} + 2\sqrt[4]{32} \cdot \sqrt[4]{4}$ **44.** $8\sqrt[3]{48} + 10\sqrt[3]{3} \cdot \sqrt[3]{18}$

Simplify each expression. Assume that all variables represent nonnegative real numbers. See Example 3.

45. $\sqrt{9x} + \sqrt{49x} - \sqrt{16x}$ **46.** $\sqrt{4a} - \sqrt{16a} + \sqrt{9a}$ **47.** $\sqrt{4a} + 6\sqrt{a} + \sqrt{25a}$

48. $\sqrt{6x^2} + x\sqrt{54}$ **49.** $\sqrt{75x^2} + x\sqrt{300}$ **50.** $\sqrt{20y^2} - 3y\sqrt{5}$

51. $3\sqrt{8x^2} - 4x\sqrt{2}$ **52.** $6r\sqrt{27r^2s} + 3r^2\sqrt{3s}$ **53.** $6\sqrt[3]{8p^2} - 2\sqrt[3]{27p^2}$

54. $5\sqrt[4]{m^3} + 8\sqrt[4]{16m^3}$ **55.** $5\sqrt[4]{m^4} + 3\sqrt[3]{81m^4}$ **56.** $10\sqrt[3]{4m^3} - 3m\sqrt[3]{32}$

Review Exercises *Find each product. See Section 3.6.*

57. $(m + 3)(m + 5)$ **58.** $(p - 2)(p + 7)$ **59.** $(2k - 3)(3k - 4)$

60. $(4z + 2)(5z - 8)$ **61.** $(3x - 1)^2$ **62.** $(2y + 5)^2$

63. $(a + 3)(a - 3)$ **64.** $(2n + 3)(2n - 3)$ **65.** $(4k + 5)(4k - 5)$

8.5 Simplifying Radicals

⊡ Simplify sums of radicals.

⊡ Simplify radical products.

⊡ Simplify quotients with radicals.

⊡ Write quotients with radicals in lowest terms.

⊡ A decision on the "simplest" form of a radical is not always easy to make. In this book, a radical expression is simplified when the following five conditions are satisfied. Although the conditions are illustrated with square roots, they apply to higher roots as well.

Simplifying Radicals

1. If a radicand is a perfect square, then the square root should be used in place of the radical.

   For example, $\sqrt{49}$ is simplified by writing 7, and $\sqrt{\dfrac{169}{9}}$ by writing $\dfrac{13}{3}$.

2. If a radical expression contains products of radicals, the product rule for radicals, $\sqrt{x} \cdot \sqrt{y} = \sqrt{xy}$, should be used to get a single radical.

   For example, $\sqrt{3} \cdot \sqrt{2}$ is simplified to $\sqrt{6}$, and $\sqrt{5} \cdot \sqrt{x}$ to $\sqrt{5x}$.

3. If a radicand has a factor that is a perfect square, the radical should be expressed as the product of the positive square root of the perfect square and the remaining radical factor.

   For example, $\sqrt{20}$ is simplified to $\sqrt{20} = \sqrt{4 \cdot 5} = \sqrt{4} \cdot \sqrt{5} = 2\sqrt{5}$, and $\sqrt{75}$ to $5\sqrt{3}$.

4. Any radical in the denominator should be changed to a rational number.

   For example, $\dfrac{5}{\sqrt{3}}$ is rationalized as

   $$\frac{5}{\sqrt{3}} = \frac{5\sqrt{3}}{\sqrt{3} \cdot \sqrt{3}} = \frac{5\sqrt{3}}{3},$$

   and $\sqrt{\dfrac{3}{2}}$ is rationalized as

   $$\sqrt{\frac{3}{2}} = \frac{\sqrt{3}}{\sqrt{2}} = \frac{\sqrt{3}}{\sqrt{2}} \cdot \frac{\sqrt{2}}{\sqrt{2}} = \frac{\sqrt{6}}{2}.$$

5. If a radical expression contains sums or differences of radicals, the distributive property should be used to combine terms, if possible.

   For example, $3\sqrt{2} + 4\sqrt{2}$ is combined as $7\sqrt{2}$, but $3\sqrt{2} + 4\sqrt{3}$ cannot be further combined.

EXAMPLE 1   Simplify each of the following.

(a) $\sqrt{16} + \sqrt{9}$

   Here $\sqrt{16} + \sqrt{9} = 4 + 3 = 7$.

(b) $5\sqrt{2} + 2\sqrt{18}$

First simplify $\sqrt{18}$.

$$5\sqrt{2} + 2\sqrt{18} = 5\sqrt{2} + 2(\sqrt{9} \cdot \sqrt{2})$$
$$= 5\sqrt{2} + 2(3\sqrt{2})$$
$$= 5\sqrt{2} + 6\sqrt{2}$$
$$= 11\sqrt{2} \quad \bullet$$

2   The next examples show how to simplify products.

EXAMPLE 2   Simplify $\sqrt{5}(\sqrt{8} - \sqrt{32})$.

Start by simplifying $\sqrt{8}$ and $\sqrt{32}$.

$$\sqrt{8} = 2\sqrt{2} \quad \text{and} \quad \sqrt{32} = 4\sqrt{2}$$

Now simplify inside the parentheses.

$$\sqrt{5}(\sqrt{8} - \sqrt{32}) = \sqrt{5}(2\sqrt{2} - 4\sqrt{2})$$
$$= \sqrt{5}(-2\sqrt{2})$$
$$= -2\sqrt{5 \cdot 2}$$
$$= -2\sqrt{10} \quad \bullet$$

EXAMPLE 3   Simplify the product $(\sqrt{3} + 2\sqrt{5})(\sqrt{3} - 4\sqrt{5})$.

The products of these sums of radicals can be found in much the same way that we found the product of binomials in Chapter 3. The pattern of multiplication is the same, using the FOIL method.

$$(\sqrt{3} + 2\sqrt{5})(\sqrt{3} - 4\sqrt{5})$$
$$= \sqrt{3} \cdot \sqrt{3} + \sqrt{3}(-4\sqrt{5}) + 2\sqrt{5} \cdot \sqrt{3} + 2\sqrt{5}(-4\sqrt{5})$$
$$= 3 - 4\sqrt{15} + 2\sqrt{15} - 8 \cdot 5$$
$$= 3 - 2\sqrt{15} - 40$$
$$= -37 - 2\sqrt{15} \quad \bullet$$

EXAMPLE 4   Simplify the product $(\sqrt{3} + \sqrt{21})(\sqrt{3} - \sqrt{7})$.

$$(\sqrt{3} + \sqrt{21})(\sqrt{3} - \sqrt{7})$$
$$= \sqrt{3}(\sqrt{3}) + \sqrt{3}(-\sqrt{7}) + \sqrt{21}(\sqrt{3}) + \sqrt{21}(-\sqrt{7})$$
$$= 3 - \sqrt{21} + \sqrt{63} - \sqrt{147}$$
$$= 3 - \sqrt{21} + \sqrt{9} \cdot \sqrt{7} - \sqrt{49} \cdot \sqrt{3}$$
$$= 3 - \sqrt{21} + 3\sqrt{7} - 7\sqrt{3}$$

Since there are no like radicals, no terms may be combined. $\bullet$

Just as we used the FOIL method above, the special products of binomials discussed in Chapter 3 can be used to find products of radicals. Example 5 uses the difference of two squares,

$$(a + b)(a - b) = a^2 - b^2.$$

EXAMPLE 5 Simplify each product.

(a) $(4 + \sqrt{3})(4 - \sqrt{3})$

Follow the pattern given above. Let $a = 4$ and $b = \sqrt{3}$.

$$(4 + \sqrt{3})(4 - \sqrt{3}) = (4)^2 - (\sqrt{3})^2$$
$$= 4 \cdot 4 - \sqrt{3} \cdot \sqrt{3} = 16 - 3 = 13$$

(b) $(\sqrt{12} - \sqrt{3})(\sqrt{12} + \sqrt{3}) = (\sqrt{12})^2 - (\sqrt{3})^2$
$$= \sqrt{12} \cdot \sqrt{12} - \sqrt{3} \cdot \sqrt{3} = 12 - 3 = 9 \quad \bullet$$

Both products in Example 5 resulted in rational numbers. The expressions in these products, such as $4 + \sqrt{3}$ and $4 - \sqrt{3}$, are called **conjugates** of each other.

3 We can use products of radicals similar to those in Example 5 to rationalize the denominators in more complicated expressions, such as

$$\frac{2}{4 - \sqrt{3}}.$$

By Example 5(a), if this denominator, $4 - \sqrt{3}$, is multiplied by $4 + \sqrt{3}$, then the product $(4 - \sqrt{3})(4 + \sqrt{3})$ is the rational number 13. Multiplying numerator and denominator by $4 + \sqrt{3}$ gives

$$\frac{2}{4 - \sqrt{3}} = \frac{2(4 + \sqrt{3})}{(4 - \sqrt{3})(4 + \sqrt{3})} = \frac{2(4 + \sqrt{3})}{13}.$$

The denominator now has been rationalized; it contains no radical signs.

EXAMPLE 6 Rationalize the denominator in the quotient

$$\frac{4}{3 + \sqrt{5}}.$$

To eliminate the radical in the denominator, multiply numerator and denominator by $3 - \sqrt{5}$.

$$\frac{4}{3 + \sqrt{5}} = \frac{4(3 - \sqrt{5})}{(3 + \sqrt{5})(3 - \sqrt{5})}$$
$$= \frac{4(3 - \sqrt{5})}{3^2 - (\sqrt{5})^2} = \frac{4(3 - \sqrt{5})}{9 - 5}$$
$$= \frac{4(3 - \sqrt{5})}{4} = 3 - \sqrt{5}$$

The last step gives the result in lowest terms. $\bullet$

EXAMPLE 7   Simplify $\dfrac{6 + \sqrt{2}}{\sqrt{2} - 5}$.

Multiply numerator and denominator by $\sqrt{2} + 5$.

$$\frac{6 + \sqrt{2}}{\sqrt{2} - 5} = \frac{(6 + \sqrt{2})(\sqrt{2} + 5)}{(\sqrt{2} - 5)(\sqrt{2} + 5)}$$

$$= \frac{6\sqrt{2} + 30 + 2 + 5\sqrt{2}}{2 - 25}$$

$$= \frac{11\sqrt{2} + 32}{-23} = -\frac{11\sqrt{2} + 32}{23} \quad \bullet$$

4   The final example shows how to write quotients in lowest terms.

EXAMPLE 8   Write $\dfrac{3\sqrt{3} + 15}{12}$ in lowest terms.

Factor the numerator, and then divide numerator and denominator by any common factors.

$$\frac{3\sqrt{3} + 15}{12} = \frac{3(\sqrt{3} + 5)}{12} = \frac{\sqrt{3} + 5}{4} \quad \bullet$$

8.5 EXERCISES

Simplify each expression. Use the five rules given in the text. See Examples 1–5.

1. $3\sqrt{5} + 8\sqrt{45}$
2. $6\sqrt{2} + 4\sqrt{18}$
3. $9\sqrt{50} - 4\sqrt{72}$
4. $3\sqrt{80} - 5\sqrt{45}$
5. $\sqrt{2}(\sqrt{8} - \sqrt{32})$
6. $\sqrt{3}(\sqrt{27} - \sqrt{3})$
7. $\sqrt{5}(\sqrt{3} + \sqrt{7})$
8. $\sqrt{7}(\sqrt{10} - \sqrt{3})$
9. $2\sqrt{5}(\sqrt{2} + \sqrt{5})$
10. $3\sqrt{7}(2\sqrt{7} - 4\sqrt{5})$
11. $-\sqrt{14} \cdot \sqrt{2} - \sqrt{28}$
12. $\sqrt{6} \cdot \sqrt{3} - 2\sqrt{50}$
13. $(2\sqrt{6} + 3)(3\sqrt{6} - 5)$
14. $(4\sqrt{5} - 2)(2\sqrt{5} + 3)$
15. $(5\sqrt{7} - 2\sqrt{3})(3\sqrt{7} + 3\sqrt{3})$
16. $(2\sqrt{10} + 5\sqrt{2})(3\sqrt{10} - 4\sqrt{2})$
17. $(3\sqrt{2} + 4)(3\sqrt{2} + 4)$
18. $(4\sqrt{5} - 1)(4\sqrt{5} - 1)$
19. $(2\sqrt{7} - 3)^2$
20. $(3\sqrt{5} + 5)^2$
21. $(3 - \sqrt{2})(3 + \sqrt{2})$
22. $(7 - \sqrt{5})(7 + \sqrt{5})$
23. $(2 + \sqrt{8})(2 - \sqrt{8})$
24. $(3 + \sqrt{11})(3 - \sqrt{11})$
25. $(\sqrt{6} - \sqrt{5})(\sqrt{6} + \sqrt{5})$
26. $(\sqrt{11} + \sqrt{10})(\sqrt{11} - \sqrt{10})$
27. $(\sqrt{2} + \sqrt{3})(\sqrt{6} - \sqrt{2})$
28. $(\sqrt{3} + \sqrt{5})(\sqrt{15} - \sqrt{5})$
29. $(\sqrt{8} - \sqrt{2})(\sqrt{2} + \sqrt{4})$
30. $(\sqrt{6} - \sqrt{3})(\sqrt{3} + \sqrt{18})$
31. $(\sqrt{5} + \sqrt{30})(\sqrt{6} + \sqrt{3})$
32. $(\sqrt{10} - \sqrt{20})(\sqrt{2} - \sqrt{5})$

Write each quotient in lowest terms. See Example 8.

33. $\dfrac{5\sqrt{7} - 10}{5}$

34. $\dfrac{6\sqrt{5} - 9}{3}$

35. $\dfrac{2\sqrt{3} + 10}{8}$

36. $\dfrac{4\sqrt{6} + 6}{10}$

37. $\dfrac{12 - 2\sqrt{10}}{4}$

38. $\dfrac{9 - 6\sqrt{2}}{12}$

39. $\dfrac{16 + 8\sqrt{2}}{24}$

40. $\dfrac{25 + 5\sqrt{3}}{10}$

Rationalize the denominators. See Examples 6 and 7.

41. $\dfrac{5}{2 + \sqrt{5}}$

42. $\dfrac{6}{3 + \sqrt{7}}$

43. $\dfrac{7}{2 - \sqrt{11}}$

44. $\dfrac{38}{5 - \sqrt{6}}$

45. $\dfrac{\sqrt{2}}{1 + \sqrt{2}}$

46. $\dfrac{\sqrt{7}}{2 - \sqrt{7}}$

47. $\dfrac{\sqrt{5}}{1 - \sqrt{5}}$

48. $\dfrac{\sqrt{3}}{2 + \sqrt{3}}$

49. $\dfrac{\sqrt{12}}{\sqrt{3} + 1}$

50. $\dfrac{\sqrt{18}}{\sqrt{2} - 1}$

51. $\dfrac{2\sqrt{3}}{\sqrt{3} + 5}$

52. $\dfrac{\sqrt{12}}{2 - \sqrt{10}}$

53. $\dfrac{\sqrt{2} + 3}{\sqrt{3} - 1}$

54. $\dfrac{\sqrt{5} + 2}{2 - \sqrt{3}}$

55. $\dfrac{6 - \sqrt{5}}{\sqrt{2} + 2}$

56. $\dfrac{3 + \sqrt{2}}{\sqrt{2} + 1}$

57. $\dfrac{3 + \sqrt{5}}{\sqrt{2} + 1}$

58. $\dfrac{8 - \sqrt{2}}{\sqrt{3} + 1}$

59. $\dfrac{\sqrt{3} - 7}{\sqrt{3} + 4}$

60. $\dfrac{\sqrt{10} - 3}{\sqrt{10} + 5}$

61. $\dfrac{2\sqrt{6} + 1}{\sqrt{2} + 5}$

62. $\dfrac{3\sqrt{2} - 4}{\sqrt{3} + 2}$

63. $\dfrac{\sqrt{7} + \sqrt{2}}{\sqrt{3} - \sqrt{2}}$

64. $\dfrac{\sqrt{6} + \sqrt{5}}{\sqrt{3} + \sqrt{5}}$

Review Exercises   *Solve each equation. See Section 4.5.*

65. $y^2 - 4y + 3 = 0$

66. $x^2 - x - 20 = 0$

67. $2m^2 + m = 15$

68. $3a^2 = 14a + 5$

69. $k - 1 = (k - 1)^2$

70. $(t + 2)^2 = -(t + 2)$

8.6   Equations with Radicals

1 Solve equations with radicals.

2 Identify equations with no solutions.

3 Solve equations by squaring a binomial.

1   How can we solve an equation with radicals, such as

$$\sqrt{x + 1} = 3 \ ?$$

The addition and multiplication properties of equality will not help us here; we need another property, a squaring property. To find this property, recall that if $a = b$, then $a^2 = b^2$. For example, if $y = 4$, then squaring both sides gives

$$y^2 = 4^2 \quad \text{or} \quad y^2 = 16.$$

This last equation, $y^2 = 16$, has *two* solutions, 4 or -4, while the original equation, $y = 4$, has only *one* solution, 4.

As shown by this example, squaring both sides of an equation can lead to a new equation with more solutions than the original equation. Because of this possibility, all proposed solutions from the squared equation must be checked in the *original* equation.

In summary, we have the **squaring property of equality.**

Squaring Property

> If both sides of a given equation are squared, all solutions of the original equation are *among* the solutions of the squared equation.

EXAMPLE 1   Solve the equation $\sqrt{p + 1} = 3$.

To use the squaring property of equality, first square both sides of the equation and then solve this new equation.

$$(\sqrt{p + 1})^2 = 3^2$$
$$p + 1 = 9$$
$$p = 8$$

Now check this answer in the original equation.

$$\sqrt{p + 1} = 3$$
$$\sqrt{8 + 1} = 3$$
$$\sqrt{9} = 3$$
$$3 = 3 \qquad \text{True}$$

Since this statement is true, the solution of $\sqrt{p + 1} = 3$ is the number 8. In this case the squared equation had just one solution, which also satisfied the original equation.   ●

EXAMPLE 2   Solve $3\sqrt{x} = \sqrt{x + 8}$.

Squaring both sides gives

$$(3\sqrt{x})^2 = (\sqrt{x + 8})^2$$
$$3^2(\sqrt{x})^2 = (\sqrt{x + 8})^2$$
$$9x = x + 8$$
$$8x = 8$$
$$x = 1.$$

Check this proposed solution.

$$3\sqrt{x} = \sqrt{x + 8}$$
$$3\sqrt{1} = \sqrt{1 + 8}$$
$$3(1) = \sqrt{9}$$
$$3 = 3 \qquad \text{True}$$

The check shows that the solution of the given equation is 1.   •

2   Not all equations with radicals even have a solution, as Example 3 shows.

EXAMPLE 3   Solve the equation $\sqrt{y} = -3$.
Square both sides.

$$(\sqrt{y})^2 = (-3)^2$$
$$y = 9$$

Check this proposed answer in the original equation.

$$\sqrt{y} = -3$$
$$\sqrt{9} = -3$$
$$3 = -3 \qquad \text{False}$$

Since the statement $3 = -3$ is false, the number 9 is not a solution of the given equation, and $\sqrt{y} = -3$ has no solution. Since $\sqrt{y}$ represents the *nonnegative* square root, we might have seen immediately that there is no solution.   •

EXAMPLE 4   Solve $a = \sqrt{a^2 + 5a + 10}$.
Square both sides.

$$(a)^2 = (\sqrt{a^2 + 5a + 10})^2$$
$$a^2 = a^2 + 5a + 10$$
$$0 = 5a + 10$$
$$a = -2$$

Check the proposed solution $a = -2$ in the original equation.

$$a = \sqrt{a^2 + 5a + 10}$$
$$-2 = \sqrt{(-2)^2 + 5(-2) + 10}$$
$$-2 = \sqrt{4 - 10 + 10}$$
$$-2 = 2 \qquad\qquad\qquad \text{False}$$

Since $a = -2$ leads to a false result, there is no solution.   •

3   The next examples use the facts that

$$(a + b)^2 = a^2 + 2ab + b^2 \qquad \text{and} \qquad (a - b)^2 = a^2 - 2ab + b^2.$$

EXAMPLE 5   Solve the equation $\sqrt{2y - 3} = y - 3$.
To square both sides, first square $y - 3$ using the pattern above.

$$(y - 3)^2 = y^2 - 2(y)(3) + (3)^2 = y^2 - 6y + 9$$

Now square both sides of the given equation.

$$(\sqrt{2y - 3})^2 = (y - 3)^2$$
$$2y - 3 = y^2 - 6y + 9$$

This equation is quadratic, because of the y^2 term. To solve the equation, first make one side equal to 0. Subtract $2y$ and add 3, getting

$$0 = y^2 - 8y + 12.$$

This equation can be solved by factoring.

$$0 = (y - 6)(y - 2)$$

Set each factor equal to 0.

$$y - 6 = 0 \quad \text{or} \quad y - 2 = 0$$
$$y = 6 \quad \text{or} \quad y = 2$$

Check both of these proposed solutions in the original equation.

If $y = 6$,   If $y = 2$,

$$\sqrt{2y - 3} = y - 3 \qquad\qquad \sqrt{2y - 3} = y - 3$$
$$\sqrt{2(6) - 3} = 6 - 3 \qquad\qquad \sqrt{2(2) - 3} = 2 - 3$$
$$\sqrt{12 - 3} = 3 \qquad\qquad\qquad \sqrt{4 - 3} = -1$$
$$\sqrt{9} = 3 \qquad\qquad\qquad\quad \sqrt{1} = -1$$
$$3 = 3. \quad \text{True} \qquad\qquad 1 = -1. \quad \text{False}$$

Only 6 is a solution of the equation.   ●

Sometimes it is necessary to write an equation in a different form before squaring both sides. The next example shows why.

EXAMPLE 6   Solve the equation $\sqrt{x} + 1 = 2x$.

Squaring both sides gives

$$(\sqrt{x} + 1)^2 = (2x)^2$$
$$x + 2\sqrt{x} + 1 = 4x^2,$$

an equation that is more complicated, and still contains a radical. It would be better instead to rewrite the original equation so that the radical is alone on one side of the equals sign. To do this, subtract 1 from both sides to get

$$\sqrt{x} = 2x - 1.$$

Now square both sides.

$$(\sqrt{x})^2 = (2x - 1)^2$$
$$x = 4x^2 - 4x + 1$$

Subtract x from both sides.

$$0 = 4x^2 - 5x + 1$$

This equation is a quadratic equation, which can be solved by factoring.

$$0 = (4x - 1)(x - 1)$$
$$4x - 1 = 0 \quad \text{or} \quad x - 1 = 0$$
$$x = \frac{1}{4} \quad \text{or} \quad x = 1$$

Both of these proposed solutions must be checked in the original equation.

If $x = \dfrac{1}{4}$,

$$\sqrt{x} + 1 = 2x$$

$$\sqrt{\frac{1}{4}} + 1 = 2\left(\frac{1}{4}\right)$$

$$\frac{1}{2} + 1 = \frac{1}{2}. \qquad \text{False}$$

If $x = 1$,

$$\sqrt{x} + 1 = 2x$$

$$\sqrt{1} + 1 = 2(1)$$

$$2 = 2. \qquad \text{True}$$

The only solution to the original equation is 1.   ●

Some equations with radicals require squaring twice, as in the next example.

EXAMPLE 7   Solve $\sqrt{21 + x} = 3 + \sqrt{x}$.
Square both sides.

$$(\sqrt{21 + x})^2 = (3 + \sqrt{x})^2$$
$$21 + x = 9 + 6\sqrt{x} + x$$

Combine terms and simplify.

$$12 = 6\sqrt{x}$$
$$2 = \sqrt{x}$$

Square both sides a second time.

$$4 = x$$

Check the proposed solution.

If $x = 4$,
$$\sqrt{21 + x} = 3 + \sqrt{x}$$
$$\sqrt{21 + 4} = 3 + \sqrt{4}$$
$$5 = 5. \qquad \text{True}$$

The solution is 4.   ●

Here is a summary of the steps to use when solving an equation with a radical.

Solving Equations with Radicals		
	Step 1	Arrange the terms so that there is no more than one radical on each side of the equation.
	Step 2	Square both sides.
	Step 3	Combine like terms.
	Step 4	If there is still a term with a radical, repeat Steps 1–3.
	Step 5	Solve the equation.
	Step 6	Check all solutions from Step 5 in the original equation.

8.6 EXERCISES

Find all solutions for each equation. See Examples 1–4.

1. $\sqrt{x} = 2$

2. $\sqrt{m} = 5$

3. $\sqrt{y + 3} = 2$

4. $\sqrt{z + 1} = 5$

5. $\sqrt{t - 3} = 2$

6. $\sqrt{r + 5} = 4$

7. $\sqrt{n + 8} = 1$

8. $\sqrt{k + 10} = 2$

9. $\sqrt{m + 5} = 0$

10. $\sqrt{y - 4} = 0$

11. $\sqrt{z + 5} = -2$

12. $\sqrt{t - 3} = -2$

13. $\sqrt{k} - 2 = 5$

14. $\sqrt{p} - 3 = 7$

15. $\sqrt{y} + 4 = 2$

16. $\sqrt{m} + 6 = 5$

17. $\sqrt{5t - 9} = 2\sqrt{t}$

18. $\sqrt{3n + 4} = 2\sqrt{n}$

19. $3\sqrt{r} = \sqrt{8r + 16}$

20. $2\sqrt{r} = \sqrt{3r + 9}$

21. $\sqrt{5y - 5} = \sqrt{4y + 1}$

22. $\sqrt{2x + 2} = \sqrt{3x - 5}$

23. $\sqrt{x + 2} = \sqrt{2x - 5}$

24. $\sqrt{3m + 3} = \sqrt{5m - 1}$

25. $p = \sqrt{p^2 - 3p - 12}$

26. $k = \sqrt{k^2 - 2k + 10}$

27. $2r = \sqrt{4r^2 + 5r - 30}$

Find all solutions for each equation. Remember that $(a + b)^2 = a^2 + 2ab + b^2$ and $(\sqrt{a})^2 = a$. See Examples 5 and 6.

28. $\sqrt{5x + 11} = x + 3$

29. $\sqrt{2x + 1} = x - 7$

30. $\sqrt{5x + 1} = x + 1$

31. $\sqrt{3x + 10} = 2x - 5$

32. $\sqrt{4x + 13} = 2x - 1$

33. $\sqrt{x + 1} - 1 = x$

34. $\sqrt{3x + 3} + 5 = x$

35. $\sqrt{4x + 5} - 2 = 2x - 7$

36. $\sqrt{6x + 7} - 1 = x + 1$

37. $3\sqrt{x + 13} = x + 9$

38. $2\sqrt{x + 7} = x - 1$

39. $\sqrt{4x} - x + 3 = 0$

40. $\sqrt{2x} - x + 4 = 0$

41. $\sqrt{3x} - 4 = x - 10$

42. $\sqrt{x} + 9 = x + 3$

In the following two exercises, it is necessary to square both sides twice. See Example 7.

43. $\sqrt{x} = \sqrt{x - 5} + 1$

44. $\sqrt{2x} = \sqrt{x + 7} - 1$

Solve each word problem.

45. The square root of the sum of a number and 4 is 5. Find the number.

46. A certain number is the same as the square root of the product of 8 and the number. Find the number.

47. Three times the square root of 2 equals the square root of the sum of some number and 10. Find the number.

48. The negative square root of a number equals that number decreased by 2. Find the number.

49. To estimate the speed at which a car was traveling at the time of an accident, police sometimes use the following procedure. A police officer drives the car involved in the accident under conditions similar to those during which the accident took place, and then skids to a stop. If the car is driven at 30 miles per hour, the speed at the time of the accident is given by

$$s = 30\sqrt{\frac{a}{p}},$$

where a is the length of the skid marks left at the time of the accident and p is the length of the skid marks in the police test. Find s if

(a) $a = 900$ feet and $p = 100$ feet;

(b) $a = 400$ feet and $p = 25$ feet;

(c) $a = 80$ feet and $p = 20$ feet;

(d) $a = 120$ feet and $p = 30$ feet.

Review Exercises *Use the rules for exponents to simplify each expression. Write each answer in exponential form with only positive exponents. See Section 3.2.*

50. $(5^2)^3$

51. $3^{-4} \cdot 3^{-1}$

52. $\dfrac{a^{-2}a^3}{a^4}$

53. $(2x^3)^{-1}$

54. $\left(\dfrac{p}{3}\right)^{-2}$

55. $\left(\dfrac{2y^3}{y^{-1}}\right)^{-2}$

56. $\dfrac{(c^3)^2 c^4}{(c^{-1})^3}$

8.7 Fractional Exponents

Use fractional exponents of the form

1 $a^{1/n}$;

2 $a^{m/n}$.

3 Use rules for exponents with fractional exponents.

4 Use fractional exponents to simplify radicals.

In this section, we define exponential expressions with fractional exponents, such as $5^{1/2}$, $16^{3/4}$, and $8^{-2/3}$.

1 First, how can we define $5^{1/2}$? We want to define this expression so that all the rules for exponents developed earlier in this book still hold. In particular, the power rule should work, so that

$$(5^{1/2})^2 = 5^{2/2} = 5^1 = 5.$$

Also, from our work with square roots, we know that

$$(\sqrt{5})^2 = 5.$$

Thus, since both $(5^{1/2})^2$ and $(\sqrt{5})^2$ equal 5, we must have

$$5^{1/2} = \sqrt{5}.$$

Also,

$$(5^{1/3})^3 = 5 \quad \text{and} \quad (\sqrt[3]{5})^3 = 5,$$

so

$$5^{1/3} = \sqrt[3]{5}.$$

Generalizing from these examples,

$a^{1/n}$

> if a is a nonnegative number and n is a positive integer,
> $$a^{1/n} = \sqrt[n]{a}.$$

EXAMPLE 1 Simplify each expression by first writing it in radical form.

(a) $16^{1/2}$

By definition,

$$16^{1/2} = \sqrt{16} = 4.$$

(b) $27^{1/3} = \sqrt[3]{27} = 3$

(c) $64^{1/3} = \sqrt[3]{64} = 4$

(d) $64^{1/6} = \sqrt[6]{64} = 2$

Use the table of selected powers inside the front cover or a calculator. ●

2 Now we can define an exponential expression like $16^{3/4}$. By the power rule again,

$$16^{3/4} = (16^{1/4})^3 = (\sqrt[4]{16})^3 = 2^3 = 8.$$

However, we also could write

$$16^{3/4} = (16^3)^{1/4} = (4096)^{1/4} = \sqrt[4]{4096} = 8.$$

The expression can be evaluated either way to get the same answer. As the example suggests, taking the root first involves smaller numbers and is often easier.

Generalizing from this example,

$a^{m/n}$

> if a is a nonnegative number and m and n are integers, with $n \neq 0$,
> $$a^{m/n} = \sqrt[n]{a^m} = (\sqrt[n]{a})^m.$$

EXAMPLE 2   Simplify each expression.

(a) $9^{3/2}$

  Use the definition to write
  $$9^{3/2} = (9^{1/2})^3 = 3^3 = 27.$$

(b) $64^{2/3} = (64^{1/3})^2 = 4^2 = 16$

(c) $(-64)^{2/3} = [(-64)^{1/3}]^2 = (-4)^2 = 16$ ●

We saw earlier that
$$a^{-n} = \frac{1}{a^n}$$

for nonzero numbers a and integers n. This same result applies for negative fractional exponents:

$a^{-m/n}$

> $$a^{-m/n} = \frac{1}{a^{m/n}},$$

for $a \neq 0$.

EXAMPLE 3   Write each expression with a positive exponent and simplify.

(a) $32^{-3/5} = \dfrac{1}{32^{3/5}} = \dfrac{1}{(32^{1/5})^3} = \dfrac{1}{2^3} = \dfrac{1}{8}$

(b) $27^{-4/3} = \dfrac{1}{27^{4/3}} = \dfrac{1}{3^4} = \dfrac{1}{81}$ ●

3   All the rules for exponents hold when the exponents are fractions. The next examples show how to use these rules to simplify expressions with fractional exponents.

EXAMPLE 4   Simplify each expression. Write each answer in exponential form with only positive exponents.

(a) $3^{2/3} \cdot 3^{5/3} = 3^{2/3+5/3} = 3^{7/3}$

(b) $\dfrac{5^{1/4}}{5^{3/4}} = 5^{1/4-3/4} = 5^{-2/4} = 5^{-1/2} = \dfrac{1}{5^{1/2}}$

(c) $(9^{1/4})^2 = 9^{2(1/4)} = 9^{2/4} = 9^{1/2} = \sqrt{9} = 3$

(d) $\dfrac{2^{1/2} \cdot 2^{-1}}{2^{-3/2}} = \dfrac{2^{1/2+(-1)}}{2^{-3/2}} = \dfrac{2^{-1/2}}{2^{-3/2}} = 2^{-1/2-(-3/2)} = 2^{2/2} = 2^1 = 2$

(e) $\left(\dfrac{9}{4}\right)^{5/2} = \dfrac{9^{5/2}}{4^{5/2}} = \dfrac{(9^{1/2})^5}{(4^{1/2})^5} = \dfrac{(\sqrt{9})^5}{(\sqrt{4})^5} = \dfrac{3^5}{2^5} = \dfrac{243}{32}$ ●

EXAMPLE 5   Simplify each expression. Write each answer in exponential form with only positive exponents. Assume that all variables represent positive numbers.

(a) $m^{1/5} \cdot m^{3/5} = m^{1/5+3/5} = m^{4/5}$

(b) $\dfrac{p^{5/3}}{p^{4/3}} = p^{5/3-4/3} = p^{1/3}$

(c) $(x^2 y^{1/2})^4 = (x^2)^4 (y^{1/2})^4 = x^8 y^2$

(d) $\left(\dfrac{z^{1/4}}{w^{1/3}}\right)^5 = \dfrac{(z^{1/4})^5}{(w^{1/3})^5} = \dfrac{z^{5/4}}{w^{5/3}}$

(e) $\dfrac{k^{2/3} \cdot k^{-1/3}}{k^{5/3}} = k^{2/3+(-1/3)-5/3} = k^{-4/3} = \dfrac{1}{k^{4/3}}$ ●

4   Sometimes a radical expression can be simplified by writing it in exponential form. The next example shows how this is done.

EXAMPLE 6   Simplify each radical by writing it in exponential form.

(a) $\sqrt[6]{9^3} = (9^3)^{1/6} = 9^{3/6} = 9^{1/2} = \sqrt{9} = 3$

(b) $(\sqrt[4]{m})^2 = (m^{1/4})^2 = m^{2/4} = m^{1/2} = \sqrt{m}$

Here, we assume $m \geq 0$.   ●

8.7   EXERCISES

Simplify each expression by first writing it in radical form. See Examples 1 and 2.

1. $16^{1/2}$	**2.** $64^{1/2}$	**3.** $25^{1/2}$	**4.** $49^{1/2}$
5. $8^{1/3}$	**6.** $27^{1/3}$	**7.** $64^{1/3}$	**8.** $125^{1/3}$
9. $16^{1/4}$	**10.** $81^{1/4}$	**11.** $32^{1/5}$	**12.** $243^{1/5}$
13. $4^{3/2}$	**14.** $9^{5/2}$	**15.** $27^{2/3}$	**16.** $8^{5/3}$
17. $16^{3/4}$	**18.** $64^{5/4}$	**19.** $32^{2/5}$	**20.** $144^{3/2}$
21. $(-8)^{2/3}$	**22.** $(-27)^{5/3}$	**23.** $(-64)^{1/3}$	**24.** $(-125)^{5/3}$

Simplify each expression. Write each answer in exponential form with only positive exponents. Assume that all variables represent positive numbers. See Examples 3–5.

25. $2^{1/2} \cdot 2^{5/2}$	**26.** $5^{2/3} \cdot 5^{4/3}$	**27.** $6^{1/4} \cdot 6^{-3/4}$	**28.** $12^{2/5} \cdot 12^{-1/5}$

29. $\dfrac{15^{3/4}}{15^{5/4}}$

30. $\dfrac{7^{3/5}}{7^{-1/5}}$

31. $\dfrac{11^{-2/7}}{11^{-3/7}}$

32. $\dfrac{4^{-2/3}}{4^{1/3}}$

33. $(8^{3/2})^2$

34. $(5^{2/5})^{10}$

35. $(6^{1/3})^{3/2}$

36. $(7^{2/5})^{5/3}$

37. $(9^{1/4})^{3/2}$

38. $(13^{2/3})^{4/5}$

39. $\left(\dfrac{25}{4}\right)^{3/2}$

40. $\left(\dfrac{9}{16}\right)^{5/2}$

41. $\left(\dfrac{8}{27}\right)^{2/3}$

42. $\left(\dfrac{64}{27}\right)^{2/3}$

43. $\dfrac{2^{2/5}\cdot 2^{-3/5}}{2^{7/5}}$

44. $\dfrac{3^{-3/4}\cdot 3^{5/4}}{3^{-1/4}}$

45. $\dfrac{6^{-2/9}}{6^{1/9}\cdot 6^{-5/9}}$

46. $\dfrac{8^{6/7}}{8^{2/7}\cdot 8^{-1/7}}$

47. $p^{2/3}\cdot p^{7/3}$

48. $k^{-1/4}\cdot k^{5/4}$

49. $\dfrac{z^{2/3}}{z^{-1/3}}$

50. $\dfrac{r^{5/4}}{r^{3/4}}$

51. $(m^3 n^{1/4})^{2/3}$

52. $(p^4\cdot q^{1/2})^{4/3}$

53. $(x^{1/2}y^{2/3})^{3/4}$

54. $(z^{2/5}w^{1/5})^{4/3}$

55. $\left(\dfrac{a^{1/2}}{b^{1/3}}\right)^{4/3}$

56. $\left(\dfrac{m^{2/3}}{n^{3/4}}\right)^{1/2}$

57. $\dfrac{c^{2/3}\cdot c^{-1/3}}{c^{5/3}}$

58. $\dfrac{d^{3/4}\cdot d^{5/4}}{d^{1/4}}$

59. $\left(\dfrac{k^{1/4}\cdot k^{-3/4}}{k^{5/4}}\right)^2$

60. $\left(\dfrac{p^{3/8}\cdot p^{-2}}{p^{1/8}}\right)^4$

Simplify each radical by writing it in exponential form. Give final answers in radical form. Assume that all variables represent positive numbers. See Example 6.

61. $\sqrt[6]{4^3}$

62. $\sqrt[9]{8^3}$

63. $\sqrt[8]{16^2}$

64. $\sqrt[9]{27^3}$

65. $\sqrt[4]{a^2}$

66. $\sqrt[9]{b^3}$

67. $\sqrt[6]{k^4}$

68. $\sqrt[8]{m^4}$

Review Exercises *Find all square roots of each number. Simplify where possible. See Section 8.1.*

69. 25

70. 49

71. 14

72. 29

73. 18

74. 48

75. 80

76. 75

Chapter 8   Review Exercises

[8.1] *Find all square roots of each number.*

1. 49

2. 81

3. 225

4. 729

Find each root that exists.

5. $\sqrt{16}$

6. $-\sqrt{36}$

7. $\sqrt{-8100}$

8. $-\sqrt{4225}$

9. $\sqrt[3]{27}$

10. $\sqrt[3]{-64}$

11. $\sqrt[4]{16}$

12. $\sqrt[5]{32}$

Write rational *or* irrational *for each number. If a number is rational, give its exact value. If a number is irrational, give a decimal approximation for the number. Round approximations to the nearest thousandth.*

13. $\sqrt{15}$ **14.** $\sqrt{64}$ **15.** $-\sqrt{169}$ **16.** $-\sqrt{170}$

[8.2] *Use the product rule to simplify each expression.*

17. $\sqrt{5} \cdot \sqrt{15}$ **18.** $\sqrt{48}$ **19.** $\sqrt{160}$ **20.** $\sqrt{98} \cdot \sqrt{50}$

Use the quotient and the product rule, as necessary, to simplify each expression.

21. $\sqrt{\dfrac{9}{4}}$ **22.** $\sqrt{\dfrac{10}{169}}$ **23.** $\sqrt{\dfrac{2}{5}} \cdot \sqrt{\dfrac{2}{45}}$ **24.** $\dfrac{24\sqrt{12}}{16\sqrt{3}}$

Simplify each expression. Assume that all variables represent nonnegative real numbers.

25. $\sqrt{p} \cdot \sqrt{p}$ **26.** $\sqrt{m^2 p^4}$ **27.** $\sqrt{x^3}$ **28.** $\sqrt{\dfrac{36}{p^2}}$

Simplify each radical. Assume that all variables represent nonnegative real numbers.

29. $\sqrt[3]{\dfrac{5}{8}}$ **30.** $\sqrt[3]{\dfrac{6}{125}}$ **31.** $\sqrt[3]{54x^2}$ **32.** $\sqrt[3]{375x^4}$

[8.3] *Perform the indicated operations, and write all answers in simplest form. Rationalize all denominators.*

33. $\dfrac{10}{\sqrt{3}}$ **34.** $\dfrac{3\sqrt{2}}{\sqrt{5}}$ **35.** $\dfrac{12}{\sqrt{24}}$ **36.** $\sqrt{\dfrac{3}{5}}$

37. $\sqrt{\dfrac{2}{3}} \cdot \sqrt{\dfrac{1}{5}}$ **38.** $\sqrt{\dfrac{1}{6}} \cdot \sqrt{\dfrac{18}{5}}$ **39.** $\sqrt[3]{\dfrac{1}{3}}$ **40.** $\sqrt[3]{\dfrac{5}{4}}$

Perform the indicated operations, and write all answers in simplest form. Rationalize all denominators. Assume that all variables represent nonnegative real numbers.

41. $\sqrt{\dfrac{7}{x}}$ **42.** $\sqrt{\dfrac{9m^3}{2p}}$ **43.** $\sqrt{\dfrac{r^3 t}{5w^2}}$ **44.** $\sqrt[3]{\dfrac{k^4}{4n}}$

[8.4] *Simplify and combine terms wherever possible.*

45. $3\sqrt{2} + 5\sqrt{2}$ **46.** $3\sqrt{75} + 2\sqrt{27}$ **47.** $4\sqrt{24} - 3\sqrt{54} + \sqrt{6}$

48. $\dfrac{1}{3}\sqrt{18} + \dfrac{1}{4}\sqrt{32}$ **49.** $\dfrac{2}{5}\sqrt{75} - \dfrac{3}{4}\sqrt{160}$ **50.** $\sqrt{5} \cdot \sqrt{3} + 4\sqrt{15} - \sqrt{3}$

51. $\sqrt{15} \cdot \sqrt{2} + 5\sqrt{30}$ **52.** $3\sqrt[3]{54} - 2\sqrt[3]{16}$ **53.** $4\sqrt[4]{16} + 3\sqrt[4]{32} \cdot \sqrt[4]{2}$

Simplify each expression. Assume that all variables represent nonnegative real numbers.

54. $\sqrt{16p} + 3\sqrt{p} - \sqrt{49p}$ **55.** $\sqrt{20m^2} - m\sqrt{45}$ **56.** $3k\sqrt{8k^2n} + 5k^2\sqrt{2n}$

[8.5] *Simplify each expression.*

57. $-\sqrt{3}(\sqrt{5} - \sqrt{27})$ **58.** $3\sqrt{2}(\sqrt{3} + 2\sqrt{2})$ **59.** $(2\sqrt{3} - 4)(5\sqrt{3} + 2)$

60. $(5\sqrt{7} + 2)^2$ **61.** $(\sqrt{5} - \sqrt{7})(\sqrt{5} + \sqrt{7})$ **62.** $(2\sqrt{3} + 5)(2\sqrt{3} - 5)$

Rationalize the denominators.

63. $\dfrac{1}{2 + \sqrt{5}}$ **64.** $\dfrac{\sqrt{3}}{1 + \sqrt{3}}$ **65.** $\dfrac{\sqrt{5} - 1}{\sqrt{2} + 3}$ **66.** $\dfrac{2 + \sqrt{6}}{\sqrt{3} - 1}$

[8.6] *Find all solutions for each equation.*

67. $\sqrt{p} = -2$ **68.** $\sqrt{k + 1} = 10$ **69.** $\sqrt{x} + 2 = 1$

70. $\sqrt{5m + 4} = 3\sqrt{m}$ **71.** $\sqrt{-2k - 4} = k + 2$ **72.** $\sqrt{2 - x} + 3 = x + 7$

[8.7] *Simplify each expression.*

73. $81^{1/2}$ **74.** $125^{1/3}$ **75.** $7^{2/3} \cdot 7^{5/3}$ **76.** $\dfrac{12^{2/5}}{12^{-2/5}}$

77. $\dfrac{(7^{5/2})^{1/5}}{7^{3/2}}$ **78.** $\dfrac{x^{1/4} \cdot x^{5/4}}{x^{3/4}}$ **79.** $\sqrt[8]{49^4}$ **80.** $\sqrt[12]{125^4}$

Chapter 8 Test

In this test, assume that all variables represent positive numbers.

Find the indicated root. Use the square root table if necessary.

1. $\sqrt{100}$ **2.** $\sqrt{77}$ **3.** $-\sqrt{190}$

4. $\sqrt[3]{-27}$ **5.** $\sqrt[4]{625}$

Simplify where possible.

6. $\sqrt{27}$ **7.** $\sqrt{128}$

8. $\sqrt[3]{-32}$ **9.** $3\sqrt{6} + \sqrt{14}$

10. $3\sqrt{28} + \sqrt{63}$ **11.** $m\sqrt{20} - m\sqrt{45}$

12. $3\sqrt{27x} - 4\sqrt{48x} + 2\sqrt{3x}$ **13.** $\sqrt[3]{32x^2y^3}$

14. $\sqrt[4]{32m^3n^4p^6}$ **15.** $(6 - \sqrt{5})(6 + \sqrt{5})$

16. $(2 - \sqrt{7})(3\sqrt{2} + 1)$ **17.** $(\sqrt{5} + \sqrt{6})^2$

Rationalize each denominator.

18. $\dfrac{3\sqrt{2}}{\sqrt{6}}$

19. $\dfrac{4p}{\sqrt{k}}$

20. $\sqrt[3]{\dfrac{5}{9}}$

21. $\dfrac{-3}{4 - \sqrt{3}}$

22. $\dfrac{\sqrt{2} + 1}{3 - \sqrt{7}}$

Solve each equation.

23. $\sqrt{k + 2} + 3 = -2$

24. $\sqrt{2y + 8} = 2\sqrt{y}$

25. $6\sqrt{k} - 3 = k + 2$

26. $\sqrt{y + 3} = \sqrt{y} + 1$

Simplify each expression. Write answers with only positive exponents.

27. $8^{4/3}$

28. $5^{3/4} \cdot 5^{7/4}$

29. $\dfrac{(3^{1/4})^3}{3^{7/4}}$

30. $\dfrac{m^{2/3} \cdot m^{5/6}}{m^{4/3}}$

9

Quadratic Equations

The path a vaulter travels may have the shape of a parabola.

9.1 Solving Quadratic Equations by the Square Root Method

1 Solve equations of the form $x^2 =$ a number.

2 Solve equations of the form $(ax + b)^2 =$ a number.

In Chapter 4, we solved quadratic equations (second-degree equations) by factoring. However, not all quadratic equations can be solved by factoring. To solve equations like

$$(x - 3)^2 = 15,$$

in which the square of a binomial is equal to some number, we can use square roots.

1 If two positive numbers are equal, then they must have the same square roots or square roots that are negatives of each other. This fact is called the **square root property.**

Square Root Property

> If b is a positive number and if $a^2 = b$, then $a = \sqrt{b}$ or $a = -\sqrt{b}$.

EXAMPLE 1   Solve each equation.

(a) $x^2 = 16$

By the square root property, since $x^2 = 16$, then

$$x = \sqrt{16} = 4 \quad \text{or} \quad x = -\sqrt{16} = -4.$$

(b) $z^2 = 5$

Here $z = \sqrt{5}$ or $z = -\sqrt{5}$.

(c) $m^2 = 8$

We have $m = \sqrt{8}$ or $m = -\sqrt{8}$. Since $\sqrt{8} = 2\sqrt{2}$,

$$m = 2\sqrt{2} \quad \text{or} \quad m = -2\sqrt{2}.$$

(d) $y^2 = -4$

Since -4 is a negative number, and the square of a real number cannot be negative, there is no real number solution for this equation.

(e) $3x^2 + 5 = 11$

First solve the equation for x^2.

$$3x^2 + 5 = 11$$
$$3x^2 = 6 \qquad \text{Subtract 5}$$
$$x^2 = 2 \qquad \text{Divide by 3}$$

Now use the square root property to get

$$x = \sqrt{2} \quad \text{or} \quad x = -\sqrt{2}. \quad \bullet$$

2   We can solve the equation $(x - 3)^2 = 16$ in the same way we solved the equations in Example 1. Starting with $(x - 3)^2 = 16$, and using the square root property, gives

$$x - 3 = 4 \quad \text{or} \quad x - 3 = -4.$$

Solve each of the last two equations to get

$$x - 3 = 4 \quad \text{or} \quad x - 3 = -4$$
$$x = 7 \quad \text{or} \quad x = -1.$$

Check both answers in the original equation.

$$(7 - 3)^2 = 4^2 = 16 \quad \text{and} \quad (-1 - 3)^2 = (-4)^2 = 16$$

Both 7 and -1 are solutions.

EXAMPLE 2   Solve $(x - 1)^2 = 6$.

By the square root property,

$$x - 1 = \sqrt{6} \quad \text{or} \quad x - 1 = -\sqrt{6}$$
$$x = 1 + \sqrt{6} \quad \text{or} \quad x = 1 - \sqrt{6}.$$

Check:
$$(1 + \sqrt{6} - 1)^2 = (\sqrt{6})^2 = 6;$$
$$(1 - \sqrt{6} - 1)^2 = (-\sqrt{6})^2 = 6.$$

The solutions are $1 + \sqrt{6}$ and $1 - \sqrt{6}$.   ●

EXAMPLE 3   Solve the equation $(3r - 2)^2 = 27$.
The square root property gives

$$3r - 2 = \sqrt{27} \quad \text{or} \quad 3r - 2 = -\sqrt{27}.$$

Now simplify the radical: $\sqrt{27} = \sqrt{9 \cdot 3} = \sqrt{9} \cdot \sqrt{3} = 3\sqrt{3}$, so

$$3r - 2 = 3\sqrt{3} \quad \text{or} \quad 3r - 2 = -3\sqrt{3}$$
$$3r = 2 + 3\sqrt{3} \quad \text{or} \quad 3r = 2 - 3\sqrt{3}$$
$$r = \frac{2 + 3\sqrt{3}}{3} \quad \text{or} \quad r = \frac{2 - 3\sqrt{3}}{3}.$$

The solutions are

$$\frac{2 + 3\sqrt{3}}{3} \quad \text{and} \quad \frac{2 - 3\sqrt{3}}{3}. \quad ●$$

EXAMPLE 4   Solve $(x + 3)^2 = -9$.
The square root of -9 is not a real number. There is no real number solution.   ●

9.1   EXERCISES

Solve each equation by using the square root property. Express all radicals in simplest form. See Example 1.

1. $x^2 = 25$ **2.** $y^2 = 100$ **3.** $x^2 = 64$ **4.** $z^2 = 81$

5. $m^2 = 13$ **6.** $x^2 = 7$ **7.** $y^2 = -15$ **8.** $p^2 = -10$

9. $3p^2 = 6$ **10.** $2q^2 = 12$ **11.** $4k^2 = 5$ **12.** $5k^2 = 8$

13. $3x^2 - 8 = 64$ **14.** $2t^2 + 7 = 61$ **15.** $5a^2 + 4 = 8$ **16.** $4p^2 - 3 = 7$

17. $k^2 = 2.56$ **18.** $z^2 = 9.61$ **19.** $r^2 = 77.44$ **20.** $y^2 = 43.56$

Solve each equation by using the square root property. Express all radicals in simplest form. Round answers to the nearest hundredth in Exercises 41–44. See Examples 2–4.

21. $(x - 2)^2 = 16$ **22.** $(r + 4)^2 = 25$ **23.** $(a + 4)^2 = 10$ **24.** $(r - 3)^2 = 15$

25. $(m - 1)^2 = -4$ **26.** $(t + 2)^2 = -8$ **27.** $(x - 1)^2 = 32$ **28.** $(y + 5)^2 = 28$

29. $(2m - 1)^2 = 9$ **30.** $(3y - 7)^2 = 4$ **31.** $(6m - 2)^2 = 121$ **32.** $(7m - 10)^2 = 144$

33. $(2a - 5)^2 = 30$ **34.** $(2y + 3)^2 = 45$ **35.** $(3p - 1)^2 = 18$ **36.** $(5r - 6)^2 = 75$

37. $(2k - 5)^2 = 98$ **38.** $(4x - 1)^2 = 48$ **39.** $(3m + 4)^2 = 8$ **40.** $(5y - 3)^2 = 50$

41. $(2.11p + 3.42)^2 = 9.58$

42. $(1.71m - 6.20)^2 = 5.41$

43. $(6.95x - 1.72)^2 = 86.4$

44. $(3.76y + 4.19)^2 = 72.8$

Solve the following word problems.

45. One expert at marksmanship can hold a silver dollar at forehead level, drop it, draw his gun, and shoot the coin as it passes waist level. The distance traveled by a falling object is given by

$$d = 16t^2,$$

where d is the distance the object falls in t seconds. If the coin falls about 4 feet, estimate the time that elapses between the dropping of the coin and the shot.

46. The illumination produced by a light source depends on the distance from the source. For a particular light source, this relationship can be expressed as

$$d^2 = \frac{4050}{I},$$

where d is the distance from the source (in feet) and I is the amount of illumination in footcandles. How far from the source is the illumination equal to 50 footcandles?

Review Exercises *Simplify all radicals and combine terms. See Sections 8.2 and 5.4.*

47. $\dfrac{3}{5} - \sqrt{\dfrac{121}{25}}$

48. $\dfrac{5}{4} + \sqrt{\dfrac{169}{16}}$

49. $\dfrac{3}{2} + \sqrt{\dfrac{27}{4}}$

50. $-\dfrac{1}{4} + \sqrt{\dfrac{5}{16}}$

51. $6 + \sqrt{\dfrac{2}{3}}$

52. $5 - \sqrt{\dfrac{7}{2}}$

53. $1 - \sqrt{\dfrac{2}{54}}$

54. $-8 - \sqrt{\dfrac{3}{8}}$

9.2 Solving Quadratic Equations by Completing the Square

1 Solve quadratic equations by completing the square when the coefficient of the squared term is 1.

2 Solve quadratic equations by completing the square when the coefficient of the squared term is not 1.

1 With the properties and methods studied so far, we cannot solve

$$x^2 + 6x + 7 = 0.$$

To see how to solve this equation, recall that in the preceding section we learned to solve equations of the type

$$(x + 3)^2 = 2.$$

If we can rewrite the equation $x^2 + 6x + 7 = 0$ in the form $(x + 3)^2 = 2$, we can solve it by using the square root property. The following example shows how to do this.

EXAMPLE 1   Solve $x^2 + 6x + 7 = 0$.

To start, subtract 7 from both sides of the equation to get

$$x^2 + 6x = -7.$$

We want the quantity on the left-hand side to be a perfect square trinomial. To get this perfect square, we need to add a suitable number to both sides of the equation. To decide on the number to use, look at the perfect square trinomial $x^2 + 2ax + a^2$. The coefficient of the middle term is $2a$. To find a, we need to multiply the coefficient $2a$ by $1/2$. Then square the result, and add the square to both sides of the equation.

In our equation, $x^2 + 6x = -7$, the coefficient of x is 6, and half of 6 is 3. Squaring 3 gives 9. Therefore, if we add 9 to both sides, we will have an equation with a perfect square trinomial on the left-hand side, as desired.

$$x^2 + 6x + 9 = -7 + 9$$

or
$$(x + 3)^2 = 2$$

Now use the square root property to complete the solution.

$$x + 3 = \sqrt{2} \qquad \text{or} \qquad x + 3 = -\sqrt{2}$$
$$x = -3 + \sqrt{2} \qquad \text{or} \qquad x = -3 - \sqrt{2}$$

The solutions of the original equation are $-3 + \sqrt{2}$ and $-3 - \sqrt{2}$. Verify this by substituting $-3 + \sqrt{2}$ and $-3 - \sqrt{2}$ for x in the equation.   ●

The process of changing the form of the equation in Example 1 from

$$x^2 + 6x + 7 = 0 \qquad \text{to} \qquad (x + 3)^2 = 2$$

is called **completing the square.**

EXAMPLE 2   Solve the quadratic equation $m^2 - 8m = 5$.

We want the quantity on the left-hand side of the equation to be a perfect square trinomial. Here the coefficient of m is -8; half of -8 is -4. If we square -4, we get 16, the number to be added to both sides.

$$m^2 - 8m + 16 = 5 + 16 \qquad (1)$$

The trinomial $m^2 - 8m + 16$ is a perfect square trinomial. Factor to get

$$m^2 - 8m + 16 = (m - 4)^2,$$

with equation (1) becoming

$$(m - 4)^2 = 21.$$

Now use the square root property.

$$m - 4 = \sqrt{21} \qquad \text{or} \qquad m - 4 = -\sqrt{21}$$
$$m = 4 + \sqrt{21} \qquad \text{or} \qquad m = 4 - \sqrt{21}$$

The solutions are

$$4 + \sqrt{21} \qquad \text{and} \qquad 4 - \sqrt{21}. \quad \bullet$$

2 To complete the square, the coefficient of the squared variable must be 1. However, we still can use completing the square to solve a quadratic equation of the form $ax^2 + bx + c = 0$ by first dividing both sides of the equation by a. The next examples show this approach.

EXAMPLE 3   Solve $4y^2 + 24y = 13$.

To make the coefficient of the squared term equal 1, divide both sides of the equation by 4, which gives

$$y^2 + 6y = \frac{13}{4}.$$

Now take half the coefficient of y, or $6/2 = 3$, and square the result: $3^2 = 9$. Add 9 to both sides of the equation, and perform the addition on the right-hand side.

$$y^2 + 6y + 9 = \frac{13}{4} + 9 = \frac{49}{4}$$

Write the left side as a perfect square.

$$(y + 3)^2 = \frac{49}{4}$$

Use the square root property and solve for y.

$$y + 3 = \frac{7}{2} \qquad \text{or} \qquad y + 3 = -\frac{7}{2}$$

$$y = -3 + \frac{7}{2} \qquad \text{or} \qquad y = -3 - \frac{7}{2}$$

$$y = \frac{1}{2} \qquad \text{or} \qquad y = -\frac{13}{2}$$

The two solutions are 1/2 and $-13/2$, as can be checked by substitution into the original equation. $\bullet$

EXAMPLE 4   Solve $2x^2 - 7x = 9$.

To begin, we need the coefficient 1 for the x^2 term. Divide both sides of the equation by 2, giving

$$x^2 - \frac{7}{2}x = \frac{9}{2}.$$

Now take half the coefficient of x and square it. Half of $-7/2$ is $-7/4$, and $-7/4$ squared is $49/16$. Add $49/16$ to both sides of the equation, write the left side as a perfect square, and perform the addition on the right.

$$x^2 - \frac{7}{2}x + \frac{49}{16} = \frac{9}{2} + \frac{49}{16}$$

$$\left(x - \frac{7}{4}\right)^2 = \frac{121}{16}$$

Apply the square root property.

$$x - \frac{7}{4} = \sqrt{\frac{121}{16}} \qquad \text{or} \qquad x - \frac{7}{4} = -\sqrt{\frac{121}{16}}$$

Since $\sqrt{\dfrac{121}{16}} = \dfrac{11}{4}$,

$$x - \frac{7}{4} = \frac{11}{4} \qquad \text{or} \qquad x - \frac{7}{4} = -\frac{11}{4}$$

$$x = \frac{18}{4} \qquad \text{or} \qquad x = -\frac{4}{4}$$

$$x = \frac{9}{2} \qquad \text{or} \qquad x = -1.$$

The solutions are $9/2$ and -1.   ●

EXAMPLE 5   Solve $4p^2 + 8p + 5 = 0$.

First divide both sides by 4 to get the coefficient 1 for the p^2 term. The result is

$$p^2 + 2p + \frac{5}{4} = 0.$$

Subtract $5/4$ from both sides, which gives

$$p^2 + 2p = -\frac{5}{4}.$$

The coefficient of p is 2. Take half of 2, square the result, and add it to both sides. The left-hand side can then be written as a perfect square.

$$p^2 + 2p + 1 = -\frac{5}{4} + 1$$

$$(p + 1)^2 = -\frac{1}{4}$$

At this point, we should use the square root property. However, the square root of $-1/4$ is not a real number. This equation has no real number solution.   ●

Let us now summarize the steps to take in solving a quadratic equation by completing the square.

Solving a Quadratic Equation by Completing the Square

Step 1 If the coefficient of the squared term is 1, proceed to Step 2. If the coefficient of the squared term is not 1 but some other number a, divide both sides of the equation by a. This gives an equation that has 1 as coefficient of the squared term.

Step 2 Make sure that all terms with variables are on one side of the equals sign and that all numbers are on the other side.

Step 3 Take half the coefficient of x and square the result. Add the square to both sides of the equation. The side containing the variables now can be written as a perfect square.

Step 4 Apply the square root property. The solutions are determined by solving the two resulting equations.

9.2 EXERCISES

Find the number that should be added to each expression to make it a perfect square. See Example 1.

1. $x^2 + 2x$ **2.** $y^2 - 4y$ **3.** $x^2 + 18x$ **4.** $m^2 - 3m$

5. $z^2 + 9z$ **6.** $p^2 + 22p$ **7.** $y^2 + 5y$ **8.** $r^2 + 7r$

Solve each equation by completing the square. You may have to simplify first. Round answers to the nearest thousandth in Exercises 31–34. See Examples 2–5.

9. $x^2 + 4x = -3$ **10.** $y^2 - 4y = 0$ **11.** $a^2 + 2a = 5$

12. $m^2 + 4m = -1$ **13.** $z^2 + 6z = -8$ **14.** $q^2 - 8q = -16$

15. $x^2 - 6x + 1 = 0$ **16.** $b^2 - 2b - 2 = 0$ **17.** $c^2 + 3c = 2$

18. $k^2 + 5k - 3 = 0$ **19.** $2m^2 + 4m = -7$ **20.** $3y^2 - 9y + 5 = 0$

21. $6q^2 - 8q + 3 = 0$ **22.** $4y^2 + 4y - 3 = 0$ **23.** $-x^2 + 6x = 4$

24. $3y^2 - 6y - 2 = 0$ **25.** $2m^2 - 4m - 5 = 0$ **26.** $-x^2 + 4 = 2x$

27. $3x^2 - 2x = 1$ **28.** $-x^2 - 4 = 2x$ **29.** $m^2 - 4m + 8 = 6m$

30. $2z^2 = 8z + 5 - 4z^2$ **31.** $3r^2 - 2 = 6r + 3$ **32.** $4p - 3 = p^2 + 2p$

33. $(x + 1)(x + 3) = 2$ **34.** $(x - 3)(x + 1) = 1$

35. A rule for estimating the number of board feet of lumber that can be cut from a log depends on the diameter of the log. The diameter d required to get 9 board feet is found from the equation

$$\left(\frac{d - 4}{4}\right)^2 = 9.$$

Solve this equation for d. Are both answers reasonable?

Review Exercises *Write each quotient in lowest terms. Simplify the radicals if necessary. See Section 8.5.*

36. $\dfrac{2 + 2\sqrt{3}}{2}$

37. $\dfrac{3 + 6\sqrt{5}}{3}$

38. $\dfrac{4 + 2\sqrt{7}}{8}$

39. $\dfrac{5 + 5\sqrt{2}}{10}$

40. $\dfrac{8 + 6\sqrt{3}}{4}$

41. $\dfrac{4 + \sqrt{28}}{6}$

42. $\dfrac{6 + \sqrt{45}}{12}$

9.3 Solving Quadratic Equations by the Quadratic Formula

1. Identify the coefficients a, b, and c in a quadratic equation.
2. Use the quadratic formula to solve quadratic equations.
3. Solve quadratic equations with fractions.

Any quadratic equation can be solved by completing the square, but the method is not very handy. In this section, we work out a general formula, the quadratic formula, that gives the solution for any quadratic equation.

To get the quadratic formula, start with the general form of a quadratic equation,

$$ax^2 + bx + c = 0, \qquad a \neq 0.$$

The restriction $a \neq 0$ is important in order to make sure that the equation is quadratic. If $a = 0$, then the equation becomes $0x^2 + bx + c = 0$, or $bx + c = 0$, which is a linear, and not a quadratic, equation.

1. The first step in solving a quadratic equation is to identify the letters a, b, and c in the general form of the quadratic equation.

EXAMPLE 1 Match the coefficients of each of the following quadratic equations with the letters a, b, and c of the general quadratic equation

$$ax^2 + bx + c = 0.$$

(a) $2x^2 + 3x - 5 = 0$

In this example $a = 2$, $b = 3$, and $c = -5$.

(b) $-x^2 + 2 = 6x$

First rewrite the equation with 0 on one side to match the general form $ax^2 + bx + c = 0$.

$$-x^2 + 2 = 6x$$
$$-x^2 - 6x + 2 = 0$$

Now identify $a = -1$, $b = -6$, and $c = 2$.

(c) $2(x + 3)(x - 1) = 5$

   First multiply on the left.

$$2(x + 3)(x - 1) = 2(x^2 + 2x - 3) = 2x^2 + 4x - 6$$

The equation becomes

$$2x^2 + 4x - 6 = 5, \quad \text{or} \quad 2x^2 + 4x - 11 = 0,$$

so that $a = 2$, $b = 4$, and $c = -11$. ●

   The quadratic formula is developed by solving the equation $ax^2 + bx + c = 0$ by completing the square. First, get the coefficient 1 for the x^2 term by dividing both sides by a, which gives

$$x^2 + \frac{b}{a}x + \frac{c}{a} = 0.$$

Next add $-c/a$ to both sides, to get

$$x^2 + \frac{b}{a}x = -\frac{c}{a}.$$

Complete the square on the left: Take half the coefficient of x to get $\dfrac{b}{2a}$. Square $\dfrac{b}{2a}$

to get $\dfrac{b^2}{4a^2}$. Add $\dfrac{b^2}{4a^2}$ to both sides of the equation.

$$x^2 + \frac{b}{a}x + \frac{b^2}{4a^2} = -\frac{c}{a} + \frac{b^2}{4a^2}$$

Rewrite the left-hand side as a perfect square, and simplify the right-hand side of the equation.

$$\left(x + \frac{b}{2a}\right)^2 = \frac{b^2}{4a^2} - \frac{c}{a}$$

$$= \frac{b^2}{4a^2} - \frac{4ac}{4a^2}$$

$$= \frac{b^2 - 4ac}{4a^2}$$

Apply the square root property.

$$x + \frac{b}{2a} = \sqrt{\frac{b^2 - 4ac}{4a^2}} \quad \text{or} \quad x + \frac{b}{2a} = -\sqrt{\frac{b^2 - 4ac}{4a^2}}$$

Simplify the radical.

$$\sqrt{\frac{b^2 - 4ac}{4a^2}} = \frac{\sqrt{b^2 - 4ac}}{\sqrt{4a^2}} = \frac{\sqrt{b^2 - 4ac}}{2a}$$

Write the solutions as follows.

$$x + \frac{b}{2a} = \frac{\sqrt{b^2 - 4ac}}{2a} \qquad \text{or} \qquad x + \frac{b}{2a} = \frac{-\sqrt{b^2 - 4ac}}{2a}$$

$$x = \frac{-b}{2a} + \frac{\sqrt{b^2 - 4ac}}{2a} \qquad \text{or} \qquad x = \frac{-b}{2a} - \frac{\sqrt{b^2 - 4ac}}{2a}$$

$$x = \frac{-b + \sqrt{b^2 - 4ac}}{2a} \qquad \text{or} \qquad x = \frac{-b - \sqrt{b^2 - 4ac}}{2a}$$

In summary, the solutions of the general quadratic equation $ax^2 + bx + c = 0$, where $a \neq 0$, are

$$\frac{-b + \sqrt{b^2 - 4ac}}{2a} \qquad \text{and} \qquad \frac{-b - \sqrt{b^2 - 4ac}}{2a}.$$

For convenience, the solutions are often expressed in compact form by using the symbol $\pm$ (read "plus or minus"). The result is called the **quadratic formula.**

Quadratic Formula

> If $ax^2 + bx + c = 0$, with $a \neq 0$, then $x = \dfrac{-b \pm \sqrt{b^2 - 4ac}}{2a}$.

2   The following examples show how to use the quadratic formula.

EXAMPLE 2   Use the quadratic formula to solve $2x^2 - 7x - 9 = 0$.

Match the coefficients of the variables with those of the general quadratic equation $ax^2 + bx + c = 0$. Here, $a = 2$, $b = -7$, and $c = -9$. Substitute these numbers into the quadratic formula and simplify the result.

$$x = \frac{-b \pm \sqrt{b^2 - 4ac}}{2a}$$

$$= \frac{-(-7) \pm \sqrt{(-7)^2 - 4(2)(-9)}}{2(2)}$$

$$= \frac{7 \pm \sqrt{49 + 72}}{4}$$

$$= \frac{7 \pm \sqrt{121}}{4}$$

Since $\sqrt{121} = 11$,

$$x = \frac{7 \pm \sqrt{121}}{4} = \frac{7 \pm 11}{4}.$$

To write the two solutions separately, first use the plus sign and then use the minus sign.

$$x = \frac{7 + 11}{4} = \frac{18}{4} = \frac{9}{2} \quad \text{or} \quad x = \frac{7 - 11}{4} = -\frac{4}{4} = -1$$

The solutions of $2x^2 - 7x - 9 = 0$ are 9/2 and -1. Check by substituting back in the original equation. ●

EXAMPLE 3

Solve $x^2 = 2x + 1$.

To find a, b, and c, one side of the equation must be 0. Subtract $2x$ and 1 from both sides of the equation to get

$$x^2 - 2x - 1 = 0.$$

Then $a = 1$, $b = -2$, and $c = -1$. The solution is found by substituting these values into the quadratic formula.

$$x = \frac{-b \pm \sqrt{b^2 - 4ac}}{2a}$$

$$= \frac{-(-2) \pm \sqrt{(-2)^2 - 4(1)(-1)}}{2(1)}$$

$$= \frac{2 \pm \sqrt{4 + 4}}{2} = \frac{2 \pm \sqrt{8}}{2}$$

Since $\sqrt{8} = \sqrt{4 \cdot 2} = \sqrt{4} \cdot \sqrt{2} = 2\sqrt{2}$,

$$x = \frac{2 \pm 2\sqrt{2}}{2}.$$

Also, $2 \pm 2\sqrt{2}$ factors as $2(1 \pm \sqrt{2})$, so

$$x = \frac{2(1 \pm \sqrt{2})}{2} = 1 \pm \sqrt{2},$$

and the two solutions of this equation are

$$1 + \sqrt{2} \quad \text{and} \quad 1 - \sqrt{2}. \quad ●$$

When the quantity under the radical, $b^2 - 4ac$, equals zero, the equation has just one rational number solution. This means that the quadratic trinomial $ax^2 + bx + c$ is a perfect square.

EXAMPLE 4   Solve $4x^2 + 25 = 20x$.

Write the equation as

$$4x^2 - 20x + 25 = 0.$$

Here, $a = 4$, $b = -20$, and $c = 25$. By the quadratic formula,

$$x = \frac{-(-20) \pm \sqrt{(-20)^2 - 400}}{8} = \frac{20}{8} = \frac{5}{2}.$$

Since there is just one solution, the trinomial $4x^2 - 20x + 25$ is a perfect square.   ●

3   The next example shows how to solve quadratic equations with fractions.

EXAMPLE 5   Solve the equation $\dfrac{1}{10}t^2 = \dfrac{2}{5}t - \dfrac{1}{2}$.

To eliminate the denominators, multiply both sides of the equation by the common denominator, 10.

$$10\left(\frac{1}{10}t^2\right) = 10\left(\frac{2}{5}t - \frac{1}{2}\right)$$

$$t^2 = 4t - 5$$

Subtract $4t$ and add 5 on both sides of the equation to get

$$t^2 - 4t + 5 = 0.$$

In this form, we can identify $a = 1$, $b = -4$, and $c = 5$. Use the quadratic formula to complete the solution.

$$t = \frac{-(-4) \pm \sqrt{(-4)^2 - 4(1)(5)}}{2(1)} = \frac{4 \pm \sqrt{16 - 20}}{2} = \frac{4 \pm \sqrt{-4}}{2}$$

The radical $\sqrt{-4}$ is not a real number, so the equation has no real number solution.   ●

9.3 EXERCISES

For each equation, identify the letters a, b, and c of the general quadratic equation $ax^2 + bx + c = 0$. Do not solve. See Example 1.

1. $3x^2 + 4x - 8 = 0$

2. $9x^2 + 2x - 3 = 0$

3. $-8x^2 - 2x - 3 = 0$

4. $-2x^2 + 3x - 8 = 0$

5. $2x^2 = 3x - 2$

6. $9x^2 - 2 = 4x$

7. $x^2 = 2$

8. $x^2 - 3 = 0$

9. $3x^2 - 8x = 0$

10. $5x^2 = 2x$

11. $(x - 3)(x + 4) = 0$

12. $(x + 6)^2 = 3$

13. $9(x - 1)(x + 2) = 8$

14. $(3x - 1)(2x + 5) = x(x - 1)$

Use the quadratic formula to solve each equation. Write all radicals in simplified form. Reduce answers to lowest terms. Round answers to the nearest thousandth in Exercises 45–50. See Examples 2–4.

15. $p^2 + 2p - 2 = 0$

16. $6k^2 + 6k + 1 = 0$

17. $y^2 + 4y + 4 = 0$

18. $3r^2 - 5r + 1 = 0$

19. $z^2 = 13 - 12z$

20. $x^2 = 8x + 9$

21. $2w^2 + 12w + 5 = 0$

22. $k^2 = 20k - 19$

23. $5x^2 + 4x - 1 = 0$

24. $5n^2 + n - 1 = 0$

25. $2z^2 = 3z + 5$

26. $7r - 2r^2 + 30 = 0$

27. $z^2 + 6z + 9 = 0$

28. $x^2 - 2x + 1 = 0$

29. $4p^2 - 12p + 9 = 0$

30. $9r^2 + 6r + 1 = 0$

31. $5m^2 + 5m = 0$

32. $4y^2 - 8y = 0$

33. $6p^2 = 10p$

34. $3r^2 = 16r$

35. $m^2 - 20 = 0$

36. $k^2 - 5 = 0$

37. $9r^2 - 16 = 0$

38. $4y^2 - 25 = 0$

39. $2x^2 + 2x + 4 = 4 - 2x$

40. $3x^2 - 4x + 3 = 8x - 1$

41. $2x^2 + x + 7 = 0$

42. $x^2 + x + 1 = 0$

43. $2x^2 = 3x - 2$

44. $x^2 = 5x - 20$

45. $x^2 = 1 + x$

46. $2x^2 + 2x = 5$

47. $5x^2 = 3 - x$

48. $3x^2 + 1 = 6x$

49. $x^2 + 6x + 2 = 0$

50. $5x + 2 = x^2$

Use the quadratic formula to solve each equation. See Example 5.

51. $\frac{1}{2}x^2 = 1 - \frac{1}{6}x$

52. $\frac{3}{2}r^2 - r = \frac{4}{3}$

53. $\frac{2}{3}m^2 - \frac{4}{9}m - \frac{1}{3} = 0$

54. $\frac{3}{5}x - \frac{2}{5}x^2 = -1$

55. $\frac{r^2}{2} = r + \frac{1}{2}$

56. $\frac{m^2}{4} + \frac{3m}{2} + 1 = 0$

57. $k^2 = \frac{2k}{3} + \frac{2}{9}$

58. $\frac{2y^2}{7} + \frac{10}{7}y + 1 = 0$

59. $\frac{m^2}{2} = \frac{m}{2} - 1$

60. $\frac{3k^2}{8} - k = -\frac{17}{24}$

61. $2 = \frac{4}{x} - \frac{3}{x^2}$

62. The time t in seconds under certain conditions for a car to skid 48 feet is given (approximately) by

$$48 = 64t - 16t^2.$$

Solve this equation for t. Are both answers reasonable?

Review Exercises *Use the product rule to simplify each expression. See Section 8.2.*

63. $\sqrt{27}$

64. $\sqrt{24}$

65. $\sqrt{48}$

66. $\sqrt{72}$

67. $\sqrt{44}$

68. $\sqrt{800}$

69. $\sqrt{288}$

70. $\sqrt{150}$

MISCELLANEOUS QUADRATIC EQUATIONS

We now have introduced three methods for solving quadratic equations written in the form $ax^2 + bx + c = 0$. The chart below gives some advantages and disadvantages of each method.

Methods for Solving Quadratic Equations

Method	Advantages	Disadvantages
1. Factoring	Usually the fastest method	Not all equations are factorable
		Some factorable equations are hard to factor
2. Completing the square	None for solving equations (the procedure is useful in other areas of mathematics)	Requires more steps than other methods
3. Quadratic formula	Can always be used	More difficult than factoring because of the square root
4. Square root method	Simplest method for solving equations of the form $(x + a)^2 = b$	Few equations are given in this form

Solve each quadratic equation.

1. $y^2 + 3y + 1 = 0$

2. $p^2 + 3p + 2 = 0$

3. $2x^2 - x = 1$

4. $2a^2 + 1 = a$

5. $8m^2 = 2m + 15$

6. $8x^2 + 2x = 15$

7. $3p^2 + 5p + 1 = 0$

8. $2q^2 + 3q = 1$

9. $5k^2 + 8 = 22k$

10. $5k^2 + 2k = 1$

11. $3z^2 = 4z + 1$

12. $2c^2 + 11c + 12 = 0$

13. $4x^2 = 5x - 1$

14. $4x^2 + 5x = 1$

15. $15t^2 + 58t + 48 = 0$

16. $12d^2 + 19d = 21$

17. $p^2 + 5p + 5 = 0$

18. $a^2 - 3a - 3 = 0$

19. $3c^2 - 4c = 4$

20. $5k^2 + 17k = 12$

21. $2x^2 - 5x + 1 = 0$

22. $z^2 - z + 3 = 0$

23. $4m^2 - 11m + 10 = 0$

24. $2a^2 - 7a + 4 = 0$

25. $(2p - 1)^2 = 10$

26. $(3r + 2)^2 = 5$

27. $(a + 6)^2 = 121$

28. $(7m - 1)^2 = 32$

29. $(2q + 9)^2 = 48$

30. $(5r - 7)^2 = -1$

9.4 Complex Solutions of Quadratic Equations

① Write complex numbers like $\sqrt{-5}$ as multiples of i.

② Add and subtract complex numbers.

③ Multiply complex numbers.

④ Divide complex numbers.

⑤ Solve quadratic equations with complex number solutions.

We have seen that some quadratic equations have no real number solutions. For example, the solution

$$x = \frac{-3 + \sqrt{-5}}{2}$$

is not a real number because of $\sqrt{-5}$. In order for every quadratic equation to have a solution, we need a new set of numbers, which includes the real numbers. This new set of numbers is called the *complex numbers*.

① In work with complex numbers, a new number i is defined such that

i

$$i = \sqrt{-1} \quad \text{and} \quad i^2 = -1.$$

The symbol $\sqrt{-1}$ is always replaced with i. This means that we can write numbers like $\sqrt{-5}$, $\sqrt{-4}$, and $\sqrt{-8}$ as multiples of i. This is done with a generalization of the product rule for radicals, as in the next example.

EXAMPLE 1   Write each number as a multiple of i.

(a) $\sqrt{-5} = \sqrt{-1 \cdot 5} = \sqrt{-1} \cdot \sqrt{5} = i\sqrt{5}$

We usually write $i\sqrt{5}$ rather than $\sqrt{5}\,i$ to avoid confusion with $\sqrt{5i}$.

(b) $\sqrt{-4} = \sqrt{-1} \cdot \sqrt{4} = i\sqrt{4} = i \cdot 2 = 2i$

(c) $\sqrt{-8} = i\sqrt{8} = i \cdot 2 \cdot \sqrt{2} = 2i\sqrt{2}$ ●

Now we can define a **complex number.**

Complex
Number

A **complex number** is a number of the form $a + bi$, where a and b are real numbers.

For example, the real number 2 is a complex number since it can be written as $2 + 0i$. Also, $3i = 0 + 3i$ is a complex number. Other examples of complex numbers are

$$3 - 2i, \quad 1 + i\sqrt{2}, \quad \text{and} \quad -5 + 4i.$$

A complex number written in the form $a + bi$ (or $a + ib$) is in **standard form.**

2   All the properties of real numbers also apply to complex numbers. Therefore, to add or subtract complex numbers, combine like terms.

EXAMPLE 2   Add or subtract.

(a) $(2 - 6i) + (7 + 4i) = (2 + 7) + (-6 + 4)i = 9 - 2i$

(b) $3i + (-2 - i) = -2 + (3 - 1)i = -2 + 2i$

(c) $(2 + 6i) - (-4 + i) = [2 - (-4)] + (6 - 1)i = 6 + 5i$

(d) $(-1 + 2i) - 4 = (-1 - 4) + 2i = -5 + 2i$ ●

3   Multiplication of complex numbers, using the FOIL method, is handled in much the same way as multiplication of polynomials.

EXAMPLE 3   Find the following products.

(a) $3i(2 - 5i) = 6i - 15i^2$

$\qquad\qquad\quad = 6i - 15(-1)$ Recall: $i^2 = -1$

$\qquad\qquad\quad = 6i + 15$

$\qquad\qquad\quad = 15 + 6i$

The last step gives the result in standard form.

(b) $(4 - 3i)(2 + 5i) = 4(2) + 4(5i) + (-3i)(2) + (-3i)(5i)$

$\qquad\qquad\qquad\quad = 8 + 20i - 6i - 15i^2$

$\qquad\qquad\qquad\quad = 8 + 14i - 15(-1)$

$\qquad\qquad\qquad\quad = 8 + 14i + 15$

$\qquad\qquad\qquad\quad = 23 + 14i$

(c) $(5 - 2i)(5 + 2i) = 25 + 10i - 10i - 4i^2$

$\qquad\qquad\qquad\quad = 25 - 4(-1)$

$\qquad\qquad\qquad\quad = 25 + 4 = 29$ ●

The complex numbers $5 - 2i$ and $5 + 2i$ are *conjugates*. That is, the **conjugate** of the complex number $a + bi$ is $a - bi$.

4   The quotient of two complex numbers, such as the quotient

$$\frac{2 - 5i}{4 + 3i},$$

can be expressed in standard form by changing the denominator into a real number. Following what was done in Example 3(c), multiply numerator and denominator of the given quotient by $4 - 3i$, where $4 - 3i$ is the conjugate of the denominator, as shown on the next page.

$$\frac{2-5i}{4+3i}\cdot\frac{4-3i}{4-3i}=\frac{8-6i-20i+15i^2}{16-9i^2}$$

$$=\frac{8-26i+15(-1)}{16-9(-1)}$$

$$=\frac{8-26i-15}{16+9}$$

$$=\frac{-7-26i}{25}=\frac{-7}{25}-\frac{26}{25}i$$

The last step gives the result in standard form. This procedure is similar to the one used to rationalize radical expressions in Chapter 8.

EXAMPLE 4   Write the following quotients in standard form.

(a) $\dfrac{-4+i}{2-i}$

Multiply numerator and denominator by the conjugate of the denominator, $2+i$.

$$\frac{-4+i}{2-i}\cdot\frac{2+i}{2+i}=\frac{-8-4i+2i+i^2}{4-i^2}$$

$$=\frac{-8-2i-1}{4-(-1)}$$

$$=\frac{-9-2i}{5}=-\frac{9}{5}-\frac{2}{5}i$$

(b) $\dfrac{3+i}{-i}$

Here, the conjugate of $0-i$ is $0+i$, or i.

$$\frac{3+i}{-i}\cdot\frac{i}{i}=\frac{3i+i^2}{-i^2}=\frac{-1+3i}{-(-1)}=-1+3i \quad\bullet$$

5   Now we are ready to solve quadratic equations that have no real number solutions.

EXAMPLE 5   Solve $(x+3)^2=-25$.

Use the square root property.

$$(x+3)^2=-25$$

$$x+3=\sqrt{-25} \quad\text{or}\quad x+3=-\sqrt{-25}$$

Since $\sqrt{-25}=5i$,

$$x+3=5i \quad\text{or}\quad x+3=-5i$$

$$x=-3+5i \quad\text{or}\quad x=-3-5i.$$

In standard form, the two complex solutions are $-3+5i$ and $-3-5i$. $\bullet$

EXAMPLE 6   Solve $t^2 - 4t + 5 = 0$.

The polynomial on the left cannot be factored, so use the quadratic formula, with $a = 1$, $b = -4$, and $c = 5$. The solutions are

$$t = \frac{-(-4) \pm \sqrt{(-4)^2 - 4(1)(5)}}{2(1)}$$

$$= \frac{4 \pm \sqrt{16 - 20}}{2} = \frac{4 \pm \sqrt{-4}}{2} = \frac{4 \pm 2i}{2}.$$

Factor out the common factor of 2 in the numerator and reduce to get

$$t = \frac{2(2 \pm i)}{2} = 2 \pm i.$$

The two complex solutions are $2 + i$ and $2 - i$. ●

EXAMPLE 7   Solve $2p^2 = 4p - 5$.

Write the equation as $2p^2 - 4p + 5 = 0$. Then $a = 2$, $b = -4$, and $c = 5$. The solutions are

$$p = \frac{-(-4) \pm \sqrt{(-4)^2 - 4(2)(5)}}{2(2)}$$

$$= \frac{4 \pm \sqrt{16 - 40}}{4} = \frac{4 \pm \sqrt{-24}}{4}.$$

Since $\sqrt{-24} = i\sqrt{24} = i \cdot \sqrt{4} \cdot \sqrt{6} = i \cdot 2 \cdot \sqrt{6} = 2i\sqrt{6}$,

$$p = \frac{4 \pm 2i\sqrt{6}}{4}$$

$$= \frac{2(2 \pm i\sqrt{6})}{4} = \frac{2 \pm i\sqrt{6}}{2}.$$

The solutions are the complex numbers

$$\frac{2 + i\sqrt{6}}{2} \quad \text{and} \quad \frac{2 - i\sqrt{6}}{2}. ●$$

9.4 EXERCISES

Write the following numbers as multiples of i. See Example 1.

1. $\sqrt{-9}$ **2.** $\sqrt{-18}$ **3.** $\sqrt{-20}$ **4.** $\sqrt{-27}$

5. $\sqrt{-36}$ **6.** $\sqrt{-50}$ **7.** $\sqrt{-125}$ **8.** $\sqrt{-98}$

Add or subtract as indicated. See Example 2.

9. $(2 + 8i) + (3 - 5i)$ **10.** $(4 - 5i) + (7 - 2i)$ **11.** $(16 + 5i) + (2 - 7i)$

12. $(6 + 3i) + (-1 - 4i)$ **13.** $(8 - 3i) - (2 + 6i)$ **14.** $(1 + i) - (3 - 2i)$

15. $(3 - 4i) + (6 - i) - (3 + 2i)$ **16.** $(5 + 8i) - (4 + 2i) + (3 - i)$

Find each product. See Example 3.

17. $(3 + 2i)(4 - i)$

18. $(9 - 2i)(3 + i)$

19. $(5 - 4i)(3 - 2i)$

20. $(10 + 6i)(8 - 4i)$

21. $(3 + 6i)(3 - 6i)$

22. $(11 - 2i)(11 + 2i)$

23. $(5 - 3i)(5 + 3i)$

24. $(7 + 2i)(7 - 2i)$

Write each quotient in standard form. See Example 4.

25. $\dfrac{-2 + i}{1 - i}$

26. $\dfrac{6 + i}{2 + i}$

27. $\dfrac{3 - 4i}{2 + 2i}$

28. $\dfrac{7 - i}{3 - 2i}$

29. $\dfrac{5 + 2i}{1 + 3i}$

30. $\dfrac{4 + 6i}{2 - 3i}$

31. $\dfrac{4 - 3i}{i}$

32. $\dfrac{-i}{1 + 2i}$

Solve each quadratic equation by the square root property. See Example 5.

33. $(a + 1)^2 = -4$

34. $(p - 5)^2 = -36$

35. $(k - 3)^2 = -5$

36. $(y + 6)^2 = -12$

37. $(3x + 2)^2 = -18$

38. $(4z - 1)^2 = -20$

Solve each quadratic equation by the quadratic formula. See Examples 6 and 7.

39. $m^2 - 2m + 2 = 0$

40. $b^2 + b + 3 = 0$

41. $2r^2 + 3r + 5 = 0$

42. $3q^2 = 2q - 3$

43. $2r^2 + 5 = 4r$

44. $4q^2 + 2q + 3 = 0$

Review Exercises *Complete the ordered pairs using the given equation. Then plot the ordered pairs. See Section 6.1.*

Equation	Ordered pairs			
45. $2x - 3y = 6$	(0,)	(, 0)	(, 2)	(−3,)
46. $4x - y = 8$	(0,)	(, 0)	(4,)	(, −4)
47. $3x + 5y = 15$	(0,)	(, 0)	(−5,)	(, −3)
48. $6x + 4y = 12$	(0,)	(, 0)	(−2,)	(, −3)
49. $y - 2x = 0$	(0,)	(3,)	(, 5)	(, 2)
50. $x - 3y = 0$	(0,)	(3,)	(, 4)	(4,)

9.5 Graphing Quadratic Equations

■ Graph quadratic equations.

■ Find the vertex of a parabola.

■ In Chapter 6, we graphed straight lines to represent the solutions of linear equations. Now we graph quadratic equations in two variables of the form $y = ax^2 + bx + c$. Perhaps the simplest such quadratic equation is

$$y = x^2$$

(or $y = 1x^2 + 0x + 0$). The graph of this equation cannot be a straight line since only linear equations, which can be put in the form

$$ax + by + c = 0,$$

have graphs that are straight lines. However, we can graph $y = x^2$ in much the same way that we graphed straight lines, by finding ordered pairs that satisfy the equation $y = x^2$.

EXAMPLE 1   Graph $y = x^2$.

Select values for x. Then find the corresponding y-values. For example, if we select $x = 2$, then

$$y = 2^2 = 4,$$

and the point (2, 4) belongs to the graph of $y = x^2$. (Recall that in an ordered pair such as (2, 4), the x-value comes first and the y-value second.) In the same way we can find the ordered pairs (−3, 9), (−2, 4), (−1, 1), (0, 0), (1, 1), and (3, 9).

If we plot all these points on a coordinate system and draw a smooth curve through them, we get the graph shown in Figure 9.1. This graph is called a **parabola.** The point (0, 0), the lowest point on this graph, is the **vertex** of the parabola.   ●

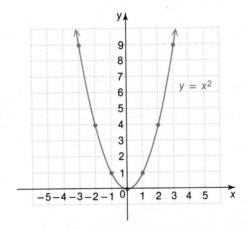

Figure 9.1

Every quadratic equation of the form

$$y = ax^2 + bx + c$$

has a graph that is a parabola. Because of its many useful properties, the parabola occurs frequently in real-life applications. For example, if an object is thrown into the air, the path that the object follows is a parabola (discounting wind resistance). The cross sections of radar, spotlight, and telescope reflectors also form parabolas.

EXAMPLE 2   Graph the parabola $y = -x^2$.

We could select values for x and then find the corresponding y-values. But for a given x-value, the y-value here will be the negative of the corresponding y-value of the parabola $y = x^2$ discussed above. Because of this, the new parabola has the same shape as the one in the preceding figure but opens downward, as shown in Figure 9.2. Here the vertex, (0, 0), is the *highest* point on the graph.   ●

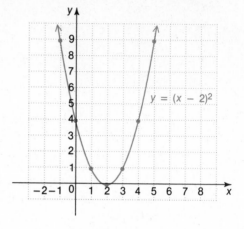

Figure 9.2   **Figure 9.3**

2   The next examples show how to find the vertex of a parabola from its equation.

EXAMPLE 3   Graph the parabola $y = (x - 2)^2$.

The vertex of a parabola is the point where y has its largest or smallest value. Since $(x - 2)^2$ is always nonnegative, y will be nonnegative. The smallest y-value, the y-value of the vertex, will be 0. To find x at the vertex, let $y = 0$ in the equation and solve for x.

$$y = (x - 2)^2$$
$$0 = (x - 2)^2$$
$$0 = x - 2$$
$$x = 2$$

The vertex is (2, 0).

To find some other points on the graph, select values for x and find the corresponding y-values. For example, if we let $x = -1$, then

$$y = (-1 - 2)^2 = (-3)^2 = 9.$$

In this way we find the ordered pairs (−1, 9), (3, 1), (0, 4), (4, 4), (1, 1), (5, 9), and (2, 0). Plotting these points and joining them gives the graph shown in Figure 9.3. This parabola has the same shape as the graph of $y = x^2$, but is shifted two units to the right, with vertex (2, 0).   ●

EXAMPLE 4   Graph the parabola $y = x^2 - 3$.

The smallest value of y will occur when $x = 0$ and $y = 0 - 3$, or $y = -3$. Thus, the vertex of this parabola is $(0, -3)$. The graph is shown in Figure 9.4. This time the graph is shifted three units downward, as compared with the graph of $y = x^2$.   ●

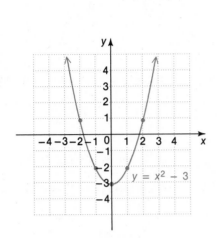

Figure 9.4

$y = x^2 - 3$

Figure 9.5

$y = (x - 2)^2 - 3$

$(2, -3)$

EXAMPLE 5   Graph $y = (x - 2)^2 - 3$.

As shown in Figure 9.5, the vertex is $(2, -3)$. The graph is the same shape as that of $y = x^2$, but is shifted two units to the right and three units downward. See Examples 3 and 4 to see why.   ●

We can now summarize our results on graphing parabolas.

Graphing Parabolas

The graph of

$$y = a(x - h)^2 + k$$

is a parabola with vertex at (h, k).

The parabola opens upward if $a > 0$ and downward if $a < 0$.

The parabola is "fatter" than $y = x^2$ if $0 < |a| < 1$, and it is "thinner" than $y = x^2$ if $|a| > 1$.

Suppose we want to graph $y = x^2 + 6x + 5$. To identify the vertex, the equation must be in the form $y = (x - h)^2 + k$. We need to find appropriate numbers for h and k, which we do by completing the square (as in Section 9.2).

EXAMPLE 6   Complete the square of $y = x^2 + 6x + 5$ and write the equation in the form $y = (x - h)^2 + k$.

Here we want to leave the left side of the equation alone, so we work only on the right side. Write the equation as

$$y = (x^2 + 6x) + 5.$$

Take half the coefficient of x and square it:

$$\frac{1}{2}(6) = 3 \quad \text{and} \quad 3^2 = 9.$$

Add 9 and subtract 9 on the right side. (We are adding $9 + (-9) = 0$, so the value of the equation remains unchanged.)

$$y = (x^2 + 6x + 9) + 5 - 9$$

Write the first three terms as $(x + 3)^2$ and combine the last two terms.

$$y = (x + 3)^2 - 4$$

Writing the equation in this form shows that the vertex is $(-3, -4)$. The graph is given in Figure 9.6.   ●

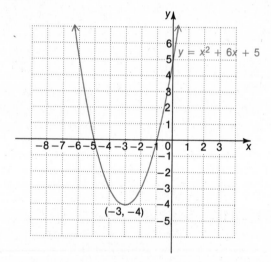

Figure 9.6

In the last example we graphed the equation $y = x^2 + 6x + 5$. If $y = 0$, the equation becomes

$$0 = x^2 + 6x + 5.$$

The solutions of this equation can be found by factoring.

$$0 = (x + 5)(x + 1)$$

$$x + 5 = 0 \quad \text{or} \quad x + 1 = 0$$

$$x = -5 \quad \text{or} \quad x = -1$$

Now look at Figure 9.6, which gives the graph of $y = x^2 + 6x + 5$. The x-intercepts (the points where $y = 0$) are -5 and -1. The two solutions of the quadratic equation $x^2 + 6x + 5 = 0$ give the intercepts of the graph of the equation $y = x^2 + 6x + 5$. This is always the case.

Intercepts of a Quadratic Equation

> The real number solutions of a quadratic equation $ax^2 + bx + c = 0$ are the x-intercepts of the graph of $y = ax^2 + bx + c$.

Since a parabola can cross the x-axis in two, one, or no places, this result shows why some quadratic equations have two solutions, some have one, and some have no real solutions.

EXAMPLE 7

Decide from the indicated graph how many solutions the corresponding quadratic equation with $y = 0$ will have.

(a) Figure 9.4 shows the graph of an equation with two solutions, $x = \sqrt{3}$ and $x = -\sqrt{3}$.

(b) Figure 9.3 shows the graph of an equation with one solution, $x = 2$.

(c) Figure 9.7 gives the graph of $y = x^2 + 2$. Since there are no x-intercepts, the equation $x^2 + 2 = 0$ has no *real* number solutions. The equation *does* have two complex solutions, $i\sqrt{2}$ and $-i\sqrt{2}$. ●

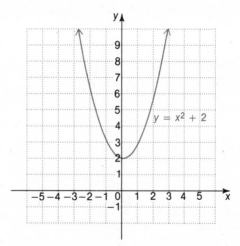

Figure 9.7

9.5 EXERCISES

Sketch the graph of each equation. Identify each vertex. See Examples 1–5.

1. $y = 2x^2$ **2.** $y = -2x^2$ **3.** $y = (x + 1)^2$ **4.** $y = (x - 2)^2$

5. $y = -(x + 1)^2$ **6.** $y = -(x - 2)^2$ **7.** $y = x^2 + 1$ **8.** $y = -x^2 - 2$

9. $y = 2 - x^2$　　　**10.** $y = -4 + x^2$　　　**11.** $y = \dfrac{1}{2}x^2 + 2$　　　**12.** $y = -\dfrac{1}{3}x^2 + 1$

13. $y = (x + 1)^2 + 2$　　**14.** $y = (x - 2)^2 - 1$　　**15.** $y = (x - 4)^2 - 1$　　**16.** $y = (x + 3)^2 + 3$

Sketch the graph of each equation. Identify each vertex. See Example 6.

17. $y = x^2 - 6x + 5$　　　　**18.** $y = x^2 - 4x + 2$　　　　**19.** $y = x^2 - 8x + 9$

20. $y = x^2 - 2x - 1$　　　　**21.** $y = x^2 + 3x + 2$　　　　**22.** $y = x^2 + 5x - 2$

Decide from the graph how many real number solutions the corresponding equation has. Find any real solutions from the graph. See Example 7.

23.

24.

25.

26.

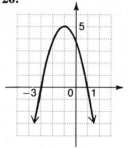

Chapter 9　Review Exercises

[9.1] *Solve each equation by using the square root property. Express all radicals in simplest form.*

1. $y^2 = 49$　　　　**2.** $x^2 = 15$　　　　**3.** $m^2 = 48$　　　　**4.** $(k + 2)^2 = 9$

5. $(r - 3)^2 = 7$　　**6.** $(2p + 1)^2 = 11$　　**7.** $(3k + 2)^2 = 12$　　**8.** $\left(x + \dfrac{1}{2}\right)^2 = \dfrac{3}{4}$

[9.2] *Solve each equation by completing the square.*

9. $m^2 + 6m + 5 = 0$

10. $p^2 + 4p = 7$

11. $-x^2 + 5 = 2x$

12. $2y^2 + 8y = 3$

13. $5k^2 - 3k - 2 = 0$

14. $(4a + 1)(a - 1) = -3$

[9.3] *Use the quadratic formula to solve each equation.*

15. $x^2 - 2x - 4 = 0$

16. $-m^2 + 3m + 5 = 0$

17. $3k^2 + 2k + 3 = 0$

18. $5p^2 = p + 1$

19. $2p^2 - 3 = 4p$

20. $-4a^2 + 7 = 2a$

21. $\dfrac{c^2}{4} = 2 - \dfrac{3}{4}c$

22. $\dfrac{3}{2}r^2 = \dfrac{1}{2} - r$

Use the most suitable of the following methods to solve each quadratic equation: factoring, the square root property, completing the square, or the quadratic formula.

23. $(2t - 1)(t + 5) = 0$

24. $(2p + 1)^2 = 4$

25. $(k + 2)(k - 1) = 3$

26. $6t^2 + 7t - 3 = 0$

27. $2x^2 + 3x + 2 = x^2 - 2x$

28. $x^2 + 2x + 1 = 3$

29. $(3x + 5)(3x + 5) = 7$

30. $\dfrac{1}{2}r^2 = \dfrac{7}{2} - r$

31. $\dfrac{2}{m} - 3 = \dfrac{-1}{m^2}$

32. $(2y - 3)^2 = 7$

33. $x^2 + 4x - 1 = 0$

34. $7x^2 - 8 = 5x^2 + 16$

[9.4] *Perform the indicated operation.*

35. $(3 + 5i) + (2 - 6i)$

36. $(-2 - 8i) - (4 - 3i)$

37. $(-1 + i) - (2 - i)$

38. $(4 + 3i) + (-2 + 3i)$

39. $(6 - 2i)(3 + i)$

40. $(2 + 3i)(4 - 2i)$

41. $(5 + 2i)(5 - 2i)$

42. $(8 - i)(8 + i)$

43. $\dfrac{1 + i}{1 - i}$

44. $\dfrac{3 + 2i}{1 + i}$

45. $\dfrac{2 - 4i}{3 + i}$

46. $\dfrac{5 + 6i}{2 + 3i}$

Solve each quadratic equation.

47. $(m + 2)^2 = -3$

48. $(x - 1)^2 = -2$

49. $(3p - 2)^2 = -8$

50. $(4p + 1)^2 = -12$

51. $3k^2 = 2k - 1$

52. $h^2 + 3h = -8$

53. $4q^2 + 2 = 3q$

54. $9z^2 + 2z + 1 = 0$

[9.5] *Sketch the graph of each equation. Identify each vertex.*

55. $y = 3x^2$

56. $y = -3x^2$

57. $y = -x^2 + 3$

58. $y = x^2 - 1$

59. $y = (x - 4)^2$

60. $y = -(2x + 1)^2$

61. $y = (x + 2)^2 - 3$

62. $y = -(x - 1)^2 + 4$

63. $y = \dfrac{1}{2}(x - 3)^2 + 1$

64. $y = x^2 + 8x + 14$

65. $y = x^2 - 10x + 24$

66. $y = x^2 + 2x + 1$

Decide from the graph how many real number solutions the corresponding equation has. Find any real solutions from the graph.

67.

68.

69.

Chapter 9 Test

Solve by completing the square.

1. $2z^2 - 5z = 0$ **2.** $5x^2 = 2 - 9x$

Solve by using the square root property.

3. $x^2 - 5 = 0$ **4.** $(k - 3)^2 = 49$ **5.** $(3r - 2)^2 = 35$

Solve by the quadratic formula.

6. $m^2 = 3m + 10$ **7.** $3z^2 + 2 = 7z$ **8.** $y^2 - \dfrac{5}{3}y + \dfrac{1}{3} = 0$

Solve by the most appropriate method.

9. $m^2 - 2m = 1$ **10.** $(2x - 1)^2 = 18$ **11.** $(x - 5)(3x + 2) = 0$

12. $(q - 5)(3q - 2) = 4$ **13.** $(x - 5)(x - 5) = 8$ **14.** $y^2 = 6y - 2$

15. $p^2 = 5p - 7$ **16.** $3m^2 + 1 = 2m$

Perform the indicated operations.

17. $(3 + i) + (5 - 2i) - (1 + i)$ **18.** $(4 - 3i)(6 + i)$

19. $(2 + 5i)(2 - 5i)$ **20.** $\dfrac{1 + 2i}{3 - i}$

Sketch the graph and identify the vertex of each equation.

21. $y = -(x + 3)^2$ **22.** $y = (x - 4)^2 + 1$ **23.** $y = x^2 + 6x + 7$

24. From your answer to Exercise 23, decide how many real number solutions the equation $x^2 + 6x + 7 = 0$ has.

Appendices

Appendix A Review of Decimals and Percents

1 Add and subtract decimals.

2 Multiply and divide decimals.

3 Convert percents to decimals and decimals to percents.

4 Find percentages by multiplication.

1 A **decimal** is a number written with a decimal point, such as 4.2. The operations on decimals—addition, subtraction, multiplication, and division—are explained in the next examples.

EXAMPLE 1 Add or subtract as indicated.

(a) $6.92 + 14.8 + 3.217$

Place the numbers in a column, with decimal points lined up. Then add. If you want, attach 0's to make all the numbers the same length; this is a good way to avoid errors. For example,

$$
\begin{array}{r}
6.92 \\
14.8 \\
+\ 3.217 \\
\hline
24.937
\end{array}
\qquad \text{or} \qquad
\begin{array}{r}
6.920 \\
14.800 \\
+\ 3.217 \\
\hline
24.937.
\end{array}
$$

Decimal points lined up

(b) $47.6 - 32.509$

Write the numbers in a column, attaching 0's to 47.6.

$$
\begin{array}{r}
47.6 \\
-32.509 \\
\end{array}
\qquad \text{becomes} \qquad
\begin{array}{r}
47.600 \\
-32.509 \\
\hline
15.091
\end{array}
$$

(c) $3 - .253$

$$
\begin{array}{r}
3.000 \\
-\ \ .253 \\
\hline
2.747
\end{array}
$$

2 Now we can multiply and divide decimals.

EXAMPLE 2   Multiply.

(a) 29.3×4.52

Multiply as if the numbers were whole numbers. Then, place the decimal points as shown.

$$
\begin{array}{r}
29.3 \\
\times 4.52 \\
\hline
5\ 86 \\
14\ 6\ 5 \\
117\ 2 \\
\hline
132.4\ 36
\end{array}
$$

1 decimal place
2 decimal places

3 decimal places in answer

(b) 7.003×55.8

$$
\begin{array}{r}
7.003 \\
\times\ 55.8 \\
\hline
5\ 602\ 4 \\
35\ 015 \\
350\ 15 \\
\hline
390.767\ 4
\end{array}
$$

3 decimal places
1 decimal place

4 decimal places in answer ●

EXAMPLE 3   Divide: $279.45 \div 24.3$.

Move the decimal point in 24.3 one place to the right, to get 243. Move the decimal point the same number of places in 279.45. By doing this, we make 24.3 into the whole number 243.

$$24.3\,\overline{)279.4\,5}$$

Bring the decimal point straight up and divide as with whole numbers.

$$
\begin{array}{r}
11.5 \\
243\overline{)2794.5} \\
243 \\
\hline
364 \\
243 \\
\hline
121\ 5 \\
121\ 5 \\
\hline
0
\end{array}
$$
●

3 One of the main uses of decimals comes from percent problems. The word **percent** means "per one hundred." Percent is written with the sign %. One percent means "one per one hundred," or

Percent

$$
1\% = .01 \quad \text{or} \quad 1\% = \frac{1}{100}.
$$

EXAMPLE 4   Convert.

(a) 75% to a decimal

Since $1\% = .01$,
$$75\% = 75 \cdot \mathbf{1\%} = 75 \cdot (\mathbf{.01}) = .75.$$

We also can convert 75% to a decimal using the fraction form $1\% = 1/100$.

$$75\% = 75 \cdot \mathbf{1\%} = 75 \cdot \left(\frac{1}{100}\right) = .75$$

(b) 2.63 to a percent

$$2.63 = 263 \cdot (\mathbf{.01}) = 263 \cdot \mathbf{1\%} = 263\% \quad \bullet$$

4   A part of a whole is called a **percentage**. For example, since 50% represents $50/100 = 1/2$ of a whole, 50% of 800 is half of 800, or 400. Percentages are found by multiplication, as in the next example.

EXAMPLE 5   Find the percentages.

(a) 15% of 600

The word *of* indicates multiplication here. For this reason, we can find 15% of 600 by multiplying.

$$15\% \cdot 600 = (.15) \cdot 600 = 90$$

(b) 125% of 80

$$125\% \cdot 80 = (1.25) \cdot 80 = 100 \quad \bullet$$

APPENDIX A   EXERCISES

Perform the indicated operations. See Examples 1–3.

1. $14.23 + 9.81 + 74.63 + 18.715$ **2.** $89.416 + 21.32 + 478.91 + 298.213$

3. $19.74 - 6.53$ **4.** $27.96 - 8.39$

5.	**6.**	**7.**	**8.**
48.96	9.71	8.6	27.8
37.421	4.8	-3.751	-13.582
$+\ 9.72$	3.6		
	5.2		
	$+8.17$		

9. $39.6 \cdot (4.2)$ **10.** $18.7 \cdot (2.3)$ **11.** $.042 \cdot (3.2)$ **12.** $.571 \cdot (2.9)$

13. $7.6266 \div 3.42$ **14.** $14.9202 \div 2.43$ **15.** $2.496 \div .52$ **16.** $3.57 \div .034$

Convert the following percents to decimals. See Example 4(a).

17. 53%   **18.** 38%   **19.** 129%   **20.** .1%

Convert the following decimals to percents. See Example 4(b).

21. .8   **22.** .75   **23.** .007   **24.** 1.4

Find each of the following percentages. See Example 5.

25. 14% of 780   **26.** 20% of 1500   **27.** 5% of 80   **28.** 125% of 2000
29. 400% of 3200   **30.** 118% of 125.8

Solve the word problems.

31. A retailer has $23,000 invested in her business. She finds that she is earning 12% per year on this investment. How much money is she earning per year?

32. Harley Dabler recently bought a duplex for $144,000. He expects to earn 16% per year on the purchase price. How many dollars per year will he earn?

33. For a recent tour of the eastern United States, a travel agent figured that the trip totaled 2300 miles, with 35% of the trip by air. How many miles of the trip were by air?

34. Capitol Savings Bank pays 8.9% interest per year. What is the annual interest on an account of $3000?

35. An ad for steel-belted radial tires promises 15% better mileage when the tires are used. Alexandria's Escort now goes 420 miles on a tank of gas. If she switched to the new tires, how many extra miles could she drive on a tank of gas?

36. A home worth $77,000 is located in an area where home prices are increasing at a rate of 12% per year. By how much would the value of this home increase in one year?

Appendix B Sets

■ List the elements of a set.
② Learn the vocabulary and symbols used to discuss sets.
③ Decide whether a given set is a subset of another set.
④ Find the union and the intersection of two sets.

■   A **set** is a collection of things. The objects in a set are called the **elements** of the set. A set is represented by listing its elements between **set braces,** { }. The order in which the elements of a set are listed is unimportant.

EXAMPLE 1 Represent the following sets by listing the elements.

(a) The set of states in the United States that border on the Pacific Ocean = {California, Oregon, Washington, Hawaii, Alaska}.

(b) The set of all counting numbers less than $6 = \{1, 2, 3, 4, 5\}$.   ●

2   Capital letters are used to name sets. To state that 5 is an element of

$$S = \{1, 2, 3, 4, 5\},$$

we write $5 \in S$. The statement $6 \notin S$ means that 6 is not an element of S.

A set with no elements is called the **empty set,** or the **null set.** The symbols $\emptyset$ or $\{\ \}$ are used for the empty set. If we let A be the set of all cats that fly, then A is the empty set.

$$A = \emptyset \qquad \text{or} \qquad A = \{\ \}$$

The **universal set**, denoted U, includes all the elements under consideration. For example, if a discussion is about presidents of the United States, then the set of all presidents of the United States is the universal set.

Two sets are **equal** if they have exactly the same elements. Thus, the set of natural numbers and the set of positive integers are equal sets. Also, the sets

$$\{1, 2, 4, 7\} \qquad \text{and} \qquad \{4, 2, 7, 1\}$$

are equal. The order of the elements does not make a difference.

3   If all the elements of a set A are also elements of some set B, then we say that A is a **subset** of B, written $A \subset B$. We use the symbol $A \not\subset B$ to mean that A is not a subset of B.

EXAMPLE 2 Let $A = \{1, 2, 3, 4\}$, $B = \{1, 4\}$, and $C = \{1\}$. Then $B \subset A$, $C \subset A$, and $C \subset B$, but $A \not\subset B$, $A \not\subset C$, and $B \not\subset C$.   ●

4   The **union** of two sets A and B, written $A \cup B$, is the set of all elements of A together with all elements of B. For example, if set $A = \{a, b, c\}$ and set $B = \{a, d, f, g\}$,

$$A \cup B = \{a, b, c, d, f, g\}.$$

EXAMPLE 3 If $M = \{2, 5, 7\}$ and $N = \{1, 2, 3, 4, 5\}$, then $M \cup N = \{1, 2, 3, 4, 5, 7\}$.   ●

The **intersection** of two sets A and B, written $A \cap B$, is the set of all elements that belong to both A and B. For example, if

$$A = \{\text{Jose, Ellen, Marge, Kevin}\}$$

and

$$B = \{\text{Jose, Patrick, Ellen, Sue}\},$$

then

$$A \cap B = \{\text{Jose, Ellen}\}.$$

EXAMPLE 4   Suppose that $P = \{3, 9, 27\}$, $Q = \{2, 3, 10, 18, 27, 28\}$, and $R = \{2, 10, 28\}$.

(a) $P \cap Q = \{3, 27\}$ (b) $Q \cap R = \{2, 10, 28\} = R$

(c) $P \cap R = \emptyset$ ●

A pair of sets like P and R in Example 4 that have no elements in common are called **disjoint sets.**

APPENDIX B EXERCISES

List the elements of each of the following sets. See Example 1.

1. The set of all natural numbers less than 8
2. The set of all integers between 4 and 10
3. The set of seasons
4. The set of months of the year
5. The set of women presidents of the United States
6. The set of all living humans more than 200 years old

Tell whether each of the following is true or false.

7. $5 \in \{1, 2, 5, 8\}$
8. $6 \in \{1, 2, 3, 4, 5\}$
9. $7 \notin \{2, 4, 6, 8\}$
10. $7 \notin \{1, 3, 5, 7\}$
11. $\{2, 4, 9, 12, 13\} = \{13, 12, 9, 4, 2\}$
12. $\{7, 11, 4\} = \{7, 11, 4, 0\}$

Let $A = \{1, 3, 4, 5, 7, 8\}$, $B = \{2, 4, 6, 8\}$, $C = \{1, 3, 5, 7\}$, $D = \{1, 2, 3\}$, $E = \{3, 7\}$, and $U = \{1, 2, 3, 4, 5, 6, 7, 8, 9, 10\}$. Tell whether each of the following is true or false. See Examples 2–4.

13. $D \subset B$ **14.** $E \subset C$ **15.** $D \not\subseteq E$ **16.** $E \not\subseteq A$
17. $\{3, 1, 0\} \cap \{0, 2, 4\} = \{0\}$ **18.** $\{3, 9, 12\} \cup \emptyset = \emptyset$
19. $\{1, 2, 3\} \cup \{1, 2, 3\} = \{1, 2, 3\}$ **20.** $\{3, 5, 7, 9\} \cup \{4, 6, 8\} = \emptyset$

Let $U = \{a, b, c, d, e, f, g, h\}$, $A = \{a, b, c, d, e, f\}$, $B = \{a, c, e\}$, $C = \{a, f\}$, $D = \{d\}$. List the elements in the following sets. See Examples 3 and 4.

21. $A \cap B$ **22.** $B \cap D$ **23.** $B \cap C$ **24.** $A \cup B$
25. $B \cup D$ **26.** $B \cup C$ **27.** $A \cap \emptyset$ **28.** $B \cup \emptyset$

Appendix C The Metric System

The basic units used in the metric system are listed in the following table.

Basic unit	*Used for*
meter	length
gram	weight
liter	volume

Prefixes are used with the basic units to indicate larger or smaller measures. The most common prefixes are listed below.

Prefix	Definition	Example
milli-	1/1000	1 millimeter = 1/1000 meter
centi-	1/100	1 centiliter = 1/100 liter
deci-	1/10	1 decigram = 1/10 gram
kilo-	1000	1 kilogram = 1000 grams

Eventually, people will think in the metric system as easily as they now think in the English system. To help you "think metric," get in the habit of estimating in the metric system. As an aid, use the *approximate* conversion table shown below.

METRIC TO ENGLISH   **ENGLISH TO METRIC**

From	to	Multiply by	From	to	Multiply by
meters	yards	1.094	yards	meters	.9144
meters	feet	3.281	feet	meters	.3048
meters	inches	39.37	inches	meters	.0254
kilometers	miles	.6214	miles	kilometers	1.6093
grams	pounds	.00220	pounds	grams	454
kilograms	pounds	2.20	pounds	kilograms	.454
liters	quarts	1.057	quarts	liters	.946
liters	gallons	.264	gallons	liters	3.785

Answers to Selected Exercises

> If you need further help with algebra, you might want to get a copy of the *Study Guide* and *Student Solutions Manual* designed to go along with this book. Your local college bookstore either has these books or can order them for you.

CHAPTER 1

1. $\frac{1}{2}$ **3.** $\frac{5}{6}$ **5.** $\frac{8}{9}$ **7.** $\frac{2}{3}$ **9.** $\frac{2}{3}$ **11.** $\frac{5}{6}$ **13.** $\frac{9}{20}$ **15.** $\frac{3}{25}$

17. $\frac{6}{5}$ or $1\frac{1}{5}$ **19.** $\frac{3}{10}$ **21.** $\frac{1}{9}$ **23.** $\frac{3}{20}$ **25.** $\frac{7}{18}$ **27.** $\frac{13}{6}$ or $2\frac{1}{6}$ **29.** 8

31. $\frac{2}{3}$ **33.** $\frac{1}{2}$ **35.** $\frac{4}{5}$ **37.** $\frac{10}{9}$ or $1\frac{1}{9}$ **39.** $\frac{19}{22}$ **41.** $\frac{1}{15}$ **43.** $\frac{8}{15}$

45. $3\frac{3}{8}$ **47.** $\frac{49}{6}$ or $8\frac{1}{6}$ **49.** $1\frac{5}{12}$ **51.** $\frac{49}{30}$ or $1\frac{19}{30}$ **53.** $\frac{13}{28}$ **55.** $\frac{5}{24}$

57. $\frac{17}{24}$ of the debt   **59.** $14\frac{7}{16}$ tons   **61.** $8\frac{23}{24}$ hours   **63.** 36 yards

Section 1.2   (page 8)

1. $<$ **3.** $<$ **5.** $>$ **7.** $<$ **9.** $<$ **11.** $>$ **13.** $\leq$ **15.** $\geq$ **17.** $\leq$
19. $\leq$ **21.** $<$, $\leq$ **23.** $\geq$, $>$ **25.** $\leq$, $\geq$ **27.** $\geq$, $>$ **29.** $>$, $\geq$
31. $<$, $\leq$ **33.** $<$, $\leq$ **35.** $<$, $\leq$ **37.** $7 = 5 + 2$ **39.** $3 < \frac{50}{5}$
41. $12 \neq 5$ **43.** $0 \geq 0$ **45.** True   **47.** True   **49.** True   **51.** True
53. True   **55.** False   **57.** False   **59.** False   **61.** False   **63.** True
65. $14 > 6$ **67.** $3 \leq 15$ **69.** $8 < 9$ **71.** $6 \geq 0$ **73.** $15 \leq 18$ **75.** $.439 \leq .481$

Section 1.3   (page 13)

1. 1, 2, 3, 5, 6, 10, 15, 30   **3.** 1, 2, 5, 10, 25, 50   **5.** 1, 5, 13, 65   **7.** 1, 2, 4, 5, 10, 20, 25, 50, 100   **9.** 1, 17   **11.** 1, 29   **13.** 36   **15.** 64   **17.** 289   **19.** 125
21. 1296   **23.** 32   **25.** 729   **27.** 1/4   **29.** 8/125   **31.** 64/125   **33.** .475
35. 3.112   **37.** $16 \leq 16$; true   **39.** $0 \leq 0$; true   **41.** $61 \leq 60$; false   **43.** $0 \leq 0$; true
45. $60 \leq 0$; false   **47.** $65 > 60$; true   **49.** $46 \leq 45$; false   **51.** $66 > 72$; false   **53.** $2 \geq 3$; false   **55.** $20/6 > 4$ or $10/3 > 4$; false   **57.** $3 \leq 3$; true   **59.** $66 \geq 63$; true   **61.** $29 \geq 30$; false   **63.** $21.912 \geq 21.92$; false   **65.** $10 - (7 - 3) = 6$ **67.** No parentheses needed, or $(3 \cdot 5) + 7 = 22$ **69.** $3 \cdot (5 - 4) = 3$ **71.** No parentheses needed, or $(3 \cdot 5) + (2 \cdot 4) = 23$
73. $(3 \cdot 5 + 2) \cdot 4 = 68$ **75.** No parentheses needed, or $(3 \cdot 5) - (2 \cdot 4) = 7$ **77.** No parentheses needed, or $(100 \div 20) \div 5 = 1$ **79.** $100 \div (20 \div 5) = 25$ **81.** $(2^2 + 4) \cdot 2 = 16$
83. $(3^3 - 2) \cdot 4 = 100$ **85.** $(6^2 - 2) \cdot 5 = 170$ **87.** $(5 \cdot 52) - 4 = 256$

Section 1.4   (page 18)

1. (a) 12   (b) 24   **3.** (a) 15   (b) 75   **5.** (a) 14   (b) 38   **7.** (a) 4/3   (b) 16/3   **9.** (a) 2/3   (b) 4/3   **11.** (a) 30   (b) 690   **13.** (a) 19.377   (b) 96.885   **15.** (a) .8195   (b) 16.9115   **17.** (a) 43   (b) 28   **19.** (a) 24   (b) 33   **21.** (a) 6   (b) 9/5   **23.** (a) 23/6   (b) 4/3   **25.** (a) 150   (b) 195   **27.** (a) 2   (b) 17/7   **29.** (a) 5/6   (b) 16/27   **31.** (a) 28   (b) 55   **33.** (a) 10/3   (b) 13/3   **35.** (a) 14.736   (b) 8.841   **37.** $8x$ **39.** $5x$ **41.** $4 + x$ **43.** $x - 9$ **45.** $5x - 6$ **47.** Yes   **49.** No   **51.** Yes   **53.** Yes   **55.** Yes   **57.** Yes   **59.** No   **61.** $x + 8 = 12$; 4   **63.** $x + 2 = 10$; 8   **65.** $2x + 5 = 13$; 4

67. $3x = 2 + 2x$; 2   **69.** $\dfrac{20}{5x} = 2$; 2

Section 1.5   (page 24)

1. -8 **3.** 9   **5.** 2   **7.** -15 **9.** -8 **11.** -12 **13.** -12 **15.** -8 **17.** 3   **19.** $|-3|$ or 3   **21.** $-|-6|$ or -6 **23.** $|5 - 3|$ or 2   **25.** True   **27.** True   **29.** False   **31.** True   **33.** True   **35.** True   **37.** True   **39.** True   **41.** True   **43.** False   **45.** True   **47.** False   **49.** (a) 0, 3, 7   (b) -9, 0, 3, 7   (c) -9, $-1\,1/4$, $-3/5$, 0, 3, 5.9, 7   (d) $-\sqrt{7}$, $\sqrt{5}$ (e) all the numbers are real numbers   **51.**

53.
55.
57.

Many answers are possible in Exercises 59–63. We give three possible answers for each.   **59.** 1/2, 5/8, 1 3/4   **61.** $-3\,1/2$, $-2/3$, 3/7   **63.** $\sqrt{5}$, π, $-\sqrt{3}$ **65.** True   **67.** False   **69.** False (0 is a whole number, but not positive)   **71.** True   **73.** False

Section 1.6   (page 28)

1. 2   **3.** -2 **5.** -8 **7.** -12 **9.** 4   **11.** 12   **13.** 5   **15.** 2   **17.** -9 **19.** -11 **21.** 1/2   **23.** $-19/24$ **25.** $-3/4$ **27.** -7.7 **29.** -8 **31.** 0   **33.** -20 **35.** 1.7125   **37.** False   **39.** True   **41.** False   **43.** True   **45.** True   **47.** False   **49.** True   **51.** True   **53.** -3 **55.** -2 **57.** -2 **59.** 2   **61.** $-9 + 2 + 6 = -1$ **63.** $12 + [-17 + (-6)] = -11$ **65.** $[-11 + (-4)] + (-5) = -20$ **67.** \$9   **69.** -135, or 135 feet below sea level   **71.** 90   **73.** 13°   **75.** \$943.72   **77.** 17   **79.** -16

Section 1.7   (page 31)

1. -3 **3.** -4 **5.** -8 **7.** -14 **9.** 9   **11.** 17   **13.** -4 **15.** 4   **17.** 1   **19.** 3/4   **21.** $-11/8$ **23.** 15/8   **25.** 11.6   **27.** -9.9 **29.** -1.72448 **31.** 3.6863   **33.** 10   **35.** -5 **37.** 11   **39.** -10 **41.** -18 **43.** 2   **45.** -16 **47.** -12 **49.** -5.90617 **51.** -41.4616 **53.** 18   **55.** -21 **57.** 3   **59.** 1.1   **61.** $8 - (-2) = 10$ **63.** $-11 + (-4 - 2) = -17$ **65.** $[-12 + (-3)] - 4 = -19$ **67.** $-15°$ **69.** 14,776 feet   **71.** $-172.3°$ **73.** \$105,000

Section 1.8   (page 36)

1. 12   **3.** -12 **5.** 120   **7.** -48 **9.** 0   **11.** 0   **13.** -165 **15.** 5/12   **17.** $-1/6$ **19.** 6   **21.** $-.102$ **23.** -12.96 **25.** -11.9 **27.** -52.752 (rounded)   **29.** 42.100 (rounded)   **31.** -14 **33.** -3 **35.** -36 **37.** 12   **39.** 5   **41.** 12   **43.** 18   **45.** -14 **47.** -10 **49.** 45   **51.** 12   **53.** 16   **55.** -28 **57.** 12   **59.** -360 **61.** 0   **63.** -30 **65.** 44   **67.** -2 **69.** 0   **71.** -3 **73.** -2 **75.** -1 **77.** $4(-7) + (-9) = -37$ **79.** $-4 - 2(-8)(2) = 28$ **81.** $-2(3) - 3 = -9$

Section 1.9 (page 40)

1. 1/9 **3.** −1/4 **5.** 3/2 **7.** −10/9 **9.** No multiplicative inverse for 0
11. 1.150 **13.** −2 **15.** −3 **17.** −6 **19.** 15 **21.** 36 **23.** 0
25. 2/3 **27.** 2.1 **29.** −5 **31.** −4 **33.** −10 **35.** −4 **37.** −60
39. 2 **41.** 50.58 **43.** 4 **45.** 3 **47.** −3 **49.** 8 **51.** −1 **53.** 52/75
55. 1 **57.** .039 **59.** −2 **61.** 4 **63.** 0 **65.** −2 **67.** $4x = -32$; −8

69. $\dfrac{x}{-3} = -4$; 12 **71.** $\dfrac{x}{5} = -2$; −10 **73.** $\dfrac{x^2}{3} = 12$; 6 or −6 **75.** $4 + \dfrac{(-28)}{4} = -3$

77. $\dfrac{-16}{4} - 3 = -7$

Section 1.10 (page 46)

1. Commutative **3.** Associative **5.** Commutative **7.** Commutative
9. Commutative **11.** Inverse **13.** Identity **15.** Inverse **17.** Identity
19. Distributive **21.** $k + 9$ **23.** m **25.** $3r + 3m$ **27.** 1 **29.** 0 **31.** $-5 + 5$,
or 0 **33.** $-3r - 6$ **35.** 9 **37.** $k + [5 + (-6)] = k - 1$ **39.** $4z + (2r + 3k)$
41. $5m + 10$ **43.** $-4r - 8$ **45.** $-8k + 16$ **47.** $-9a - 27$ **49.** $4r + 32$
51. $-16 + 2k$ **53.** $10r + 12m$ **55.** $-12x + 16y$ **57.** $5(8 + 9) = 5(17) = 85$
59. $7(2 + 8) = 7(10) = 70$ **61.** $9(p + q)$ **63.** $5(7z + 8w)$ **65.** $-3k - 5$
67. $-4y + 8$ **69.** $4 - p$ **71.** $1 + 15r$ **73.** No **75.** Yes **77.** It is not

Chapter 1 Review Exercises (page 48)

1. 1/3 **3.** 1/5 **5.** 7/50 **7.** 3/4 **9.** 7/8 **11.** 8 1/6 **13.** 7/12 **15.** >
17. < **19.** 64 **21.** 25/64 **23.** 68 > 70; false **25.** 8/9 < 1; true **27.** 41 ≤ 40; false
29. 2/3 **31.** 137/3 **33.** $4 - x$ **35.** $x(x + 1)$ **37.** $|-7|$ or 7 **39.** $-|-7|$ or −7
41. False **43.** True **45.** False **47.** False **49.**

$$\begin{array}{ccccccc} -2\frac{4}{5} & -1\frac{1}{8} & & \frac{2}{3} & & 3\frac{1}{4} \\ \hline -4 & -2 & 0 & 2 & 4 \end{array}$$

51. −13 **53.** 23/40 **55.** 5.6 **57.** −15 **59.** −$2 **61.** $21,000
63. 18 **65.** 17/12 **67.** 0 **69.** −6 **71.** 8/7 **73.** −28.25 **75.** −60
77. 65 **79.** −38 **81.** −378 **83.** 1/10 **85.** −1 **87.** 2 **89.** Identity
91. Commutative **93.** Inverse **95.** $18k + 30r$

Chapter 1 Test (page 50)

1. 7/11 **2.** 203/120 **3.** 18/19 **4.** False **5.** True **6.** True **7.** False
8. False **9.** 46 **10.** 124/5 **11.** $-|-8|$ or −8 **12.** .705 **13.** $11 - 2x$
14. $\dfrac{9}{x - 8}$ **15.** Yes **16.** No **17.** −7 **18.** 3 1/20 **19.** 0 **20.** −1
21. −14 **22.** 3 **23.** 4 **24.** Meaningless **25.** −9 **26.** −4 **27.** −3
28. A, E **29.** H **30.** C, I **31.** B, G **32.** D, F **33.** $-3 + 4m$

CHAPTER 2

Section 2.1 (page 54)

1. 15 **3.** −22 **5.** 35 **7.** −9 **9.** 1 **11.** −1 **13.** Like terms **15.** Unlike
terms **17.** Like terms **19.** Like terms **21.** Like terms **23.** Unlike terms
25. $17y$ **27.** $-6a$ **29.** $13b$ **31.** $7k + 15$ **33.** $m - 1$ **35.** $-4y$
37. $2x + 6$ **39.** $14 - 7m$ **41.** $z + 38$ **43.** $-17 + x$ **45.** $23x$ **47.** $9y^2$
49. $-14p^3 + 5p^2$ **51.** $-2.844q^2 - 5.32q - 18.7$ **53.** $30t + 66$ **55.** $-3n - 15$
57. $4r + 15$ **59.** $12k - 5$ **61.** $-2k - 3$ **63.** $-.148y - 20.7872$ **65.** $2 - x$
67. $10x$ **69.** $-32 - 47x$ **71.** −6 **73.** 4 **75.** Add 7 **77.** Add −6

Section 2.2 (page 59)

1. 10　　**3.** −2　　**5.** 10　　**7.** −8　　**9.** −5　　**11.** −2　　**13.** 4　　**15.** −5
17. −11　　**19.** −6　　**21.** 1/2　　**23.** −5　　**25.** −2　　**27.** 7/6　　**29.** −5　　**31.** 7
33. 8　　**35.** −10　　**37.** −9　　**39.** 0　　**41.** 3　　**43.** −2　　**45.** −1　　**47.** −2
49. 17　　**51.** 18　　**53.** 26　　**55.** $3x = 17 + 2x$; 17　　**57.** $5x + 3x = 7x + 9$; 9
59. $6(2x + 5) = 13x − 8$; 38　　**61.** m　　**63.** y　　**65.** q　　**67.** r

Section 2.3 (page 64)

1. 5　　**3.** 25　　**5.** −8　　**7.** −7　　**9.** −4　　**11.** −9　　**13.** 0　　**15.** −6
17. 4　　**19.** 4　　**21.** 8　　**23.** 20　　**25.** −3　　**27.** 4　　**29.** −3　　**31.** 7
33. 32　　**35.** 49　　**37.** 9　　**39.** 8　　**41.** −80　　**43.** 15/2　　**45.** 49/2　　**47.** 3

49. −6　　**51.** .7　　**53.** −1.1　　**55.** −5.7　　**57.** $\dfrac{x}{4} = 6$; 24　　**59.** $\dfrac{x}{4} = 62$; \$248

61. $\dfrac{2x}{1.74} = -8.38$; −7.2906　　**63.** $18q + 63$　　**65.** $-20p + 10$　　**67.** $-2 + 11r$
69. $-3 − 12a$

Section 2.4 (page 70)

1. 2　　**3.** 24　　**5.** 9　　**7.** −2　　**9.** −1　　**11.** −4　　**13.** −12.5　　**15.** 2
17. −1.5　　**19.** −3　　**21.** −3　　**23.** 8　　**25.** −2　　**27.** 6　　**29.** −5　　**31.** 0
33. 4　　**35.** 0　　**37.** −1/5　　**39.** −5/7　　**41.** 1.4　　**43.** −5.2　　**45.** 1.6
47. $8 + x$　　**49.** $-1 + x$　　**51.** $x + (−18)$　　**53.** $x − 5$　　**55.** $x − 9$　　**57.** $9x$

59. $3x$　　**61.** $\dfrac{x}{6}$　　**63.** $\dfrac{x}{-4}$　　**65.** $8(x + 3)$　　**67.** $\dfrac{1}{x} − x$　　**69.** $8(x − 8)$

71. $11 − q$　　**73.** $x + 7$　　**75.** $a + 12$　　**77.** $\dfrac{t}{5}$　　**79.** $n + 2$

Section 2.5 (page 76)

1. 60　　**3.** 4　　**5.** 8　　**7.** 14　　**9.** 10　　**11.** 21　　**13.** 1.5　　**15.** 254.34

17. 113.04　　**19.** 2　　**21.** 3　　**23.** 7　　**25.** 1　　**27.** $L = \dfrac{A}{W}$　　**29.** $H = \dfrac{V}{LW}$

31. $r = \dfrac{C}{2\pi}$　　**33.** $W = \dfrac{1}{2}(P − 2L)$ or $W = \dfrac{P − 2L}{2}$　　**35.** $b = \dfrac{2A}{h} − B$

37. $h = \dfrac{S − 2\pi r^2}{2\pi r}$　　**39.** $r^2 = \dfrac{A}{4\pi}$　　**41.** $r^2 = \dfrac{3V}{\pi h}$　　**43.** 20 cm　　**45.** 10 in

47. 108 square cm　　**49.** 7 cm　　**51.** Let x be the number; $4(x + 3) = 36$; 6　　**53.** Let x be the
number; $2x + x = 90$; 30　　**55.** Let x be the number; $x − 6 = 7x$; −1　　**57.** 19 in
59. 48 points　　**61.** 36 prescriptions　　**63.** 613 gallons　　**65.** 10　　**67.** 15　　**69.** 36 quart
cartons　　**71.** 2　　**73.** 8/3　　**75.** −15/7　　**77.** −20

Section 2.6 (page 83)

1. 3/2　　**3.** 36/55　　**5.** 2/5　　**7.** 5/8　　**9.** 1/10　　**11.** 8/5　　**13.** 1/6
15. 4/15　　**17.** True　　**19.** True　　**21.** False　　**23.** True　　**25.** False　　**27.** True
29. True　　**31.** False　　**33.** 175　　**35.** 4　　**37.** 16　　**39.** 14/3　　**41.** 25/3
43. 35/8　　**45.** 15/2　　**47.** 7/15　　**49.** −31　　**51.** −11　　**53.** 2 1/2 bars
55. 9 pounds　　**57.** 9 inches　　**59.** \$67.50　　**61.** 420 miles　　**63.** \$144　　**65.** 40 miles per
hour　　**67.** 2 1/2 years

Section 2.7 (page 88)

1. 4   **3.** 3   **5.** 16   **7.** 2 1/2 cm   **9.** 25 fives   **11.** 18 of the 16¢

13. 42 tens   **15.** $12,000 at 16%   **17.** $15,000 at 14%   **19.** $8000 at 16%

21. 2 hours   **23.** 2 1/2 hours   **25.** 3 hours   **27.** 160 gallons   **29.** 160 kilograms

31. 20 pounds   **33.** 3 days   **35.** 25 miles per hour   **37.** $<$ **39.** $<$ **41.** $>$ **43.** $>$

Section 2.8 (page 96)

1.   **3.**   **5.**

7.   **9.** $a < 2$ **11.** $z \geq 1$ **13.** $p \leq 12$ **15.** $k \geq 5$

17. $x \leq 0$ **19.** $x < 6$ **21.** $n \leq -11$ **23.** $z > 5$

25. $y < 5$ **27.** $k \geq 44$ **29.** $k > -21$

31. $6 \leq p \leq 13$ **33.** $5 < y < 12$ **35.** $-21 \leq p \leq -13$

37. Let x be the number; $4x + 8 < 3x + 5$; $x < -3$ **39.** Let x be the width; $2x - x \leq 7$; 7 meters

41. Let x be the width; $4x - 3x \geq 15$; 15, 60   **43.** True; false   **45.** True; false   **47.** True; false   **49.** True; false

Section 2.9 (page 102)

1. $x < 9$ **3.** $r \geq -3$ **5.** $k \geq -6$

7. $y < -9$ **9.** $m < 7$ **11.** $r > \dfrac{8}{3}$

13. $k \geq -5$ **15.** $r < 10$ **17.** $q > -2$

19. $p > -5$ **21.** $k \leq 0$ **23.** $x < -11$

25. $r \geq -1$ **27.** $p \leq \dfrac{8}{3}$ **29.** $-1 \leq x \leq 6$

31. $1 < m < \dfrac{13}{6}$ **33.** $0 \leq q \leq \dfrac{17}{5}$ **35.** $-26 \leq z \leq 6$

37. $-3 \leq p \leq 6$ **39.** $-\dfrac{24}{5} \leq r \leq 0$

41. 83 or more   **43.** Any number greater than 11/5   **45.** 38 meters   **47.** $1100   **49.** All numbers greater than or equal to -16 **51.** 30 meters   **53.** 32   **55.** 625   **57.** 8/27
59. 128   **61.** 3   **63.** 5   **65.** 13   **67.** 3

Chapter 2   Review Exercises   (page 104)

1. $11m$ **3.** $16p^2 + 2p$ **5.** $-2m + 29$ **7.** 6   **9.** 7   **11.** 11   **13.** 5
15. 5   **17.** 64/5   **19.** -6 **21.** $-9/2$ **23.** 6   **25.** 19   **27.** 18 miles

29. 11   **31.** 2   **33.** $W = \dfrac{A}{L}$ **35.** $a = P - b - c$ **37.** 5 meters   **39.** 5/3

41. 3/4   **43.** True   **45.** False   **47.** 3.5 or 3 1/2   **49.** 7   **51.** 8 quarts
53. 3   **55.** 10 fives   **57.** $10,000 at 5%, $16,000 at 10%   **59.** 24 liters

61.   **63.**   **65.** $y \geq -3$

67. $k \geq 53$ **69.** $-8 \leq x \leq -2$ **71.** $k \geq -3$ **73.** $z < 4$ **75.** $p < -5$
77. $-2 \leq m \leq 3/2$ **79.** 50 meters

Chapter 2   Test   (page 107)

1. $-r$ **2.** 4   **3.** $4m + 6$ **4.** -5 **5.** 0   **6.** $-12/5$ **7.** 5/6   **8.** 3

9. -4 **10.** $100   **11.** $p = \dfrac{I}{rt}$ **12.** $h = \dfrac{2A}{b + B}$ **13.** True   **14.** 1

15. $-22/3$ **16.** $17.60   **17.** 20 tens   **18.** 3 hours   **19.** $11,000 at 12%
20. 10 liters   **21.** $m > 7$ **22.** $k \leq 1$

23. $r \leq 4$ **24.** $-2 < k \leq 14/3$

CHAPTER 3

Section 3.1   (page 113)

1. Base 5, exponent 12   **3.** Base 2, exponent 4   **5.** Base -24, exponent 2   **7.** Base r, exponent 5   **9.** 3^5 **11.** $(-2)^5$ **13.** $1/(-2)^3$ **15.** p^5 **17.** $1/y^4$ **19.** $(-2z)^3$
21. 90   **23.** 80   **25.** 36   **27.** 2   **29.** 2   **31.** 1/27   **33.** $-1/12$ **35.** 32
37. 2   **39.** 27/8   **41.** 5/6   **43.** 9/20   **45.** 1.041   **47.** .017   **49.** 4^5
51. $1/3^3$ **53.** $1/4^2$ **55.** $(-3)^5$ **57.** y^{14} **59.** r^{17} **61.** $1/k$ **63.** $10p^{13}$
65. $-63r^3$ **67.** 4^5 **69.** $1/8^6$ **71.** $1/6^6$ **73.** 14^3 **75.** x^{15} **77.** z^2
79. 2^5 **81.** $a^2/3^3$ **83.** $4^2k^4m^8$ **85.** $13m^3$; $36m^6$ **87.** $-p$; $-132p^2$ **89.** $15r$; $105r^3$ **91.** $-2a^{-2}$ or $-2/a^2$; $-15a^{-4}$ or $-15/a^4$ **93.** (a) -3 (b) -28 **95.** (a) -8 (b) 32

Section 3.2   (page 117)

1. 6^6 **3.** $1/9^6$ **5.** 3^{10} **7.** y^5 **9.** a^3 **11.** $1/k^4$ **13.** $1/4^9$ **15.** $1/5^9$
17. m^5 **19.** $1/a$ **21.** $1/r$ **23.** a^7 **25.** 5^3m^3 or $125m^3$ **27.** $(-2)^4p^4q^4$ or $16p^4q^4$ **29.** $(-3)^2x^{10}$ or $9x^{10}$ **31.** $5^3a^6b^3$ or $125a^6b^3$ **33.** $3^2/x^{10}$ or $9/x^{10}$ **35.** $9^2/y^{10}$ or $81/y^{10}$ **37.** $a^3/5^3$ or $a^3/125$ **39.** $3^5m^5n^5/2^5$ **41.** b/a **43.** $5^2/m^2$ or $25/m^2$

45. x^5 **47.** $1/b^2$ **49.** $\dfrac{125}{27x^2}$ **51.** $\dfrac{a^{11}}{2b^5}$ **53.** $\dfrac{108}{y^5z^3}$ **55.** $\dfrac{9z^2}{400x^3}$

57. 5^{6r} **59.** x^{-11a} or $1/x^{11a}$ **61.** a^{4y} **63.** q^{5k} **65.** $6^{-y} \cdot p^{3y}$ or $\dfrac{p^{3y}}{6^y}$ **67.** $3^{-q} \cdot m^{2q}/p^q$ or $\dfrac{m^{2q}}{3^q \cdot p^q}$ **69.** 100   **71.** 100,000   **73.** .1   **75.** .0001

Section 3.3 (page 121)

1. 6.835×10^9 **3.** 8.36×10^{12} **5.** 2.15×10^2 **7.** 2.5×10^4 **9.** 3.5×10^{-2}
11. 1.01×10^{-2} **13.** 1.2×10^{-5} **15.** $8,100,000,000$ **17.** $9,132,000$
19. $324,000,000$ **21.** $.00032$ **23.** $.041$ **25.** $800,000$ **27.** $.000004$ **29.** 420
31. 1440 **33.** $3,000,000$ **35.** $.2$ **37.** 1300 **39.** $.000008$ **41.** 4×10^{-4},
8×10^{-4} **43.** 3.68×10^{15} **45.** $35,000$ **47.** $1000, .06102$ **49.** $15m$ **51.** $4p$
53. $7m - 5$ **55.** -13 **57.** -48

Section 3.4 (page 127)

1. $-r^5$ **3.** x^5 **5.** $-p^7$ **7.** $6y^2$ **9.** 0 **11.** $9y^4 + 7y^2$
13. $14z^5 - 9z^3 + 8z^2$ **15.** $2p^7 - 8p^6 + 5p^4 - 9p$ **17.** $1.171q^2 + 1.401q - .252$ **19.** Already
simplified; degree 4; binomial   **21.** Already simplified; degree 9; trinomial   **23.** Already simplified;
degree 8; trinomial   **25.** Simplifies to x^5; degree 5; monomial   **27.** Already simplified; degree 9;
binomial   **29.** Sometimes   **31.** Never   **33.** Sometimes   **35.** (a) 38   (b) -1
37. (a) 19   (b) -2 **39.** (a) -5 (b) 1   **41.** (a) -20 (b) 7   **43.** $5m^2 + 3m$
45. $4x^4 - 4x^2$ **47.** $-n^5 - 12n^3 - 2$ **49.** $12m^3 + m^2 + 12m - 14$ **51.** $15m^2 - 3m + 4$
53. $8b^2 + 2b + 7$ **55.** $-2r^2 + 7r - 6$ **57.** $-2x^2 - x + 1$ **59.** $4x^3 + 2x^2 + 5x$
61. $-11y^4 + 8y^2 + 3y$ **63.** $5m^2 + 8m - 10$ **65.** $3.386m^2 - 12.273m + 4.953$
67. $(4 + x^2) + (-9x + 2) > 8$ **69.** $(5 + x^2) + (3 - 2x) \neq 5$ **71.** $2p^2$ **73.** $10x^3$
75. $56m^5$ **77.** $30p^9$

Section 3.5 (page 131)

1. $-32x^7$ **3.** $15y^{11}$ **5.** $30a^9$ **7.** $15pq^2$ **9.** $-18m^3n^2$ **11.** $6m^2 + 4m$
13. $-6p^4 + 12p^3$ **15.** $-16z^2 - 24z^3 - 24z^4$ **17.** $6y^3 + 4y^4 + 10y^7$
19. $28r^5 - 32r^4 + 36r^3$ **21.** $6a^4 - 12a^3b + 15a^2b^2$ **23.** $21m^5n^2 + 14m^4n^3 - 7m^3n^5$
25. $m^2 + 12m + 35$ **27.** $x^2 - 25$ **29.** $3r^2 - 13r + 4$ **31.** $6p^2 - p - 5$
33. $16m^2 + 24m + 9$ **35.** $6b^2 + 46b - 16$ **37.** $16 + 2a - 3a^2$ **39.** $-8 + 6k - k^2$
41. $2m^2 + 7mn - 15n^2$ **43.** $10r^2 - 29rs - 21s^2$ **45.** $6x^2 + 3x - 45$
47. $-24r^3 + 44r^2 + 40r$ **49.** $12x^3 + 26x^2 + 10x + 1$ **51.** $81a^3 + 27a^2 + 11a + 2$
53. $20m^4 - m^3 - 8m^2 - 17m - 15$ **55.** $6x^6 - 3x^5 - 4x^4 + 4x^3 - 5x^2 + 8x - 3$
57. $5x^4 - 13x^3 + 20x^2 + 7x + 5$ **59.** $x^2 + 14x + 49$ **61.** $a^2 - 8a + 16$
63. $4p^2 - 20p + 25$ **65.** $25k^2 + 30kq + 9q^2$ **67.** $m^3 - 15m^2 + 75m - 125$
69. $8a^3 + 12a^2 + 6a + 1$ **71.** $k^4 + 4k^3 + 6k^2 + 4k + 1$ **73.** $27r^3 - 54r^2s + 36rs^2 - 8s^3$
75. $2, 3$ **77.** $-7, 3$ **79.** $9, -6$

Section 3.6 (page 136)

1. $r^2 + 2r - 3$ **3.** $x^2 - 10x + 21$ **5.** $6x^2 + x - 2$ **7.** $6z^2 - 13z - 15$
9. $2a^2 + 9a + 4$ **11.** $8r^2 + 2r - 3$ **13.** $6a^2 + 11a - 10$ **15.** $20 + 9x - 20x^2$
17. $-12 + 5r + 2r^2$ **19.** $15 + a - 2a^2$ **21.** $p^2 + 4pq + 3q^2$ **23.** $10y^2 - 3yz - z^2$
25. $8y^2 + 31yz - 45z^2$ **27.** $21m^2 - 23mn - 88n^2$ **29.** $28.595m^2 + 6.306m - 4.32$
31. $x^2 + 16x + 64$ **33.** $z^2 - 10z + 25$ **35.** $9m^2 - 6mp + p^2$ **37.** $64a^2 - 48ab + 9b^2$
39. $81y^2 + 18yz + z^2$ **41.** $36a^2 - 18ab + \dfrac{9}{4}b^2$ **43.** $m^2 - mq + .25q^2$
45. $.4489m^2 - .2278mk + .0289k^2$ **47.** $4b^2 - 25$ **49.** $36a^2 - p^2$ **51.** $4m^2 - \dfrac{25}{9}$
53. $49y^4 - 100z^2$ **55.** $.2304q^2 - .1369r^2$ **57.** $(a + b)^2 = 49$; $a^2 + b^2 = 29$; not equal
59. $(x + 3)^2 = 5$ **61.** $(3 + x)(x - 4) > 7$ **63.** $3y^3$ **65.** $5m^4$ **67.** $\dfrac{-4}{5z^2}$ **69.** $\dfrac{3s^6}{2r^4}$

Section 3.7 (page 139)

1. $2x$ **3.** $2a^2$ **5.** $\dfrac{9k^3}{m}$ **7.** $\dfrac{-3m^2}{p^2}$ **9.** $30m^3 - 10m$ **11.** $5m^4 - 8m + 4m^2$

13. $4m^4 - 2m^2 + 2m$ **15.** $m^4 - 2m + 4$ **17.** $m - 1 + \dfrac{5}{2m}$ **19.** $-5q^2 + 2q - 1$

21. $8q^4 - 7q^2 + \dfrac{4}{q}$ **23.** $-\dfrac{3q^3}{5} - q + \dfrac{6}{5}$ **25.** $-q^2 + \dfrac{3q}{5} - \dfrac{2}{5} + \dfrac{7}{5q}$

27. $x^2 + 3x$ **29.** $4x^2 - x + 1$ **31.** $9x - 3x^2 + 6x^3$ **33.** $\dfrac{12}{x} + 8 + x$

35. $\dfrac{x}{3} + 2 - \dfrac{1}{3x}$ **37.** $4k^3 - 6k^2 - k + \dfrac{7}{2} - \dfrac{3}{2k}$ **39.** $-10p^3 + 5p^2 - 3p + \dfrac{3}{p}$

41. $\dfrac{2}{x^3} + \dfrac{4}{x^2} + \dfrac{5}{2x}$ **43.** $4y^3 - 2 + \dfrac{3}{y}$ **45.** $\dfrac{12}{x} - \dfrac{6}{x^2} + \dfrac{14}{x^3} - \dfrac{10}{x^4}$

47. 8; 13; no   **49.** $12x^5 + 9x^4 - 12x^3 + 6x^2$ **51.** $-63y^4 - 21y^3 - 35y^2 + 14y$

53. $2x^3 - 5x^2 + x$ **55.** $-20k^4 + 12k^3 - 8k^2$ **57.** $6m^{10} - 12m^8 + 3m^7$ **59.** $5x + 2$

61. $-2x^2 - 11$ **63.** $7x^2 - 10x + 1$

Section 3.8 (page 144)

1. $x + 2$ **3.** $2y - 5$ **5.** $p - 4 + \dfrac{4}{p + 6}$ **7.** $r - 5$ **9.** $6m - 1$

11. $a - 7 + \dfrac{37}{2a + 3}$ **13.** $x + 2 + \dfrac{1}{2x + 1}$ **15.** $4r + 1 + \dfrac{10}{3r - 5}$

17. $2k + 5 + \dfrac{10}{7k - 8}$ **19.** $x^2 - x + 2$ **21.** $4k^3 - k + 2$ **23.** $3y + 1$

25. $3k - 4 + \dfrac{2}{k^2 - 2}$ **27.** $x^2 + 1 + \dfrac{-6x + 2}{x^2 - 2}$ **29.** $2p^2 - 5p + 4 + \dfrac{6}{3p^2 + 1}$

31. $m^3 - 2m^2 + 4 + \dfrac{-3}{4m^2 - 3}$ **33.** $y^2 - y + 1$ **35.** $a^2 - 1$ **37.** 1, 2, 3, 4, 6, 12

39. 1, 2, 4, 5, 10, 20   **41.** 1, 2, 5, 10, 25, 50   **43.** 1, 29   **45.** $2m^3 - 2m^2 + 2m$

47. $-3y^6 - 2y^5 + y^2$

Chapter 3   Review Exercises   (page 145)

1. 80   **3.** 1/16   **5.** 256/81   **7.** 3/4   **9.** $(-4)^8$ **11.** 6^2 **13.** 5^8 **15.** y^7

17. $r^2/6$ **19.** $72r^5$ **21.** 1.58×10^7 **23.** 9.76×10^{-5} **25.** 12,000

27. 90,000,000   **29.** .0003   **31.** $22m^2$; degree 2   **33.** Already in descending powers;

degree 5   **35.** $a^3 + 4a^2$ **37.** $-13k^4 - 15k^2 + 18k$ **39.** $-y^2 - 4y + 4$

41. $7r^4 - 4r^3$ **43.** $-8m^7 + 10m^6 - 6m^5$ **45.** $144a^2 - 1$ **47.** $a^3 - 2a^2 - 7a + 2$

49. $5p^4 + 2p^3 - 3p^2 + 25p + 15$ **51.** $6k^2 - 7k - 3$ **53.** $2a^2 + 5ab - 3b^2$

55. $a^2 + 8a + 16$ **57.** $64z^2 - 48zy + 9y^2$ **59.** $25a^2 - 36b^2$ **61.** $y^3 - 2y + 3$

63. $-2m^2 + m + 6/5$ **65.** $2r + 7$ **67.** $y^2 + 5y + 1$ **69.** $k^3 + k^2 + 4k - 8$

Chapter 3   Test   (page 146)

1. 27/64   **2.** 1/25   **3.** $1/5^6$ **4.** 8^2 **5.** $\dfrac{1}{6q}$ **6.** $\dfrac{p^{24}}{2}$

7. 3.79×10^{-4} **8.** 900   **9.** .0004   **10.** $-x^2 + 6x$; degree 2; binomial

11. $2m^4 + 11m^3 - 8m^2$; degree 4; trinomial   **12.** $-13m^3 + 7m^2 - 16m + 8$

13. $x^5 - x^2 - 2x + 12$ **14.** $3y^2 - 2y - 2$ **15.** $6m^5 + 12m^4 - 18m^3 + 42m^2$

16. $15m^2 - 37m - 66$ **17.** $14t^2 + 27ts - 20s^2$ **18.** $6k^3 - 17k^2 + 10k + 16$

19. $4k^2 + 20km + 25m^2$ **20.** $4r^2 + 2rt + \dfrac{1}{4}t^2$ **21.** $36p^4 - 25r^2$ **22.** $-5y^3 - \dfrac{8y^2}{3} + 2y$

23. $2 + \dfrac{5}{r} - \dfrac{3}{r^2} + \dfrac{8}{5r^3}$ **24.** $3x^2 + 4x + 2$ **25.** $5r^2 + 2r - 5 + \dfrac{5}{2r^2 - 3}$

CHAPTER 4

Section 4.1   (page 153)

1. 1, 2, 7, 14   **3.** 1, 3, 9, 27   **5.** 1, 3, 5, 9, 15, 45   **7.** 1, 2, 3, 4, 5, 6, 10, 12, 15, 20, 30, 60   **9.** 1, 2, 4, 5, 10, 20, 25, 50, 100   **11.** 1, 29   **13.** Composite   **15.** Prime   **17.** Composite   **19.** Composite   **21.** Prime   **23.** Composite   **25.** $2^3 \cdot 3 \cdot 5$ **27.** $2^2 \cdot 3^2 \cdot 5$ **29.** $5^2 \cdot 11$ **31.** $5^2 \cdot 19$ **33.** 12   **35.** $10p^2$ **37.** 1   **39.** $6m^2n$ **41.** $4y^3x$ **43.** x **45.** $3m^2$ **47.** $-2z^4$ **49.** xy^2 **51.** $3ab$ **53.** $-4m^2n$ **55.** $5y^5(13y^4 - 7)$ **57.** $11p^4(11p - 3)$ **59.** No common factor other than 1   **61.** $19y^2p^2(y + 2p)$ **63.** $13y^3(y^3 + 2y^2 - 3)$ **65.** $9qp^3(5q^3p^2 - 4p^3 + 9q)$ **67.** $ab^3(a^2b^2 - ab^4 + 1)$ **69.** $5z^3a^3(25z^2 - 12za^2 + 17a)$ **71.** $11y^3(3y^5 - 4y^9 + 7 + y)$ **73.** $4a^4b^2(9b + 8a - 12a^2b)$ **75.** $(a - 2)(a + 5)$ **77.** $(7z + 3m)(z + 2m)$ **79.** $(m + 3p)(5m - 2p)$ **81.** $(a^2 + b^2)(3a + 2b)$ **83.** $(1 - a)(1 - b)$ **85.** $(3 - ab)(2 + a)$ **87.** $m^2 + 7m + 12$ **89.** $r^2 - 4r - 45$ **91.** $y^2 - 12y + 32$ **93.** $a^2 - 49$

Section 4.2   (page 156)

1. $x + 3$ **3.** $r + 8$ **5.** $t - 12$ **7.** $x - 8$ **9.** $m + 6$ **11.** $p - 1$ **13.** $x - 5y$ **15.** $(x + 5)(x + 1)$ **17.** $(a + 4)(a + 5)$ **19.** $(x - 7)(x - 1)$ **21.** Prime   **23.** $(y - 4)(y - 2)$ **25.** $(s - 5)(s + 7)$ **27.** Prime   **29.** $(b - 8)(b - 3)$ **31.** $(k - 5)(k - 5)$ or $(k - 5)^2$ **33.** $(y - 15)(y + 3)$ **35.** $(x + 3a)(x + a)$ **37.** $(y + 5b)(y - 6b)$ **39.** $(x + 6y)(x - 5y)$ **41.** $(r - s)(r - s)$ or $(r - s)^2$ **43.** $(p - 5q)(p + 2q)$ **45.** $3m(m + 3)(m + 1)$ **47.** $6(a + 2)(a - 10)$ **49.** $3r(r - 4)(r - 6)$ **51.** $3x^2(x - 6)(x + 5)$ **53.** $a^3(a + 4b)(a - b)$ **55.** $yz(y + 3z)(y - 2z)$ **57.** $z^8(z - 7y)(z + 3y)$ **59.** Because $2x + 4$ has a common factor of 2   **61.** $y^2 - y - 42$ **63.** $2y^2 + y - 28$.   **65.** $15z^2 - 4z - 4$ **67.** $8p^2 - 10p - 3$

Section 4.3   (page 162)

1. $x - 1$ **3.** $b - 3$ **5.** $4y - 3$ **7.** $5x + 4$ **9.** $m + 10$ **11.** $3a - 4b$ **13.** $k + 3m$ **15.** $2x^2 - 5x - 3$; $x - 3$ **17.** $6m^2 + 7m - 20$; $2m + 5$ **19.** $(2x + 1)(x + 3)$ **21.** $(3a + 7)(a + 1)$ **23.** $(4r - 3)(r + 1)$ **25.** $(3m - 1)(5m + 2)$ **27.** $(2m - 3)(4m + 1)$ **29.** $(5a + 3)(a - 2)$ **31.** $(3r - 5)(r + 2)$ **33.** $(y + 17)(4y + 1)$ **35.** $(19x + 2)(2x + 1)$ **37.** $(2x + 3)(5x - 2)$ **39.** $(2w + 5)(3w + 2)$ **41.** $(2q + 3)(3q + 7)$ **43.** $(5m - 4)(2m - 3)$ **45.** $(4k - 5)(2k + 3)$ **47.** $(5m - 8)(2m + 3)$ **49.** $(4x - 1)(2x - 3)$ **51.** $(8m - 3)(5m + 2)$ **53.** $2m(m + 5)(m - 4)$ **55.** $2a^2(4a - 1)(3a + 2)$ **57.** $4w^4(z - 1)(8z + 3)$ **59.** $(4p - 3q)(3p + 4q)$ **61.** $(5a + 2b)(5a + 3b)$ **63.** $(3a - 5b)(2a + b)$ **65.** $2k^2(2k - 3w)(k + w)$ **67.** $m^4n(3m + 2n)(2m + n)$ **69.** $3zy(3z + 7y)(2z - 5y)$ **71.** $25p^2 - 9q^2$ **73.** $x^3 - 1$ **75.** $27k^3 - 1$

Section 4.4   (page 166)

1. $(x + 4)(x - 4)$ **3.** $(p + 2)(p - 2)$ **5.** $(m + n)(m - n)$ **7.** $(a + b)(a - b)$ **9.** $(3m + 1)(3m - 1)$ **11.** $(5m + 4)(5m - 4)$ **13.** $4(3t + 2)(3t - 2)$ **15.** $(5a + 4r)(5a - 4r)$ **17.** Prime   **19.** $(p^2 + 6)(p^2 - 6)$ **21.** $(a^2 + 1)(a + 1)(a - 1)$ **23.** $(m^2 + 9)(m + 3)(m - 3)$ **25.** $(a + 2)^2$ **27.** $(x - 5)^2$ **29.** $(a + 7)^2$ **31.** $(k + 11)^2$ **33.** Not a perfect square   **35.** Not a perfect square   **37.** $(4a - 5b)^2$

39. $25(2m + 1)^2$ **41.** $(7x + 2y)^2$ **43.** $(2c + 3d)^2$ **45.** $(5h - 2y)^2$ **47.** $xy(x + 3y)^2$
49. $(2a + 1)(4a^2 - 2a + 1)$ **51.** $(3x - 5)(9x^2 + 15x + 25)$ **53.** $(2p + q)(4p^2 - 2pq + q^2)$
55. $(3a - 4b)(9a^2 + 12ab + 16b^2)$ **57.** $(4x + 5y)(16x^2 - 20xy + 25y^2)$
59. $(5m - 2p)(25m^2 + 10mp + 4p^2)$ **61.** $(10z + 3x)(100z^2 - 30zx + 9x^2)$
63. $(4y^2 + 1)(16y^4 - 4y^2 + 1)$ **65.** $(2k^2 - 3q)(4k^4 + 6k^2q + 9q^2)$
67. $(10a - 7b^3)(100a^2 + 70ab^3 + 49b^6)$ **69.** 10   **71.** 9   **73.** 2   **75.** 2/3
77. $-9/7$ **79.** $-5/8$

Miscellaneous Factoring Exercises   (page 167)
1. $(a - 6)(a + 2)$ **3.** $6(y - 2)(y + 1)$ **5.** $6(a + 2b + 3c)$ **7.** $(p - 11)(p - 6)$
9. $(5z - 6)(2z + 1)$ **11.** $(5z - 1)(z + 5)$ **13.** $8a^3(a - 3)(a + 2)$ **15.** $(z - 5a)(z + 2a)$
17. $(3n - 2)(2n - 5)$ **19.** $(2m - 1)(m + 3)$ **21.** $4(4x + 5)$ **23.** $(3y - 4)(2y + 1)$
25. $(6z + 1)(z + 5)$ **27.** $(2k - 3)^2$ **29.** $6(3m + 2z)(3m - 2z)$ **31.** $(3k - 2)(k + 2)$
33. $7k(2k + 5)(k - 2)$ **35.** $(y^2 + 4)(y + 2)(y - 2)$ **37.** $8m(1 - 2m)$
39. $(z - 2)(z^2 + 2z + 4)$ **41.** $8m^3(4m^6 + 2m^2 + 3)$ **43.** $(4r + 3m)^2$
45. $(5h + 7g)(3h - 2g)$ **47.** $(k - 5)(k - 6)$ **49.** $3k(k - 5)(k + 1)$
51. $(10p + 3)(100p^2 - 30p + 9)$ **53.** $(2 + m)(3 + p)$ **55.** $(4z - 1)^2$ **57.** $3(6m - 1)^2$
59. Prime   **61.** $8z(4z - 1)(z + 2)$ **63.** $(x - 4)(x - 5)$ **65.** $(4 + m)(5 + 3n)$
67. $2(3a - 1)(a + 2)$ **69.** $(2k - 5z)^2$ **71.** $(8m - 5n)^2$ **73.** $(4k - 3h)(2k + h)$
75. $(5y - 6z)(2y + z)$ **77.** Prime   **79.** $(8a - b)(a + 3b)$ **81.** $(3m + 8)(3m - 8)$
83. Prime   **85.** $(a + 4)^2$

Section 4.5   (page 173)
1. $2, -4$ **3.** $-5/3, 1/2$ **5.** $-1/5, 1/2$ **7.** $-9/2, 1/3$ **9.** $1, -5/3$
11. $7/3, -4$ **13.** $-2, -3$ **15.** $-1, 6$ **17.** $-7, 4$ **19.** $-8, 3$ **21.** $-1, 3$
23. $-1, -2$ **25.** -4 **27.** $1/3, -2$ **29.** $5/2, -2$ **31.** $-4/3, 1/2$
33. $1/3, -5/2$ **35.** $-4, 5/2$ **37.** $5/3, -4$ **39.** $2/5, -1/3$ **41.** $3/2, -3$
43. $5/4, -5/4$ **45.** $2, -2$ **47.** $5, 2$ **49.** $-12, 11/2$ **51.** $3, -1$ **53.** $1/4, 4$
55. $5/2, 1/3, 5$ **57.** $-7/2, 3, -1$ **59.** $0, -5, 5$ **61.** $0, 7/3, -7/3$ **63.** $0, 4, -2$
65. $0, -5, 4$ **67.** 2 or -5 **69.** 7 meters   **71.** 18

Section 4.6   (page 178)
1. 6 cm   **3.** 10 m   **5.** 4 in   **7.** 2   **9.** 5 cm   **11.** 16 square m   **13.** 19 ft
15. 6 ft   **17.** 12   **19.** 8   **21.** 4 or -1 **23.** 12, 14, 16 or $-2, 0, 2$ **25.** -9 and -5
or 6 and 10   **27.** -2 **29.** 256 ft   **31.** 10 seconds   **33.** 48 ft   **35.** 48 ft
37. False   **39.** True   **41.** True

Section 4.7   (page 184)
1. $-2 < m < 5$

3. $t \le -6$ or $t \ge -5$

5. $-3 < a < 3$

7. $a \le -6$ or $a \ge 7$

9. $m < -3$ or $m > -2$

11. $-1 \le z \le 5$

13. $-1 < m < \dfrac{2}{5}$

15. $-\dfrac{1}{2} < r < \dfrac{4}{3}$

17. $-4 < a < 4$

19. $r \le -10$ or $r \ge 10$

21. $-\dfrac{3}{2} \le k \le 5$

23. $-\dfrac{1}{2} \le r \le \dfrac{2}{5}$

25. $r < -4$ or $r > 4$ **27.** $-2 \le a \le \dfrac{1}{3}$ or $a \ge 4$ **29.** $r < -1$ or $2 < r < 4$

31. 2/3   **33.** 1/3   **35.** 25/36   **37.** 1/6

Chapter 4   Review Exercises   (page 184)

1. $2^4 \cdot 3$ **3.** $2^3 \cdot 3 \cdot 5^2$ **5.** $6(1 - 3r^5 + 2r^3)$ **7.** $5m^2n^4(3m - 4n + 10mn^2)$
9. $(2p + 3)(3p + 2)$ **11.** $(3m + 4p)(5m - 4p)$ **13.** $(r - 9)(r + 3)$ **15.** $(z - 11)(z + 4)$
17. $(r - 12s)(r + 8s)$ **19.** $(y - 5z)(y - 3z)$ **21.** $5p^4(p - 7)(p - 2)$ **23.** $(3z - 1)(z + 4)$
25. $3m(m - 5)(2m + 3)$ **27.** $(z + 5y)(2z - y)$ **29.** $(7m - 2n)(m + 3n)$
31. $(10a + 3)(10a - 3)$ **33.** $36(2p + q)(2p - q)$ **35.** Prime   **37.** $(4m + 5n)^2$
39. $6x(3x - 2)^2$ **41.** $(7x + 4)(49x^2 - 28x + 16)$ **43.** $2, -5$ **45.** 3, 5
47. $7/10, -7/10$ **49.** $1/3, -1, -2$ **51.** $0, 3, -3$ **53.** 4 m   **55.** 4 and 6 or -2 and 0
57. $q < -5$ or $q > 3$ **59.** $2 \le m \le 3$ **61.** $p \le -4$ or $p \ge 3/2$

Chapter 4   Test   (page 186)

1. $2^4 \cdot 5$ **2.** $3^3 \cdot 5^2$ **3.** $8m^2(2 - 3m + 4m^2)$ **4.** $14p(2q + 1 + 4pq^3)$
5. $(m - 9)(m - 3)$ **6.** $(2 - a)(6 + b)$ **7.** $(x - 9)(x + 5)$ **8.** $3p^2q(p + 7)(p - 1)$
9. $(3a - 2)(a + 5)$ **10.** $3z^3(5z + 1)(2z - 5)$ **11.** $p^2(4r + 5)(3r + 1)$
12. $(3t - 2x)(2t + x)$ **13.** $2(5m + 7)(5m - 7)$ **14.** $(12a + 13b)(12a - 13b)$
15. $(a^2 + 25)(a + 5)(a - 5)$ **16.** $(2p + 3)^2$ **17.** $(5z - 1)^2$ **18.** $4y(y + 2)^2$
19. $(2p - 5)(4p^2 + 10p + 25)$ **20.** $(3r + 4t^2)(9r^2 - 12rt^2 + 16t^4)$ **21.** $1/3, -2$ **22.** $5/2, -4$
23. $3, 5/2, -2/3$ **24.** $0, 4, -4$ **25.** 3 in   **26.** 8 and 17 or -7 and 2   **27.** 8
28.   **29.**   **30.**

CHAPTER 5

Section 5.1   (page 190)

1. 0   **3.** 4   **5.** -5 **7.** 5, 3   **9.** $3/2, -1$ **11.** None; the rational expression is always
defined   **13.** (a) 1   (b) 14/9   **15.** (a) 2   (b) $-14/3$ **17.** (a) 256/15   (b) meaningless
19. (a) -5 (b) 5/23   **21.** (a) -5 (b) 15/2   **23.** (a) Meaningless   (b) 1/10   **25.** $2k$

27. $\dfrac{-4y^3}{3}$ **29.** $\dfrac{4m}{3p}$ **31.** 3/4   **33.** $\dfrac{x - 1}{x + 1}$ **35.** $2(r - 2)$ or $2r - 4$

37. $4m^2 - 3$ **39.** $\dfrac{8y + 5}{6}$ **41.** Cannot be reduced further   **43.** $m - n$ **45.** $\dfrac{m}{2}$

47. $2(2r + s)$ or $4r + 2s$ **49.** $\dfrac{m - 2}{m + 3}$ **51.** $\dfrac{x + 4}{x + 1}$ **53.** -1 **55.** 1   **57.** $-(x + 1)$ or
$-x - 1$ **59.** -1 **61.** 15/32   **63.** 32/9   **65.** 4   **67.** 81/10

Section 5.2   (page 194)

1. $\dfrac{3m}{4}$ **3.** $\dfrac{3}{32}$ **5.** $2a^4$ **7.** $\dfrac{1}{4}$ **9.** $\dfrac{1}{6}$ **11.** $\dfrac{2}{r^5}$ **13.** $\dfrac{6}{a + b}$

15. $\dfrac{2}{9}$ **17.** $\dfrac{3}{10}$ **19.** $\dfrac{2r}{3}$ **21.** $(y + 4)(y - 3)$ **23.** $\dfrac{18}{(m - 1)(m + 2)}$

25. $-\dfrac{7}{8}$ **27.** -1 **29.** $m - 4$ **31.** $\dfrac{k + 2}{k + 3}$ **33.** $\dfrac{z + 4}{z - 4}$

35. $\dfrac{4k-1}{3k-2}$ **37.** $\dfrac{m-3}{2m-3}$ **39.** $\dfrac{m+4p}{m+p}$ **41.** $(x+2)(x+1)$ **43.** $\dfrac{10}{x+10}$

45. $2^2 \cdot 3$ **47.** $2^3 \cdot 3^2$ **49.** $x(x-4)$ **51.** $(2y-1)(y+3)$

Section 5.3 (page 198)

1. 60   **3.** 120   **5.** 1800   **7.** x^5 **9.** $30p$ **11.** $150m$ **13.** $180y^4$

15. $300r^5$ **17.** $15a^5b^3$ **19.** $12p(p-2)$ **21.** $32r^2(r-2)$ **23.** $18(r-2)$

25. $12p(p+5)$ **27.** $8(y+2)(y+1)$ **29.** $m-3$ or $3-m$ **31.** $p-q$ or $q-p$

33. $a(a+6)(a-3)$ **35.** $(k+7)(k-5)(k+8)$ **37.** $(2y-1)(y+4)(y-3)$

39. $(3r-5)(2r+3)(r-1)$ **41.** $\dfrac{42}{66}$ **43.** $\dfrac{54}{6r}$ **45.** $\dfrac{-88}{8m}$

47. $\dfrac{24y^2}{70y^3}$ **49.** $\dfrac{60m^2k^3}{32k^4}$ **51.** $\dfrac{57z}{6z-18}$ **53.** $\dfrac{-4a}{18a-36}$ **55.** $\dfrac{6(k+1)}{k(k-4)(k+1)}$

57. $\dfrac{36r(r+1)}{(r-3)(r+2)(r+1)}$ **59.** $\dfrac{7}{3}$ **61.** $\dfrac{9}{10}$ **63.** $\dfrac{2}{3}$ **65.** $\dfrac{19}{72}$

Section 5.4 (page 203)

1. $\dfrac{7}{p}$ **3.** $\dfrac{-3}{k}$ or $-\dfrac{3}{k}$ **5.** 1   **7.** $\dfrac{-2q}{3}$ or $-\dfrac{2q}{3}$ **9.** m **11.** $q-2$

13. $\dfrac{2m+3}{6}$ **15.** $\dfrac{28-5z}{20}$ **17.** $\dfrac{4y-3}{3y}$ **19.** $\dfrac{m}{6}$ **21.** $\dfrac{k+2}{2}$

23. $\dfrac{5m+8}{6}$ **25.** $\dfrac{5m+11}{4m}$ **27.** $\dfrac{6-2y}{y^2}$ **29.** $\dfrac{9p-8}{2p^2}$ **31.** $\dfrac{3x-y}{x^2y}$

33. $\dfrac{4(x+6)}{(x-2)(x+2)}$ **35.** $\dfrac{x}{2(x+y)}$ **37.** $\dfrac{m}{3(m+3)(m-3)}$ **39.** $\dfrac{3}{(m+1)(m-1)(m+2)}$

41. $\dfrac{3}{q-2}$ or $\dfrac{-3}{2-q}$ **43.** $\dfrac{-6}{4p-5}$ or $\dfrac{6}{5-4p}$ **45.** $\dfrac{43m+1}{5m(m-2)}$ **47.** $\dfrac{9r+2}{r(r+2)(r-1)}$

49. $\dfrac{4k^2-10k+5}{(k+4)(k-2)(k-1)}$ **51.** $\dfrac{11y^2-y-11}{(2y-1)(y+3)(3y+2)}$ **53.** $\dfrac{2x^2+6xy+8y^2}{(x+y)(x+y)(x+3y)}$ or

$\dfrac{2x^2+6xy+8y^2}{(x+y)^2(x+3y)}$ **55.** $\dfrac{14}{3}$ **57.** $\dfrac{1}{5}$

Section 5.5 (page 208)

1. $\dfrac{31}{50}$ **3.** $\dfrac{5}{18}$ **5.** $\dfrac{1}{pq}$ **7.** $\dfrac{1}{x}$ **9.** $\dfrac{mp}{40}$ **11.** $\dfrac{x(x+1)}{4(x-3)}$

13. $\dfrac{18q}{1-q}$ **15.** $\dfrac{5(2x+3)}{4(x-1)}$ **17.** $\dfrac{2}{y}$ **19.** $\dfrac{8}{x}$ **21.** $\dfrac{x^2+1}{4+xy}$

23. $\dfrac{5p+15}{5+p}$ **25.** $\dfrac{40-12p}{85p}$ **27.** $\dfrac{5y-2x}{3+4xy}$ **29.** $\dfrac{a-2}{2a}$ **31.** $\dfrac{z-5}{4}$

33. $\dfrac{-m}{m+2}$ **35.** $\dfrac{3m(m-3)}{(m-1)(m-8)}$ **37.** $\dfrac{1}{3}$ **39.** $\dfrac{19r}{15}$ **41.** $12x+2$

43. $44p^2-27p$ **45.** -2 **47.** $\dfrac{-13}{3}$ **49.** $\dfrac{2}{3}$

Section 5.6 (page 214)

1. 1/2   **3.** 12   **5.** 21/8   **7.** 2/5   **9.** 24   **11.** 2   **13.** −7   **15.** 1
17. 2   **19.** 5   **21.** −8   **23.** 8   **25.** 5   **27.** 2/7   **29.** 6   **31.** 1
33. 4   **35.** 0   **37.** 3   **39.** −19/6   **41.** −3   **43.** 1   **45.** No solution
47. 3, −1/3   **49.** No solution   **51.** 1/2, −6   **53.** 1, −4/3   **55.** 3, −3/5

57. $y = \dfrac{xz}{x + z}$ **59.** $z = \dfrac{3y}{5 - 9xy}$ **61.** $R = \dfrac{E - Ir}{I}$ **63.** $r = \dfrac{S - a}{S}$

65. $r_1 = \dfrac{Rr_2}{r_2 - R}$ **67.** $r = \dfrac{d}{10}$ **69.** $\dfrac{1}{x}$

Miscellaneous Exercises (page 216)

1. $\dfrac{8}{m}$ **3.** $\dfrac{3}{4x^2(x + 3)}$ **5.** $\dfrac{r + 4}{r + 1}$ **7.** −43   **9.** $\dfrac{17}{3(y - 1)}$ **11.** 2, 1/5

13. $\dfrac{-19}{18z}$ **15.** $\dfrac{3m + 5}{(m + 3)(m + 2)(m + 1)}$

Section 5.7 (page 222)

1. 9   **3.** 12/17   **5.** 6, 9   **7.** 2/3 or −3   **9.** 2/3 or 1   **11.** Father's were $120, son's
were $48   **13.** $32,000   **15.** 2 miles per hour   **17.** 150 miles each way   **19.** 37/2 miles
per hour   **21.** 6/5 hours or 1 hour 12 minutes   **23.** 84/19 hours   **25.** 28/5 days or 5 3/5
days   **27.** 100/11 minutes   **29.** 3 hours   **31.** 63/2   **33.** 125   **35.** 5/2
37. 4/9   **39.** 69.08 cm   **41.** 144 ft   **43.** 20 lb   **45.** (a) 1   (b) −23
47. (a) 7   (b) −17   **49.** (a) 4/7   (b) 22/7   **51.** (a) −2/3   (b) 4/3

Chapter 5 Review Exercises (page 225)

1. 0   **3.** 4, −2   **5.** (a) 9/5   (b) 1   **7.** (a) 24/7   (b) 8   **9.** 3p   **11.** $\dfrac{3x - 4}{2}$

13. $\dfrac{40}{3p^2}$ **15.** 7/2   **17.** −1   **19.** $\dfrac{2p - 1}{2p + 3}$ **21.** 90   **23.** $y(y + 2)(y + 4)$

25. $\dfrac{20}{45}$ **27.** $\dfrac{9m}{24m^3}$ **29.** $\dfrac{-10k}{15k + 75}$ **31.** $\dfrac{1}{r}$ **33.** $\dfrac{35 - 2k}{5k}$

35. $\dfrac{16 - 3r}{2r^2}$ **37.** $\dfrac{-y - 5}{(y + 1)(y - 1)}$ **39.** $\dfrac{8p - 30}{p(p - 2)(p - 3)}$ **41.** 4   **43.** $\dfrac{1 - a - b}{1 + a + b}$

45. 1/7   **47.** −4   **49.** 10/3   **51.** −6   **53.** No solution   **55.** $r = \dfrac{3zk}{5k - z}$

57. $y = \dfrac{xz}{3 - 2x}$ **59.** 15/11   **61.** $180, $120   **63.** 150 km per hour   **65.** 6 days

67. 36/5   **69.** 9/4

Chapter 5 Test (page 227)

1. 3, 1   **2.** (a) 1/3   (b) meaningless   **3.** $\dfrac{4}{3mp^3}$ **4.** $\dfrac{5y(y - 1)}{2}$ **5.** a

6. −40/27   **7.** $\dfrac{3m - 2}{3m + 2}$ **8.** $\dfrac{a + 3}{a + 4}$ **9.** $150p^5$ **10.** $(2r + 3)(r + 2)(r - 5)$

11. $\dfrac{77r}{49r^2}$ **12.** $\dfrac{15m}{24m^2 - 48m}$ **13.** $-\dfrac{1}{x}$ **14.** $\dfrac{-13}{6(a + 1)}$ **15.** $\dfrac{m^2 - m - 1}{m - 3}$
or $\dfrac{1 + m - m^2}{3 - m}$ **16.** $\dfrac{2k^2 + 2k + 3}{(2k - 1)(k + 2)(k + 1)}$ **17.** $\dfrac{3(1 - 2k)}{k(1 + 3k)}$ **18.** $\dfrac{-2p - 7}{2p + 9}$

19. 6   **20.** No solution   **21.** 1   **22.** 1/4 or 1/2   **23.** 20 miles per hour
24. 20/9 hours   **25.** 56/3

CHAPTER 6

Section 6.1   (page 235)

1. Yes   **3.** Yes   **5.** No   **7.** Yes   **9.** Yes   **11.** No   **13.** 11   **15.** 29
17. −4   **19.** 3   **21.** (3, 7), (0, 1), (−1, −1)   **23.** (2, 2), (0, 8), (−3, 17)
25. (0, 9), (3, 3), (12, −15)   **27.** (−4, 6), (−4, 2), (−4, −3)   **29.** (−9, 8), (−9, 3), (−9, 0)
31. (−2, 6), (0, 0), (2, −6)   **33.** (2, 5)   **35.** (−5, 5)   **37.** (7, 3)
39–49.   **51.** I   **53.** II   **55.** III   **57.** II   **59.** IV   **61.** none

63.   **65.**   **67.**   **69.**

71.   **73.** 8/3   **75.** −9   **77.** 1   **79.** 15

Section 6.2   (page 244)

1.   **3.**   **5.**   **7.**

9.

11. $x = 3$; $y = 2$ **13.** $x = 3$; $y = -9/5$ **15.** $x = 0$; $y = 0$

17. $x = -4$; no y-intercept

19.

21.

23.

25.

27.

29.

31.

33.

35.

37.

39.

41.

43. $x = y + 2$

45. $y = 2x - 3$

47. $3 + y = 2x - 4$

$y = 2x - 7$

49. (a) 121   (b) 132   (c) 154   (d) 176   **51.** (a)

(e)

(b) about $5200

53. 8/5   **55.** −4   **57.** −1   **59.** −2

Section 6.3   (page 251)
1. −1/2   **3.** 2/7   **5.** 0   **7.** 7/6   **9.** 9/2   **11.** −5/8   **13.** 0
15. Undefined   **17.** −1.020   **19.** −1   **21.** −5   **23.** −2   **25.** 3/2
27. −2/5   **29.** 0   **31.** Perpendicular   **33.** Parallel   **35.** Perpendicular
37. Neither   **39.** Neither   **41.** Neither   **43.** $y = 2x - 11$ **45.** $y = -x - 5$
47. $y = -3x - 1$ **49.** $y = -x/2 - 21/10$

Section 6.4   (page 256)
1. $y = 3x + 5$ **3.** $y = -x - 6$ **5.** $20y = 8x - 5$ **7.** $y = -5$
9. $y = 4.61x - 2.38$

11.

13.

15.

17.

19.

21.

23.

25. $y = 2x - 7$ **27.** $y = -2x - 4$ **29.** $3y = 2x + 9$ **31.** $4y = -3x - 17$
33. $11y = -8x + 48$ **35.** $3x - 5y = -11$ **37.** $3x + 5y = -11$
39. $2x + 3y = 6$ **41.** $2x + y = -1$ **43.** $x - 3y = -4$ **45.** $88x - 72y = -133$
47. $y = 12x + 100$ **49.** (a) $700   (b) $1600   **51.** (a) (1, 24); (5, 48)   (b) $y = 6x + 18$
53. $m < 7$ **55.** $p \le 1/2$ **57.** $p > -3$ **59.** $p < -11$

Section 6.5 (page 262)

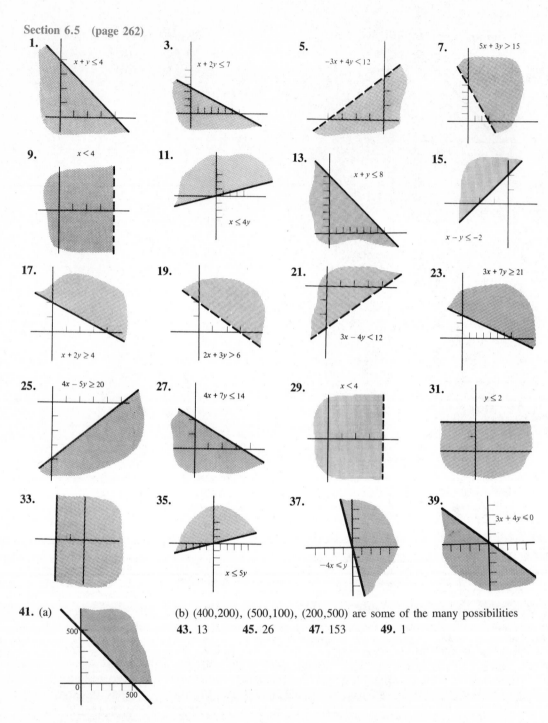

1. $x + y \leq 4$

3. $x + 2y \leq 7$

5. $-3x + 4y < 12$

7. $5x + 3y > 15$

9. $x < 4$

11. $x \leq 4y$

13. $x + y \leq 8$

15. $x - y \leq -2$

17. $x + 2y \geq 4$

19. $2x + 3y > 6$

21. $3x - 4y < 12$

23. $3x + 7y \geq 21$

25. $4x - 5y \geq 20$

27. $4x + 7y \leq 14$

29. $x < 4$

31. $y \leq 2$

33.

35. $x \leq 5y$

37. $-4x \leq y$

39. $3x + 4y \leq 0$

41. (a)

500

0   500

(b) (400,200), (500,100), (200,500) are some of the many possibilities
43. 13   **45.** 26   **47.** 153   **49.** 1

Section 6.6 (page 268)

1. Yes   **3.** No   **5.** No   **7.** Yes   **9.** Yes   **11.** Yes   **13.** No   **15.** No

17. Yes   **19.** Yes   **21.** No   **23.** Yes   **25.** No   **27.** Both domain and range are set of all real numbers   **29.** Both domain and range are set of all real numbers   **31.** Domain is set of all real numbers, range is set of all $y \geq -3$ **33.** Domain is set of all real numbers, range is set of all $y \geq 0$ **35.** Domain is set of all real numbers, range is set of all $y \leq 6$ **37.** Domain is set of all real numbers, range is set of all $y \leq 0$ **39.** Domain is set of all real numbers, range is set of all $y \geq 2$ **41.** Domain is set of all real numbers, range is set of all $y \geq 0$ **43.** 8; 2; -7 **45.** 2; 4; 7   **47.** -12; -4; 8   **49.** 6; 2; 11   **51.** 1; 9; 36   **53.** -4; -2; -1 **55.** 0; 3; 8   **57.** 9; 24; -11 **59.** 1; -62; -7 **61.** $4x$ **63.** $2b$

Chapter 6   Review Exercises   (page 269)
1. Yes   **3.** No   **5.** Yes   **7.** $(-1, -5)$; $(0, -2)$; $(7/3, 5)$ **9.** $(0, 3)$; $(9/4, 0)$; $(-2, 17/3)$ **11.** $(-4, -3)$; $(-4, 0)$; $(-4, 5)$

13.   **15.**   **17.**   **19.**

21. $x = 5/2$; $y = -5$ **23.** $x = 8/3$; $y = -8$ **25.** 2/3   **27.** 2   **29.** 3
31. 0   **33.** Parallel   **35.** Perpendicular   **37.** $y = 3x - 2$ **39.** $3y = 2x + 15$
41. $y = -3x + 30$ **43.** $3y = 2x + 14$ **45.** $-4y = x - 6$ **47.** $x = 5$
49.   **51.**   **53.**

55. No   **57.** Yes   **59.** Yes   **61.** Yes   **63.** Domain is set of all real numbers, range is set of all real numbers   **65.** Domain is set of all real numbers, range is set of all $y \geq 0$
67. (a) 7   (b) 1   **69.** (a) 5   (b) 2

Chapter 6   Test   (page 271)
1. $(0, -6)$; $(-2, -16)$; $(4, 14)$ **2.** $(0, 3)$; $(21/2, 0)$; $(3, 15/7)$; $(7/2, 2)$ **3.** $(0, 0)$; $(6, 2)$; $(8, 8/3)$; $(-12, -4)$ **4.** $(5, 2)$; $(4, 2)$; $(0, 2)$; $(-3, 2)$
5. 4; 4   **6.** 3; 6   **7.** 6; $-\dfrac{9}{2}$ **8.** 0; 0

9. −5; none

10. None; 2

11. −3/7   **12.** −3/4   **13.** −4/7
14. Undefined   **15.** $4x + y = 1$
16. $3x − y = 1$ **17.** $3x + 4y = 8$
18. $9x − y = −12$

19.

20.

21. No   **22.** Yes   **23.** No   **24.** Domain is the set of all real numbers, range is the set of $y \geq 0$ **25.** −20; 28

CHAPTER 7

Section 7.1 (page 277)

1. Yes   **3.** No   **5.** No   **7.** Yes   **9.** No   **11.** Yes   **13.** (4, 2)
15. (0, 4)   **17.** (2, 2)   **19.** (1, 3)   **21.** (3, −2)   **23.** (2, −1)   **25.** (−4, 1)
27. (−4, 3)   **29.** (5, 0)   **31.** (0, −2)   **33.** (1, 2)   **35.** (−1, 3)   **37.** (2, −3)
39. (6, −2)   **41.** (2, 7)   **43.** No solution   **45.** No solution   **47.** Same line
49. Same line   **51.** Same line   **53.** $10p + 7q$ **55.** $8r$ **57.** $2a$ **59.** 0

Section 7.2 (page 284)

1. (1, −2)   **3.** (2, 0)   **5.** (6, 2)   **7.** (−2, 6)   **9.** (1/2, 2)   **11.** (3/2, −2)
13. (3, 0)   **15.** (2, −3)   **17.** (4, 4)   **19.** (2, −5)   **21.** (4, 9)   **23.** (−4, 0)
25. (4, −3)   **27.** (−9, −11)   **29.** (6, 3)   **31.** (6, −5)   **33.** (−6, 0)
35. (1/2, 3)   **37.** (−3, 2)   **39.** (2.283, .071)   **41.** (−7, −1)   **43.** No solution
45. Same line   **47.** No solution   **49.** (2, −5)   **51.** (4, 9)   **53.** (0, 0)   **55.** No
solution   **57.** (3/8, 5/6)   **59.** (2/3, −1/5)   **61.** 4   **63.** 9   **65.** −7   **67.** 14/13

Section 7.3 (page 290)

1. (2, 4)   **3.** (6, 4)   **5.** (8, −1)   **7.** No solution   **9.** (2, −4)   **11.** (5, 1)
13. Same line   **15.** (4, 1)   **17.** (−2, 5)   **19.** (−6, 2)   **21.** (−5, 3)   **23.** (3, 2)
25. (7, 0)   **27.** Same line   **29.** (6, 5)   **31.** (4, −6)   **33.** (18, −12)   **35.** (3, 2)
37. (3, −1)   **39.** (12, 6)   **41.** 21   **43.** 8 feet   **45.** 13

Section 7.4 (page 296)

1. 43 and 9   **3.** 72 and 24   **5.** 55° and 35°   **7.** 10 inches by 20 inches   **9.** 22 tens,
63 twenties   **11.** 74 at 8¢, 96 at 10¢   **13.** 80 fives, 44 tens   **15.** 21 at $7, 18 at $4
17. $7500 at 10%, $2500 at 14%   **19.** 4 liters of 90%, 16 liters of 75%   **21.** 4 of 25%,
8 of 55%   **23.** 30 of $6, 60 of $3   **25.** 30 barrels of $40 olives, 20 barrels of $60 olives
27. 2 mph, 10 mph   **29.** plane, 470 mph; wind, 70 mph   **31.** John, 3 1/4 mph; Harriet,
2 3/4 mph   **33.** 4 girls, 3 boys

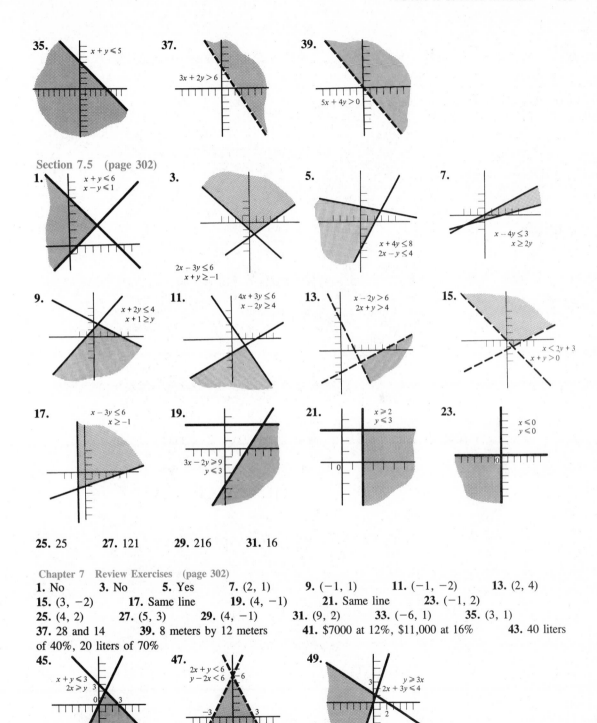

35. $x + y \leqslant 5$

37. $3x + 2y > 6$

39. $5x + 4y > 0$

Section 7.5 (page 302)

1. $x + y \leqslant 6$ $x - y \leqslant 1$

3. $2x - 3y \leqslant 6$ $x + y \geqslant -1$

5. $x + 4y \leqslant 8$ $2x - y \leqslant 4$

7. $x - 4y \leqslant 3$ $x \geqslant 2y$

9. $x + 2y \leqslant 4$ $x + 1 \geqslant y$

11. $4x + 3y \leqslant 6$ $x - 2y \geqslant 4$

13. $x - 2y > 6$ $2x + y > 4$

15. $x < 2y + 3$ $x + y > 0$

17. $x - 3y \leqslant 6$ $x \geqslant -1$

19. $3x - 2y \geqslant 9$ $y \leqslant 3$

21. $x \geqslant 2$ $y \leqslant 3$

23. $x \leqslant 0$ $y \leqslant 0$

25. 25   **27.** 121   **29.** 216   **31.** 16

Chapter 7 Review Exercises (page 302)
1. No   **3.** No   **5.** Yes   **7.** (2, 1)   **9.** (−1, 1)   **11.** (−1, −2)   **13.** (2, 4)
15. (3, −2)   **17.** Same line   **19.** (4, −1)   **21.** Same line   **23.** (−1, 2)
25. (4, 2)   **27.** (5, 3)   **29.** (4, −1)   **31.** (9, 2)   **33.** (−6, 1)   **35.** (3, 1)
37. 28 and 14   **39.** 8 meters by 12 meters   **41.** \$7000 at 12%, \$11,000 at 16%   **43.** 40 liters
of 40%, 20 liters of 70%
45. $x + y \leqslant 3$ $2x \geqslant y$

47. $2x + y < 6$ $y - 2x < 6$

49. $y \geqslant 3x$ $2x + 3y \leqslant 4$

Chapter 7 Test (page 304)
1. $(4, -3)$ **2.** $(6, -5)$ **3.** $(4, 1)$ **4.** $(6, 5)$ **5.** $(4, 3)$ **6.** Same line
7. $(3/2, -2)$ **8.** No solution   **9.** $(-11/14, -8/7)$ **10.** $(3, -5)$ **11.** $(-6, 8)$
12. Same line   **13.** $(-6, 4)$ **14.** 12 and 27   **15.** 2 at \$5, 4 at \$7.50   **16.** 75 liters of
40%, 25 liters of 60%   **17.** 45 mph and 60 mph
18.   **19.**   **20.**

$2x + 7y \leq 14$
$x - y \geq 1$

$2x - y \leq 6$
$4y + 12 \geq -3x$

$3x - 5y < 15$
$y < 2$

CHAPTER 8

Section 8.1 (page 310)
1. $3, -3$ **3.** $11, -11$ **5.** $20/9, -20/9$ **7.** $25, -25$ **9.** $39, -39$
11. $63, -63$ **13.** 2   **15.** 5   **17.** -8 **19.** $13/7$ **21.** $30/11$ **23.** -41
25. 51   **27.** -70 **29.** Does not exist   **31.** Does not exist   **33.** Rational; 4
35. Irrational; 3.873   **37.** Irrational; 6.856   **39.** Irrational; 8.246   **41.** Rational; -11
43. Irrational; 10.488   **45.** Rational; 20   **47.** Irrational; -14.142 **49.** 23.896
51. 28.249   **53.** 1.985   **55.** .095   **57.** $c = 10$ **59.** $b = 15$ **61.** $c = \sqrt{164}$ or
12.806   **63.** $a = \sqrt{95}$ or 9.747   **65.** 10   **67.** 5   **69.** -2 **71.** -2 **73.** 1
75. Does not exist   **77.** -3 **79.** 1   **81.** -2.378 **83.** 2.280   **85.** 1.092
87. 4.036   **89.** 1, 2, 3, 4, 6, 8, 12, 24   **91.** 1, 2, 3, 4, 5, 6, 10, 12, 15, 20, 25, 30, 50, 60, 75,
100, 150, 300   **93.** 1, 2, 3, 4, 6, 8, 9, 12, 18, 24, 36, 72   **95.** 1, 2, 3, 6, 10, 15, 25, 50, 75, 150

Section 8.2 (page 315)
1. 4   **3.** 6   **5.** 21   **7.** $\sqrt{21}$ **9.** $3\sqrt{3}$ **11.** $2\sqrt{7}$ **13.** $3\sqrt{2}$
15. $4\sqrt{3}$ **17.** $5\sqrt{5}$ **19.** $10\sqrt{7}$ **21.** $30\sqrt{3}$ **23.** $4\sqrt{5}$ **25.** 36   **27.** 60
29. $7\sqrt{3}$ **31.** $15\sqrt{3}$ **33.** $20\sqrt{3}$ **35.** $10\sqrt{10}$ **37.** 10/3   **39.** 6/7
41. $\sqrt{5}/4$ **43.** $\sqrt{30}/7$ **45.** 2/5   **47.** 4/25   **49.** 5   **51.** 4   **53.** $3\sqrt{5}$
55. $5\sqrt{10}$ **57.** y **59.** $\sqrt{xz}$ **61.** x **63.** x^2 **65.** xy^2 **67.** $x\sqrt{x}$
69. $4/x$ **71.** $\sqrt{11}/r^2$ **73.** $2\sqrt[3]{5}$ **75.** $3\sqrt[3]{2}$ **77.** $4\sqrt[3]{2}$ **79.** $2\sqrt[4]{5}$ **81.** 2/3
83. 10/3   **85.** 27/39   **87.** 10/15   **89.** $\dfrac{6}{3x}$ **91.** $\dfrac{10}{2\sqrt{3}}$

Section 8.3 (page 318)
1. $6\sqrt{5}/5$ **3.** $\sqrt{5}$ **5.** $3\sqrt{7}/7$ **7.** $8\sqrt{15}/5$ **9.** $\sqrt{30}/2$ **11.** $8\sqrt{3}/9$
13. $3\sqrt{2}/10$ **15.** $\sqrt{2}$ **17.** $9\sqrt{2}/8$ **19.** 2   **21.** $\sqrt{2}$ **23.** $2\sqrt{30}/3$
25. $\sqrt{2}/2$ **27.** $\sqrt{70}/7$ **29.** $3\sqrt{5}/5$ **31.** $\sqrt{21}/3$ **33.** $\sqrt{15}/10$ **35.** $3\sqrt{14}/4$
37. $\sqrt{3}/5$ **39.** $4\sqrt{3}/27$ **41.** $\sqrt{6p}/p$ **43.** $p\sqrt{2pm}/m$ **45.** $\dfrac{x\sqrt{y}}{2y}$ **47.** $3a\sqrt{5r}/5$
49. $\sqrt[3]{4}/2$ **51.** $\sqrt[3]{2}/4$ **53.** $\sqrt[3]{121}/11$ **55.** $\sqrt[3]{50}/5$ **57.** $\sqrt[3]{6}/2$ **59.** $\sqrt[3]{42}/6$
61. $4x$ **63.** $-2m - 3$ **65.** $3y + 8z$

Section 8.4 (page 321)
1. $7\sqrt{3}$ **3.** $-5\sqrt{7}$ **5.** $2\sqrt{6}$ **7.** $3\sqrt{17}$ **9.** $4\sqrt{7}$ **11.** $12\sqrt{2}$ **13.** $7\sqrt{5}$
15. $10\sqrt{2}$ **17.** $3\sqrt{3}$ **19.** $20\sqrt{2}$ **21.** $19\sqrt{7}$ **23.** $-12\sqrt{5}$ **25.** $6\sqrt{2} + 7\sqrt{3}$
27. $-16\sqrt{2} + 8\sqrt{3}$ **29.** $20\sqrt{2} + 6\sqrt{3} + 15\sqrt{5}$ **31.** $2\sqrt{2}$ **33.** $3\sqrt{3} - 2\sqrt{5}$
35. $3\sqrt{21}$ **37.** $5\sqrt{3}$ **39.** $-\sqrt[3]{2}$ **41.** $24\sqrt[3]{3}$ **43.** $10\sqrt[4]{2} + 4\sqrt[4]{8}$ **45.** $6\sqrt{x}$

47. $13\sqrt{a}$ **49.** $15x\sqrt{3}$ **51.** $2x\sqrt{2}$ **53.** $6\sqrt[3]{p^2}$ **55.** $14m$ **57.** $m^2 + 8m + 15$
59. $6k^2 - 17k + 12$ **61.** $9x^2 - 6x + 1$ **63.** $a^2 - 9$ **65.** $16k^2 - 25$

Section 8.5 (page 326)
1. $27\sqrt{5}$ **3.** $21\sqrt{2}$ **5.** -4 **7.** $\sqrt{15} + \sqrt{35}$ **9.** $2\sqrt{10} + 10$ **11.** $-4\sqrt{7}$
13. $21 - \sqrt{6}$ **15.** $87 + 9\sqrt{21}$ **17.** $34 + 24\sqrt{2}$ **19.** $37 - 12\sqrt{7}$ **21.** 7
23. -4 **25.** 1 **27.** $2\sqrt{3} - 2 + 3\sqrt{2} - \sqrt{6}$ **29.** $2 + 2\sqrt{2}$
31. $\sqrt{30} + \sqrt{15} + 6\sqrt{5} + 3\sqrt{10}$ **33.** $\sqrt{7} - 2$ **35.** $\dfrac{\sqrt{3} + 5}{4}$ **37.** $\dfrac{6 - \sqrt{10}}{2}$
39. $\dfrac{2 + \sqrt{2}}{3}$ **41.** $-10 + 5\sqrt{5}$ **43.** $-2 - \sqrt{11}$ **45.** $-\sqrt{2} + 2$ **47.** $\dfrac{-\sqrt{5} - 5}{4}$
49. $3 - \sqrt{3}$ **51.** $\dfrac{-3 + 5\sqrt{3}}{11}$ **53.** $\dfrac{\sqrt{6} + \sqrt{2} + 3\sqrt{3} + 3}{2}$
55. $\dfrac{-6\sqrt{2} + 12 + \sqrt{10} - 2\sqrt{5}}{2}$ **57.** $3\sqrt{2} - 3 + \sqrt{10} - \sqrt{5}$ **59.** $\dfrac{-31 + 11\sqrt{3}}{13}$
61. $\dfrac{-4\sqrt{3} - \sqrt{2} + 10\sqrt{6} + 5}{23}$ **63.** $\sqrt{21} + \sqrt{14} + \sqrt{6} + 2$ **65.** $1, 3$ **67.** $5/2, -3$
69. $1, 2$

Section 8.6 (page 332)
1. 4 **3.** 1 **5.** 7 **7.** -7 **9.** -5 **11.** No solution **13.** 49
15. No solution **17.** 9 **19.** 16 **21.** 6 **23.** 7 **25.** No solution **27.** 6
29. 12 **31.** 5 **33.** $0, -1$ **35.** 5 **37.** 3 **39.** 9 **41.** 12 **43.** 9
45. 21 **47.** 8 **49.** (a) 90 mph (b) 120 mph (c) 60 mph (d) 60 mph **51.** $1/(3^5)$
53. $1/(2x^3)$ **55.** $1/(2^2 y^8)$

Section 8.7 (page 336)
1. 4 **3.** 5 **5.** 2 **7.** 4 **9.** 2 **11.** 2 **13.** 8 **15.** 9 **17.** 8
19. 4 **21.** 4 **23.** -4 **25.** 2^3 **27.** $1/(6^{1/2})$ **29.** $1/(15^{1/2})$ **31.** $11^{1/7}$
33. 8^3 **35.** $6^{1/2}$ **37.** $9^{3/8}$ **39.** $125/8$ **41.** $4/9$ **43.** $1/(2^{8/5})$ **45.** $6^{2/9}$
47. p^3 **49.** z **51.** $m^2 n^{1/6}$ **53.** $x^{3/8} y^{1/2}$ **55.** $(a^{2/3})/(b^{4/9})$ **57.** $1/(c^{4/3})$
59. $1/(k^{7/2})$ **61.** 2 **63.** 2 **65.** $\sqrt{a}$ **67.** $\sqrt[3]{k^2}$ **69.** $5, -5$
71. $\sqrt{14}, -\sqrt{14}$ **73.** $3\sqrt{2}, -3\sqrt{2}$ **75.** $4\sqrt{5}, -4\sqrt{5}$

Chapter 8 Review Exercises (page 337)
1. $7, -7$ **3.** $15, -15$ **5.** 4 **7.** Does not exist **9.** 3 **11.** 2 **13.** Irrational;
3.873 **15.** Rational; -13 **17.** $5\sqrt{3}$ **19.** $4\sqrt{10}$ **21.** $3/2$ **23.** $2/15$
25. p **27.** $x\sqrt{x}$ **29.** $\sqrt[3]{5}/2$ **31.** $3\sqrt[3]{2x^2}$ **33.** $(10\sqrt{3})/3$ **35.** $\sqrt{6}$
37. $\sqrt{30}/15$ **39.** $\sqrt[3]{9}/3$ **41.** $\sqrt{7x}/x$ **43.** $\dfrac{r\sqrt{5rt}}{5w}$ **45.** $8\sqrt{2}$ **47.** 0
49. $2\sqrt{3} - 3\sqrt{10}$ **51.** $6\sqrt{30}$ **53.** $8 + 6\sqrt[4]{4}$ **55.** $-m\sqrt{5}$ **57.** $-\sqrt{15} + 9$
59. $22 - 16\sqrt{3}$ **61.** -2 **63.** $-2 + \sqrt{5}$ **65.** $\dfrac{-\sqrt{10} + 3\sqrt{5} + \sqrt{2} - 3}{7}$ **67.** No
solution **69.** No solution **71.** -2 **73.** 9 **75.** $7^{7/3}$ **77.** $1/7$ **79.** 7

Chapter 8 Test (page 339)
1. 10 **2.** 8.775 **3.** -13.784 **4.** -3 **5.** 5 **6.** $3\sqrt{3}$ **7.** $8\sqrt{2}$
8. $-2\sqrt[3]{4}$ **9.** Cannot be simplified **10.** $9\sqrt{7}$ **11.** $-m\sqrt{5}$ **12.** $-5\sqrt{3x}$
13. $2y\sqrt[3]{4x^2}$ **14.** $2np\sqrt[4]{2m^3 p^2}$ **15.** 31 **16.** $6\sqrt{2} + 2 - 3\sqrt{14} - \sqrt{7}$

17. $11 + 2\sqrt{30}$ **18.** $\sqrt{3}$ **19.** $4p\sqrt{k}/k$ **20.** $\sqrt[3]{15}/3$ **21.** $\dfrac{-12 - 3\sqrt{3}}{13}$

22. $\dfrac{3\sqrt{2} + \sqrt{14} + 3 + \sqrt{7}}{2}$ **23.** No solution   **24.** 4   **25.** 1, 25   **26.** 1

27. 16   **28.** $5^{5/2}$ **29.** 1/3   **30.** $m^{1/6}$

CHAPTER 9

Section 9.1   (page 343)

1. 5, -5 **3.** 8, -8 **5.** $\sqrt{13}$, $-\sqrt{13}$ **7.** No real number solution   **9.** $\sqrt{2}$, $-\sqrt{2}$
11. $\sqrt{5}/2$, $-\sqrt{5}/2$ **13.** $2\sqrt{6}$, $-2\sqrt{6}$ **15.** $2\sqrt{5}/5$, $-2\sqrt{5}/5$ **17.** 1.6, -1.6
19. 8.8, -8.8 **21.** 6, -2 **23.** $-4 + \sqrt{10}$, $-4 - \sqrt{10}$ **25.** No real number solution
27. $1 + 4\sqrt{2}$, $1 - 4\sqrt{2}$ **29.** 2, -1 **31.** 13/6, $-3/2$ **33.** $\dfrac{5 + \sqrt{30}}{2}$, $\dfrac{5 - \sqrt{30}}{2}$

35. $\dfrac{1 + 3\sqrt{2}}{3}$, $\dfrac{1 - 3\sqrt{2}}{3}$ **37.** $\dfrac{5 + 7\sqrt{2}}{2}$, $\dfrac{5 - 7\sqrt{2}}{2}$ **39.** $\dfrac{-4 + 2\sqrt{2}}{3}$, $\dfrac{-4 - 2\sqrt{2}}{3}$

41. $-.15$, -3.09 **43.** 1.58, -1.09 **45.** About 1/2 second   **47.** $-8/5$

49. $\dfrac{3 + 3\sqrt{3}}{2}$ **51.** $\dfrac{18 + \sqrt{6}}{3}$ **53.** $\dfrac{9 - \sqrt{3}}{9}$

Section 9.2   (page 348)

1. 1   **3.** 81   **5.** 81/4   **7.** 25/4   **9.** -1, -3 **11.** $-1 + \sqrt{6}$, $-1 - \sqrt{6}$

13. -2, -4 **15.** $3 + 2\sqrt{2}$, $3 - 2\sqrt{2}$ **17.** $\dfrac{-3 + \sqrt{17}}{2}$, $\dfrac{-3 - \sqrt{17}}{2}$ **19.** No real number

solution   **21.** No real number solution   **23.** $3 + \sqrt{5}$, $3 - \sqrt{5}$ **25.** $\dfrac{2 + \sqrt{14}}{2}$,

$\dfrac{2 - \sqrt{14}}{2}$ **27.** 1, $-1/3$ **29.** $5 + \sqrt{17}$, $5 - \sqrt{17}$ **31.** $\dfrac{3 + 2\sqrt{6}}{3}$, $\dfrac{3 - 2\sqrt{6}}{3}$

or 2.633, $-.633$ **33.** $-2 + \sqrt{3}$, $-2 - \sqrt{3}$ or $-.268$, -3.732 **35.** 16; no

37. $1 + 2\sqrt{5}$ **39.** $\dfrac{1 + \sqrt{2}}{2}$ **41.** $\dfrac{2 + \sqrt{7}}{3}$

Section 9.3   (page 353)

1. 3, 4, -8 **3.** -8, -2, -3 **5.** 2, -3, 2   **7.** 1, 0, -2 **9.** 3, -8, 0   **11.** 1, 1,
-12 **13.** 9, 9, -26 **15.** $-1 + \sqrt{3}$, $-1 - \sqrt{3}$ **17.** -2 **19.** 1, -13
21. $\dfrac{-6 + \sqrt{26}}{2}$, $\dfrac{-6 - \sqrt{26}}{2}$ **23.** 1/5, -1 **25.** 5/2, -1 **27.** -3 **29.** 3/2

31. 0, -1 **33.** 0, 5/3   **35.** $2\sqrt{5}$, $-2\sqrt{5}$ **37.** 4/3, $-4/3$ **39.** 0, -2 **41.** No real

number solutions   **43.** No real number solutions   **45.** $\dfrac{1 + \sqrt{5}}{2}$, $\dfrac{1 - \sqrt{5}}{2}$ or 1.618, $-.618$

47. $\dfrac{-1 + \sqrt{61}}{10}$, $\dfrac{-1 - \sqrt{61}}{10}$ or .681, $-.881$ **49.** $-3 + \sqrt{7}$, $-3 - \sqrt{7}$ or $-.354$, -5.646

51. $\dfrac{-1 + \sqrt{73}}{6}$, $\dfrac{-1 - \sqrt{73}}{6}$ **53.** $\dfrac{2 + \sqrt{22}}{6}$, $\dfrac{2 - \sqrt{22}}{6}$ **55.** $1 + \sqrt{2}$, $1 - \sqrt{2}$

57. $\dfrac{1 + \sqrt{3}}{3}$, $\dfrac{1 - \sqrt{3}}{3}$ **59.** No real number solutions   **61.** No real number solutions

63. $3\sqrt{3}$ **65.** $4\sqrt{3}$ **67.** $2\sqrt{11}$ **69.** $12\sqrt{2}$

Miscellaneous Quadratic Equations   (page 355)

1. $\dfrac{-3 + \sqrt{5}}{2}, \dfrac{-3 - \sqrt{5}}{2}$ **3.** $-1/2, 1$ **5.** $-5/4, 3/2$ **7.** $\dfrac{-5 + \sqrt{13}}{6}, \dfrac{-5 - \sqrt{13}}{6}$

9. $2/5, 4$ **11.** $\dfrac{2 + \sqrt{7}}{3}, \dfrac{2 - \sqrt{7}}{3}$ **13.** $1/4, 1$ **15.** $-6/5, -8/3$ **17.** $\dfrac{-5 + \sqrt{5}}{2},$

$\dfrac{-5 - \sqrt{5}}{2}$ **19.** $-2/3, 2$ **21.** $\dfrac{5 + \sqrt{17}}{4}, \dfrac{5 - \sqrt{17}}{4}$ **23.** No real number solutions

25. $\dfrac{1 + \sqrt{10}}{2}, \dfrac{1 - \sqrt{10}}{2}$ **27.** $5, -17$ **29.** $\dfrac{-9 + 4\sqrt{3}}{2}, \dfrac{-9 - 4\sqrt{3}}{2}$

Section 9.4   (page 359)

1. $3i$ **3.** $2i\sqrt{5}$ **5.** $6i$ **7.** $5i\sqrt{5}$ **9.** $5 + 3i$ **11.** $18 - 2i$ **13.** $6 - 9i$

15. $6 - 7i$ **17.** $14 + 5i$ **19.** $7 - 22i$ **21.** 45 **23.** 34 **25.** $-\dfrac{3}{2} - \dfrac{1}{2}i$

27. $-\dfrac{1}{4} - \dfrac{7}{4}i$ **29.** $\dfrac{11}{10} - \dfrac{13}{10}i$ **31.** $-3 - 4i$ **33.** $-1 + 2i, -1 - 2i$

35. $3 + i\sqrt{5}, 3 - i\sqrt{5}$ **37.** $\dfrac{-2 + 3i\sqrt{2}}{3}, \dfrac{-2 - 3i\sqrt{2}}{3}$ **39.** $1 + i, 1 - i$

41. $\dfrac{-3 + i\sqrt{31}}{4}, \dfrac{-3 - i\sqrt{31}}{4}$ **43.** $\dfrac{2 + i\sqrt{6}}{2}, \dfrac{2 - i\sqrt{6}}{2}$

45.   **47.**   **49.**

Section 9.5   (page 365)

1.   **3.**   **5.**   **7.**

9.   **11.**   **13.**   **15.**

17.

(3, −4)
$y = x^2 − 6x + 5$

19.

$y = x^2 − 8x + 9$

(4, −7)

21.

$(−\frac{3}{2}, −\frac{1}{4})$

$y = x^2 + 3x + 2$

23. One solution: 2   **25.** Two solutions: −2 and 2

Chapter 9   Review Exercises   (page 366)

1. 7, −7   **3.** $4\sqrt{3}, −4\sqrt{3}$ **5.** $3 + \sqrt{7}, 3 − \sqrt{7}$ **7.** $\dfrac{−2 + 2\sqrt{3}}{3}, \dfrac{−2 − 2\sqrt{3}}{3}$

9. −5, −1   **11.** $−1 + \sqrt{6}, −1 − \sqrt{6}$ **13.** 1, −2/5   **15.** $1 + \sqrt{5}, 1 − \sqrt{5}$ **17.** No real

number solution   **19.** $\dfrac{2 + \sqrt{10}}{2}, \dfrac{2 − \sqrt{10}}{2}$ **21.** $\dfrac{−3 + \sqrt{41}}{2}, \dfrac{−3 − \sqrt{41}}{2}$

23. 1/2, −5   **25.** $\dfrac{−1 + \sqrt{21}}{2}, \dfrac{−1 − \sqrt{21}}{2}$ **27.** $\dfrac{−5 + \sqrt{17}}{2}, \dfrac{−5 − \sqrt{17}}{2}$

29. $\dfrac{−5 + \sqrt{7}}{3}, \dfrac{−5 − \sqrt{7}}{3}$ **31.** 1, −1/3   **33.** $−2 + \sqrt{5}, −2 − \sqrt{5}$ **35.** $5 − i$

37. $−3 + 2i$ **39.** 20   **41.** 29   **43.** i **45.** $\dfrac{1}{5} − \dfrac{7}{5}i$ **47.** $−2 + i\sqrt{3}, −2 − i\sqrt{3}$

49. $\dfrac{2 + 2i\sqrt{2}}{3}, \dfrac{2 − 2i\sqrt{2}}{3}$ **51.** $\dfrac{1 + i\sqrt{2}}{3}, \dfrac{1 − i\sqrt{2}}{3}$ **53.** $\dfrac{3 + i\sqrt{23}}{8}, \dfrac{3 − i\sqrt{23}}{8}$

55.

$y = 3x^2$

(0, 0)

57.

(0, 3)

$y = −x^2 + 3$

59.

$y = (x − 4)^2$

(4, 0)

61. $y = (x + 2)^2 − 3$

(−2, −3)

63.

(3, 1)

$y = \frac{1}{2}(x − 3)^2 + 1$

65.

(5, −1)

$y = x^2 − 10x + 24$

67. Two solutions: −2 and 2   **69.** Two solutions: −1 and 4

Chapter 9   Test   (page 368)

1. 0, 5/2   **2.** 1/5, −2   **3.** $\sqrt{5}, −\sqrt{5}$ **4.** 10, −4   **5.** $\dfrac{2 + \sqrt{35}}{3}, \dfrac{2 − \sqrt{35}}{3}$

6. 5, −2   **7.** 2, 1/3   **8.** $\dfrac{5 + \sqrt{13}}{6}, \dfrac{5 - \sqrt{13}}{6}$ **9.** $1 + \sqrt{2}, 1 - \sqrt{2}$ **10.** $\dfrac{1 + 3\sqrt{2}}{2},$

$\dfrac{1 - 3\sqrt{2}}{2}$ **11.** 5, −2/3   **12.** $\dfrac{17 + \sqrt{217}}{6}, \dfrac{17 - \sqrt{217}}{6}$ **13.** $5 + 2\sqrt{2}, 5 - 2\sqrt{2}$

14. $3 + \sqrt{7}, 3 - \sqrt{7}$ **15.** $\dfrac{5 + i\sqrt{3}}{2}, \dfrac{5 - i\sqrt{3}}{2}$ **16.** $\dfrac{1 + i\sqrt{2}}{3}, \dfrac{1 - i\sqrt{2}}{3}$

17. $7 - 2i$ **18.** $27 - 14i$ **19.** 29   **20.** $\dfrac{1}{10} + \dfrac{7}{10}i$

21.

22.

23.

24. 2

APPENDICES

Appendix A   (page 371)
1. 117.385   **3.** 13.21   **5.** 96.101   **7.** 4.849   **9.** 166.32   **11.** .1344   **13.** 2.23
15. 4.8   **17.** .53   **19.** 1.29   **21.** 80%   **23.** .7%   **25.** 109.2   **27.** 4
29. 12,800   **31.** $2760   **33.** 805 miles   **35.** 63 miles

Appendix B   (page 374)
1. {1, 2, 3, 4, 5, 6, 7}   **3.** {winter, spring, summer, fall}   **5.** ∅   **7.** True   **9.** True
11. True   **13.** False   **15.** True   **17.** True   **19.** True   **21.** {a, c, e} = B   **23.** {a}
25. {a, c, d, e}   **27.** ∅

Index

Absolute value, 23
Addition
  of complex numbers, 357
  of fractions, 4
  of polynomials, 125
  of radicals, 320
  of rational expressions, 200
  of real numbers, 25
Addition method for linear
    systems, 279
Addition property of equality, 57
Addition property of inequality, 93
Additive inverse, 22
Algebraic expression, 14
Associative property, 43
Axes, 232

Base, of an exponential
    expression, 10, 109
Binomial, 124
  square of, 135
Binomial products, 132
Braces, set, 17

Centimeter, 375
Coefficient, 122
  numerical, 53
Combining like terms, 54
Common denominator, 196
Common factor, 2, 150
Commutative property, 42
Completing the square, 345
Complex fractions, 205
Complex numbers, 356
Composite numbers, 149
Conjugates, 325, 357
Consecutive integers, 73, 177
Consistent system, 276
Conversion table, metric to
    English, 375

Coordinate system, 232
Cross products, 81
Cube root, 309
Cubes
  difference of, 165
  sum of, 166

Decimal, 369
Degree, of a polynomial, 123
Demand, 245
Denominator, 1
  common, 196
  rationalizing, 316
Dependent equations, 276
Descending powers, 123
Difference, 30
Difference of two cubes, 165
Difference of two squares, 135,
    163
Direct variation, 220
Disjoint sets, 374
Distributive property, 45
Division
  of complex numbers, 357–58
  of fractions, 3
  of polynomials, 137, 141
  of radicals, 314
  of rational expressions, 193
  of real numbers, 39
Domain, 17, 266

Elements, 372
Empty set, 373
English system, 375
Equal sets, 373
Equation, 16
  dependent, 276
  independent, 276
  linear, 56, 229
  quadratic, 169

radical, 327
  with rational expressions, 210
  in two variables, 229
Equation of a line, 252
  point-slope form, 254
  slope-intercept form, 253
Exponent, 10, 109
  fractional, 333
  negative, 111
  power rule, 115
  product rule, 110
  quotient rule, 112
  rules for, 117
  variable, 117
  zero, 111
Exponential expression, 109
Expression
  algebraic, 14
  exponential, 109
  rational, 187

Factor, 10, 148
  greatest common factor, 2
Factored form, 148
  prime, 149
Factoring, 154
  by grouping, 152
  perfect square trinomial, 164
Factoring out, 151
Factoring trinomials, 154
Fixed cost, 257
FOIL method, 133
Formulas
  See inside back cover
Fourth root, 309
Fractional exponents, 333
Fractions, 1
  adding, 4
  complex, 205
  denominator, 1
  dividing, 3

Fractions
  lowest terms, 2
  multiplying, 2
  numerator, 1
  subtracting, 5
Function, 264
  domain, 266
  range, 266
  vertical line test, 265
Fundamental property of rational
    expressions, 189

Gram, 374–75
Graph
  of a linear inequality, 258
  of a parabola, 361
  of a quadratic inequality, 182
  of a straight line, 238–39
  of a system of linear equations,
    274
  of a system of linear
    inequalities, 300
Graphical solution
  of a quadratic inequality, 182
  of a system of linear equations,
    274
  of a system of linear
    inequalities, 300
Greater than, 7
Greatest common factor, 2, 150
Grouping, factoring by, 152

Horizontal line, 242, 249

i, 356
Identity element
  for addition, 44
  for multiplication, 4
Identity property, 44
Inconsistent system, 276
Independent equations, 276
Inequality
  linear, 258
  linear system, 299
  quadratic, 181
Inner product, 133
Integers, 20
  consecutive, 73, 177
Intercepts, 240
Interest, 86
Intersection, 373

Inverse
  additive, 22
  multiplicative, 38
Inverse property, 44
Inverse variation, 221
Irrational numbers, 20, 308

Kilometer, 375

Least common denominator, 196
Less than, 7
Like radicals, 320
Like terms, 53
Linear equation, 56, 229
  graphing, 238–39
  summary, 256
  system of, 273
  in two variables, 229
Linear inequality, 258
  graphing, 258
  system of, 299
Liter, 374–75
Lowest terms, 2

Median, 245
Meter, 374–75
Metric system, 374–75
Millimeter, 375
Monomial, 124
Multiplication
  of complex numbers, 357
  of fractions, 2
  of polynomials, 129
  of radicals, 312
  of rational expressions, 192
  of real numbers, 35
Multiplication property of equality,
    61
Multiplication property of
    inequality, 98
Multiplicative inverse, 38

Negative exponent, 111
Negative numbers, 20
Null set, 373
Number line, 19
Numbers
  complex, 356
  composite, 149
  integers, 20

  irrational, 20, 308
  negative, 20
  positive, 20
  prime, 149
  rational, 20
  real, 21
  signed, 20
  whole, 1, 19
Numerator, 1
Numerical coefficient, 53

Operations with signed numbers, 40
Opposite, 22
Order of operations, 11
Ordered pair, 230
Origin, 232
Outer product, 133

Parabola, 361
Parallel lines, 250
Percent, 370
Percentage, 371
Perfect cube, 315
Perfect square, 307
Perfect square trinomial, 164
Perimeter, 74, 175
Perpendicular lines, 250
Plotting points, 233
Point-slope form, 254
Polynomial, 123
  adding, 125
  degree, 123
  in descending powers, 123
  dividing, 137, 141
  multiplying, 129
  prime, 156
  subtracting, 126
  term, 122–23
  in *x*, 123
Positive numbers, 20
Power (exponent), 10, 109
Power rule for exponents, 115
Prime factored form, 149
Prime number, 149
Prime polynomial, 156
Product, 2
Product rule for exponents, 110
Product rule for radicals, 312
Properties of addition and
    multiplication, 46
Proportion, 80
Pythagorean formula, 176, 309

Quadrant, 232
Quadratic equation, 169
  completing the square, 345
  factoring method of solution,
    172
  quadratic formula, 351
  square root method, 341
Quadratic formula, 351
Quadratic inequality, 181
Quotient, 3
Quotient rule for exponents, 112
Quotient rule for radicals, 313

Radical, 307
  equations, 327
  like, 320
  product rule, 312
  quotient rule, 313
  simplified form, 312, 323
Radical sign, 307
Radicand, 307
Range, 266
Ratio, 80
Rational expressions, 187
  adding, 200
  dividing, 193
  equations, 210
  fundamental property, 189
  multiplying, 192
  subtracting, 202
Rational numbers, 20
Rationalizing the denom-
  inator, 316
Real numbers, 21
Reciprocal, 3, 38
Rise, 246
Root, 306
  cube, 309
  fourth, 309
  square, 307
Rules for exponents, 117
Run, 246

Scatter diagram, 237
Scientific notation, 119

Set, 17, 372
  disjoint, 374
  empty, 373
  equal, 373
  intersection, 373
  null, 373
  union, 373
  universal, 373
Set braces, 17, 372
Signed numbers, 20
Simplified form of radicals, 312
Simplifying radicals, 323
Slope, 246
Slope-intercept form, 253
Solution of an equation, 16
Solution of a system, 273
Solving for a specified variable,
  75, 213
Square of a binomial, 135
Square root, 307
  See table inside front cover
Square root property, 341
Squares
  difference of, 135, 163
  sum of, 163
Squaring property of equality, 328
Standard form, of a complex
  number, 357
Subset, 373
Substitution method for linear
  systems, 286
Subtraction
  of complex numbers, 357
  of fractions, 5
  of polynomials, 126
  of radicals, 320
  of rational expressions, 202
  of real numbers, 30
Sum, 4
Sum of two cubes, 166
Sum of two squares, 163
Symbols, 7
System of linear equations, 273
  addition method, 279
  consistent, 276
  graphing method, 274
  inconsistent, 276
  substitution method, 286

Systems
  English, 375
  of linear equations, 273
  of linear inequalities, 299
  metric, 374–75

Term, 53
  combining, 54
  like, 53
  unlike, 53
Terms of a proportion, 80
Trinomial, 124
  factoring, 154
  perfect square, 164

Union, 373
Universal set, 373
Unlike terms, 53

Variable, 14
  specified, 75, 213
Variable cost, 257
Variable exponents, 117
Variation, 220
Varies directly, 220
Varies inversely, 221
Vertex, 361
Vertical line, 242, 249
Vertical line test, 265

Whole numbers, 1, 19
Word problems, 71, 84
  with two variables, 291

x-axis, 232
x-intercept, 240

y-axis, 232
y-intercept, 240

Zero exponent, 111
Zero-factor property, 169

FORMULAS

Rectangle   The length is L; the width is W.

    Perimeter $P = 2L + 2W$
    Area $A = LW$

Square   Each side is s.

    Perimeter $P = 4s$
    Area $A = s^2$

Trapezoid   The two parallel sides are b and B. Altitude (height) is h.

    Area $A = \frac{1}{2}(b + B)h$

Rectangular solid   The height is H.

    Volume $V = LWH$

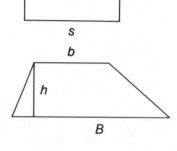

Triangle   The sides are a, b, c, where b is the base. Altitude is h.

    Perimeter $P = a + b + c$
    Area $A = \frac{1}{2}bh$

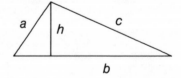

Distance r is rate (or speed); t is time.

    $d = rt$